The Fifth Kingdom
Second Edition

The Fifth Kingdom
Second Edition

Bryce Kendrick
University of Waterloo

Dedication
To Laurie

Frontispiece: Poison arrow frog sitting in apothecial ascoma of *Cookeina* (Pezizales)

96 97   •   10 9 8 7 6 5 4 3

Focus Texts
Focus Information Group, Inc.
PO Box 369
Newburyport MA 01950

Table of Contents

Preface

"Fungi probably rival flowering plants in their species diversity, and outweigh the animal kingdom. Whilst wielding great destructive power as agents of disease and decay, they drive the global carbon cycle, sustain our forests and grasslands via mycorrhizal associations, and clothe, as lichens, what would otherwise be bare parts of the planet. Their developmentally versatile body forms provide immense scope for industrial exploitation as well as experimentally accessible systems for studying fundamental biological issues. Yet most people's appreciation of fungi stops at mushrooms, mouldy food and fairy tales.

Challenged by such ignorance, mycologists need to overcome some deeply rooted prejudices. On the one hand, the variety, edibility and toxicity of fungal fruit bodies has always been a source of fascination which can be relied on to deliver new recruits to the cause of mycology, but if that fascination becomes an obsession, the cause is lost.

On the other hand, mycologists working on disease control, taxonomy or some industrial process often find it difficult to communicate the wider interest of what they are doing. Because of the vicious cycle of neglect, their task is made harder by the need to use 'technical' terms: plant scientists can assume that their audience knows what leaves, roots and stems are; mycologists always have to explain what hyphae and mycelium are.

So there are two images of the mycologist—one of the eccentric amateur, the other of the remote professional working on esoteric problems. Both are damaging." So writes Professor Alan Rayner, one of mycology's most articulate spokespersons, and it is impossible to disagree with him. Perhaps this book can do something to produce a more balanced understanding and appreciation of fungi among university students and intelligent laypersons. Interest is the best stimulant to learning, and at least some of the stories in this book will surely tickle even the most jaded palate, since the fungal lifestyle is so bizarre, the facts so strange. Science fiction writers, look no further. Plots lie within.

So far, we have described about 70,000 fungi, yet we estimate these to represent less than one-tenth of the Earth's mycota. Part of this book, then, is a celebration of biodiversity: just think, there are over ten thousand species of mushrooms alone. Tragically, the world is gradually losing its biological richness. As a result of human activities, species of living organisms, fungi among them, are being driven irretrievably into extinction every day. We need you, the readers of this book, to help stop those losses. There are many kinds of environmental action: may I urge you to become personally involved in some of them. Our grandchildren will thank us, but only if we succeed.

Acknowledgments

Mycology has now become so multifaceted, and each of its many aspects so specialized, that it is increasingly difficult for one person to write a truly comprehensive text. This book may well prove that point, though I did not write it unaided. I am grateful to Professor Joan Bennett (Tulane University), for a critical reading of the chapter on fungal genetics that appeared in the first edition. Professor Bernie Glick (University of Waterloo), and Professor Jim Anderson (Erindale Campus, University of Toronto) have made valuable input to the second version of that chapter. Dr. Donald Barr (Biosystematics Research Institute, Ottawa), made sure the original chapter on protoctistan fungi was up-to-date, and supplied several original illustrations. Professor George Barron (University of Guelph) supplied interesting new information for the revision of the chapter on fungi exploiting microscopic animals. Professor Alan Watson (Macdonald College of McGill University) sent me new material on biological control of weeds by fungi, Professor John Rippon (University of Chicago) provided most helpful comments on medical mycology. Professors Dave Malloch and Michèle Heath (University of Toronto) scanned the 'preview' edition and provided feedback that saved me from making a few mistakes. Dr. Zheng Ru-yong (Academia Sinica, Beijing), has given me invaluable advice about the Erysiphales. I am particularly grateful to Dr. Henry Descals for a detailed and most helpful critique, which has been of great value in the preparation of the second edition. I also thank the following Professors who used the first edition in their courses, and provided me with useful feedback: Margaret Barr, George Barron, Lynn Margulis, Peter Neumann, G.B. Ouellette, R.D. Reeleder, John Rippon, Suzanne Schwab, Don Thomas. Prof. Mike Tansey reviewed the second edition and I have incorporated many of his suggestons in its second printing. For the egregious errors and misinterpretations that undoubtedly remain, I accept sole responsibility.

I would like to thank many of my third- and fourth-year mycology students, on-campus and correspondence, and my own graduate students, who struggled through early versions of several chapters in order to provide me with constructive criticism. University life has provided me with wonderful opportunities for continuing my own education, and my students have certainly taught me a lot—perhaps more than I have succeeded in teaching them. I hope this book will help to redress the balance.

Since the fungi are so unfamiliar to most students, good illustrations are an essential part of any mycology textbook. I have been fortunate to have Mary Ann Milne as my artistic collaborator. She has drawn most of the illustrations with obvious skill, delicacy and taste. Her versatility in producing accurate line drawings from a wide variety of sources—vaguely phrased oral instructions, indistinct pencil sketches, line drawings, photographs, colour transparencies, microscope preparations and macroscopic specimens—is deeply appreciated. Some drawings were kindly provided by Dr. Frank DiCosmo, a former graduate student of mine who is now a professor at University of Toronto, and Ms. Gracia Murase, my able and versatile technician, executed a number of drawings and diagrams.

In 1984-5 I composed the original manuscript on an Apple II+ Microcomputer, using the Easywriter Word-processing Program (which miraculously camouflaged my almost total lack of typing skill). In 1985, the camera-ready copy was produced by a Multiwriter IV daisywheel printer, using multistrike carbon ribbons. The text for the second edition was prepared in 1991 on a new-generation PC: an MS-DOS clone with an Intel 386 microprocessor running at 25 MHz, using WordPerfect 5.1.

Throughout the preparation of the manuscript, Ms. Gracia Murase helped in innumerable ways—compiling the glossary and the index, making drawings and calligraphing titles, retyping lost files, doing paste-ups of plates, proof-reading and editing, numbering and labelling, to name but a few—and I am deeply indebted to her for her help, without which the publiction of the book would have been much delayed.

"Learn About Fungi? Who? Me?"

Imagine the picnic of your dreams. You and your loved one float across a flower-filled meadow, coming to rest under the shade of a giant white pine. There you spread out the magic ingredients—the champagne, wine, or beer, the fresh crusty bread, the pâté au truffe, the creamy camembert, brie or roquefort cheese. You may add other ingredients, but up to this point your tryst is a tribute to the beneficent influence of fungi on our diet and our scenery.

The grass, the flowers in the meadow, and the pine tree all have specialized phosphorus-gathering fungi growing in and around their roots in an obligate mutually beneficial symbiotic relationship. Without these fungi we believe that neither grass nor tree would exist. Champagne, wine and beer—all three are direct products of fungal action on specific sugary substrates, and the alcohol they contain is a fungal metabolite highly prized by those who need an occasional escape from reality. (Some people are particularly unstinting in their praise—I recently saw a T-shirt emblazoned with the motto 'Booze is the ONLY answer'). Reality may also be kept at arm's length with psilocybin or LSD, both psychotropic substances derived from fungi.

Bread owes lightness and texture to the 'raising' activities of a fungus. The mouthwatering flavour of your pâté is enhanced by the presence of pieces of black truffle, a subterranean fungus from Europe. The cheeses are ripened and given their unique texture and taste by specific moulds.

But fungi, like people, have a darker side. On closer inspection, the flowers in the meadow may be found to be suffering from a host of fungal diseases—leaf spots, wilts, mildews, blights and more—and the pine tree may have problems with root rot, heart rot, blister rust and needle cast, all caused by fungi. Some of the food in your picnic may have been insidiously infiltrated by fungi. Those ripe, juicy peaches you brought along for dessert may reveal rapidly spreading brown areas. You must trust that societal regulatory mechanisms have ensured that the bread wasn't made from wheat containing vomitoxin, or if it's rye bread, that no ergot, with its multitude of toxic alkaloids and hallucinogens, was in the grain. Even your peanut butter may contain one of the most poisonous of all mycotoxins.

Homeowners know this other face, too. Has your wooden garden fence or your deck become rotten and needed rebuilding? Has your shade-providing elm tree died, or your chestnut been defoliated by leaf blight? Are your roses besmirched by black spot, your lilacs by powdery mildew, your hollyhocks by rust? Do your tomatoes suffer from early blight, your potatoes from late blight, your grapes from downy mildew, your strawberries from grey mould? Are your peaches attacked by leaf curl or soft rot, your apples by scab? Does damping-off cause your seedlings to keel over? Does food go mouldy, turning green, pink or brown, or growing whiskers, even in the refrigerator? And is there a creeping black stain around its door or in the shower? Have you ever had Athlete's foot, or jock itch, or ringworm of the scalp? All of these, too, are the results of fungal activity.

But there's still another side to the fungi. The blister rust on your pine tree may itself be attacked and controlled by another fungus, as may the powdery mildew on the grass. Specialized fungi can control infestations of insects in your garden. A fungal metabolite is used world-wide to control many bacterial infections (including gonorrhea), while another can cure some of the fungal diseases that afflict people from time to time. Organ transplantation is now a common procedure, but only because a fungal metabolite safely prevents the body from rejecting the new organ, and this same substance seems to interrupt the onset of juvenile diabetes—the first time this has been possible.

These are a few of the reasons why you should know something about mycology. I hope that after you have read this book you will be able to add other reasons of your own.

Chapter 1

Kingdoms and Classification

Five Kingdoms

Let me begin by suggesting that you read this page and see whether you find the subject matter, and especially the words printed in **bold face**, reasonably familiar, or absolutely incomprehensible. If they are familiar, you may press on into the main text. But if they seem very strange, may I recommend that you find and read a first year University Biology textbook before going any further. You could of course compromise by looking up the meanings of the words you don't know in the comprehensive glossary which precedes the index at the end of this book.

You are about to become a member of an elite group. Although many people now know that there are literally millions of different kinds (**species**) of living organisms on Earth (thus far, although our species is doing its best to drive many of them into extinction), surprisingly few people are aware that these organisms are now divided up among no fewer than **FIVE** Kingdoms. Before I can effectively develop the theme of this book I must explain these five major patterns, and those of some of the more than 80 distinctive evolutionary pathways which make up the five Kingdoms. These are officially called **Divisions** in plants, **Phyla** in animals. Since most people recognize the word Phylum, I will use it in this book.

The really basic division among life forms is between the simpler **Prokaryotes** and the more complex **Eukaryotes**. Look at Fig. 1.1: it shows the way in which we think the Kingdoms evolved. The earliest forms of life, which appeared more than 3,500 million years ago, were **prokaryotes**. We tend to define them by their relative morphological simplicity, and by the absence of many features found in more modern cells. Although they had a single **chromosome**, this was not found inside a **nucleus**, and their cytoplasm contained no **mitochondria** or **plastids** (**cytoplasmic organelles**). We feel fairly sure of these things because there are successful living descendants of those early forms. These still lack nuclei and cytoplasmic organelles, and they make up the baseline Kingdom Monera—Archaeobacteria and Eubacteria.

As Fig. 1.1 shows, prokaryotes had the world to themselves for more than 2,000 million years (they did invent photosynthesis during that time). Not until about 1.4 billion years ago did life take the next giant step, the evolution of the **eukaryotic cell**. Many biologists now believe that this arose as a result of the mutually beneficial **symbiotic** union of several different kinds of prokaryote with another host prokaryote. The dotted lines in Fig. 1.1 indicate possible

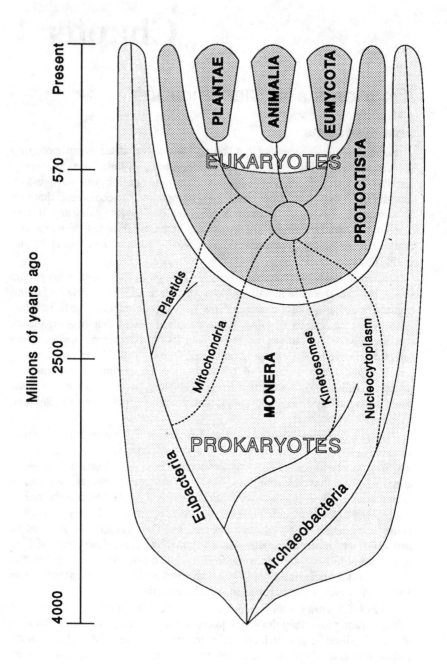

Fig. 1.1 History of the living Kingdoms.

origins for the variety of **organelles** now found in the cytoplasm of eukaryotes. (1) **Mitochondria** specialize in the oxidation of 3-carbon organic acids (the **Krebs cycle**), providing an immediately available energy supply in the form of **ATP**. (2) **Plastids** may contain photosynthetic pigments and enzymes (chloroplasts), or may store food. Many of us are convinced that mitochondria, plastids and even (3) **flagella** were once free-living prokaryotes, which were engulfed and co-opted during the evolution of the eukaryotic cell to become specialized and efficient components of the new, more sophisticated system.

Eukaryotic cells also have their **DNA** organized into a number of discrete chromosomes, which are found inside a membrane-bounded **nucleus**. Cell division in eukaryotes involves a complex process called **mitosis**. The nuclear membrane breaks down, a **mitotic spindle** of **microtubules** develops, and the chromosomes are duplicated. Then the daughter chromosomes separate and are pulled to opposite poles by the spindle fibres. Each set of chromosomes then becomes enclosed by a new nuclear membrane, and the cell finally divides into two.

Prokaryotic cells have only a single chromosome, and do not undergo mitosis. They usually divide by a much simpler process called **binary fission**. Mitosis, with its very accurate duplication and sharing of the genetic material, seems to have been a crucial invention. Only eukaryotic cells, with their precisely regulated genetic mechanisms, apparently had the potential to evolve into more complex, multicellular organisms in which cells are organized into different tissues and organs. All prokaryotes are still microbes.

Now look at Fig. 1.1 again. The Archaeobacteria and the Eubacteria are prokaryotes. The eukaryotes encompass all the other Kingdoms, and it is in these other Kingdoms that the dazzling evolutionary explosion of new taxa has occurred. Although Fig. 1.1 shows only four eukaryote Kingdoms, the molecular biologists are suggesting that the admittedly heterogeneous Kingdom Protoctista should be divided into three: ciliates, flagellates and microsporidia.

The burst of eukaryote evolution was made possible by, among other things, a modified form of mitosis called **meiosis** or **reduction division**. In many organisms this produces special sex cells called **gametes**. These cells have a single set of chromosomes (we say that they are **haploid**). When two gametes from compatible parent organisms fuse, the resulting cell (the **zygote**) has two sets of chromosomes (we call this condition **diploid**). In plants and animals, zygotes develop into diploid, multicellular organisms, but in most fungi the vegetative phase is always haploid, so meiosis must take place in the zygote. Whether meiosis happens in the zygote, or at the other end of the life cycle, during the formation of gametes, it is responsible for the reassortment of the genetic information built into the chromosomes. New features are constantly being added to the pool of genetic material by the process of **mutation**, but sexual reproduction is the mechanism by which this pool is recombined each generation in most eukaryotic organisms, producing an endless supply of variation upon which the processes of natural selection can work. This is one of the key secrets of eukaryote diversity.

Kingdom **Protoctista**, with about 35 phyla (three considered here as protoctistan fungi), shows how the evolution of the eukaryotic cell expanded life's horizons. But the full potential of the new teamwork—I call it that, since several prokaryotes cooperate to make one functional eukaryotic cell—was not realized until cells, as well as cell components, began to cooperate. When organisms became multicellular, different cells could assume different, specialised functions. This division of labour eventually led to the development of **tissues** and **organs**, and ultimately permitted the evolution of complex beings like ourselves, beings with almost infinitely expanded capabilities (both wonderful and terrible).

Three new multicellular Kingdoms arose, exemplifying three different ways of life. Multicellular organisms which could **photosynthesize**—make their own food from simple inorganic precursors—were eaten by other multicellular organisms that lacked this talent, and both were recycled after death by a third group. These groups we call producers, consumers and decomposers—the plants, the animals and the fungi. We recognize about 10 Phyla of plants, about 33 Phyla of multicellular animals, and 5 Phyla of fungi (3 protoctistan and 2 eumycotan).

The world being what it is, the picture is not as simple as we might like. Some of the divergent paths of evolution have come together again, almost as they did at the birth of the eukaryotes, and many organisms that seem unitary are in fact partnerships or even consortia. Lichens, for example, always incorporate both an alga (eukaryotic or prokaryotic) and a fungus.

How can fungi fit into two Kingdoms? The answer lies in the way we define the term **fungus** (plural: **fungi**). Fungi are **eukaryotic, heterotrophic, absorptive organisms that develop a rather diffuse, branched, tubular body and reproduce by means of spores**. This describes, not a single **phylogenetic** line, but rather a way of life shared by organisms of different evolutionary backgrounds. So we can say that there are **protoctistan fungi** as well as **eumycotan fungi** in what we may call the **fungal Union**.

If you find this strange, consider the 'algae' for a moment—they include representatives of three Kingdoms: prokaryotes (the blue-green cyanobacteria), protoctistans such as diatoms and dinoflagellates, and complex multicellular plants such as the giant brown kelps. Both algae and fungi are defined functionally or ecologically, rather than phylogenetically.

At this point it becomes clear that this book does not, as its title implies, deal exclusively with the Fifth Kingdom, Eumycota, but also discusses some elements of Kingdom Protoctista. Yet by far the greater part of the book is in fact concerned with the Eumycotan fungi, and I hope readers will forgive my little deception: I wanted the book to have a catchy, original title.

Biological Classification

The first part of this book deals with the classification of the fungi. You can certainly ignore chapters 2-7, and move quickly to the more accessible and, to many people, more interesting chapters later in the book which deal with the numerous ways in which fungi impact on human existence. However, I don't think I am overstating the case if I say that unless you understand something about how the main groups of fungi differ in morphology and behaviour, you will not be able to make much sense of the more 'relevant' sections of the book. If you can develop a sort of 'cognitive map' of the main classes, recognizing them on sight, and understanding the unique abilities of each, you will find the study of fungi—**mycology**—infinitely more rewarding.

Biological Nomenclature

Every **species** of living organism is a collection of individuals which are very similar (genetically, if not always in appearance), and each species has a unique name made up of two words, which may actually be from the ancient Latin lexicon, but are far more often new, pseudo-Latin words coined for the occasion. This two-epithet name is the **binomial**. You and I belong to the species *Homo sapiens*. The supermarket mushroom belongs to the species *Agaricus brunnescens*. In each case the first of these two Latin words is the **generic** name or epithet (this places the organism in a **genus**, a collection of similar and/or related species). The second Latin word is the epithet applied to one particular species of the genus. But notice that the name of the species consists of **both** epithets together. This is because only the two-word combination is actually unique to that species. The generic epithet is shared by all other species in that genus. The same species epithet may also be applied to species in other genera (for example, many Canadian spring flowers, though belonging to different genera, have the same species epithet, *canadensis*, as does the national animal of Canada, the beaver). So remember that only the two epithets together—the binomial—properly specify a species. *Homo sapiens* is the only extant species in the genus *Homo*, but most genera contain more than one species, and some, for example the mushroom genus *Cortinarius*, are made up of hundreds of species.

For purposes of classification (which is actually a method of information storage and retrieval), related genera are grouped into **families**, families are grouped into **orders**, orders into **classes**, classes into **Phyla**, and Phyla into **Kingdoms**. Here is a sample of how an organism is classified in this **hierarchical** (boxes within boxes) system. Note that the binomial is in *italics*, as it is in most scientific publications, while the names of higher-ranking taxa (families, orders, etc.) are not in italics. If you refer to a binomial in writing, it should be underlined, to show that it would be printed in italics.

Kingdom: EUMYCOTA
   Phylum: Dikaryomycota
      Subphylum: Basidiomycotina
         Class: Holobasidiomycetes
            Order: Agaricales
               Family: Agaricaceae
                  Genus: *Agaricus*
                     Species: *Agaricus brunnescens*—the mushroom.
Why do we use this binomial nomenclature, which is so unfamiliar to the man-or-woman-in-the-street? Why not use common names wherever they exist? For three good reasons: (1) the common names of many organisms differ from country to country, and even from district to district; (2) the same common name is sometimes applied to different organisms—for example, the British and North American "Robins"; (3) common names can be downright misleading: Irish moss is a red alga, Spanish moss is a flowering plant, clubmoss is a fern ally, and reindeer moss is a lichen. Let's face it, common names are too unreliable and confusing to be of any use to scientists, who rely heavily on international communication and cooperation. Please take the time to learn the proper scientific names of the more important organisms you encounter in these pages. If you ever want to know more about any of them, you'll find that their binomials are the key to almost everything that has been written about them.

"But why **Latin** or pseudo-Latin binomials?" I can hear you saying plaintively. That's easy too: (1) Latin is officially a dead language, so although scientists do coin new words, the grammar, vocabulary and usage will change much more slowly than those of all living languages. In a changing world, we need the relative stability of Latin for our scientific names. (2) The use of Latin for names and diagnoses of all new taxa also means that no-one can be offended by being forced to use someone else's language. Latin has once again become a useful international standard, ably assisted by many Greek word roots.

Further Reading

Crowson, R.A. (1970) **Classification and Biology**. Heinemann, London.

Jaques, H.E. (1946) **Living Things: How to Know Them**. Wm.C. Brown, Dubuque.

Margulis, L. and R. Guerrero (1991) Kingdoms in turmoil. New Scientist, 23 March 1991, 46-50.

Margulis, L. and K.V. Schwartz (1982) **Five Kingdoms**. Freeman, San Francisco.

Raven, P.H., R.F. Evert and S.E. Eichhorn (1986) **Biology of Plants**. 4th Edn. Worth, New York.

Woese, C.R., O. Kandler and M.L. Wheelis (1990) Towards a natural system of organisms: Proposal for the domains Archaea, Bacteria, and Eucarya. Proceedings of the National Academy of Science **87**:4576-4579.

Chapter 2

Protoctistan Fungi and Protoctistan Others

Phyla CHYTRIDIOMYCOTA, HYPHOCHYTRIOMYCOTA, and OOMYCOTA and the "Slime Moulds"

First let me elaborate a little on the definition of fungi given earlier. Fungi (whether protoctistan or eumycotan) are **heterotrophic** (non-photosynthesizing) **eukaryotes** that **absorb** their food, typically at the many growing points of their rather diffuse, indefinite 'body' (often called a **thallus** or **mycelium**), which is made up of fine branching tubes called **hyphae** (only narrower rhizoids are produced by some protoctistan fungi). The wall of the tubes is mainly composed of **chitin** or **cellulose**, and within this wall the cytoplasm and nuclei live and move, protected from the outside world, but able to explore small parts of it inside their apically extending, microscopic, hyphal tunnels, and much more of it by means of their detachable reproductive units called **spores.**

But before I discuss real fungi, four peripheral or extracurricular groups must be mentioned. These are the so-called "slime-moulds," the inappropriately named Myxomycota, Acrasiomycota, Labyrinthulomycota and Plasmodiophoromycota. Although they were long considered fungi, and are still dealt with in some current mycological literature, and in some mycology courses, this seems to be phylogenetically incorrect. Here's why. The vegetative phases of three of these four groups are basically amoeboid: none of the four ever produces hyphae (a diagnostic feature of most true fungi), and the assimilative plasmodia have no cell walls. The names currently applied to some of these groups are misleading, in that they imply a fungal nature, so in three cases I have supplied new names reflecting their non-fungal affiliations. I hope you will agree with me after you have read the thumbnail sketches below and compared them with my later descriptions of the wall-possessing hyphal fungi. These phyla are included in some mycology courses because some of them (particularly Myxostelida) tend to turn up when we look for fungi. And if mycologists, who have historically looked after them, abandon them, which other group of organismic biologists will agree to add these organisms to their already crowded course schedules?

Phylum MYXOSTELIDA (formerly MYXOMYCOTA)

Phylum Myxostelida (Figure 2.1) is the only one of these four non-fungal phyla you are likely to find if you go out looking for fungi in Autumn. The macroscopic, slimy, amoeboid plasmodium of *Stemonitis fusca*, populated by diploid nuclei, oozes around in the soil or in decaying wood or other organic matter, eating (yes, actually **ingesting** bacteria and other tiny food particles). Eventually the slowly pulsating plasmodium emerges into the light, finds a dry spot, and **metamorphoses** dramatically into a cluster of stalked, dry sporangia full of powdery resting spores. Spore formation involves reduction division (meiosis), so when the haploid spore germinates to release a cell that may be either amoeboid or biflagellate, this cell can act as a gamete. Fusion of two compatible gametes produces a diploid zygote which can then fuse with other zygotes, begin to feed, and eventually grow into a plasmodium once more.

Phylum DICTYOSTELIDA (formerly ACRASIOMYCOTA)

In the assimilative phase, *Dictyostelium discoideum*, (Fig. 2.2), consists of independent, individual amoebae which feed phagotrophically by ingesting

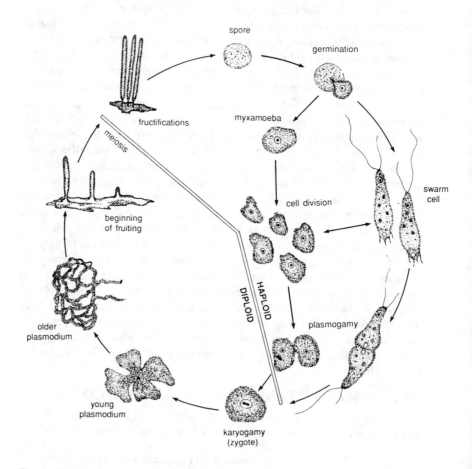

Fig. 2.1 Myxostelida: life cycle of **Stemonitis fusca**.

bacteria. The reproductive phase is entered when the amoebae begin to secrete cyclic adenosine monophosphate (cAMP), a sort of pheromone which causes the amoebae to be mutually attracted. They stream together and form aggregations called pseudoplasmodia or slugs (these differ from true plasmodia in that each amoeba retains its cell membrane). Each slug crawls around until dry conditions prompt it to undergo differentiation, heaping itself up and eventually forming a sorocarp with a slim cellulosic stalk and an expanded head containing spores. *Dictyostelium* has been used as an experimental organism by many scientists because it provides a simple system for studying differentiation.

Phylum LABYRINTHULIDA (formerly LABYRINTHULOMYCOTA)

The colourless colonies of *Labyrinthula* (Fig. 2.3) cause a wasting disease of eel grass (*Zostera*, one of the few marine flowering plants). The spindle-shaped,

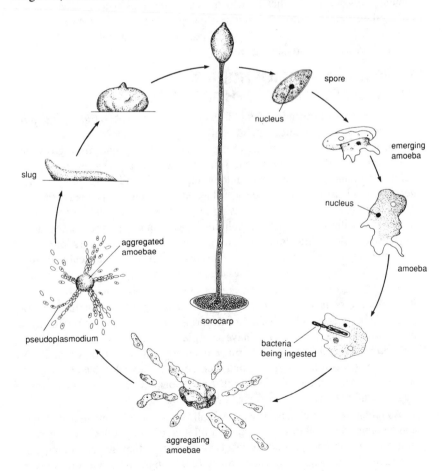

spore

nucleus

emerging amoeba

nucleus

slug

amoeba

aggregated amoebae

pseudoplasmodium

sorocarp

bacteria being ingested

aggregating amoebae

Fig. 2.2 Dictyostelida: life cycle of *Dictyostelium discoideum*.

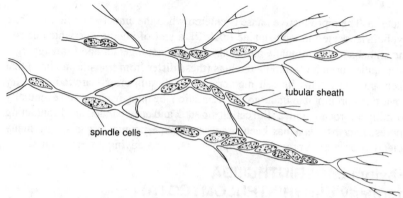

Fig. 2.3 Labyrinthulida: *Labyrinthula*.
naked cells of the colony live and move entirely within a network of narrow, tubular, polysaccharide sheaths which they themselves secrete. They release biflagellate gametes, and the zygote divides mitotically to generate a new colony, whose cells are presumably diploid. Most other members of this group are also marine, parasitising algae.

Phylum PLASMODIOPHORIDA (formerly PLASMODIOPHOROMYCOTA)

All members of this group (Fig. 2.4) are obligate parasites. *Plasmodiophora brassicae* produces uninucleate, biflagellate primary zoospores which penetrate a root hair of its host, cabbage (*Brassica oleracea*). Inside, they grow into multinucleate but still microscopic primary plasmodia. These eventually develop a wall and divide internally into uninucleate secondary sporangia. These germinate, releasing four secondary, biflagellate zoospores which leave the host. These may also act as gametes, fusing in pairs, but soon infect a root again, developing within host cells into multinucleate secondary plasmodia. At maturity, these can cleave into uninucleate cysts, each containing a single spore, which can persist in the soil for many years. This parasite stimulates the cabbage roots to become grossly swollen, a serious disease condition known as "club root."

The four groups just outlined are all clearly non-fungal members of the Kingdom Protoctista, but the current arrangement of phyla within that kingdom places them in three rather different categories. The Dictyostelida is one of four phyla which lack flagella, but have complex sexual cycles (group II). The Labyrinthulida and Plasmodiophorida are among fourteen phyla which display reversible formation of flagella, and lack complex sexual cycles (group III); while the Myxostelida and eleven other phyla display reversible formation of flagella, and exhibit complex sexual cycles (group IV).

As I mentioned in chapter 1, what we call "fungi" share many morphological and behavioural similarities in their assimilative phase, but they do not have a uniform genetic background. It seems obvious that they have evolved from several different ancestral lineages. Some fungi can produce cells that swim by means of one or two very fine whiplike extensions called **flagella** (rather like the tails of sperms). Three Phyla—**Chytridiomycota, Hyphochytriomycota,** and **Oomycota**—fall into this category. Because many of them also have microscopic, often unicellular thalli, they are clearly members of the Kingdom Protoctista, and I call them the **protoctistan fungi.** The other two fungal Phyla never have motile cells, and these—the **Zygomycota** and **Dikaryomycota**— make up Kingdom Eumycota, and are thus called **eumycotan fungi,** though only the Dikaryomycota produce highly differentiated, multicellular reproductive phases, as you will see.

Phyla CHYTRIDIOMYCOTA

The vegetative phases of chytridiomycetes vary widely in appearance, but they all produce zoospores with a single, posteriorly directed, **whiplash flagel-**

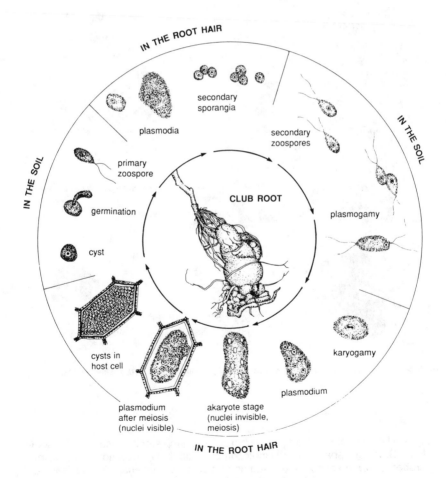

Fig. 2.4 Plasmodiophorida: life cycle of *Plasmodiophora brassicae*.

lum. I will discuss members of four orders: the **Chytridiales, Spizellomycetales, Blastocladiales**, and **Monoblepharidales**. Although these orders were formerly separated on the morphology of their microscopic thalli, we now know that this is too variable to be reliable, and emphasis has switched to ultrastructural features of the zoospore, some of which are illustrated in Fig 2.5. Unfortunately, although conservative, and therefore taxonomically valuable, these can be seen only in the transmission electron microscope after elaborate preparative

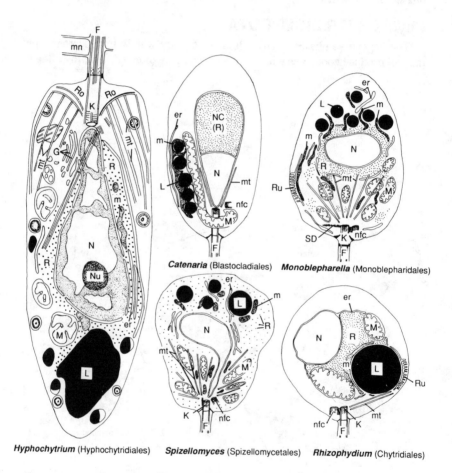

Hyphochytrium (Hyphochytridiales)   ***Spizellomyces*** (Spizellomycetales)   *Rhizophydium* (Chytridiales)

Fig. 2.5 Ultrastructure of fungal zoospores: *er*, endoplasmic reticulum; *F*, flagellum; *G*, golgi apparatus; *K*, kinetosome; *L*, lipid; *M*, mitochondrion; *m*, microbody; *mn*, mastigoneme; *mt*, microtubules; *N*, nucleus; *NC*, nuclear cap (ribosomes); *nfc* - non-functional centrioles; *Nu*, nucleolus; *R*, ribosomes; *Ro*, rootlet; *Ru*, rumposome; *SD*, striated disc.

techniques. Despite this, I would like you at least to be aware of the direction taken by contemporary taxonomic thought about this group.

Orders Chytridiales and **Spizellomycetales**. These orders look very alike under the light microscope, and it takes an expert to tell them apart. However, most Chytridiales are aquatic, while most Spizellomycetales live in soil. Until important differences were found in the ultrastructure of their zoospores (Fig. 2.5), the two orders were considered to be one. These most primitive protoctistan fungi do not produce hyphae. They are often parasitic, and their vegetative thallus may consist of a single cell. This is ultimately either entirely converted into a reproductive sporangium (the **holocarpic** mode: Fig. 2.6 B), as in *Olpidium brassicae*, or the thallus can be differentiated into assimilative **rhizoids** and a sporangium (the **eucarpic** mode: Fig. 2.6 A), as in *Chytridium lagenaria* or *Spizellomyces punctatus*. Other chytrids have a more extensive system of rhizoids, called **rhizomycelium**, which may nourish several sporangia, as in *Cladochytrium* (Fig. 2.6 C). We describe this condition as **polycentric** to differentiate it from the **monocentric** forms just mentioned, which produce only a single sporangium. The difference between rhizoids and rhizomycelium is that rhizoids are generally anucleate, and usually less than a millimetre long, while rhizomycelia contain nuclei and can be much more extensive.

You might be interested in the activities of some of the members of these two orders, including the fungi just named. The holocarpic *Olpidium brassicae* does not itself cause much damage to plant roots, but is known to be the vector of some destructive viruses. The eucarpic *Chytridium lagenaria* and *Spizellomyces punctatus* parasitize pollen grains, and the polycentric *Cladochytrium* is **saprobic**, growing on decaying aquatic vegetation. At least one chytrid is of considerable economic importance: *Synchytrium endobioticum* causes wart disease of potato. This produces dark brown, cauliflower-like growths on the tubers, and a catastrophic reduction in yield. Fortunately, although the pathogen is widespread in Europe, and has spread to Newfoundland, resistant varieties of potato help to keep the disease under control. Other microscopic chytrids that parasitize unicellular planktonic algae can be so numerous as to cause epidemics which significantly, if temporarily, reduce primary productivity in lakes. Sexual reproduction in chytrids and Spizellomycetales requires critical reexamination: it was formerly assumed that any zoospore with two flagella, and every resting spore, resulted from nuclear fusion. Now we know that some biflagellate zoospores originate through incomplete differentiation of cytoplasm during zoospore formation, and many resting spores are just thick-walled sporangia that can survive dry periods.

Order Blastocladiales. Here the thallus is made up of broad true hyphae and narrow rhizoids. *Allomyces arbusculus*, whose life cycle is illustrated in Fig. 2.7, exhibits what we call **alternation of generations**—a rotation between haploid and diploid thalli. Haploid thalli produce gametes in specialized **gametangia**, while diploid thalli produce flagellate zoospores and resting sporangia. In *Allomyces* the gametes come in two sizes, a condition called

anisogamy. The general principle underlying anisogamy is division of labour: the smaller, more mobile gamete (which we can now think of as male) actively seeks out the larger, less active (female) gamete, which has sacrificed some range in order to carry enough food to give the next generation a good start. In *Allomyces arbusculus*, both kinds of gamete are formed on the same haploid thallus. The colourless female gametangia are borne at the tips of hyphal branches, with the orange male gametangia just below.

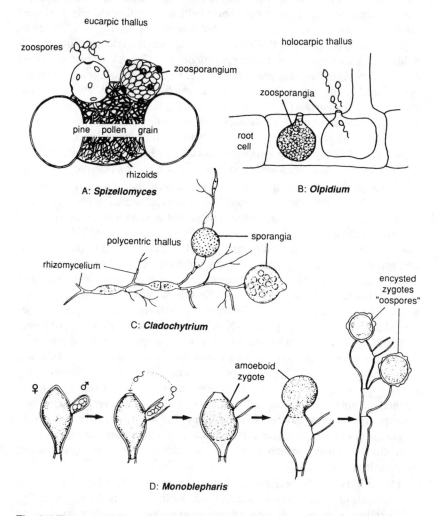

Fig. 2.6 Types of thalli and reproductive structures among the Chytridiomycota. A: eucarpic thallus of **Spizellomyces punctatus** (Spizellomycetales) in pine pollen; B: holocarpic thallus of **Olpidium brassicae** (Chytridiales) in cell of cabbage root; C: polycentric thallus of **Cladochytrium** (Chytridiales); D: stages of oogamous reproduction in **Monoblepharis polymorpha** (Monoblephari-dales).

Zygotes develop into diploid thalli, which bear two kinds of sporangia. The nuclei of thin-walled sporangia undergo repeated mitosis and produce mitospores, which in this case are diploid, uniflagellate zoospores (Fig. 2.5) that can establish new diploid thalli. The other kind of reproductive structures, resistant sporangia, are thick-walled, brown, and can survive for 30 years. These are eventually the site of reduction division (meiosis), and the resultant haploid meiospores develop into sexual thalli. *Coelomomyces* is another genus of the Blastocladiales in which some species are obligate parasites of mosquito larvae, and attempts are being made to use them in biological control of these insects (see Chapter 14).

Order Monoblepharidales. *Monoblepharis polymorpha* (Figs. 2.5, 2.6), found on twigs of birch, ash, elm or oak submerged in slightly alkaline freshwater pools, is the first fungus we have met that has gone all the way to complete sexual differentiation of gametes. The male gamete is motile (a sperm), but the female (an egg) is not. This style of sexuality is called **oogamy**. Sperms form in gametangia called **antheridia**, while eggs develop in **oogonia**, which are found on the same hypha just below the antheridia. Sperms are often released before the adjacent oogonium is ripe. This may be a mechanism for avoiding self-fertilization, and ensuring outbreeding (called **heterothallism** in fungi). After the egg has been fertilized, the resulting zygote becomes amoeboid, moves out onto the top of the oogonium, and encysts, developing a thick wall. Meiosis probably occurs when this resting spore germinates, producing a **germ tube** (another name for a first hypha).

Although the Chytridiomycota vary in so many things: in the morphology of their assimilative phase, in their patterns of sexuality, and in their adoption of parasitic or saprobic lifestyles; they all have posteriorly uniflagellate spores, and their cell walls, like those of the eumycotan fungi, are largely made of **chitin** (a polysaccharide very similar to the stuff of which insect exoskeletons are made). Chytridiomycetes have similar wall chemistry to that of the main group of terrestrial fungi (Phylum Dikaryomycota), they synthesize lysine by the same pathway (see chapter 8), and the more advanced members of the group produce true hyphae. It seems probable that the Chytridiomycota may represent a modern survival of the ancestral line that evolved into the eumycotan fungi, but this is still a matter of hot debate among mycologists. The current arrangement of major groups in Kingdom Protoctista places the Chytridiomycota in group IV (reversible formation of flagella, complex sexual cycles).

Division HYPHOCHYTRIOMYCOTA

This group is like the chytridiomycetes in many ways: they live in fresh water or soil; they can be parasites or saprobes; they may be holocarpic or eucarpic, the latter kind having assimilative rhizoids; the sporangia release uniflagellate zoospores. So why aren't they chytridiomycetes? A single character visible under the light microscope gave the original clue, and was soon supplemented by several ultrastructural features accessible only to the transmission electron microscope (Fig. 2.5). The 'visible' feature concerns the behaviour of the flagellum on the zoospore. In chytridiomycetes this propels the spore from the rear, but in hyphochytriomycetes the flagellum is seen to be attached at the **front** of the cell. Other differences emerge in the transmission electron microscope. In chytridiomycetes the axis of the flagellum is smooth (a **whiplash** flagellum), while in the hyphochytrids the axis of the flagellum bears many fine lateral filaments (mastigonemes) that give it the name **tinsel** flagellum. These may

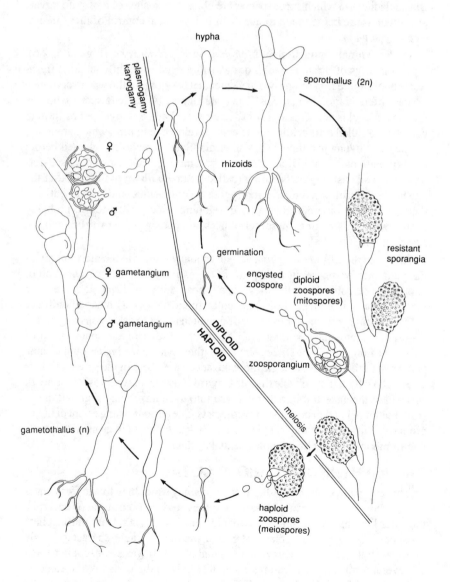

Fig. 2.7 Blastocladiales: life cycle of *Allomyces arbusculus*.

appear to be insignificant differences, but biologists consider flagellation to be an extremely conservative character—one likely to remain unchanged over vast stretches of time, perhaps even hundreds of millions of years. This makes it an important indicator, which is amply confirmed by the ultrastructural differences illustrated in Fig. 2.5, and justifies the recognition of Phylum Hyphochytriomycota, although I think the name is long and clumsy. There are few well-documented species in this Phylum, but *Hyphochytrium catenoides* is common in soil, and is often found in pollen when this is used to 'bait' soil in the laboratory. This species may be of some importance in the natural biological control of plant pathogenic Oomycetes (see below), by parasitizing their oospores. No hypho-

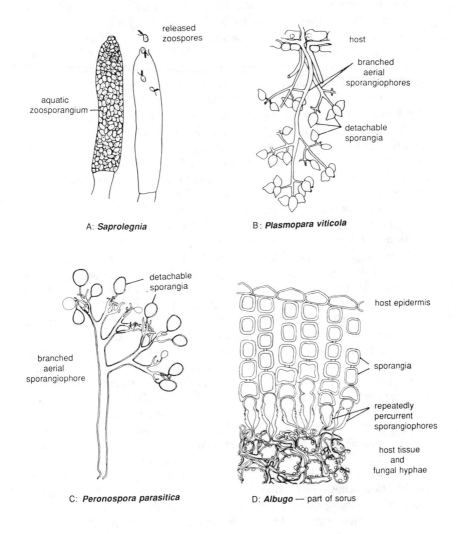

Fig. 2.8 Asexual reproduction in Oomycota. A: Saprolegniales; B-D: Peronosporales.

chytrid has yet been seen to reproduce sexually. The modern arrangement of major groups within the Kingdom Protoctista places the Hyphochytriomycetes in group III (reversible formation of flagella, no complex sexual cycle)

Phylum OOMYCOTA

Having just heard about the minute but basic differences between the two previous groups, you won't be surprised to learn that similar inconspicuous features distinguish the oomycetes, our last and most important group of protoctistan fungi. Oomycetous zoospores have **two flagella**: one tinsel, one whiplash (Fig. 2.8 A). The nuclei in assimilative hyphae of oomycetes are **diploid** and the walls of the hyphae usually contain a **cellulose-like** material (a poorly crystallized hexose polymer), though this makes up only a fraction of the cell wall, and chitin has been found in some oomycetes. All of these characters separate them from the eumycotan fungi. But the feature that gives the group its name is its **oogamous** sexual reproduction, and the fact that each zygote develops into a thick-walled, persistent **oospore** (Fig. 2.9 A,B). In the current classification of Kingdom Protoctista, the Oomycota are placed in group IV (reversible formation of flagella, complex sexual cycle).

Chytridiomycetes and Hyphochytriomycetes are often extremely inconspicuous, as befits organisms that can devote a lifetime to exploiting a single pollen grain. Oomycetes, though they also include some holocarpic and eucarpic unicells, often produce extensive hyphal networks (mycelia). These fungi, covering a dead fish like a whitish fur coat, or devastating crops such as grapes, hops, lettuce, cabbage, radishes, potatoes and tobacco, have spawned a number of common names—**water moulds** and **white rusts, downy mildews** and **damping off**. We'll take a look at some examples.

Order Saprolegniales. The water mould, *Saprolegnia parasitica*, attacks fish and their eggs. After establishing itself, the fungus soon reproduces asexually. The tips of the normally non-septate hyphae become modified into long mitosporangia delimited by a basal **septum** (a cross-wall). These sporangia (Fig. 2.8 A) produce and liberate biflagellate zoospores, often called **swarm spores**, that swim actively for a while, then **encyst**: they stop swimming and develop a thick wall. Later, they germinate again as secondary zoospores which, if they are lucky, will find a new substrate and develop into new assimilative thalli. Eventually, either when food is running out, or when other conditions are becoming unfavourable, sex supervenes. Male and female gametangia develop. Most *Saprolegnia* species form compatible antheridia and oogonia on the same mycelium, thus being **homothallic**. Since the assimilative thallus is diploid, meiosis must take place inside the gametangia. Each globose oogonium contains several **eggs** (Fig. 2.9 A). A number of antheridia may grow toward and touch a single oogonium, penetrating its wall at pre-formed thin spots and sending in **fertilization tubes** which deliver the male nuclei to the eggs. Fertilization is made more reliable because neither gamete is exposed to the vagaries of a free-swimming existence. The whole life cycle is illustrated in Fig. 2.10.

As I mentioned earlier, the zygotes develop thick, resistant walls and obviously function as survival spores that can live through such catastrophes as the drying up of the pond or stream. Homothallic species may have dispensed with the enhanced variation provided by outbreeding, but they still need the long-term insurance that is a by-product of the sexual process.

Order Peronosporales. Many members of this order are obligately parasitic on higher plants. In some cases they cause epidemics that devastate important crops. The build-up of these epidemics is facilitated, both by our need to grow dense stands of single plant species, and by aerial transmission of the fungi, made possible by their invention of airborne mitosporangia (often wrongly called conidia) (Fig. 2.8 B,C). Oogonia are also formed, each containing a single egg (Fig. 2.9 B). Sexual reproduction is usually homothallic.

Damping off is a soil-borne disease, so its causal agents, species of *Pythium*, have no need of airborne sporangia, since they persist saprobically in most soils, and spread by zoospores during wet conditions. When these motile cells find young plants, they cause infections which release toxins and also produce a pectinase enzyme which dissolves the middle lamella that glues plant cells together. Seedlings of many plants collapse rapidly when this disease strikes at the base of their delicate shoots. Damping-off is, unhappily, familiar to gardeners who try to get a head start on the growing season by germinating seeds indoors. The disease can be controlled by using heat-sterilized soil, by dusting seeds with Benomyl (a very safe fungicide—see chapter 13), or by watering seedlings with other fungicides such as Zineb or No-damp. The life cycle of *Pythium* is illustrated in Fig. 2.11.

White rust of crucifers (cabbage, radish, etc.) is caused by *Albugo candida*, which produces extensive white blisters on leaves and stems. These blisters contain innumerable unicellular mitosporangia developing in chains from the tips of short, tightly packed sporangiophores (Fig. 2.8 D). When the host epidermis bursts, the sporangia are wind- or rainsplash-dispersed to other host plants where each can germinate to release eight biflagellate zoospores. Oogonia

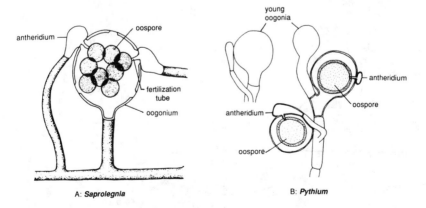

A: *Saprolegnia*   B: *Pythium*

Fig. 2.9 Sexual reproduction in Oomycota. A: Saprolegniales; B: Peronosporales.

develop later, inside the host stem or leaves, and sexual reproduction is usually heterothallic, or outbreeding.

A fairly broad interpretation of the term **downy mildew** includes **late blight** of potato and **blue mould** of tobacco, as well as downy mildew of grape. Since

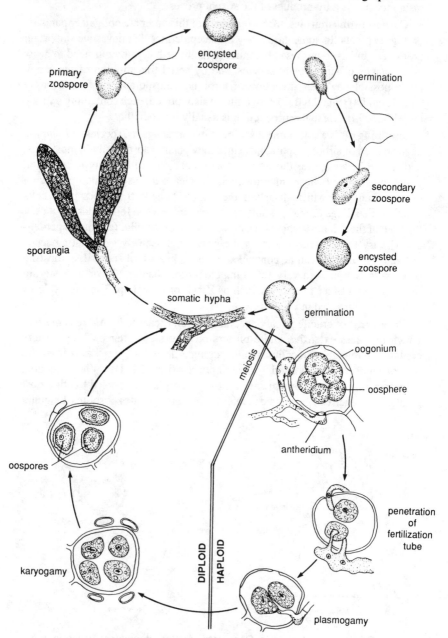

Fig. 2.10 Saprolegniales: life cycle of *Saprolegnia*.

these diseases have great historic or economic importance, I'll tell you something about each of them. In this group the mitosporangia are no longer unspecialized hyphal tips, but are borne on highly differentiated, branched, aerial sporangiophores (Figs. 2.8 B,C). The individual sporangia, like those of the white rusts, no longer merely release zoospores *in situ* but are themselves set free and blown or splashed away. The sporangia of the genus *Peronospora*

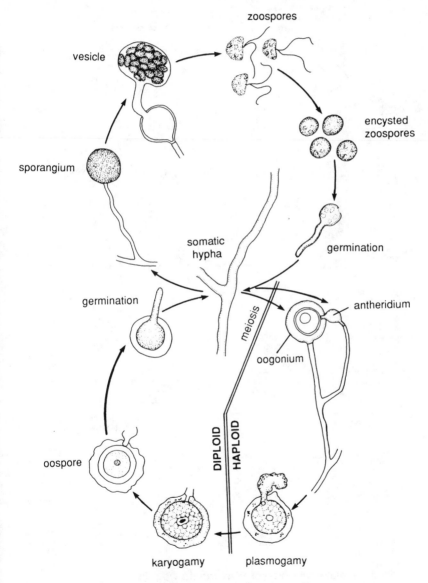

Fig. 2.11 Peronosporales: life cycle of *Pythium*.

germinate by producing a hypha, though those of most other members of the group still release zoospores.

Plasmopara viticola (Fig. 2.8 C), an oomycete native to America, causes downy mildew of grapes; you can find it attacking wild grapes every summer. But because it evolved along with its North American host, a biological balance

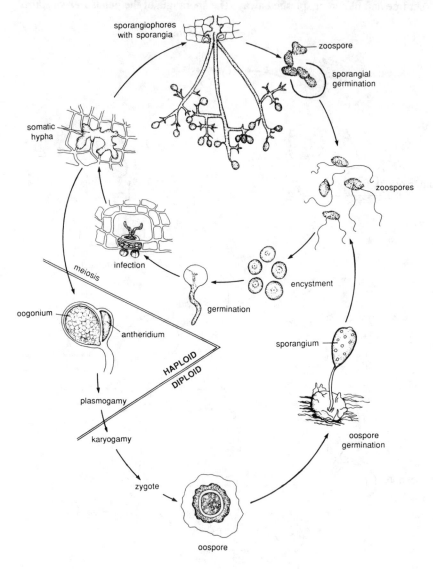

Fig. 2.12 Peronosporales: life cycle of ***Plasmopara viticola***.

has been struck, and the wild *Vitis* species aren't seriously damaged. When this fungus was accidentally introduced to Europe in the 1870's, it was a different story. The French grape vines (*Vitis vinifera*) had no resistance to the new pathogen, and were quickly devastated. Only the concoction of Bordeaux Mixture, one of the world's first practical fungicides, by a University Professor (yes, we occasionally have good ideas), saved the day. The rather strange story behind this invention is told in chapter 13. The life cycle of *Plasmopara* is illustrated in Fig. 2.12

Late blight of potato. Earlier in the 19th century, another American oomycete had caused even more havoc. Unintentionally imported to Ireland, *Phytophthora infestans* wiped out the Irish potato crop in the damp, cool summers of the years 1845-1847, causing widespread famine in that poor, one-crop economy. It is estimated that the ravages of *Phytophthora* contributed to a million deaths, and drove millions to emigrate from Ireland. Ten years after the first epidemic, the population of Ireland had fallen from 8 million to 4 million. The airborne sporangia of the potato blight fungus clearly constitute an efficient short-range dispersal mechanism, but Man was clearly the long-range **vector**. Potato blight is still a threat, though it is controlled by spraying with fungicide at times carefully chosen by plant pathologists (nowadays with the aid of special blight-forecasting computer programs), by destroying infected foliage before harvest, and by planting disease-resistant seed potatoes.

My last example of a downy mildew fungus is *Peronospora tabacina* (cf. Fig. 2.8 B), which causes **blue mould** of tobacco. This disease was first recorded in Ontario in 1938, was epidemic in 1945-1947, and was not seen from 1966 until 1979. In that year seedlings inffected with the pathogen were imported to Canada from the U.S., escaping detection at the border. The weather that year favoured the development and spread of the fungus, and a large-scale epidemic ensued. About 30% of the Ontario crop, worth $100 million, was lost. Blue mould helped to put the Ontario tobacco industry on a slippery slope, and the decline in tobacco acreage is still continuing, though it is now driven by changing societal attitudes toward smoking.

Further Reading

Barr, D.J.S. (1990) Phylum Chytridiomycota. pp. 454-466 (in) **Handbook of Protoctista**. (Eds.) L. Margulis, J.O. Corliss, M. Melkonian and D.J. Chapman. Jones and Bartlett, Boston.

Barron, G.L. (1991) Protoplasm in motion. Seasons **31**(2): 20-25.

Bonner, J.T. (1967) **The Cellular Slime Molds**. 2nd Edn. Princeton University Press.

Buczacki, S.T. (Ed.) (1983) **Zoosporic Plant Pathogens, a Modern Perspective**. Academic Press, New York.

Cavender, J.C. (1990) Phylum Dictyostelida. pp. 88-101 (in) **Handbook of Protoctista**. (Eds.) L. Margulis, J.O. Corliss, M. Melkonian and D.J. Chapman. Jones and Bartlett, Boston.

Dick, M.W. (1990) Phylum Oomycota. pp. 661-685 (in) **Handbook of Protoctista.** (Eds.) L. Margulis, J.O. Corliss, M. Melkonian and D.J. Chapman. Jones and Bartlett, Boston.

Dylewski, D.P. (1990) Phylum Plasmodiophoromycota. pp. 399-416 (in) **Handbook of Protoctista.** (Eds.) L. Margulis, J.O. Corliss, M. Melkonian and D.J. Chapman. Jones and Bartlett, Boston.

Frederick, L. (1990) Phylum plasmodial slime molds: class Myxomycota. pp. 467-483 (in) **Handbook of Protoctista.** (Eds.) L. Margulis, J.O. Corliss, M. Melkonian and D.J. Chapman. Jones and Bartlett, Boston.

Fuller, M.S. (1990) Phylum Hyphochytriomycota. pp. 380-387. (in) **Handbook of Protoctista.** (Eds.) L. Margulis, J.O. Corliss, M. Melkonian and D.J. Chapman. Jones and Bartlett, Boston.

Fuller, M.S. and A. Jaworski (Eds.) (1987) **Zoosporic Fungi in Teaching and Research.** Southeastern Publishing Co., Athens.

Gray, W.D. and C.J. Alexopoulos (1968) **Biology of the Myxomycetes.** Ronald, New York.

Hagiwara, H. (1989) The taxonomic study of Japanese Dictyostelid slime molds. National Science Museum, Tokyo.

Karling, J.S. (1977) **Chytridiomycetarum Iconographia.** Cramer, Vaduz.

Large, E.C. (1962) **The Advance of the Fungi.** Dover, New York.

Margulis, L., J.O. Corliss, M. Melkonian and D.J. Chapman (Eds.) (1990) **Handbook of Protoctista.** Jones and Bartlett, Boston.

Muehlstein, L.K., D. Porter and F.T. Short (1991) *Labyrinthula zosterae* sp. nov., the causative agent of wasting disease of eelgrass, *Zostera marina.* Mycologia **83**: 180-191.

Olive, L.S. (1975) **The Mycetozoans.** Academic Press, New York.

Porter, D. (1990) Phylum Labyrinthulomycota. pp. 388-398 (in) **Handbook of Protoctista.** (Eds.) L. Margulis, J.O. Corliss, M. Melkonian and D.J. Chapman. Jones and Bartlett, Boston.

Sparrow, F.K. (1960) **Aquatic Phycomycetes.** 2nd Edn. University of Michigan Press, Ann Arbor.

Spencer, D.M. (Ed.) (1981) **The Downy Mildews.** Academic Press, New York.

Webster, J. (1980) **Introduction to Fungi.** 2nd Edn. Cambridge University Press, Cambridge.

Chapter 3

Eumycotan Fungi:
(1) Phylum Zygomycota

Introduction

Now we come to the two Phyla, Zygomycota and Dikaryomycota, that make up Kingdom Eumycota. This pair, and particularly the second one, far outnumber in species diversity all three Phyla of the protoctistan fungi. We already know of about 70,000 eumycotan fungi, and it is obvious to those of us who work with them that these are just the tip of the iceberg. We estimate that there may be over a million species waiting to be found and described. Hundreds of new fungal taxa are described every year. For example, in 1990, Rafael Castañeda and I described 14 new genera and 40 new species of microscopic fungi from dead leaves of Cuban plants, and we have dozens more new taxa awaiting description. This wealth of species is a measure of fungal success in evolutionary terms, just as the existence of millions of species of insects tells us that they, too, are winners (though their total biomass is far less than that of the fungi). Before we look at the eumycotan fungi in detail, it is worth enquiring into the reasons for their success.

Earlier, I introduced the idea that the number, kind and arrangement of motility organelles (flagella) found in the protoctistan fungi are very basic features. As a corollary of this, the **absence** of motile cells from the life cycle of the eumycotan fungi must also be considered important. This seems to reflect a radical shift in evolutionary direction. It shows very clearly that the true fungi are basically **terrestrial**, and must have been so for a long time. Many more ecological niches and substrates are available on land than in the water, and the challenges of survival and dispersal are very different. Even entirely aquatic members of Kingdom Eumycota have no organs of motility: this strongly suggests that they are derived from the terrestrial forms, rather than vice versa.

Fungi are heterotrophic, and therefore depend on energy-rich carbon compounds manufactured by other organisms. But this doesn't seem to have been a serious disadvantage. Fungi have evolved enzymes that can digest some extremely recalcitrant substrates. Chitin (insect exoskeletons), keratin (skin, hair, horn, feathers), cellulose (most plant debris) and lignin (wood), nourish many fungi, though cellulose and lignin remain completely unavailable to almost all animals (except with the collaboration of microbial symbionts). Their unusual ability to exploit cellulose and lignin gives some saprobic fungi almost exclusive access to the massive quantities of plant debris produced every year, and may well make them the world's number one recyclers. Only man-made plastics are, perhaps unfortunately, immune to their attacks, which means that we, not the fungi, must take responsibility for recycling these substances.

The fungal hypha, with its strong, waterproof chitinous wall, the repertoire of enzymes it can secrete at its growing tip, and the hydrostatic pressures it can bring to bear, is ideally suited for actively penetrating, exploring and exploiting solid substrates in a manner (Fig. 3.1) that the bacteria, chief competitors of the fungi in the recycling business, cannot match.

The non-motile microscopic spores of eumycotan fungi, which come in a dazzling array of forms (Fig. 3.2) to fit specific functions, are often produced very quickly (in a matter of days or even hours after the initial colonization of the substrate), and in enormous numbers. They are dispersed by wind, water, or

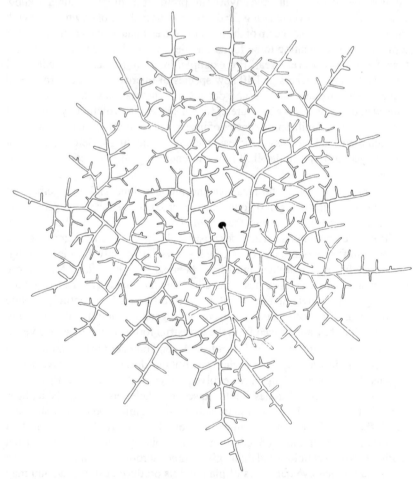

Fig. 3.1 Young colony of *Phycomyces* arising from a mitospore. Note the large number of hyphal tips.

animal vectors, and they can often survive long periods, sometimes even years, of unfavourable conditions such as freezing, starvation or desiccation (which means drying out, and is spelt with one 's,' two 'c's). Like bacteria, fungal spores are everywhere, even in the air we breathe.

Fungi have learned to cope with environmental extremes. They can grow at temperatures as low as -5° Celsius and as high as 60° Celsius. They include the most **xerotolerant** organisms known: some moulds will grow at the amazingly low water activity of 0.65 (most plants wilt permanently at a water activity of 0.98). Other moulds grow in oxygen concentrations as low as 0.2% (air contains 20% oxygen). Certain fungi can grow under extremely acid conditions (pH 1): others can tolerate alkalinity up to pH 9.

As I have already noted, the saprobic fungi are recyclers par excellence, but they are also among the world's greatest opportunists, and don't restrict their

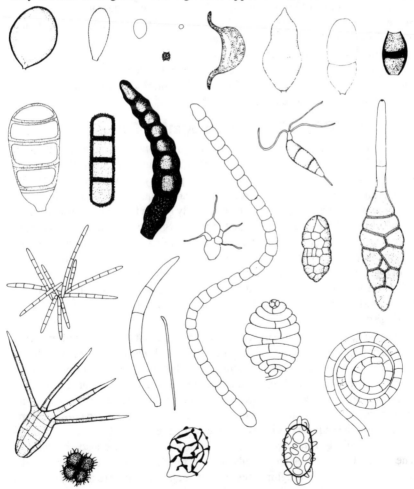

Fig. 3.2 Diversity of spores among Eumycotan fungi.

attentions to naturally occurring dead wood and leaves. Where there is a trace of moisture, their omnipresent spores will attack food and fabric, paper and paint, or almost any other kind of organic matter. Some of their metabolites (**mycotoxins**) are extremely dangerous—even carcinogenic—if they contaminate food. And parasitic fungi cause the majority of serious plant diseases, as well as some of animals and people.

Fortunately, there is a brighter side to fungal intervention in human affairs: we have harnessed the biochemical virtuosity of the saprobic fungi in the production of beer, wine, bread, some gourmet cheeses, soy sauce, some antibiotics and immunosuppressants, organic acids, and many other useful chemicals. Fungi are even being used to convert plant waste into high-protein animal feed. We ourselves eat a number of the large, spore-producing structures developed by fungi—mushrooms, chanterelles, morels and truffles are all familiar to devotees of French cuisine, who prize them for their unique flavours. Some of the parasitic forms are now being recruited to attack insects, weeds and other fungi which threaten our welfare. And fungi in intimate, obligatory association with the roots of almost all higher plants (forming **mycorrhizae**), silently and invisibly perpetuate one of the world's oldest and most successful forms of mutualistic symbiosis. You will find more detail on many of these topics in the appropriate chapters of this book.

Phylum ZYGOMYCOTA: Conjugating Fungi

The first eumycotan Phylum is the Zygomycota. Although this Phylum contains fewer than 1% of the species of fungi, its members are distinctive, and some of them are common, fast-growing, primary colonizers of substrates containing accessible carbon sources like sugar or starch. Their name is derived from the way in which they reproduce sexually by the fusion or **conjugation** of morphologically similar gametangia to form a **zygosporangium** (the **teleomorphic** phase). 'Zygos' is Greek for a yoke or joining, and the unfolding of this diagnostic process in the genus *Phycomyces* is illustrated by a sequence of four drawings (Fig. 3.3). The gametangia arise from hyphae of a single mycelium in **homothallic** species, or from different but sexually compatible mycelia in **heterothallic** species. Zygosporangia usually develop thick walls, and act as resting spores.

Zygosporangia are not really common in Nature, but asexual or **anamorphic** phases of zygomycetes are easily found on mouldy bread or peaches, or on horse dung. (You may snicker or turn up your nose, but the truth is that if you collect some fresh horse dung, keep it in a damp chamber, and look at it through a dissecting microscope every day, you should be rewarded by the sequential appearance of fruiting structures of a large number of specialized **coprophilous** fungi—and the sequence is likely to begin with one or two spectacular zygomycetes, particularly *Pilobolus*, which is discussed below: see also chapter 11). The asexual mitospores are usually formed inside mitosporangia borne at the tips of specialized sporangiophores. Zygomycete cell walls are mainly of **chitin** and the nuclei in their vegetative hyphae are haploid.

Phylum Zygomycota contains two major taxa: **Classes Zygomycetes** and **Trichomycetes**. I will concentrate on the first of these, since many of its members are common and successful saprobes. The Trichomycetes, on the other hand, live attached to the lining of the guts of insects or aquatic arthropods, and don't exactly draw attention to themselves. Within the Class Zygomycetes, I will introduce you to four orders: the **Mucorales**, the **Entomophthorales**, the **Kickxellales**, and the **Glomales**. The affinities of the Glomales are still uncertain, since they almost never reproduce sexually, but their mutualistic symbiotic relationships with the roots of most higher plants are so important that they are the subject of half of chapter 17.

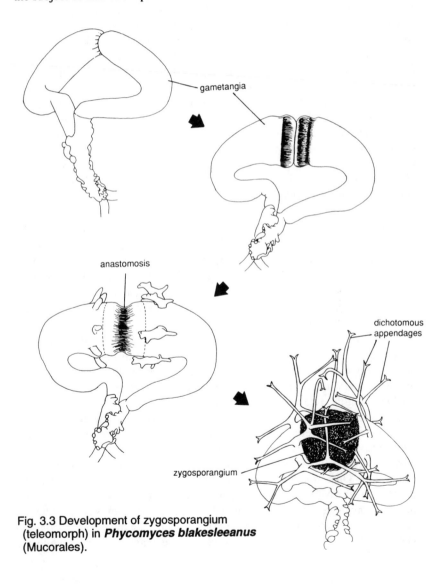

Fig. 3.3 Development of zygosporangium
(teleomorph) in **Phycomyces blakesleeanus**
(Mucorales).

1) **Order Mucorales** has 12 families which include all the common saprobic zygomycetes. Here belong the ubiquitous bread mould, *Rhizopus stolonifer* (Fig. 3.4 A), and the equally common genus *Mucor*. Each spherical **mitosporangium** of these fungi contains hundreds of non-motile spores, and these mitosporangia are produced at the ends of tall, stout, simple or branched hyphae called **sporangiophores**. The trade-mark of the family Mucoraceae is a swollen extension of the sporangiophore called a **columella** (Fig. 3.4 A), which protrudes into the mitosporangium, and often persists after the delicate outer peridium of the sporangium has disappeared and the sporangiospores have been dispersed. Other families often have fewer spores per sporangium, and their sporangia have no columella. *Thamnidium elegans* (Fig. 3.4 D), seems to compromise: its tall sporangiophores have one large, terminal, columellate sporangium, but lower on the stalk there are branches which fork repeatedly in a dichotomous manner, the final branchlets ending in tiny mitosporangia which contain only a few spores (if you don't know what 'dichotomous' means, please look it up in the glossary: get used to looking up every new word you come across). The reductionist tendency is also evident in *Blakeslea trispora* (Fig. 3.4 B), which has only three spores per mitosporangium; and the trend reaches its logical conclusion in *Cunninghamella* (Fig. 3.4 C), which has only one spore per mitosporangium, and in which the walls of spore and sporangium appear to have fused. Now the whole mitosporangium becomes detached and acts as a dispersal unit. Reduced mitosporangia which produce only one or a few spores are often called **sporangioles**.

Although mucoralean fungi can go through cycle after cycle—spore, mycelium, sporangium, spore—producing only asexual mitosporangia (the **anamorph**), they do on occasion form sexual zygosporangia (the **teleomorph**), perhaps as a survival mechanism, perhaps for the benefits conferred by genetic recombination, or perhaps because compatible strains of a heterothallic species have had one of their rare encounters. The anamorph-teleomorph alternation is illustrated in Fig. 3.5 for one of the commonest and most successful members of the Mucorales, *Rhizopus stolonifer*.

When compatible strains of *Phycomyces blakesleeanus* meet, individual hyphae establish very intimate contact, as you can see in Fig. 3.3, where they develop finger-like outgrowths and seem to grapple with one another. This intimate contact allows them to exchange chemical identification signals which establish that the two mycelia are indeed sexually compatible. Then the two hyphae grow apart again, only to loop back, swelling as they approach each other, and finally meeting each other head-on. They have become **gametangia**, which fuse when their tips touch. This is the only time in the life of a zygomycete when different cells fuse (though as we shall see later, such fusion is a common event in the Dikaryomycota, even between non-reproductive, assimilative hyphae). After the walls between the two gametangial tips have broken down and their multinucleate contents have mixed, the mixture is quickly isolated by two septa, and the paired-off nuclei fuse. The structure is now called a **zygosporangium**, and it develops a thick and often ornamented wall, even while still supported on either side by the former gametangia, which are now called **suspensors**. Although the two suspensors are now just empty appendages, they give zygosporangia a highly diagnostic appearance.

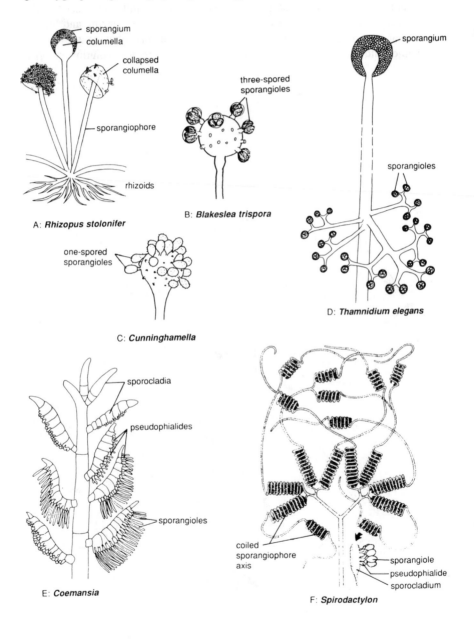

Fig. 3.4 Anamorphs in the Zygomycota. A-D: Mucorales; E,F: Kickxellales.

Zygosporangia vary in minor ways from one genus to another, and among families and orders, but they are generally rather similar, so if they are present, they are the easiest way to tell if a fungus is a zygomycete (Figs. 3.3, 3.6 D,F). By contrast, the anamorphic phases of zygomycetes—mitosporangia and the structures on which they are borne—have evolved some amazing and bizarre adaptations (Fig. 3.4). This contrast between teleomorphic constancy and anamorphic diversity is presumably the result of differing evolutionary pres-

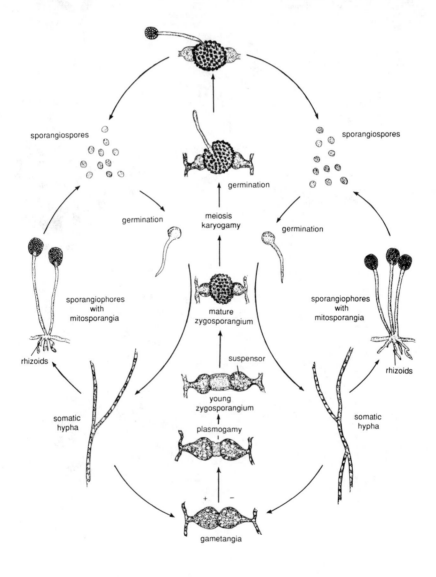

Fig. 3.5 Mucorales: life cycle of *Rhizopus stolonifer*.

sures. Long-term survival, one of the main objectives of the teleomorph, is presumably best ensured by structures with minimal surface area and thick, protective walls. Dispersal, the main purpose of most anamorphs, can be achieved in many ways. I will describe three of the more specialized zygomycetous anamorphs.

Pilobolus crystallinus (Fig. 3.6 A-D) is an atypical but fascinating **coprophilous** (dung-inhabiting) member of the order Mucorales. It grows very rapidly, and is one of the first fungi to fruit in the extended succession that occurs on dung (see chapter 11). Its unbranched sporangiophores are 2-4 cm tall, and have a unique explosive dispersal mechanism. Beneath the black apical mitosporangium is a lens-like **subsporangial vesicle**, with a light-sensitive 'retina' at its base that controls the growth of the sporangiophore very precisely (Fig. 3.6 B,C), aiming it accurately toward any light source. In a word, it is **phototropic**. Osmotically active compounds cause pressure in the sporangiophore and the subsporangial vesicle to build up until it is more than 100 pounds per square inch (7 kilograms per square centimetre). This pressure eventually causes the vesicle to explode, hurling the mitosporangial head away to a distance of up to 2 metres, directly toward the light. The mucilaginous contents of the subsporangial vesicle go with the sporangium, and glue it to whatever it lands on. Can you explain why *Pilobolus* needs such a specialized mechanism for spore dispersal: such a powerful cannon, so carefully aimed? You can find the answer in chapter 11. Note that the originality of *Pilobolus* extends only to the behaviour of its anamorph—the teleomorph (the zygosporangium, shown in Fig. 3.6 D) is fairly conventional.

2) **Order Entomophthorales.** As the name implies, these fungi often attack insects. *Entomophthora muscae* infects, and eventually kills, houseflies. Dying flies, their bodies riddled by the fungus, usually crawl into exposed situations —I find them on windows, and on the growing tips of shrubs in my garden— where the fungal infection bursts through the insects' exoskeleton and produces tightly-packed masses of sporangiophores (Fig. 3.6 E). Each sporangiophore bears one unicellular, sticky mitosporangium that is forcibly shot away at maturity. When the fly dies on a window, this barrage produces a whitish halo of mitosporangia on the glass. These sporangia, though rather short-lived, can infect other unsuspecting flies that come to pay their last respects. As you may already have guessed, species of *Entomophthora* are being investigated for their potential in biological control of insect pests. Note again that their zygosporangia, though developing in an unusual way, by the fusion of hyphal bodies inside the fly, are still recognizable (Fig. 3.6 F).

3) **Order Kickxellales** (Named after a mycologist called Kickx). Members of this order are atypical of the Zygomycetes in that they often have regularly septate hyphae. Their teleomorphs are unremarkable, but they develop some of the most complex anamorphs known. I have found *Coemansia* (Fig. 3.4 E) on bat dung from a cave. Its tall sporangiophore bears many fertile side branches called **sporocladia**. Each of these produces a row of lateral cells called **pseudo-**

phialides (true phialides are discussed in chapter 4). Finally, from the apex of each pseudophialide arises an elongate, one-spored mitosporangium (a sporangiole). That's complex enough, but it looks simple beside *Spirodactylon* (Fig. 3.4 F). This, surely the most elaborate of all zygomycetous anamorphs, produces a tall, branched sporangiophore that is repeatedly thrown into tight coils. Within these coils arise the sporocladia, which bear pseudophialides, which bear one-spored sporangioles. It is hard to imagine why this strange configuration might have evolved, until one learns that the fungus grows on mouse and rat dung. Coprophilous fungi have various highly evolved strategies for getting back inside the gut of the animals that produce their preferred substrate. This isn't too difficult for genera like *Pilobolus*, that grow on herbivore dung, since all they have to do is get their spores onto the animal's food, which is all around. But rats and mice are not herbivores, and it is essentially impossible for the fungus to ensure that its spores will be present on their food. The only alternative

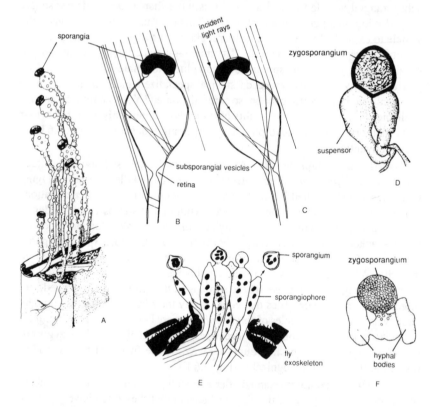

Fig. 3.6 A-D: *Pilobolus* (Mucorales). A: habit of sporangiophores (anamorph) on dung: beaded appearance is caused by condensation droplets; B,C: action of subsporangial vesicle and retinal area in phototropism; D: zygosporangium (teleomorph). E,F: *Entomophthora* (Entomophthorales). E: section through the anamorph sporulating on a fly; F: zygosporangium (teleomorph) arising by fusion of hyphal bodies.

(as I see it) is to attach spores to the animal itself, in the hope that they will be ingested during grooming activities. Rats and mice are creatures of habit, using well-trodden paths each day. Along these trails they deposit dung, and there, later, the coils of *Spirodactylon* become entangled in their hair. Only the zygosporangia of the Kickxellales convince us that these strange fungi are indeed zygomycetes.

4) **Order Glomales**. These soil-inhabiting fungi are placed in the Zygomycota only tentatively, since almost none of them form either zygosporangia or asexual sporangiospores. Nevertheless, they are extremely important, because their hyphae enter the living root cells of perhaps 90% of all higher plants and establish with them obligate mutualistic symbioses called **vesicular-arbuscular mycorrhizae (VAM)** or **endomycorrhizae**. These are discussed in detail in chapter 17, where the six endomycorrhizal genera—*Glomus, Gigaspora, Acaulospora, Sclerocystis, Entrophospora* and *Scutellospora*—are also illustrated. VAM fungi won't grow in **axenic** culture: they must be associated with a plant root. Their generally very large and thick-walled resting spores are common in most soils, and are stimulated to germinate by the proximity of plant roots (almost any plant will do, because these fungi have such wide host-ranges). Their largely non-septate hyphae ramify through the soil and enter living roots, where they develop two kinds of diagnostic structures: (A) intracellular, finely branched, tree-like **arbuscules** which are the interface across which the fungus exchanges mineral nutrients, especially phosphorus, for photosynthates; (B) intra- and inter-cellular swollen cells called **vesicles** or **intramatrical spores**, which store lipids and may act as resting spores. The soil-inhabiting mycelium is very efficient at mobilising insoluble phosphorus and translocating it to the plant. Since the low level of available phosphorus in poor soils is often the limiting nutrient for plant growth, VAM fungi help plants to thrive in such soils, and are therefore of great potential value in agriculture.

Further Reading

Benjamin, R.K. (1959) The merosporangiferous Mucorales. Aliso **4**:321-453.

Benjamin, R.K. (1979) Zygomycetes and their spores. pp. 573-621 (in) **The Whole Fungus**. Vol. 2. (Ed. B. Kendrick) National Museums of Canada, Ottawa.

Cerda-Olmedo, E. and E.D. Lepson (Eds.) (1987) *Phycomyces*. Cold Spring Harbor, N.Y.

Fuller, M.S. (Ed.) (1978) **Lower Fungi in the Laboratory**. Department of Botany, University of Georgia, Athens.

Ingold, C.T. (1978) **The Biology of Mucor and its Allies**. Edward Arnold, London.

Kendrick, B. and S.M. Berch (1985) Mycorrhizae: applications in agriculture and forestry. pp. 109-152 (in) **Comprehensive Biotechnology**. Vol. 3. (Ed.) C. Robinson. Pergamon, Oxford.

Morton, J.B. and G.L. Benny (1990) Revised classification of arbuscular mycorrhizal fungi (Zygomycetes): a new order, Glomales, two new suborders, Glomineae and Gigasporineae, and two new families, Acaulosporaceae and Gigasporaceae, with an emendation of Glomaceae. Mycotaxon **37**: 471-491.

O'Donnell, K.L. (1979) **Zygomycetes in Culture**. Department of Botany, University of Georgia, Athens.

Schenck, N.C. (1982) **Methods and Principles of Mycorrhizal Research**. American Phytopathological Society, St. Paul.

Zycha, H., R. Siepmann and G. Linnemann (1969) **Mucorales. Eine Beschreibung aller Gattungen und Arten dieser Pilzgruppe**. Cramer, Lehre.

Chapter 4

Eumycotan Fungi:
(2) Phylum Dikaryomycota
(A) Subphylum Ascomycotina

Introduction

Zygomycetes are terrestrial fungi: there's no doubt about that. But they thrive and sporulate only in damp places where the atmosphere is more or less saturated with moisture. For example, *Rhizopus stolonifer* will colonize the moist interior of a loaf of bread, but won't produce its characteristic sporangiophores and mitosporangia on the outside of the bread unless the surrounding atmosphere is humid. If we induce sporulation by keeping the loaf in a damp chamber (a plastic bag containing a little water will do) and then remove the bag, the sporangiophores will quickly collapse. The same is true of *Pilobolus* on dung.

Hyphae of most zygomycetes are wide, thin-walled, and **coenocytic**—continuous tubes which have no internal mechanical support. By contrast, hyphae of Phylum Dikaryomycota (**Ascomycetes** plus **Basidiomycetes**) are narrower, and are **septate**—they have cross-walls called septa at regular intervals. These miniature bulkheads both strengthen the hyphae and limit loss of cytoplasm if a hypha is damaged. As a result, we find that dikaryomycotan fungi have a wider ecological range: they can often grow and fruit in drier conditions than zygomycetes could tolerate. Some dikaryomycotan anamorphs grow in dead leaves and stems of desert plants, and others are the most **xerotolerant** of all organisms, able to grow at water activities below 0.70 (for example, on jams, salt fish and other substrates of extremely high osmotic pressure).

While many zygomycetes can assimilate only 'accessible' substrates like sugars and starch, ascomycetes can often exploit cellulose, and many basidiomycetes can digest both cellulose and lignin, carbon sources available to remarkably few other organisms. Though fungi cannot fix atmospheric nitrogen (this talent seems to be restricted to the prokaryotes), dikaryomycotan fungi can use many different forms of combined nitrogen: some ascomycetes even specialize in metabolizing the protein keratin, the main structural component of hair and skin. In case you were wondering if members of this group constitute a health hazard—they do. Some other orders are obligate parasites of plants. Remember the 'downy mildews' caused by oomycetes? Well, there are also plant diseases called 'powdery mildews' that are caused by ascomycetes: the similarity of terminology is unfortunate, but try to remember the difference, because although the groups of fungi involved are both obligately biotrophic, the diseases are different in many important ways, such as host ranges and methods of control. This is just one example of how taxonomy has practical implications (see chapter 12).

Thousands of basidiomycetes, and a quite a few ascomycetes, establish intimate mutualistic symbioses (mycorrhizae) with the roots of trees, especially conifers (see chapter 17). Nearly 18,000 ascomycetes, and a few basidiomycetes, have domesticated algae, thus becoming lichens, which can live in some of the world's harshest climates, and colonize the barest and most inhospitable substrates (see chapter 7). Some dikaryomycotan fungi have even re-entered the water and, lacking motile cells, have evolved other mechanisms, such as long appendages, to aid spore dispersal. Dikaryomycotan fungi range from unspecialized, almost omnivorous saprobes, to fungi so specialized and ecologically demanding that they are found only on one particular leg of one species of insect. Some dikaryomycotan fruit bodies are microscopic (as in many ascomycetes), but often (especially among the basidiomycetes), they are large and complex, and most of the common names applied to fungi refer to the visible teleomorphs of basidiomycetes, and in a few cases, ascomycetes. You may already be acquainted with some of these: I will introduce you to many more in the pages ahead.

Characteristics of Teleomorphs

Most dikaryomycotan fungi share a number of important features —(1) chitinous cell walls; (2) hyphae with regular cross-walls called **septa** (centrally perforated to allow movement of cytoplasm, and sometimes nuclei, between compartments) (note that many yeasts are unicellular, so don't produce hyphae); (3) the ability of somatic, assimilative hyphae to fuse with one another (**anastomosis**) and to exchange nuclei; and (4) the occurrence in their life cycles (or at least in those which produce a teleomorph) of a unique nuclear phenomenon called the **dikaryon**. After sexually compatible nuclei from different mycelia have been brought together, they pair off, but don't fuse immediately to form a diploid zygote. Instead, they go on dividing synchronously to populate what are called dikaryotic hyphae, in which each compartment has two compatible haploid nuclei. Oh, yes, they do fuse eventually, but not before the plot has thickened considerably, and often (at least in basidiomycetes) not for a long time. Read on.

If ascomycetes and basidiomycetes share all these things, how do they differ? Actually, in many ways, and with experience it's usually easy to tell their sexual fructifications apart with the naked eye. But their microscopic, unicellular meiosporangia are most diagnostic of all (Fig. 4.1). Those of ascomycetes are called **asci** (singular, **ascus**). They look like little cylinders or sacs, and they often contain **eight** haploid meiospores (**ascospores**) which are usually forcibly expelled all at once into the air through the top of the meiosporangium at maturity. The meiosporangia of basidiomycetes are called **basidia** (singular, **basidium**): they usually have **four** tiny projections called **sterigmata**, each bearing a haploid meiospore (**basidiospore**) which is shot away individually at maturity. The formation of asci or basidia always marks the end of the dikaryophase: the paired nuclei have finally fused and the resulting zygote nucleus has then undergone meiosis (and a subsequent mitosis in ascomycetes) to produce the 8 haploid ascospores or the 4 haploid basidiospores.

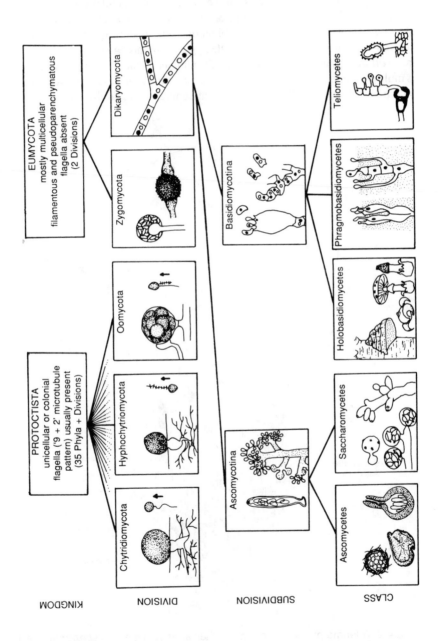

Fig. 4.1 Diagnostic chart of fungal Phyla, and the Classes of Dikaryomycota.

Now let me explain the sexual (teleomorphic) part of the ascomycete life cycle from the beginning (Fig. 4.2). When an ascospore germinates, it establishes a haploid mycelium. In heterothallic ascomycetes, this cannot undergo sexual reproduction until it meets another compatible haploid mycelium. When this presumably rare event takes place, the fungus very cleverly maximizes the ensuing potential for genetic recombination. One would expect there to be a single sexual fusion resulting in a single zygote. But most ascomycetes interpolate a **dikaryophase**. During this phase the number of pairs of compatible nuclei is multiplied enormously as dikaryotic hyphae (often called ascogenous hyphae) which have two compatible nuclei in each compartment, ramify within a mass

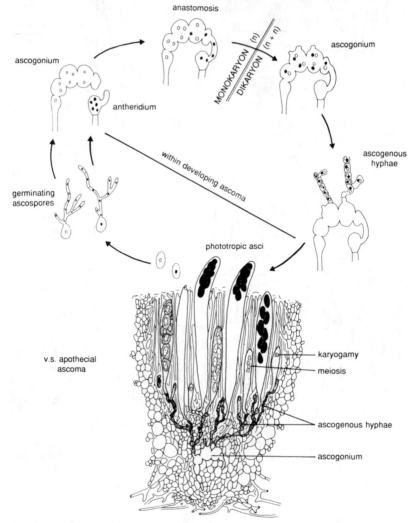

Fig. 4.2 Teleomorphic cycle of an apothecial ascomycete, **Ascobolus** (Pezizales) (see text for full explanation).

of monokaryotic (haploid) tissue which is the framework of the future fruit body (the **ascoma**).

Eventually, the ultimate branches of the dikaryotic hyphae, which in larger ascomata are by now very numerous, reach their ordained positions in the future hymenium and the long-delayed sexual fusions take place. The genome is reshuffled during the ensuing meiosis in each ascus (this recombination is due to crossing-over, which is explained in chapter 10). Each meiosis will produce a different arrangement of the genome. In this way the products of a single encounter are multiplied, and meiosis then generates a lot of genetic diversity. Not only is the dikaryon itself an unusual phenomenon, but during the dikaryo-phase an effectively diploid mycelium is growing within, and drawing nourishment from, the haploid ascoma tissue. This phenomenon has interesting parallels in the red algae, though I and most other mycologists don't think these imply any close relationship between the two groups (both lack motile gametes and appear to have simply hit upon the same solution to the problem posed by the rarity of sexual encounters).

Ascospores are not motile, in the sense of self-propelling, but most ascomycetes nevertheless send their ascospores on their way with a burst of kinetic energy. The ascus is a tiny spore-gun, which works by building up internal pressure, then releasing it through the tip. The job of many asci is to get their ascospores into the turbulent airflow above the ascoma. The mature asci of the dung-inhabiting *Ascobolus* shown in Fig. 4.2 project above the hymenium and point toward the light before discharging their spores. In this way they ensure that the spores will not run into any obstacles on their upward flight (see chapter 8).

The multicellular structures (ascomata) that produce the asci, and act as the platforms from which the spores are launched, come in four main designs, sectional views of which are shown in Fig. 4.3. The construction of the ascoma may allow many asci to discharge simultaneously (the **apothecial ascoma**); it may permit discharge of only one ascus at a time (**perithecial** and **pseudothecial ascomata**), or it may lack an opening entirely (the **cleistothecial ascoma**). This last condition indicates that the asci no longer shoot their spores, and that the fungus has evolved another dispersal strategy. This may happen because the fungus always fruits in a confined space (for example, under bark, or below the surface of the ground) where airborne dispersal cannot operate. We often find that the spores of such fungi are dispersed by animals: later I will introduce you to two excellent examples of this.

But before we go on to explore the many orders of ascomycetes, we must take a closer look at the ascus itself (Fig. 4.3). All asci are not the same. Asci come in two basic kinds, called **unitunicate** and **bitunicate**. Unitunicate asci, as their name suggests, appear to have a single wall. Sometimes these asci have a tiny built-in lid or **operculum**: at maturity the lid pops open so that the spores can be ejected. These asci are called **unitunicate-operculate**, and are found only in apothecial ascomata. Other asci have no operculum, but have a special elastic ring mechanism built into their tip. This is a pre-set pressure release valve, or sphincter, and the ring eventually stretches momentarily, or turns inside out, to let the spores shoot through. Such asci are called **unitunicate-inoperculate**, and are found in most perithecial and some apothecial ascomata. But some unitunicate asci have no active spore-shooting mechanism. These asci are usually more or less spherical, and are found in cleistothecial (occasionally perithecial) ascomata. Sometimes the wall of

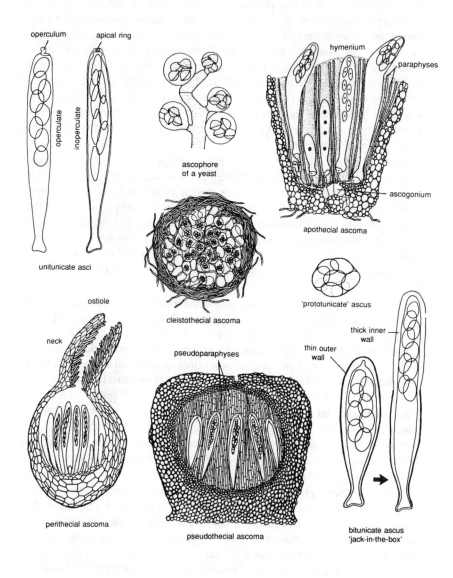

Fig. 4.3 Teleomorphs: asci, ascophore and sectional views of ascomata.

this kind of ascus dissolves at maturity and releases the ascospores, which can then ooze, rather than be shot, out of the ascoma; or they may wait inside until it decays or is ruptured. These asci are sometimes called **prototunicate**. Yet perhaps because they are found in several otherwise rather different orders, it seems very probable that they represent a secondary condition, and have evolved several times from unitunicate asci.

The other basic kind of ascus is called **bitunicate** because it has a double wall. There is a thin, inextensible outer layer, and a thick, elastic inner layer. At maturity the thin outer wall splits, and the thick inner wall absorbs water and expands upward, carrying the ascospores with it. This 'Jack-in-a-box' design allows the ascus to stretch up into the narrow neck of the ascoma to expel its spores. The structure and the dehiscence mechanism of the bitunicate ascus are so different from those of the unitunicate ascus that we can only assume these two diverged a long time ago. This impression is reinforced when we discover that although the pseudothecial ascomata in which bitunicate asci develop are often superficially similar to perithecial ascomata, their internal arrangements are rather different.

In many unitunicate ascomycetes, the perithecial ascoma develops only after the sexual stimulus, so that the asci can grow into an actively enlarging cavity. In many bitunicate ascomycetes, fertilization doesn't happen until after a solid primordium or stroma has developed, so room has to be made for the asci by dissolving away existing tissue. In some cases the asci themselves do the job, but in others it is carried out by special sterile hyphae (pseudoparaphyses) growing down from the upper layer of the stroma; the asci then grow up between them. Remember that these pseudothecial ascomata always produce bitunicate asci.

Characteristics of Anamorphs

In any modern consideration of the Ascomycetes, we cannot ignore their asexual reproductive phases. You already know that zygomycetes have a wide range of mitosporangial asexual phases producing numerous mitospores. So you won't be surprised to discover that many ascomycetes have comparable asexual (anamorphic) phases during which they reproduce rapidly, and often relatively cheaply, by means of mitospores called **conidia**. The asexually reproducing phase of the ascomycete life cycle was more or less ignored for many years in favour of teleomorph studies. But when we consider that the anamorph is an important (and sometimes the only) phenotypic expression of many ascomycete genotypes, we realize that it has much to tell us.

Though they play essentially the same role in the life cycle, the anamorphs of ascomycetes differ from those of zygomycetes in two very important respects. (A) While zygomycete mitospores orginate by **free-cell formation** inside a sporangium, mitospores (conidia) of ascomycetes are basically modified bits of hyphae, either budded out as a new structure, or converted from an existing cell: completely different techniques. (B) In zygomycetes, anamorph and teleomorph often occur together (especially in homothallic species) and always share the same binomial. In ascomycetes, anamorph and teleomorph often develop at different times, and on different substrates. In many cases each phase has often been collected in total ignorance of the existence of the other, and because of this, the Botanical Code of Nomenclature maintains that it is legal to give them separate binomials. Even though a few thousand anamorph-teleomorph connections have now been established, these represent only a small proportion of the total number of taxa, either of anamorphs or teleomorphs. Because anamorphs so often occur alone, it is still normal and accepted practice to go on using separate binomials for them, as you will see. Nevertheless, I find it completely unacceptable to talk about conidial fungi, as many other texts do, as if they constituted a separate major high-level taxon called the 'Deuteromycotina.' This ignores both the evidence that they are all expressions of dikaryomycotan genomes, and the thousands of connections that have already been established with teleomorphs.

Of about 30,000 known ascomycetes, over 4,000 have been connected to their anamorphs. What about the many thousands of conidial fungi that are still 'orphans'? It is likely that many anamorphic fungi have given up sex altogether, and become 'anamorphic-holomorphs,' though they seem to have retained genetic flexibility by: (a) having more than one kind of nucleus in their mycelia (**heterokaryosis**) as a result of occasional anastomosis; (b) undergoing a complex **parasexual** process involving rare somatic diploidization, mitotic crossing-over, and finally a return to the haploid condition (this process is more fully explained in chapter 10).

It turns out that the conidial fungi are a mixed bag: although most of them are (or were) part of ascomycete life cycles, some are (or were) connected with basidiomycetes. Despite this mixed ancestry, we have had to set up a single classification for all of them, because it is often impossible to tell in which subphylum the connection lies. Unfortunately, our scheme for classifying the anamorphs has so far been able to make little reference to teleomorphs, for several reasons: (1) teleomorphs are known for only 10-15% of anamorphic species; (2) members of what seems to be a single anamorph genus may have teleomorphs in many different teleomorph genera (which may belong to different orders)—this must be due to convergent evolution among anamorphs; (3) anamorphs belonging to several different anamorph genera can have sexual phases in a single teleomorph genus—this must be due to radiative evolution among anamorphs. So our attempts to classify anamorphs have concentrated on: (A) their mitospores (**conidia**), (B) the diverse structures (**conidiogenous cells, conidiophores** and **conidiomata**) which bear them, and (C) the ways in which they develop (**conidiogenesis**).

Morphology of Anamorphs

There are over 1650 described genera of conidial fungi, and at least 20,000 described species, and these numbers are increasing rapidly. The first really useful classification of dikaryomycotan anamorphs, established in the late 19th century, was based on mature morphology (Fig. 4.4). The principal characteristics used were: (1) colour, septation and shape of conidia; (2) conidiophore aggregation, or lack of it; (3) the production of conidia in enclosed structures or the absence of such enclosure.

The easiest decision to make is usually which Anamorph-Class (an artificial but convenient taxon) a conidial fungus belongs to—Hyphomycetes or Coelomycetes. You can recognize a hyphomycete because its conidiophores can be single or aggregated in various ways, but are never enclosed within a covered conidioma. Coelomycetes form their conidia in a variety of enclosed conidiomata, which usually develop just beneath the surface of their plant substrate. The first kind is the **acervular conidioma** or acervulus (Fig. 4.4). This may develop at various depths within the host: it can be subcuticular (covered only by the host cuticle); intraepidermal (arising within the cells of the epidermis); subepidermal; or developing beneath several layers of host cells. Under this roof of host material, fungal hyphae aggregate and soon form a flat fertile layer of short conidiophores that produce many conidia. The pressure of accumulating conidia, and often of accessory mucilage, eventually ruptures the host integument and allows the conidia to escape.

At the other end of the spectrum is the flask-shaped **pycnidial conidioma** or pycnidium (Fig. 4.4) in which the fungus itself provides the integument, and conidia eventually escape through an apical **ostiole**. Although these were the only two structures recognized in older literature, we have observed that there are many intermediate conditions—for example, the roof of an apparently acervular conidioma may contain fungal as well as host tissue, or the ostiole of an apparently pycnidial conidioma may open very widely at maturity. These intermediates have led us to coin the terms **acervuloid** and **pycnidioid** for such conidiomata, depending on which of the archetypes they resemble more. Among the hyphomycetes, conidiophores are usually solitary, though they sometimes form columnar aggregations called **synnematal conidiomata** or synnemata (Fig. 4.4) or cushion-shaped masses called **sporodochial conidiomata** or sporodochia (Fig. 4.4).

Next we examine the characters of the conidia. Presence or absence of pigment is often an important feature. Shape and septation are next on the list. There are seven categories, all illustrated at the top of Fig. 4.4. (1) Commonest of all are relatively nondescript, single-celled **amerospores**. (2) The addition of one cross-wall makes them **didymospores**. (3) Two or more septa, arranged like the rungs of a ladder, characterize **phragmospores**. (4) Septa running two ways, like the meshes of a net, or the mortar layers of a brick wall, identify **dictyospores**. (5) Conidia curved through more than a half-circle, or coiled in two or three dimensions, are called **helicospores**. (6) Those with several conspicuous, radiating arms or other projections are called **staurospores**. (7) Finally, those which are long and thin (more than 15 times as long as they are wide), are called **scolecospores** (which, appropriately enough, means 'worm-like').

Conidiogenesis

It was discovered that conidial fungi use a number of different techniques to produce their spores. Since these represent genuine 'embryological' differences, they have become important elements of our classification. Initially we check an anamorph to see which of two basic patterns of development it exhibits. In **blastic conidiogenesis** (Fig. 4.5 A), the young conidium is recognizable before it is cut off by a cross-wall (this is an extension of the idea of cells 'budding'). In **thallic conidiogenesis** (Fig. 4.5 B), the cross-wall is laid down before

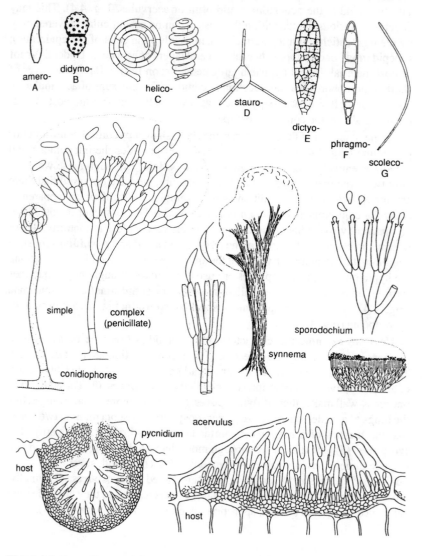

Fig. 4.4 Anamorphs: conidia, conidiophores and conidiomata.

differentiation of the conidium begins. Ripe conidia may also be liberated in two basic ways, schizolytic and rhexolytic. In **schizolytic dehiscence** the halves of a double septum split apart by the breakdown of a kind of middle lamella (Fig. 4.5 C). In **rhexolytic dehiscence** the outer wall of a cell beneath or between conidia breaks down (Fig. 4.5 D). We will examine eight different kinds of conidium development: six blastic, two thallic.

Type I: blastic-acropetal or blastic-synchronous conidiogenesis (Fig. 4.6)

In the *Cladosporium* anamorph of *Mycosphaerella tassiana* (Bitunicatae: Dothideales), a common mould on decaying organic matter; and in the *Monilia* anamorph of *Monilinia fructicola* (Unitunicatae-Inoperculatae: Leotiales), the brown rot fungus of peach and other stone fruits, conidia develop in chains by

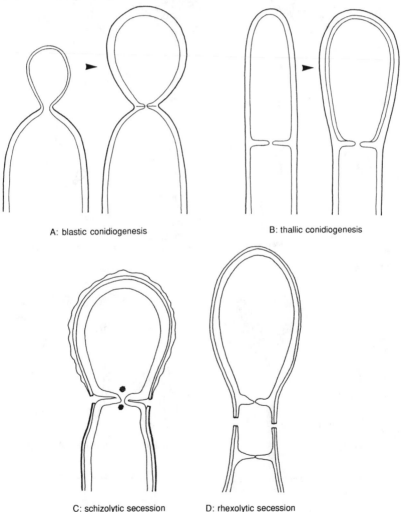

A: blastic conidiogenesis

B: thallic conidiogenesis

C: schizolytic secession   D: rhexolytic secession

Fig. 4.5 Basic modes of conidium development and release.

apical budding. The youngest conidium is at the tip of the chain. The chain branches when two buds, rather than one, develop on a terminal conidium. Note that food must be translocated up the chain through all existing conidia if new conidia are to go on forming. This is clearly just a modified form of hyphal growth. The *Botrytis* anamorphs of *Botryotinia* spp. (Unitunicatae-Inoperculatae: Leotiales), and the hyphomycete, *Gonatobotryum* (teleomorph unknown),

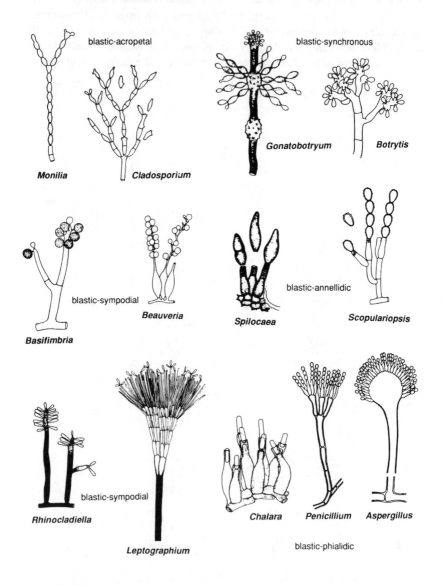

Fig. 4.6 Representative anamorphs with blastic conidiogenesis.

produce many conidia synchronously on a swollen cell: *Gonatobotryum* goes on to form acropetal chains of secondary conidia, while *Botrytis* does not.

Type II: blastic-sympodial conidiogenesis (Fig.4.6)

In species of *Beauveria*, hyphomycetous insect pathogens which are now being used in biological control of potato beetle, the narrow apex of the conidiogenous cell extends sympodially: each new apex becomes converted into a blastic conidium, then the next apex grows out from behind and to one side of it. The more conidia are produced, the longer the conidiogenous cell becomes. Although *Leptographium* anamorphs of *Ophiostoma* (Prototunicatae: Ophiostomatales) have single conidiophores, these have complex heads with several tiers of supporting cells (metulae), the ultimate ones bearing many sympodially (or percurrently) extending conidiogenous cells, and innumerable conidia accumulate in a slimy head; these spores are insect-dispersed. *Basifimbria* (teleomorph unknown), which is common on horse dung, has simple conidiophores that elongate sympodially during conidiation.

Type III: blastic-annellidic, blastic-percurrent conidiogenesis (Fig. 4.7 A)

In the *Spilocaea* anamorph of *Venturia inaequalis* (Bitunicatae: Dothideales), the apple scab fungus, each seceding conidium leaves a ring-like scar, an annellation, around the conidiogenous cell, which then grows on through the scar ('percurrently') to produce the next conidium. Conidiogenous cells that have produced seven spores bear seven annular scars—hence the name annellidic. The *Scopulariopsis* anamorph of *Microascus* (Prototunicatae: Ophiostomatales) has several annellidic conidiogenous cells on each conidiophore. The *Graphium* anamorphs of *Ophiostoma* (Ophiostomatales) produce synnematal conidiomata with many percurrent conidiogenous cells producing slimy conidia. The hyphomycete *Cephalotrichum* is similar, but has dry conidia.

It has recently been confirmed that some individual anamorphs can be both annellidic and sympodial. I'll give you two examples of how this knowledge may change our classification. When it was thought, not many years ago, that conidiogenesis in the synnematal anamorphs of *Ophiostoma* species was either exclusively sympodial or exclusively percurrent, they were segregated into two anamorph genera (*Pesotum* and *Graphium*), but now it has been shown that both kinds of conidiogenesis can occur on the same conidiophore, they are being united again in the older genus, *Graphium*. In exactly the same way, some complex mononematous anamorphs of *Ophiostoma* species were segregated into the 'exclusively sympodial' *Verticicladiella* and the 'exclusively percurrent' *Leptographium*, but are now united under the older name.

Type IV: blastic-phialidic conidiogenesis (Fig. 4.6, 4.7 B)

Many common moulds produce conidia in rapid basipetal succession from the open end of special conidiogenous cells called **phialides**. The *Penicillium* anamorphs of *Talaromyces*, the *Aspergillus* anamorphs of *Eurotium* and *Emericella* (both Prototunicatae: Eurotiales), and the *Chalara* anamorphs of *Ceratocystis* (Prototunicatae: Ophiostomatales) as well as plant pathogenic hyphomycetes like *Fusarium* and *Verticillium*, anamorphs of *Nectria* and *Hypocrea* (Unitunicatae-Inoperculatae: Hypocreales), both of which cause serious wilt diseases of crop plants (and we must not forget the many species of these anamorph genera that have no known teleomorph)—all of these and thousands more produce phialides. Most phialides don't change in length while producing many successive conidia, though some elongate sympodially or percurrently

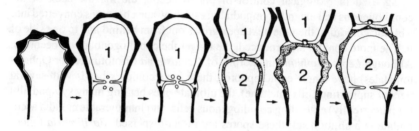

A: blastic-percurrent / blastic-annellidic

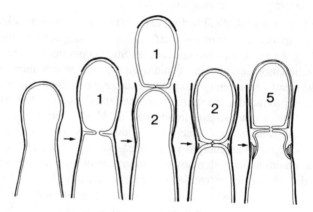

B: blastic-phialidic

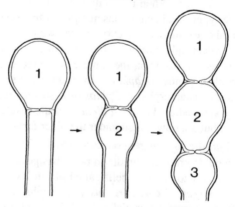

C: blastic-retrogressive

Fig. 4.7 Analysis of three modes of blastic conidiogenesis.

between conidiogenous episodes. *Penicillium* and *Aspergillus* are dry-spored, *Fusarium* and *Verticillium* have slimy spores. Phialidic ontogeny is basically rather similar to type III - percurrent.

Type V: blastic-retrogressive conidiogenesis (Fig. 4.7 C)

In the *Basipetospora* anamorph of *Monascus ruber* (a thermotolerant fungus used in Indonesia in the preparation of a red food colouring called Ang-kak), a conidium forms at the tip of the relatively undifferentiated conidiogenous hypha and is delimited by a cross-wall; then a short zone of the hypha just below the conidium balloons out evenly all around to produce the second conidium. After it has been delimited by a septum, the next segment of the hypha plasticizes and blows out. As the chain of conidia elongates, the conidiogenous hypha becomes shorter. A similar pattern of development occurs in *Trichothecium*, and in the *Cladobotryum* anamorphs of *Hypomyces* (Unitunicatae: Hypocreales). This appears to be a relatively rare type of conidiogenesis.

Type VI: basauxic conidiogenesis (Fig. 4.19)

In the *Oidium* anamorph of *Erysiphe graminis* (Unitunicatae: Erysiphales), whitish chains of conidia (the 'powdery mildew') cover the host leaves. Each chain consists of a graded series of gradually maturing conidia, the oldest at the tip, the youngest barely differentiated from the hyphal cell just below it. New material is added at the base of the chain in a form of **intercalary** growth, arising from a sometimes swollen mother cell which appears to be a highly modified phialide.

Type VII: thallic-arthric conidiogenesis (Fig. 4.8 A,B)

In the *Geotrichum* anamorphs of *Dipodascus* spp. (Saccharomycetes), an assimilative hypha stops growing, then becomes divided up into short lengths by irregularly arising septa. These are double septa which split apart schizolyti-cally to give a 'chain' of short cylindrical 'fission arthroconidia' that disarticu-lates and appears jointed (hence 'arthric'). In *Coremiella* (Fig. 4.8 B) some hyphal cells degenerate to release the intervening cells as 'alternate arthroconi-dia.' In *Oidiodendron* (Fig. 4.8 A), a common soil mould, the branches of an often tree-like conidiophore disarticulate into conidia, ultimately leaving only the denuded 'trunk,' (the stipe). Many basidiomycetes produce thallic-arthric conidia (Fig. 4.1).

Type VIII: thallic-solitary conidiogenesis (Fig. 4.8 C)

The *Microsporum* anamorphs of *Nannizzia* (Prototunicatae: Onygenales), which can digest keratin, and cause skin diseases in humans (see chapter 23), develop large thallic phragmospores at the ends of hyphae. These conidia are liberated rhexolytically.

One of the earliest kinds of 'developmental' information was the observation that some moulds produced conidia in chains, while others did not. But looking back over the various kinds of conidiogenesis I have just described, I think you could probably come up with no fewer than seven ways in which look-alike 'chains' of conidia can develop. These are seven good reasons why we no longer rely entirely on mature morphology in our classification of conidial fungi.

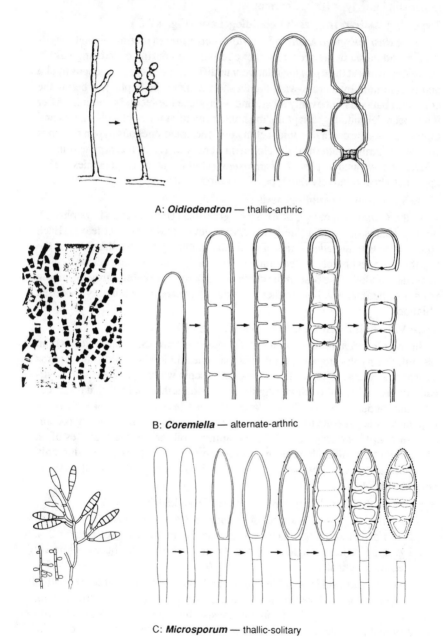

A: *Oidiodendron* — thallic-arthric

B: *Coremiella* — alternate-arthric

C: *Microsporum* — thallic-solitary

Fig. 4.8 Developmental analyses of thallic conidiogenesis.

Relevance of Conidial Anamorphs

Why is it important to be able to identify conidial fungi? Some of them literally grow on you. The most prevalent fungal diseases of humans (mycoses) are caused by conidial fungi. Various superficial mycoses, ranging from ringworm of the scalp, through jock itch (more vulgarly known as crotch-rot), to athlete's foot, are caused by keratin-attacking species of *Microsporum, Epidermophyton*, and *Trichophyton*. Although many of these have teleomorphs in the family Arthrodermataceae of order Onygenales (Prototunicatae), those teleomorphs never seem to develop when the fungus is growing on you.

When I compiled the fungi causing important plant diseases, I found that 62 were conidial fungi (hyphomycetes and coelomycetes), as compared to 111 from all other fungal groups combined. One of the most serious outbreaks of plant disease in recent years was the southern corn blight, caused by *Drechslera (Helminthosporium) maydis*, the anamorph of *Cochliobolus heterostrophus* (Bitunicatae: Dothideales), which devastated the U.S. corn crop in 1970. The special 'Texas male sterile' strain of corn becoming widely used for seed at that time was also highly susceptible to the fungus, which produces a toxin that disrupts membranes, especially those of the mitochondria, reducing the production of ATP. The toxin also reduces photosynthesis: it inhibits uptake of potassium by the guard cells of the stomates, causing the stomates to close and thereby reducing the intake of CO_2. Southern corn blight has now been brought under control again by changing the strain of corn used by growers.

Cellulolytic hyphomycetes cause blue stain and soft rot of wood, biodeterioration of cotton materials (*Stachybotrys* is particularly troublesome in the tropics), and moulding of almost any damp organic substrate.

When growing on peanuts (among other substrates) *Aspergillus flavus* produces a mycotoxin called **aflatoxin,** which causes liver damage even at very low concentrations, and is the most potent carcinogenic (cancer-inducing) substance known. *Fusarium graminearum*, the anamorph of *Gibberella zeae* (Unitunicatae-Inoperculatae: Hypocreales), growing on feed corn, produces another mycotoxin, **zearalenone**, which is a steroid, and causes **oestrogenic syndrome**—vaginal and rectal prolapse—in young female pigs. Many other mycotoxins have been discovered in recent years. They are potential threats to human and animal health of which we are only now becoming fully aware, and they have necessitated the development of new techniques for toxin monitoring and new programmes for plant protection and food storage. Mycotoxins are discussed in detail in chapter 21.

On the positive side, hyphomycetous and coelomycetous anamorphs are among the prime colonizers and decomposers of plant debris, playing a vital role in the carbon and nitrogen cycles. Hyphomycetes dominate the soil mycota in Canadian forests. The economy of many streams is based on the dead leaves of land-based plants. These are colonized by aquatic hyphomycetes, which usually form tetraradiate (four-armed) conidia, and are tolerant of low temperatures so can grow during the winter and even under ice. These fungi make the dead leaves much more palatable and nutritious for the various detritivorous invertebrates which eat them, and thus the fungi act as vital intermediaries in energy flow in northern stream systems. The terrestrial and aquatic ecology of conidial fungi is discussed in chapter 11.

Some soil-inhabiting hyphomycetous anamorphs have evolved specialized traps with which they catch small animals—nematodes, rotifers, tardigrades, amoebae and even springtails—these truly predaceous fungi are discussed in chapter 15.

We also use conidial fungi (those mentioned below have no known teleomorph) for our own purposes: the enzymes of *Penicillium camembertii* produce the soft, smooth texture of Camembert and Brie cheeses, and metabolites of *Penicillium roquefortii* put the zip in various blue cheeses—Roquefort, Danish Blue, Stilton and Gorgonzola. *Aspergillus oryzae* is used in the Far East to turn soya protein into such delicacies as soy sauce (or its sweet Indonesian variant, Ket-jap, the word which became Ketchup in English). Finally, some beneficial secondary metabolites: a substance which gave *Penicillium chrysogenum* an edge over competing bacteria in the natural habitat is now one of our most potent weapons against bacterial disease—**penicillin**; and **cyclosporine,** a metabolite recently isolated from *Tolypocladium inflatum*, has turned out to be the most effective and least toxic immunosuppressant yet discovered: it has enormously improved the success rate of organ transplant operations by preventing recipients' immune systems from rejecting the implant, without the serious side-effects caused by the chemicals used previously. This substance or its derivatives also hold out some hope for treatment of severe auto-immune diseases like some kinds of juvenile diabetes, rheumatoid arthritis, multiple sclerosis, myasthenia gravis, aplastic anaemia, Addison's disease, and systemic lupus erythematosus.

In addition, conidial anamorphs can now be genetically transformed to act as hosts for vectors carrying multiple copies of genes from other eukaryotic organisms (including humans), and have already been persuaded to express and secrete a number of eukaryotic gene products, which thus far include insulin, human growth factor, human tissue plasminogen activator (used to dissolve blood clots), bovine chymosin (an enzyme used in cheese-making), and amylase and cellulase enzymes (see chapter 10). Obviously, the biotechnological potential of the moulds is tremendous.

A Survey of Ascomycetous Holomorphs

Now to put anamorph and teleomorph together, and talk about the whole fungus (the **holomorph**). I will make a brief survey of the Ascomycetes, linking the different life-forms together in as many cases as possible. Although 44 orders of ascomycetes are recognized in one recent classification, I will discuss (and provide a key to) only 17. If you are (or become) curious about the others, check the references given at the end of this chapter.

(1) **Order Taphrinales:** 9 genera, 120 species. This is an outlying group which causes serious diseases of some plants in the Rosaceae and the Amentiferae (catkin-bearing trees). *Taphrina deformans* (Fig. 4.9) attacks the leaves of

peach trees, causing them to become thickened and distorted, whence the name 'peach leaf curl' for the disease. This fungus has four unique or unusual features. (A) The assimilative mycelium is dikaryotic—this would immediately distinguish it from most other ascomycetes (and indeed raises questions about the placement of this order). (B) It produces an exposed layer of asci on the surface of the host leaf. Since there is no surrounding or supporting fungal tissue, there is nothing we could call an ascoma. (C) The ascospores often bud in a rather yeast-like manner while still inside the ascus. (D) When the asci dehisce, they tend to split across the tip, rather than around it, so they are distinctly atypical of the operculate group. As you may have guessed by now, this group sits uneasily among the other ascomycetes, and one eminent authority recently grouped the Taphrinales with the smut fungi (see order Ustilaginales in chapter 5); both are yeast-like when grown in axenic culture. Compare its features for yourself with some of the orders that follow.

Series Unitunicatae-Operculatae

(2) **Order Pezizales:** 150 genera, 900 species. The '**operculate discomycetes**'—we'll consider 8 of the 13 families currently recognized.

a) Family Pezizaceae. Classic 'cup-fungi' producing apothecial ascomata that are actually shaped more like saucers or goblets, usually without stalks, and found growing on wood, dung or soil. They vary so much in colour, texture and ornamentation that most discomycete specialists split the Pezizaceae into several tribes or even families. Their asci have a diagnostic pop-open lid or operculum (Fig. 4.10 B), and the tips of the asci are amyloid (I$^+$: turning blue in an iodine solution known as Melzer's reagent). A small species of *Peziza* (Fig. 4.10 B) often crops up on soil in greenhouses, frequently preceded by its blastic-synchronous *Chromelosporium* anamorph (Fig. 4.10 A). Larger species,

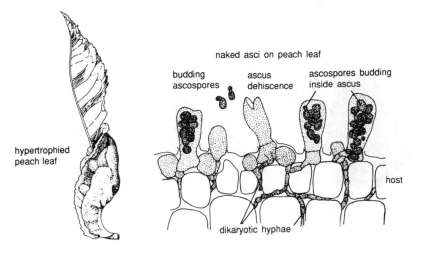

Fig. 4.9 Taphrinales: *Taphrina deformans*.

producing rather brittle apothecial ascomata several centimetres across, with light brown or orange hymenia, can be found on the ground in Spring and Fall.

b) Family Sarcosomataceae. Wood-inhabiting fungi with apothecia that are often stalked, relatively tough, and brightly coloured. The asci are sub-operculate, and non-amyloid. The scarlet cups of *Sarcoscypha coccinea*, growing from buried hemlock branches, brighten up the early Spring in Canadian woodlands. The brightly coloured apothecia of *Cookeina* are a common sight in the Neotropics, and sometimes provide a camouflaged perch for the equally colourful poison arrow frog, as you may have already seen in the frontispiece.

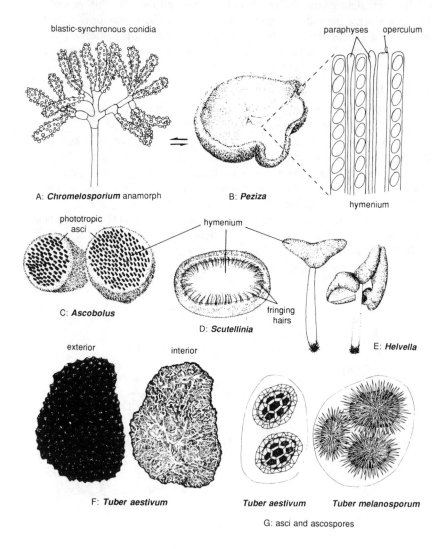

Fig. 4.10 Representative Pezizales (Unitunicatae-Operculatae).

c) Family Humariaceae. *Scutellinia scutellata* (Fig. 4.10 D), its orange apothecia rimmed with dark hairs, and with non-amyloid asci, is one of the commonest cup-fungi, growing on rotten wood. The small, often confluent, pink, cushion-like apothecia of *Pyronema* can often be found on burnt ground. Anamorphs don't seem to be produced.

d) Family Ascobolaceae. Students of mycology who have, willingly or of necessity, followed the succession of fungal fructifications appearing on horse dung, will be familiar with the two most important genera of this largely coprophilous family—*Ascobolus* (Fig. 4.10 C) and *Saccobolus*. Both produce minute, translucent apothecia; their asci are broad, and project from the hymenium when mature, so that their tips may become oriented toward the light. The ascospores have a purple or brown outer wall layer. *Ascobolus* shoots its ascospores individually, while *Saccobolus* sticks all eight together in a bundle, and they are expelled as a single projectile, which gives them extra range. I have not seen any anamorphs in this family, though a few are recorded in the literature.

e) Family Helvellaceae. The large and unusually configured apothecial ascomata of these Spring-fruiting fungi have earned two common names—saddle fungi and false morels. All are stalked, with beige to brown, hymenium-covered caps. The apothecia of *Helvella* species (Fig. 4.10 E) have a drooping flap on either side which earns them their common name. The ascomata of *Gyromitra* species, among the largest ascomycete fructifications, often contain the toxin gyromitrin, a precursor of the deadly monomethylhydrazine. By causing some fatal poisonings, the Spring-fruiting *Gyromitra esculenta* has earned its place in chapter 22 on poisonous mushrooms, and it is vital for morel-hunters to be able to distinguish the convoluted head of *Gyromitra* (Fig. 22.1 D) from the ridged and pitted head of the delicious true morel (Fig. 22.1 C).

f) Family Morchellaceae. While *Gyromitra* is numbered among the few lethally toxic fungi, its cousin, *Morchella*, the true morel (Fig. 22.1 C), is enshrined as one of the finest of all edible fungi. The several species of *Morchella* have a broad, hollow stalk, and a pitted and ridged, sponge-like, more or less conical or ellipsoidal head. Since the hymenium doesn't cover the ridges, it seems likely that a morel is a compound ascoma, each pit representing an individual apothecium. Morels have a broad geographic range, but are common in relatively few areas, of which Michigan is the best-known. People throng to the woods in May to hunt this elusive delicacy, and Boyne City holds an annual morel-hunting championship. Not long ago, dried morels cost over $400 per kilogram in Toronto. Morels are discussed in chapter 18. Just to confuse the issue a little, a second genus of Morchellaceae, *Verpa*, also fruits in May. The wrinkled thimble-cap, *Verpa bohemica*, looks like a morel, but while the cap and stalk of true morels are firmly united, those of *Verpa* are attached only at the apex.

g) Family Geneaceae. This group has closed but hollow ascomata, with cylindrical or clavate asci which are arranged in an extensive flat hymenium, but do not shoot their spores. These apparently contradictory features show that this family is becoming **sequestrate** and **hypogeous**, an evolutionary process illustrated in Fig. 4.11 (a *Genea*-like fungus is shown as the second step).

h) Family Tuberaceae. Here, the evolutionary process still active in the Geneaceae has run its course. The ascomata are sequestrate, subterranean and solid (Fig. 4.10 F), and the asci, produced in a convoluted hymenium, are rounded and thin-walled (Fig. 4.10 G) with no trace of an operculum or other shooting mechanism. Only by examining a series of microscopic characters, and considering some intermediate forms that trace the probable course of evolution in the group (Fig. 4.11) can we tell that these fungi are related to the 'operculate

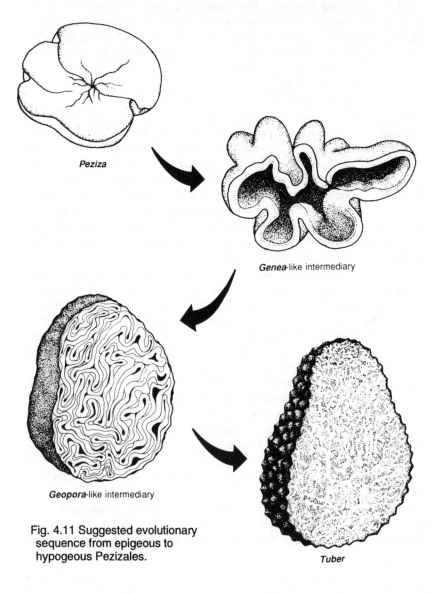

Peziza

Genea-like intermediary

Geopora-like intermediary

Fig. 4.11 Suggested evolutionary sequence from epigeous to hypogeous Pezizales.

Tuber

discomycetes.' Although it doesn't make taxonomy any easier, we must now logically place these hypogeous families with their epigeous relatives in the order Pezizales.

The hypogeous habit has necessitated the evolution of new methods for passive spore dispersal, in which some agency other than the fungus supplies the energy for dispersal. Members of the Tuberaceae, especially species of the genus *Tuber* (the truffles), have achieved this by developing what can only be called fascinating smells. These odours are released when the ascospores are mature, and lead many mammals unerringly to the ascomata, which they unearth and consume, subsequently depositing the still-viable spores elsewhere. *Tuber* is dependent, not only on mammalian vectors, but on the roots of oak and hazelnut trees, with which it establishes an **ectomycorrhizal** relationship (see chapter 17). *Tuber melanosporum* and *Tuber magnatum* are, respectively, the black and white truffles of French and Italian haute cuisine, the most highly esteemed of all edible fungi, and are therefore discussed in chapter 18.

(3) **Order Elaphomycetales:** 1 genus, 20 species. At first sight the hypogeous ascomata of *Elaphomyces* look just like truffles; and they are even called 'deer truffles'. But they have no hymenium, the spherical, non-shooting asci being produced randomly throughout the interior of the ascoma. Since it no longer offers much in the way of visual clues about its possible epigeous ancestors, *Elaphomyces* may be the oldest of the hypogeous ascomycetes.

Series Unitunicatae-Inoperculatae

Although none of them have lids (opercula), the asci of this group are not as uniform in appearance as we might like (Fig. 4.12 A-G). Most have thicker walls at their tips, pierced by a fine pore. Many have diagnostic sphincter-like rings inside these thickened tips, which control the expulsion of the spores. Some of those rings are **amyloid** (they stain blue in iodine), others don't react with iodine, and are called **chitinoid**. Some asci don't have rings at all, and in one such order (the lichenized Lecanorales), the ascal apex is extremely thick and pierced by a narrow canal. The true relationships among these orders have yet to be fully worked out.

(4) **Order Sphaeriales:** 225 genera, 1300 species. Many members of this order produce dark, brittle, globose to pear-shaped individual perithecial ascomata with prominent ostioles. Others have many perithecial cavities immersed in a single stroma to form a compound fructification. Asci often have an apical ring or sphincter, which is often, though not always, amyloid. Thread-like, sterile elements called paraphyses are present in the hymenium of some members, absent from others. Ascospores can be light or dark, simple or septate, with or without germ pore or slit, sometimes with gelatinous sheaths or appendages. In *Xylaria* (Fig. 4.13 C) a common, stromatic, wood-inhabiting genus, the asci always have amyloid apical rings, and the unicellular ascospores are dark, asymmetrical, and have a germ slit. This order also includes such pathogens as *Hypoxylon pruinatum*, which causes poplar canker, a disease that kills millions of trees every year.

(5) **Order Sordariales:** 5 families, 75 genera, 600 species. This is a generally saprobic group producing solitary perithecial ascomata, and found on dung or decaying plant remains. Their asci sometimes have non-amyloid apical sphincters, sometimes lack any apical apparatus. Several representatives are important tools in fungal genetics and biochemistry. First and foremost is *Neurospora*, which has justifiably been called the '*Drosophila* of the fungus world.' It was on *Neurospora crassa* that the science of haploid genetics was founded. The uses of *Neurospora* and *Sordaria* mutants are explored in chapter 10.

Many species of the genera *Sordaria* and *Podospora* (Fig. 4.13 A) fruit on herbivore dung, and shoot their ascospores from perithecial ascomata whose necks are positively phototropic (point toward the light). Different species of *Podospora* have 4, 8, 16, 32, 64, 128, 256, 512, 1024 or 2048 ascospores per ascus, and the various combinations of tubular and gelatinous ascospore appendages not only help in species identification, but also stick the spores to grass after they have been shot away from the dung on which the ascomata develop. Some species have *Phialophora* anamorphs (Fig. 4.13 A). *Chaetomium* (Fig. 4.13 B) is an important cellulolytic genus that damages fabrics and paper in the tropics. It differs from most other Sordariales in that its asci, though cylindrical, deliquesce or autolyse at maturity: since they don't shoot their spores, they have no apical ring mechanism, and the mucilaginous, lemon-shaped ascospores ooze out of the ascoma into a characteristic mass of coiled or dichotomously branched hairs that develop on the top of the ascoma. *Chaetomium* has *Botryotrichum* anamorphs (Fig. 4.13 B)

(6) **Order Diatrypales:** 20 genera, 125 species. The bark on dead branches of trees often develops small eruptions that mark the immersed stromata (compound ascomata) and the grouped ostioles of such common genera as *Diatrype* (Fig. 4.13 D) and *Quaternaria*. The asci have an amyloid apical ring, and the small ascospores are characteristically sausage-shaped (allantoid).

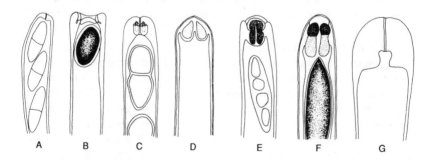

A B C D E F G

Fig. 4.12 Unitunicate-inoperculate asci. A: *Nectria* (Hypocreales); B: *Sordaria* (Sordariales); C: *Melanconis* (Diaporthales); D: *Claviceps* (Clavicipitales); E: *Microglossum* (amyloid ring, Leotiales); F: *Rosellinia* (amyloid ring, Sphaeriales); G: *Lecanora* (Lecanorales).

(7) **Order Hypocreales:** 80 genera, 550 species. This order is recognized by its brightly coloured, simple or compound, perithecial ascomata—usually yellow, orange or red—which are fleshy or waxy in texture, and usually borne on supporting layers of mycelium (subicula) or in stromata. Four genera are especially well-known. (1) *Nectria* (Fig. 4.14) has bright red, superficial ascomata containing 2-celled, boat-shaped ascospores, and some species cause cankers and die-backs of trees. *Nectria* sensu lato has a variety of conidial

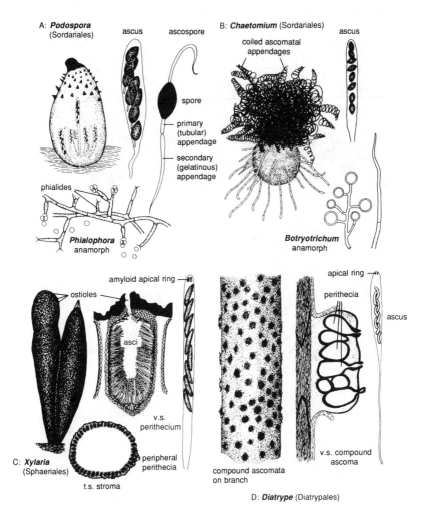

Fig. 4.13 Representative perithecial ascomycetes (Unitunicatae-Inoperculatae).

anamorphs, all of them phialidic (Fig. 4.15). The erumpent pink sporodochia of one commonly encountered anamorph, *Tubercularia* (Fig. 4.14), cause a condition known as coral spot. Here, anamorph and teleomorph often occur together, as shown in Fig. 4.14. But the most important nectriaceous anamorphs are *Fusarium* species (Figs. 4.15, 21.1), many of which cause destructive wilt diseases of higher plants, or produce mycotoxins. (2) *Gibberella* (which also has *Fusarium* anamorphs), causes a disease of rice called 'foolish seedling' in which seedlings grow too rapidly and consequently fall over. The active principle, a plant growth hormone called gibberellic acid, has been extracted and is widely used to stimulate plant growth. (3) *Hypomyces* parasitizes the agaric

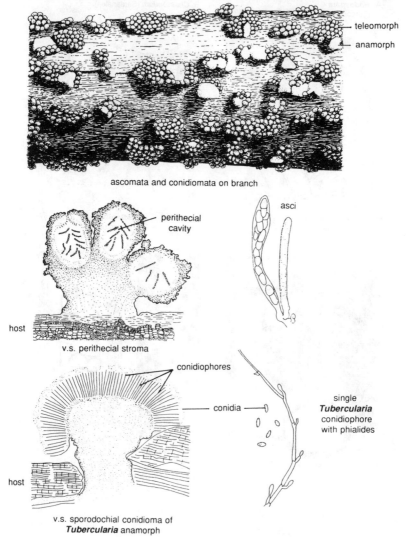

Fig. 4.14 Hypocreales: ***Nectria cinnabarina*** and its ***Tubercularia*** anamorph.

genera *Lactarius* and *Russula*, producing a myriad of bright orange perithecial ascomata on a subiculum that completely covers the aborted mushroom and gives it the name 'lobster fungus.' The anamorph of *Hypomyces* is the blastic-retrogressive hyphomycete, *Cladobotryum*. (4) *Hypocrea* forms fleshy stromata on wood, but is recorded far less often than its green-spored, phialidic anamorph, *Trichoderma* (Fig. 14.3) which, perhaps because it is a broad-spectrum myco-parasite, and produces cellulases and antibiotics, is one of the most important moulds in forest soils. It is now being exploited in biological control of pathogenic fungi (see chapter 14), and in the production of enzymes which can convert cellulose to glucose.

(8) **Order Diaporthales**: 90 genera, 500 species. Here several beaked, perithecioid ascomata are usually immersed in a single stroma; paraphyses are often absent; and the asci, which have an amyloid apical ring, become free inside the ascoma, and then autolyse. This rather paradoxical situation suggests that evolution is in progress here. Two important genera stand out. *Cryphonectria (Endothia) parasitica* causes chestnut blight, which has almost extinguished an important species of North American tree in about 50 years: you can read the full story in chapter 12. Because of this, you may not be able to find specimens of *Cryphonectria*, but another member of this order, *Gaeumannomyces graminis*, which causes 'whiteheads' or 'take-all' of wheat, is common. It rots the roots of afflicted plants, and causes premature drying out of the plant, sometimes reducing yields to zero. *Diaporthe impulsa* is illustrated in Fig. 4.16.

(9) **Order Leotiales**: 11 families, 350 genera, 2000 species. The '**inopercu-late discomycetes**.' The apothecial ascomata are superficially similar to those of the Pezizales, but the asci are inoperculate, and usually have amyloid apical

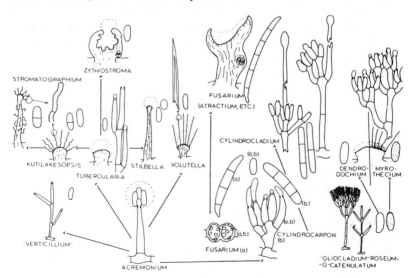

Fig. 4.15 Hypocreales: anamorphs of **Nectria** sensu lato. Arrows indicate pos-sible lines of derivation.

rings. This suggests to me that the two major kinds of apothecial ascomata are examples of parallel or convergent evolution.

(a) Family Sclerotiniaceae. As the name implies, these fungi often form **sclerotia**, which may be solid masses of fungal tissue, or may be of mixed origin—fungal hyphae riddling a mummified host such as a peach or plum. Having overwintered in this guise, they germinate in spring and use the stored energy to produce stalked apothecial ascomata. Ascospores are shot when the host is in flower, and infect new hosts through the stigma. Secondary spread is by the various conidial anamorphs. Many members of this family have distinctive anamorphs, while the teleomorphs are relatively uniform. So the genera erected for the teleomorphs have in several cases been distinguished largely on the basis of the anamorphs. Thus we have *Sclerotinia* with *Sclerotium* anamorphs, *Monilinia* with *Monilia* anamorphs (Fig. 4.17 A: blastic-acropetal), *Botryotinia* with *Botrytis* anamorphs (Fig. 4.6: blastic-synchronous), and *Streptotinia* with *Streptobotrys* anamorphs (blastic-sympodial).

Sclerotium, Monilia and *Botrytis* cause several serious plant diseases (chapter 12), but when *Botrytis* grows on overripe grapes in certain areas of France, Germany, Hungary, and South Africa it is called the 'noble rot,' because the small quantities of sweet wine that can be made from such shriveled grapes have exquisite flavour, and can be sold for very high prices. Find out what a bottle of Chateau d'Yquem sauternes (or a 'Trockenbeerenauslese') costs at your local wine store: be prepared for a shock.

(b) Family Phacidiaceae. Some members cause snow blight diseases of conifers. This family is atypical in that the ascomata develop inside host tissue, and are at first covered by a thick roof of dark fungal tissue. But at maturity the roof splits open and exposes the hymenium. The apical ring in the asci is amyloid. *Phacidium* (Fig. 4.17 D) has coelomycetous anamorphs: those of pathogenic species belong to *Apostrasseria*, those of saprobes to *Ceuthospora*.

(c) Family Geoglossaceae produces unusual stalked ascomata. The hymenium doesn't line a cup or saucer, but covers the convex surface of a club-shaped or tongue-shaped ascoma which is tough and black in *Microglossum* and *Geoglossum* (Fig. 4.17 B), fleshy and yellow in *Spathularia*.

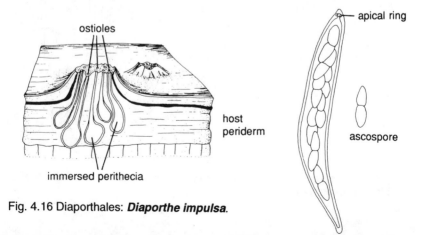

Fig. 4.16 Diaporthales: *Diaporthe impulsa*.

(d) Family Leotiaceae contains many typical 'discomycetes' such as *Bisporella*, which produces those small yellow apothecia so common on fallen, decorticated tree-trunks, while *Chlorociboria*, also fairly common, both stains the wood green and forms small green apothecia. The spectacular ascomata of *Leotia* are much larger, stalked, jelly-like, and have convex green or yellow heads (Fig. 4.17 C).

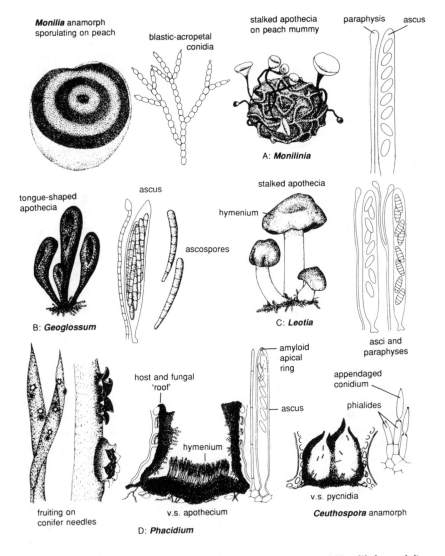

Fig. 4.17 Representative 'inoperculate discomycetes.' A: *Monilinia* and its *Monilia* anamorph; B: *Geoglossum*; C: *Leotia*; D: *Phacidium* and its *Ceuthospora* anamorph.

(10) **Order Rhytismatales**: 65 genera, 320 species. The ascomata, like those of the Phacidiaceae, develop immersed in host tissue or a fungal stroma, which ultimately ruptures to expose the hymenium. The asci often have apical rings, but these are small and chitinoid (do not stain blue in iodine). The ascospores are usually long and thin, and have a slimy sheath (absent in the Phacidiaceae). *Lophodermium* causes needle-cast of pines, and *Rhytisma* attacks the leaves of many plants, its developing shiny black ascomata giving rise to such epithets as 'tar-spot' of maple.

(11) **Order Clavicipitales**: 27 genera, 270 species. Highly evolved and sophisticated parasitic fungi with: (a) frequently stalked, all-fungal stromata, (b) long asci without apical rings, but with extremely thickened tips, and (c) long, thread-like ascospores that in some taxa fragment at or following release. Three bizarre and spectacular genera, *Claviceps*, *Cordyceps* and *Epichloë*, represent this order.

Claviceps purpurea (Fig. 4.18 A-C) discharges its ascospores when its host, rye, is in flower, and infection takes place through the stigma. As the infection progresses, the fungus takes over the food being channeled into seed-production by the host. The ovarian tissues are replaced by a mycelial mat that produces masses of conidia of the *Sphacelia* anamorph in a sweet-smelling nectar. Insects are attracted to the nectar, and spread the conidia to other host plants. The mycelial mat hardens and becomes a purplish sclerotium—the **ergot**—which replaces the grain (Fig. 4.18 A). Sclerotia fall to the ground during harvesting, overwinter, and germinate the following Spring, each producing several stalked stromata (Fig. 4.18 B). Each stroma has a spherical head within which many perithecia develop (Fig. 4.18 C). Because this fungus has a small target, the stigma of the rye flower, which is available only during a narrow time-window, and spores can reach it only by chance, the fungus must disperse a large number of ascospores. I have calculated that a single ergot can give rise to 5 stromata, each of those may contain 100 perithecia, each with 50 asci, each ascus producing eight ascospores: a total of 5 x 100 x 50 x 8 = 200,000 propagules.

If the sclerotia are accidentally consumed by cattle, or if rye bread made from ergoty rye is eaten by humans, alkaloids found in the ergot cause a form of poisoning known as **ergotism**, or, more picturesquely, St. Anthony's Fire. Human victims frequently hallucinate and feel that they are burning (see chapter 21 for a fuller account of this mycotoxicosis). The alkaloids **ergotamine** and **ergotaline** cause contractions of the smooth muscles, and the ensuing restriction of the peripheral blood supply can lead to gangrene and even death. St. Anthony's Fire was fairly common in the Middle Ages, and sporadic outbreaks occurred until recently. Ergot, the only fungus in the British Pharmacopoeia Codex, has been used in obstetrics both to induce childbirth and to control post-partural bleeding. *Claviceps* won renewed fame, or perhaps I should say notoriety, as the original source of LSD (lysergic acid diethylamide), one of the most powerful psychedelic drugs (it is a hundred times more potent than psilocybin, the active ingredient of 'magic' mushrooms).

Cordyceps (Fig. 4.18 D-F) parasitizes insects, spiders, and the deer truffle, *Elaphomyces*, and its large stromata spring up directly from its victims. These perithecial stromata, arising from an insect larva or pupa, are known as vegetable caterpillars. These strange 'two Kingdom' structures are used in traditional

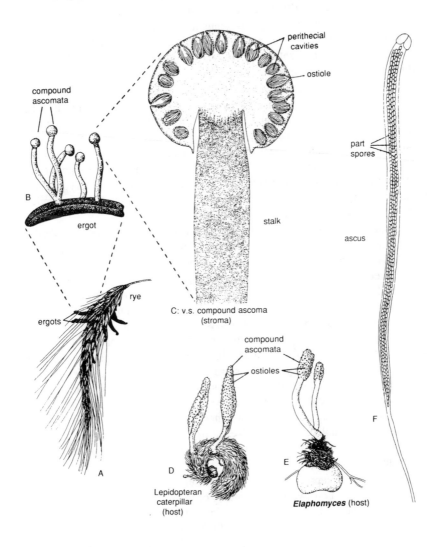

Fig. 4.18 Representative Clavicipitales. A-C: *Claviceps*; D-F: *Cordyceps.*

Chinese medicine, as a treatment for "general debility after illness, weakness, spitting of blood caused by TB, chronic coughing and asthma...night sweating...anaemia...malignant tumour." This fungus, which must infect target organisms far scarcer than rye flowers, goes one step further than *Claviceps* in its multiplication of propagules: its long ascospores break up into about 100 part-spores, often while still in the ascus (Fig. 4.18 F). I estimate that the usually single large stroma produced by this genus from its fungal or insect host may bear as many as 800 perithecial ascomata, each containing at least 50 asci, each with 8 spores, each fragmenting into 100 part-spores, for a total of 800 x 50 x 8 x 100 = 32,000,000 propagules.

Epichloë causes a disease called choke of grasses. The energy that was to have gone into the inflorescence is appropriated by the fungus to produce its own fructification, a perithecial stroma that surrounds the stalk of the grass, which does not flower. In a recently discovered twist to this story, this apparently damaging parasitic fungus is seen to have a mutualistic symbiosis with the grass. The *Acremonium* anamorph of *Epichloë* grows systemically throughout the grass plant without producing any disease symptoms, and apparently protects the grass from herbivores by producing a virulent neurotoxin. A more detailed discussion of this relationship is given in chapter 21.

(12) **Order Erysiphales**: 28 genera, 100 species. All members of this order are obligate parasites on leaves and fruits of higher plants, causing diseases called **powdery mildews**. These fungi have superficial mycelium which extracts nourishment from the host plant through specialized hyphae that penetrate the epidermal cells of the host and develop special absorbing organs called **haustoria** (Fig. 4.19). Basauxic chains of conidia of the *Oidium* anamorph (Fig. 4.19), whose appearance gives these diseases their name, arise from the mycelium in early summer. Airborne conidia spread the disease from plant to plant, and are later succeeded by ascomata which mature slowly in fall, and release ascospores the following spring. This order parasitizes well over 1,000 higher plant species, and the powdery mildews of grapes, hops, gooseberries and cereals are economically important diseases. You should have no difficulty spotting a few powdery mildews in summer; their whitish colonies growing on living leaves are unlike anything else. In dry summers, they are particularly common on grass in shady parts of lawns, on perennial *Phlox*, on *Alnus rugosa*, and many other angiosperms.

The generic concepts in this order are unusually straightforward and easy to apply; they depend on two major features of the ascoma—the number of asci within it, and the kind of appendage growing out from it (Fig. 4.19). In one way, the Erysiphales are the antithesis of the Sclerotiniaceae. There, the anamorphs were far more distinctive and diverse than the teleomorphs; here, the reverse is true. Most anamorphs of the Erysiphales belong to the hyphomycete genus *Oidium*. Although the order Erysiphales is very easy to characterize and recognize, its systematic position is controversial. Some mycologists insist that its asci are bitunicate, which would place it alongside the Dothideales (see below), but many mycologists do not accept this, and place the order among the unitunicate ascomycetes. The asci are sometimes rather thick-walled, but one of the world experts on the group, Dr. Zheng Ru-yong, of Beijing, tells me that she has seen distinctive inner and outer wall layers only in an undescribed taxon from Tibet, and has never seen the "Jack-in-a-box" mechanism so typical of the bitunicatae. The asci seem to have neither an operculum, nor an apical ring apparatus. This information, plus their strange arrangements for dispersal and dehiscence (see chapter 8), their unique anamorphs, and their obligately parasitic yet superficial lifestyle, make them a rather peripheral (though important and interesting) group.

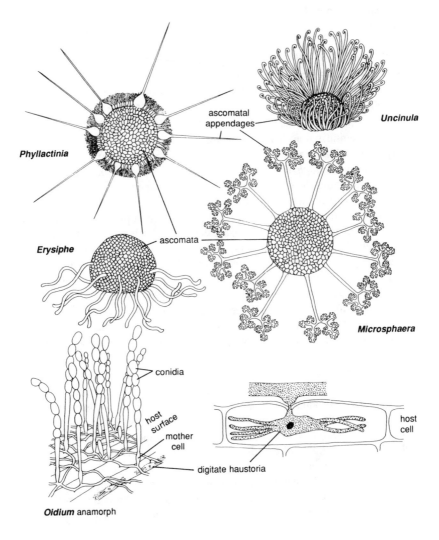

Fig. 4.19 Representative Erysiphales.

Key to Some Common Genera of Erysiphales		
	Number of asci per ascoma	
	1 only	more than 1
Appendages like assimilative hyphae	*Sphaerotheca*	*Erysiphe*
Appendages dichotomously branched at end	*Podosphaera*	*Microsphaera*
Appendages curled at end		*Uncinula*
Appendages needle-shaped, with bulbous base		*Phyllactinia*

Series Prototunicatae

In the following four orders, the walls of the asci break down when the ascospores mature, and therefore the spores cannot be forcibly ejected.

(13) **Order Onygenales:** 40 genera, 120 species. Here belong fungi which cause skin diseases in people, and can digest hair, horn and feather—all because they have the unusual ability to metabolize the resistant protein, keratin. The family Arthrodermataceae (Fig. 4.20) contains the genera *Arthroderma* (anamorphs in *Trichophyton*) and *Nannizzia* (anamorphs in *Microsporum*: Fig. 4.8 C), the infamous **dermatophytes** which cause superficial mycoses ranging from ringworm of the scalp to athlete's foot. Other members of the Onygenales can degrade cellulose, and others are coprophilous (dung-inhabiting). They all produce ascomata, but although these are theoretically cleistothecial, their walls may be very loosely woven, and in some the ascospores can simply fall out through the gaps. The asci are always more or less spherical, never shoot their spores, and tend to break down at maturity. Because of my earlier conclusion that asci evolved as spore-shooting devices, I assume that the ascoma and asci in the Onygenales are 'reduced' forms, simplified during evolution from an earlier spore-shooting design. The ascomata often bear highly characteristic coiled or branched appendages that can make identification easy—if the teleomorph is present.

If you isolate dermatophytes in pure culture, they may or may not produce teleomorphs. But they will develop characteristic thallic conidial anamorphs. Sometimes these produce small, thallic-arthric conidia (*Chrysosporium* or *Malbranchea*), sometimes large, spindle-shaped, transversely septate, solitary thallic conidia (*Trichophyton* or *Microsporum*), and sometimes the same culture will produce both kinds of conidia. When a fungus has two or more different anamorphs, these are called **synanamorphs**. The three most important anamorph genera of dermatophytes are *Epidermophyton*, *Microsporum* (Fig. 4.8 C) and *Trichophyton*. Of these, *Epidermophyton* has no known teleomorph, 9 species of *Microsporum* have teleomorphs in *Nannizzia*, and 7 species of *Trichophyton* have teleomorphs in *Arthroderma*.

(14) **Order Eurotiales:** 50 genera, 140 species. This largely cleistothecial order contains the teleomorphs of some of the most successful of all conidial

fungi—the common green and blue moulds of the hyphomycete genera *Penicillium* and *Aspergillus* (Figs. 4.6, 4.21 A, 21.1 C). These ubiquitous and almost omnivorous anamorphs are blastic-phialidic, and produce masses of dry, wind-dispersed conidia. These moulds aren't just extremely successful, they are of considerable importance to us because they produce antibiotics and mycotoxins,

Family	Ascospores	Peridia and Appendages	Anamorphs	Substrate and Habitats
ONYGENACEAE	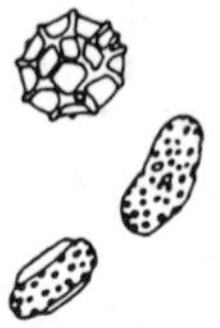 pitted; spherical, oblate, allantoid.	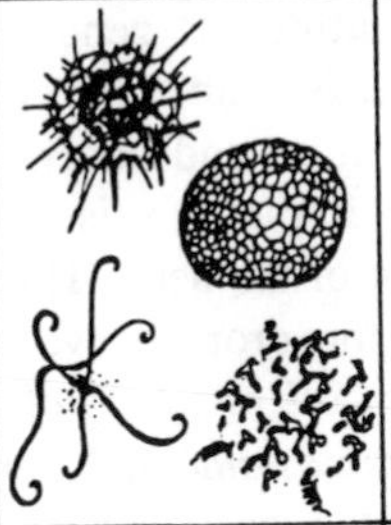	 CHRYSOSPORIUM MALBRANCHEA SPORENDONEMA	carnivore dung; soil enriched with keratin or dung; KERATIN*
ARTHRODERMATACEAE	 smooth; oblate to oblate-discoid or oblate-convex.		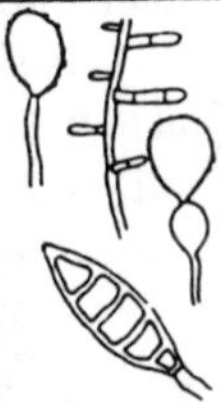 CHRYSOSPORIUM MICROSPORUM TRICHOPHYTON	decaying hoof, horn, feathers, hair and skin; some are parasitic on animals; KERATIN*
MYXOTRICHACEAE	 smooth or striate; fusiform, ellipsoid.		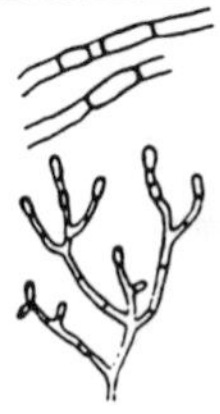 GEOMYCES MALBRANCHEA OIDIODENDRON	processed or decaying plant materials; CELLULOSE*; paper, straw, soil around the roots of plants
GYMNOASCACEAE	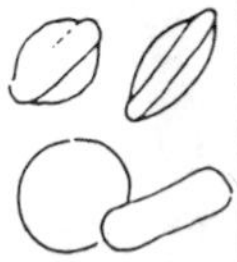 smooth or slightly irregular ("lumpy"); often with polar and/or equatorial thickenings.		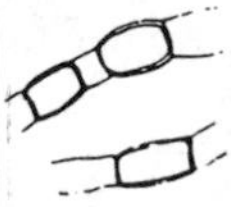 absent or of un-named arthroconidia.	decaying vegetation; soil rich in organic matter; VARIABLE*; various types of dung

Fig. 4.20 Families of the Onygenales.

and cause a lot of food spoilage. Species of *Aspergillus* have teleomorphs in *Eurotium* (Fig. 4.21 A) or *Emericella*, while many penicillia have teleomorphs in the rather similar *Talaromyces* or *Eupenicillium*. The cleistothecial ascomata of the teleomorphs have impermeable walls one or more cells thick. The asci are scattered throughout the cavity of the ascoma (i.e., never in a hymenium); they are spherical, thin-walled, and break down at spore maturity. The ascospores often have a pulley-wheel shape (Fig. 4.21 A). Again, it is thought that these fungi are 'reduced' derivatives of spore-shooting ancestors.

(15) **Order Ophiostomatales:** 15 genera, 130 species. The ascomata of this order have long, tubular necks, with the ostiole at the tip (Fig. 4.21 B). The asci are not arranged in a hymenium, and autolyse early. The spores ooze out of the ostiole and form a slimy droplet that is supported by a ring of specialized, hair-like hyphae at the top of the neck. These fungi often fruit in bark beetle tunnels, and the elevated spore drop has evolved to ensure that the beetle carries spores with it when it flies off in search of another tree. The most important genera in this order are *Ophiostoma* and *Ceratocystis*. *Ophiostoma ulmi* (Fig. 4.21 B) causes Dutch elm disease, which was introduced into the U.S. in 1930, to Canada in 1944, has since spread right across the continent, and has much more than decimated the American elm. This fungus has a *Graphium* anamorph that produces a tall, synnematal conidioma bearing a slimy droplet of conidia (Fig. 4.21 B). In producing this stalked spore drop, the anamorph is completely analogous to the teleomorph; both are trying to ensure that beetles don't leave home without them. *Ceratocystis fagacearum* and its *Chalara quercina* phialidic anamorph are the cause of another widespread and serious tree disease,

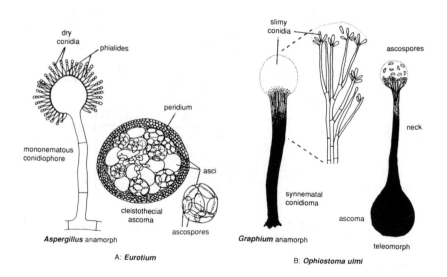

A: *Eurotium*

B: *Ophiostoma ulmi*

Fig. 4.21 Prototunicatae. A: Eurotiales; B: Ophiostomatales.

oak wilt. The teleomorphs of *Ophiostoma* and *Ceratocystis* are very similar, but the genera are easily distinguished by their anamorphs: the *Chalara* anamorph of *Ceratocystis* has solitary phialides with long, tubular collarettes (see Fig. 4.6), and forms long, cylindrical conidia; *Ophiostoma* has several different anamorphs, none anything like *Chalara*.

(16) **Order Laboulbeniales:** 75 genera, 1700 species. This group is so distinct from the other ascomycetes that some people put it in a separate Class, Laboulbeniomycetes. While that might be justifiable, it would also complicate

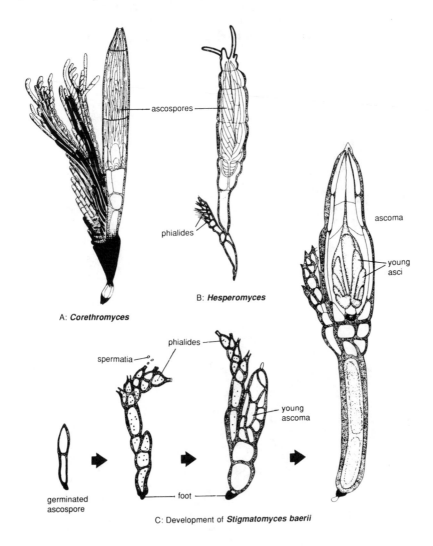

Fig. 4.22 Laboulbeniales.

our classification and make life a little more difficult for you. So, having noted the possibility of such elevated status, I will press on. All 1700 species are invariably found attached to the exoskeleton of insects, or occasionally, millipedes and mites. In *Stigmatomyces baerii* (Fig. 4.22 C), which is found on houseflies, an ascospore becomes attached to the animal, germinates, and sends a foot into the exoskeleton to absorb nutrients. Although haustoria may penetrate as far as the epidermal cells, there is never any real invasion of host tissues. The ascospore develops a median septum, and the upper cell becomes differentiated into a male organ, with several phialide-like cells that produce spermatia. The lower cell then develops an ascogonium with a trichogyne, which is fertilized by the spermatia. Several asci then develop from the ascogonium, and eventually

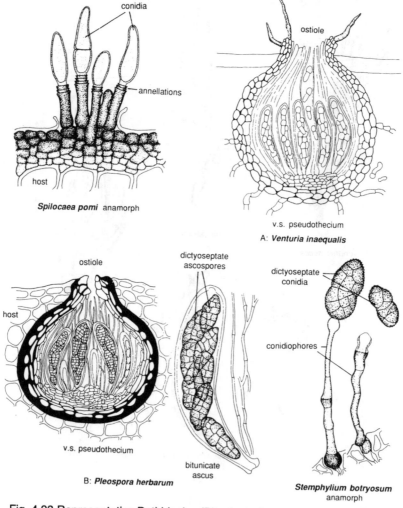

conidia

annellations

host

Spilocaea pomi anamorph

ostiole

v.s. pseudothecium

A: *Venturia inaequalis*

ostiole

host

dictyoseptate ascospores

v.s. pseudothecium

bitunicate ascus

B: *Pleospora herbarum*

dictyoseptate conidia

conidiophores

Stemphylium botryosum anamorph

Fig. 4.23 Representative Dothideales (Bitunicatae).

deliquesce. The mature ascoma is spine-like, projecting from the exterior of the host, and can be seen with a hand-lens. Other genera exhibit the same basic features (Fig. 4.22 A,B).

The Laboulbeniales apparently don't produce anamorphs, so are presumably spread from animal to animal by adhesive ascospores during mating of the hosts, or when insects form dense swarms. This goes some way toward explaining the almost incredible site-specificity of many Laboulbeniales. Various species are restricted to one part of the insect, for example, one side of a particular left limb; or even to one sex of their host, though most species are not quite so limited.

Series Bitunicatae

(17) **Order Dothideales**: 50 families, 650 genera, 6300 species. This is an extremely large and diverse order, which will obviously need to be subdivided when its taxonomy is better understood: I will mention only one or two common examples.

(a) Family Venturiaceae. *Venturia inaequalis* (Fig. 4.23 A) causes apple scab, an economically important disease. You'll find the *Spilocaea pomi* anamorph (Fig. 4.6, 4.23 A) producing its blastic-annellidic conidia on almost any unsprayed apple tree, causing large brownish spots on the leaves, and disfiguring blackish scabs on the fruit. But you won't find the teleomorph during the growing season. Its pseudothecial ascomata develop slowly in the dead apple leaves over the winter, and the ascospores are shot in spring when they can infect young leaves. *Apiosporina morbosa* causes the extremely common and disfiguring black knot of wild cherry (and of my damson plum tree), its pseudothecial ascomata developing on conspicuous black fungal stromata.

(b) Family Pleosporaceae. *Pleospora herbarum* (Fig. 4.23 B) is common on dead herbaceous stems, and has anamorphs in the hyphomycete genera *Stemphylium* (Fig. 4.23 B) and *Alternaria*. The ascospores and conidia are both dictyoseptate. Phragmoseptate or dictyoseptate ascospores are common in the Dothideales; in fact, if a fungus has ascospores of this kind, the odds are about 9:1 that it is one of the Dothideales. Coelomycetous anamorphs are also common in this group.

(c) Family Botryosphaeriaceae. *Guignardia aesculi* and its *Phyllosticta* coelomycetous anamorph cause a leaf scorch of *Aesculus* (horse chestnut, buck-eye) that effectively defoliates many of our ornamental chestnut trees a month or so before they would normally lose their leaves.

Now I will provide a dichotomous key to the 17 orders just discussed. But you will see at the very beginning of the key that this chapter has by no means dealt with all fungi that produce asci. Many thousands of fungi are always found in intimate relationships with algae, and are called lichens (see chapter 7). Many more never produce ascomata, often have unicellular thalli, and are chemically rather different from other ascus-producing fungi. These are known as yeasts (see chapter 6). I have treated yeasts and lichens separately because each group is phylogenetically diverse, and includes non-ascomycetous fungi (notably basidiomycetes).

Dichotomous Key to 17 Orders of Ascomycetes

1 No ascoma produced, asci solitary, in chains, or in
layer on host 2

1 Ascoma produced (open or closed, epigeous or
hypogeous) 3

  2 Hyphae often absent; ascus-like meiosporangia free
  or produced on individual hyphae . . . . (yeasts: ch 6)

  2 Hyphae always present; asci borne in a layer on the
  surface of the host plant . . . . **Taphrinales**

3 Thallus containing algal cells or filaments . . . . . . (lichens: ch 7)

3 Thallus without algae 4

  4 Ascus wall thick, with two functionally different
  layers (Bitunicatae) . . . . **Dothideales**

  4 Ascus wall thin, functionally single-layered, lysing at
  or before maturity in some orders 5

5 Ascus wall lysing before spore maturity; ascospores
not forcibly discharged (Prototunicatae) 6

5 Ascus wall persistent; ascospores forcibly discharged
except in hypogeous forms (Unitunicatae) 9

  6 Assimilative hyphae absent; ascomata on exterior of
  insects, appearing as spine-like outgrowths . . . . . **Laboulbeniales**

  6 Assimilative hyphae well-developed, immersed or
  superficial 7

7 Ascomata usually with ostiole; asci lysing early . . . . **Ophiostomatales**

7 Ascomata closed (cleistothecial), occasionally ostiolate; asci spherical, randomly arranged within the ascoma 8

  8 Ascomatal peridium complete; ascus wall lysing just
  before maturity; anamorphs usually blastic-phialidic **Eurotiales**

  8 Peridium often loosely woven, with characteristic appendages; anamorphs thallic . . . . **Onygenales**

9 Asci opening by circular lid (operculate), or with thin
apex; ascomata apothecial or hypogeous 10

9 Asci opening by apical pore or canal, with apical
sphincter or thick apex (inoperculate); ascomata
perithecial or apothecial 11

9 Asci without lid or sphincter; ascomata closed; obligate plant parasites with superficial assimilative hyphae . . . . **Erysiphales**

10 Ascomata apothecial or hypogeous; asci in hymenium . . . . **Pezizales**

10 Ascomata closed, hypogeous; asci random . . . . . **Elaphomycetales**

11 Mature ascomata have an exposed hymenium 12

11 Mature ascomata perithecial (closed but with ostiole) 13

12 Asci with apical sphincter blueing in iodine (amyloid) . . . . **Leotiales**

12 Asci with non-amyloid sphincter . . . . **Rhytismatales**

13 Asci with apical sphincter amyloid (blueing in iodine) 14

13 Asci with non-amyloid ring, or ring absent 15

14 Ascomata compound, perithecia radially arranged within a black stroma; ascospores sausage-shaped (allantoid) . . . . **Diatrypales**

14 Ascomata single, or compound in a stroma; ascospores not sausage-shaped . . . . **Sphaeriales**

15 Ascomata single . . . . **Sordariales**

15 Ascomata grouped in a stroma or on a subicular layer 16

16 Stroma often stalked; asci long, narrow, lacking sphincter, but apex thick, with pore; ascospores long and thread-like, often fragmenting at maturity; all obligately parasitic (on plants, arthropods or fungi) **Clavicipitales**

16 Stroma never stalked; asci and ascospores not as above 17

17 Ascomata compound, perithecia immersed, with long neck or beak; asci with apical ring but lysing . . . . . **Diaporthales**

17 Perithecia not beaked, often brightly coloured, embedded in a stroma, or superficial on a subiculum, asci not lysing . . . . **Hypocreales**

Further Reading

Ainsworth, G.C., F.K. Sparrow and A.S. Sussman (Eds.) (1973) **The Fungi: an Advanced Treatise**. Vol. 4A. Academic Press, New York.

Arx, J.A. von (1981) **The Genera of Fungi Sporulating in Pure Culture**. Cramer, Vaduz.

Arx, J.A. von and E. Muller (1975) A reevaluation of the bitunicate ascomycetes with keys to families and genera. C.B.S. Studies in Mycology **9**: 159 pp.

Barron, G.L. (1968) **The Genera of Hyphomycetes from Soil**. Williams and Wilkins, Baltimore.

Breitenbach, J. and F. Kränzlin (1984) **Fungi of Switzerland**. Vol. 1 Asomycetes. Verlag Mykologia, Lucerne.

Carmichael, J.W., B. Kendrick, I.L. Conners and L. Sigler (1980) **Genera of Hyphomycetes**. University of Alberta Press, Edmonton.

Cole, G.T. and B. Kendrick (Eds.) (1981) **Biology of Conidial Fungi**. (2 Vols.) Academic Press, New York.

Cole, G.T. and R.A. Samson (1979) **Patterns of Development in Conidial Fungi**. Pitman, London.

Dennis, R.W.G. (1968) **British Ascomycetes**. 2nd Edn. Cramer, Lehre.

Domsch, K.H., W. Gams and T-H. Anderson (1980) **Compendium of Soil Fungi**. Vols 1 & 2. Academic Press, London.

Ellis, M.B. (1971) **Dematiaceous Hyphomycetes**. Commonwealth Mycological Institute, Kew.

Ellis, M.B. (1976) **More Dematiaceous Hyphomycetes**. Commonwealth Mycological Institute, Kew.

Ellis, M.B. and J.P. Ellis (1985) **Microfungi on Land Plants. An Identification Handbook**. Croom Helm, London.

Ellis, M.B. and J.P. Ellis (1988) **Microfungi on Miscellaneous Substrates. An Identification Handbook**. Croom Helm, London.

Hawksworth, D.L., B.C. Sutton and G.C. Ainsworth (1983) **Dictionary of the Fungi**. 7th Edn. Commonwealth Mycological Institute, Kew.

Hughes, S.J. (1976) Sooty moulds. Mycologia **68**: 693-820.

Kendrick, B. (Ed.) (1979) **The Whole Fungus**. (Vols. 1 & 2). National Museums of Canada, Ottawa.

Luttrell, E.S. (1967 reprint) **Taxonomy of the Pyrenomycetes**. Bibliotheca Mycologica Vol. 6. Cramer, Lehre.

Nag Raj, T.R., G. Morgan-Jones et al. (1972-1982) **Icones generum coelomycetum**. Fascicles I-XIII. Department of Biology, Univ of Waterloo.

Seaver, F.J. (1978 reprint) **North American Cup-Fungi - Operculates**. Lubrecht and Cramer, Monticello, N.Y.

Seaver, F.J. (1978 reprint) **North American Cup-Fungi - Inoperculates**. Lubrecht and Cramer, Monticello, N.Y.

Sivanesan, A. (1984) **The Bitunicate Ascomycetes and their Anamorphs**. Cramer, Vaduz.

Sutton, B.C. (1980) **The Coelomycetes**. Commonwealth Mycological Institute, Kew.

Ying, J., X. Mao, Q. Ma, Y. Zong and H. Wen (1987) **Icons of Medicinal Fungi from China**. Science Press, Beijing.

Zheng, Ru-yong (1985) Genera of the Erysiphaceae. Mycotaxon **22**: 209-263.

Chapter 5

Eumycotan Fungi:
(2) Phylum Dikaryomycota:
(B) Subphylum Basidiomycotina

Introduction

With the Ascomycetes under your belt, you should find it easier to cope with the other half of the Phylum Dikaryomycota. The subphylum Basidiomycotina has many features in common with the Ascomycotina: chitinous hyphal walls; regularly septate hyphae; presence of central pores piercing the septa; the potential for somatic, assimilative hyphae to anastomose; the production of complex and often macroscopic sexual fruit bodies; the presence of a dikaryophase in the life cycle (except in some anamorphic holomorphs); a turgor-pressure driven mechanism for launching the meiospores into the air; production of a conidial anamorph by many species. Make no mistake, ascomycetes and basidiomycetes evolved from a common stock.

Yet they are usually relatively easy to tell apart, macroscopically, microscopically and ultrastructurally, because it is probably a long time, even in geological terms, since they evolved apart. So we can expect to find a lot of differences as well. Here are some of them.

A) The walls of ascomycete hyphae are basically two-layered, those of basidiomycete hyphae are multi-layered.

B) Dikaryomycotan hyphae are regularly septate, but the structure of the septal pore in the various classes of the two subphyla differs, as you can see in Fig. 5.1. The septa of class Ascomycetes (Fig. 5.1 A) are pierced by a simple, central pore, with a spherical **Woronin body** hovering on each side, ready to plug the pore if the hypha should be damaged. Septa of class Saccharomycetes (many yeasts and related fungi that form ascus-like meiosporangia; see chapter 6), are often perforated by multiple **micropores** (Fig. 5.1 B). In classes Holobasidiomycetes (mushrooms and bracket fungi, etc.) and Phragmobasidiomycetes (jelly fungi) the septa develop a complex, barrel-shaped structure called a **dolipore** which is covered on both sides by a cap of membrane called a **parenthesome** (Fig. 5.1 C). The septal pore of the rust fungi (atypical basidiomycotina placed in class Teliomycetes), is simpler, but is often blocked by what is called a **pulleywheel occlusion** (Fig. 5.1 D). Both basidiomycotan pore mechanisms seem to prevent the migration of nuclei: the importance of this will become clear as you read on.

C) In ascomycetes, anastomosis of somatic hyphae may establish a heterokaryon (a hypha containing more than one kind of nucleus), but it doesn't usually initiate the dikaryophase, which is restricted to the special system of ascogenous hyphae arising from the ascogonium within the ascoma (Fig. 4.2). But when monokaryotic basidiomycete hyphae anastomose, they may, if they are of compatible mating types, be establishing the dikaryophase, which can then grow assimilatively for months or years before indulging in any overtly sexual behaviour. To put it in a nutshell, ascomycetous teleomorphs have a **restricted dikaryophase**, basidiomycetes often have an **extended dikaryophase**, and

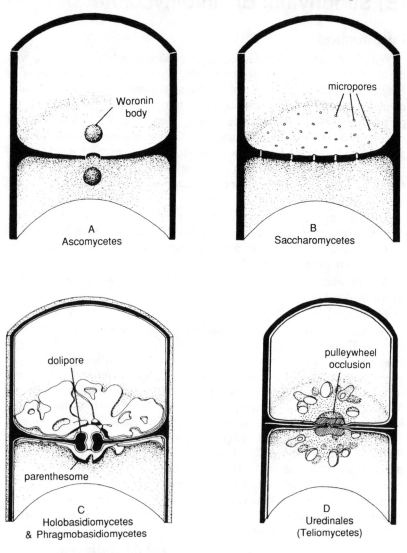

Fig. 5.1 Types of septa typical of various fungal groups.

even anamorphs can be dikaryotic, a phenomenon not found among the ascomycetes.

D) In both groups the dikaryophase comes to an end in the hymenium of the teleomorph. In many ascomycetes, at this point, each ascogenous hypha develops a reflexed tip called a **crozier**, which allows the two nuclei of the dikaryon to divide simultaneously, one in the hypha, one in the hook of the crozier, in such a way that the subsequently delimited ascus mother cell comes to contain a compatible pair of nuclei (Fig. 5.2 A). In ascomycetes, this phenomenon is generally restricted to the hymenium, but in many basidiomycetes, similar bypasses are found, not just at the base of the basidium, but at every septum in the dikaryophase. In basidiomycetes, they are called **clamp connections** (Fig. 5.2 B). If a septate, somatic hypha has regular clamp connections, it must be that of a dikaryotic basidiomycete. If clamps are absent, the hyphae could still be those of a dikaryotic basidiomycete (many boletes lack clamps), but they could equally be those of a monokaryotic basidiomycete, or of an ascomycete, or even those of a zygomycete, since members of the order Kickxellales have regularly septate hyphae.

E) While the meiospores of ascomycetes are developed **inside** meiosporangia called asci (Fig. 5.2 A), the meiospores of basidiomycetes are formed **outside** specialized meiosporangia called **basidia** (Fig. 5.2 B)—the nuclear fusion and

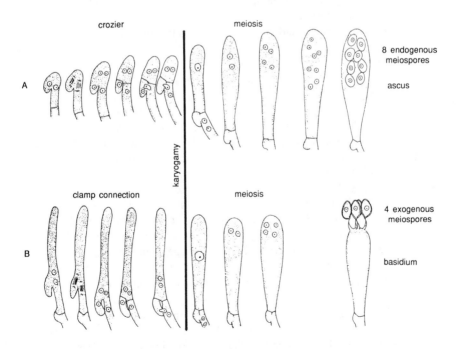

Fig. 5.2 Comparison of ascus and basidium development (see text).

the subsequent meiosis happen inside the cell, but the spores are blown out like tiny balloons at the ends of four tiny tapered outgrowths called **sterigmata**. In most basidiomycetes, these spores are then actively expelled from their perches, though, as in the ascomycetes, there is a highly significant minority which has lost the spore-shooting mechanism. These we call **sequestrate**, because the mature basidiospores are kept inside the basidioma (which may simply remain closed, or may develop underground), being released later in a variety of ways, some of which involve animal vectors.

You may be relieved to learn that you don't have to search for any of these microscopic and submicroscopic features to recognize a basidiomycete when you see one. The reason for that is that there are usually diagnostic features that are visible to the naked eye. What else do you know that looks like a mushroom? The same is true of most other basidiomycete fructifications—and you even come to recognize certain basidiomycete mycelia on sight after a while, without even using a hand lens, because they tend to form delicate but visible fan-like arrangements on decaying wood. If you can already recognize bracket fungi, puffballs, earth-stars, bird's-nest fungi and stinkhorns, you're well on the way to being able to tell a basidiomycete from an ascomycete (and from any other fungus—see Fig. 4.1).

I recognize three classes within the Subphylum Basidiomycotina. These are the Holobasidiomycetes, the Phragmobasidiomycetes, and the Teliomycetes. The first class includes all the common names just mentioned. The second includes many jelly fungi, and the third comprises the rust and smut fungi.

Class Holobasidiomycetes

All basidiomycetes with holobasidia—those that are not subdivided by septa—belong here. Again, this is an absolutely microscopic character that is often difficult to see. And again, there are macroscopic features that enable us to recognize 99% of all holobasidiomycetes as belonging to this class. I hope you will enjoy that knowledge soon. If you don't have it at your fingertips already, some time invested in looking at the various illustrations in this text, and at one of the beautifully illustrated field guides listed at the end of this chapter, will pay off handsomely when you go outdoors to look for these fungi. It's not that holobasidiomycetes are all the same: in fact, they present a dazzling diversity of form and function. But while most holobasidiomycetes develop characteristic fleshy, corky or woody basidiomata, those of phragmobasidiomycetes (which have basidia sudivided by septa) are gelatinous, and teliomycetes have nothing you could call a separate fruit body, merely forming pustules on their living hosts. And in teliomycetes, the basidia develop from a specialized resting spore called a teliospore.

The Holobasidiomycetes comprise two interrelated series, called Hymenomycetae and Gasteromycetae. Most Hymenomycetes shoot their basidiospores actively from hymenia that are exposed at maturity (Gasteromycetes do not). Basidiospores which are to be forcibly discharged (ballistospores) blow out at an angle to the fine sterigma that bears them: in other words they are asymmetrically mounted, or offset, as can be seen in Figs. 5.2, 5.3 and 5.8. Just before discharge, a droplet of fluid, enclosed within a membrane, appears at one side of the spore base. Although there is still some controversy concerning the exact nature of the mechanism involved in flipping the basidiospores into space, I am inclined to accept the theory that, as in so many other active fungal dispersal mechanisms, it is high hydrostatic pressure, turgor pressure, that operates in a syringe-like manner. However, the details of what happens at the moment of discharge are still unclear, and in need of acute observation, preferably by high-speed photomicrography.

Gasteromycetes, if they have hymenia, don't expose them when the spores are mature, and the spores are symmetrically placed on the sterigmata, and are never actively shot away. We believe that the basidium originally evolved as a spore-shooting mechanism, but that for various ecological reasons, which we will explore, it has on many separate occasions lost that function. So our assumption is that the various kinds of gasteromycete have emerged independently, on many occasions, from among the Holobasidiomycetes. Oberwinkler recognizes 19 orders of Holobasidiomycetes, but I will discuss only ten. Why the difference? He subdivides what I call the order Aphyllophorales into six orders, what I call the Agaricales into three, and recognizes one or two obscure orders I did not feel it essential to enumerate here.

(1) **Order Exobasidiales**: 5 genera, 15 species. This is an atypical order in very much the same way that the Taphrinales was atypical of the ascomycetes.

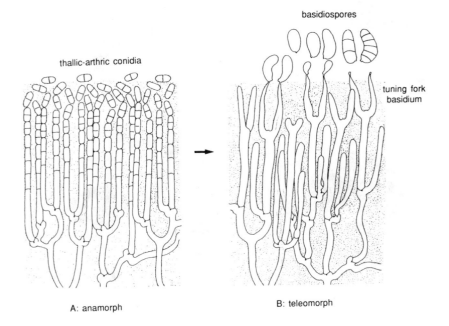

basidiospores

thallic-arthric conidia

tuning fork basidium

A: anamorph

B: teleomorph

Fig. 5.3 Dacrymycetales: *Dacrymyces stillatus.*

Unlike most members of the class, *Exobasidium* doesn't produce a basidioma, but only a layer of basidia on the surface of the host plant, which is usually a member of the Ericaceae. It produces symptoms very like those caused by the Taphrinales—excessive growth of the leaf tissues, accompanied by disturbances in photosynthesis that cause the leaves to turn red. This has led to speculation that these two orders represent some kind of connection between the subphyla.

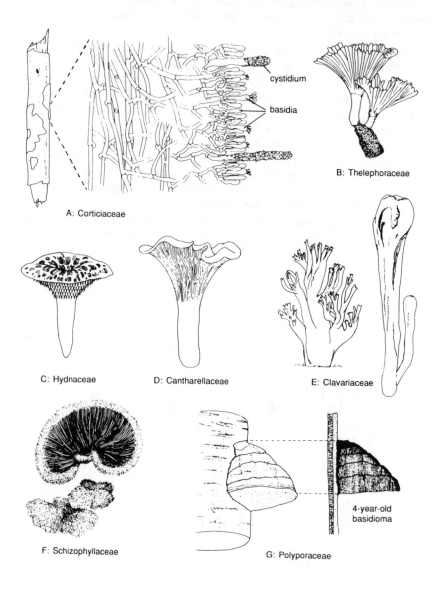

Fig. 5.4 Representative Aphyllophorales.

(2) **Order Dacrymycetales**: 11 genera, 60 species. These are all 'jelly fungi,' again very atypical of the class, that grow on rotting wood. They develop gelatinous, often bright yellow, basidiomata that are conspicuous in wet weather, but shrivel up and almost disappear in dry periods. The basidiomata of *Dacrymyces* are irregular to the point of shapelessness, and they closely resemble the fructifications of many members of the class Phragmobasidiomycetes. But their basidia are undivided and highly characteristic: we call them **tuning fork basidia** because they develop two long arms that grow up to the surface of the jelly, where their basidiospores are produced (Fig. 5.3 B). The basidiospores are also unusual in becoming multiseptate after dehiscence. The gelatinous fruit body plays a double role, in that it often produces an unnamed thallic-arthric conidial anamorph (Fig. 5.3 A) before the basidia develop.

(3) **Order Aphyllophorales**: 400 genera, 1200 species. This is one of the main groups of hymenomycetes, and one of the most diverse. Its name can be translated as 'without gills,' and it seems to be designed as a catch-all for hymenomycetes that don't fit into the fourth order, the Agaricales, which comprises the mushrooms with gills or fleshy tubes. So the Aphyllophorales embraces 8 families with conspicuous but different basidiomata—the club and coral fungi, the tooth fungi, the chanterelles and the horn of plenty, the dry rot fungi, the paint fungi, and the bracket fungi. Several of these are illustrated in Fig. 5.4. Most are saprobic on wood, and while they do us the favour of scavenging on fallen branches or logs, and recycling the nutrients in these, they are equally at home attacking either the structural timbers of our houses, if we allow these to become damp, or the wood and roots of living trees. A few are ectomycorrhizal (see chapter 17).

a) Family Corticiaceae. The basidiomata are often effuse or **resupinate** (spread out), on the surface of decaying wood (Fig. 5.4 A). The hymenium may be smooth, wrinkled or toothed, and the basidiospores are smooth in outline, colourless or pale, and non-amyloid. Although at first sight they don't appear to be particularly highly organized, their microscopic structure is often intricate. The basal tissue is usually composed of only one kind of hypha, and is thus described as **monomitic** (Fig. 5.4 A), but in some taxa the fruit bodies are **dimitic**, with thin-walled generative hyphae and thick-walled skeletal hyphae. The basidial hymenium may also incorporate specialized accessory sterile hyphae (e.g. **cystidia** such as those shown in Fig. 5.4 A). These are fungi that richly repay microscopic study.

b) Family Thelephoraceae. These are like the Corticiaceae in many ways, but most members fruit on the ground rather than on wood. The basidioma may be resupinate or fan-like or stalked, and the hymenium may be smooth, warty or toothed. The basidiospores are irregular in shape, ornamented, brown to hyaline, and non-amyloid. The dark tissue gives a green reaction with KOH. *Thelephora terrestris* (Fig. 5.4 B), with brown, fibrous, vase-shaped basidiomata and a smooth hymenium, often establishes mycorrhizal relationships with young conifers in tree nurseries (see chapter 17).

c) Family Clavariaceae. Club and coral fungi (Fig 5.4 E). Arising from the ground or from wood, the erect, beige, yellow, white or purple basidiomata may be unbranched and club-shaped, as in *Clavariadelphus*; clustered, as in *Clavaria* and *Clavulinopsis*; or repeatedly branched and coralloid, as in *Ramaria*. They are monomitic or dimitic. The hymenium covers the upper part of the basidiomata, and is not put out of action by repeated wetting, as those of most other hymenomycetes would be. Basidiospores are colourless, smooth, and non-amyloid.

d) Family Cantharellaceae. The basidiomata are monomitic (constructed from a single kind of hypha) and arise from the ground. They may be dark and funnel-shaped, as in *Craterellus cornucopioides* (the 'horn of plenty'), or yellow, stalked and rather mushroom-like, as in *Cantharellus cibarius* (the edible 'chanterelle' or 'pfifferlinge': Fig. 5.4 D). The hymenium may be smooth, wrinkled, or deeply folded in an almost gill-like configuration (as it is in the chanterelle), and the basidiospores are smooth, colourless and non-amyloid.

e) Family Coniophoraceae. The monomitic basidiomata usually appear on wood, and the hymenium can be smooth, toothed, folded or tubulate. That of *Serpula lacrymans*, the dry rot fungus, is dimpled. The basidiospores are smooth, brown and double-walled. *Serpula* and *Coniophora* (the cellar fungus) cause serious rots of structural timbers.

f) Family Hydnaceae. The tooth fungi. The basidiomata may be rather irregular and excentric, as in *Hericium* (the wood urchin, which fruits on the side of trees), or very mushroom-like, as in *Hydnum repandum*, the edible 'hedgehog mushroom' or 'sweet-tooth.' The hymenium covers tapering teeth that point vertically downward, like miniature stalactites (Fig. 5.4 C). The spores are smooth, colourless, and non-amyloid.

g) Family Schizophyllaceae. The extremely common (and therefore success-ful) *Schizophyllum commune* (Fig. 5.4 F), often seen on dead branches, looks a bit like an agaric without a stalk, but is really a compound fructification, in which the inrolled edges of contiguous cupulate basidiomata give it its misleading common name, 'split gill.' This species is easily grown in pure culture, and has been a popular subject for genetic research.

g) Family Polyporaceae. The bracket or shelf fungi. The usually persistent, poroid (or sometimes gilled) basidiomata usually arise on wood, where the larger poroid forms are often perennial, adding a layer of tubes each year (Fig. 5.4 G). Basidiomata may be monomitic, dimitic, or trimitic (constructed from one, two or three kinds of hyphae). Spores are smooth or ornamented, brown or colour-less, and non-amyloid (amyloid in *Bondarzewia*). This is by far the largest family of the Aphyllophorales, and many of its members, e.g. *Poria*, *Polyporus*, and *Ganoderma*, cause serious decays of standing and structural timber. *Hetero-basidion annosum* is highly pathogenic to many conifers, and causes serious root-rots. I have seen a forest clearing produced by this fungus, which had killed representatives of 14 different conifers, many of them introduced species. *Piptoporus betulinus* kills only birch trees. The generic concepts have changed a lot in recent years as a result of extensive anatomical and enzymological research, and are not easy for the beginner to understand.

(4) **Order Agaricales**: 280 genera, 10,000 species. This order brings together the most familiar of all fungi, the so-called mushrooms and toadstools. Since no two people agree on the precise dividing line between these two categories, it is better to call them all **agarics**, the term used by the knowledgeable, among whom you should soon be numbered. Compared to polypores, agarics are relatively ephemeral, the basidiomata persisting for anything from a few hours to a few weeks, depending on the species. They occur seasonally, fruiting mainly in late summer or fall. These fructifications arise from an extensive, perennial myce-

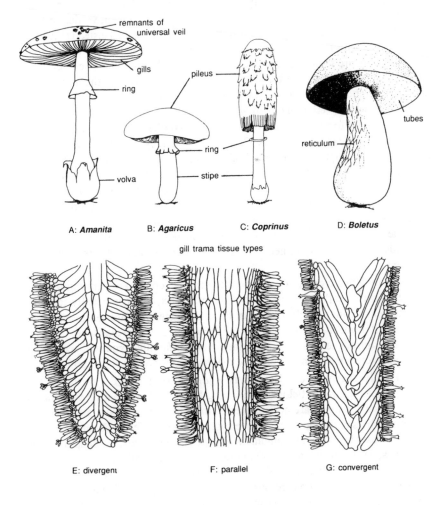

Fig. 5.5 Agaricales.

lium which ramifies, invisible to the eye, through soil, plant debris or wood, gathering energy for that once-a-year splurge. Some fairy rings (enormous, radially extending fungal colonies—compare Fig. 3.1) are estimated to be over 400 years old, and have presumably produced flushes of basidiomata in all but the driest of those years. Most agarics are either **saprobic**, exploiting dead organic matter, or **ectomycorrhizal**, establishing mutualistic symbioses with the roots of woody plants, epecially conifers of the economically important family Pinaceae. This explains why woodlands are often such excellent places to look for agarics. A more detailed discussion of the ectomycorrhizal relationship is given in chapter 17.

Most agarics share the same basic design (Fig. 5.5 A-D). There is a central, vertical **stipe**, with a horizontally spreading cap or **pileus** at the top. The underside of the pileus usually bears delicate, radially arranged, vertical plates called **gills** or **lamellae**, though some have vertical fleshy tubes instead (Fig. 5.5 D). The hymenium covers both sides of each gill, and lines each tube. Basidiospores are launched from the basidia, drop through the space between adjacent gills, and enter the turbulent outside air which carries them away. In some genera the developing basidioma may be totally enclosed within a membranous **universal veil**, remains of which can be seen on the mature, expanded basidioma in the form of a sheath or **volva** around the base of the stipe, and spots or warts on the cap (Figs. 5.5 A, 22.2 D). There may also be a **partial veil** connecting the stipe and the edge of the cap, enclosing and protecting the developing gills. This, too, may remain on the stipe of the mature agaric as a membranous **ring** or **annulus** (Fig. 5.5 A-C), or a filamentous **cortina**. A few agarics have both of these features; some others have only one, the majority have neither. Agarics are complex structures, and have many other taxonomically valuable features. The check-list given below includes many of them, and shows the kinds of information we need to collect in order to classify the thousands of different agarics.

If you look that closely at a number of agarics (a counsel of perfection), you will learn a tremendous amount about them. In fact, you can usually identify them to genus with a small fraction of those characters, though getting them to species will probably call for much more information. If you read what follows, in which I introduce you to representatives of 16 families, you will see which of the characters mentioned above are the most important in separating them.

a) Family Agaricaceae. The genus *Agaricus* (Fig. 5.5 B), to which the supermarket mushroom belongs, has a ring but no volva (a partial veil but no universal veil), its gills are not attached to the stipe, and its spore print is dark. Other members of the family may have spore prints of different colours, but they are never rusty brown or cinnamon. *Leucoagaricus naucinus*, which is common on lawns, is an all-white or cream-coloured agaric with a ring. It has an uncomfortable resemblance to the deadly poisonous *Amanita virosa* (Fig. 22.1 A), so although it is not dangerous (edible to some, a gastric irritant to others), I always advise people against making a meal of it. *Agaricus, Cystoderma,*

CHARACTERISTICS FOR THE IDENTIFICATION OF AGARICS

Locality:_____Date:_____
Habitat notes: soil type: _____
         soil pH:_____
         vegetational community:_____

BASIDIOMATA

solitary_____ in troops_____ in rings_____ on ground_____
on wood_____ on living tree_____ other (describe)_____
_____(Photograph, draw
or preferably paint general view and vertical section of fruit-body)

MACROSCOPIC CHARACTERS

CAP (PILEUS): diameter: (range) _____-_____cm
Shape: convex_____ bell-shaped_____ conical_____ umbonate_____
flat_____ depressed_____ umbilicate_____ funnel-shaped_____
cylindrical_____ (when young)_____ (when mature)_____
Colour: when immature_____ when mature_____
    when wet_____when dry_____
Surface: (circle one or more) dry • moist • greasy • viscid • gluti-
nous • peeling easily • smooth • matt • polished • irregularly
roughened • downy • zoned • velvety • scaly • splitting •
shaggy • with volva fragments
Margin: (circle one or more) regular • wavy • upcurved • incurved
 • smooth • rough • furrowed • striate • split • shaggy •
with veil fragments

GILLS (or **TUBES** or **TEETH**): (circle as appropriate)
remote • free • adnate • adnexed • sinuate • decurrent
 • crowded • distant • forked • anastomosing
easily separable from the cap-tissue: Yes • No
thick • thin
consistency: brittle • pliable • fleshy • waxy
colour: when immature_____ at maturity_____
number of different gill lengths (series)__or number of tube layers___
obvious features of gill-edge, tube-edge, e.g., colour, outline_____

_____

STIPE: central • eccentric • absent • hollow • solid •
stuffed • tapering upward • equal
Dimensions: length(range)___-___ thickness___-___
Colour: when immature_____ at maturity_____
Consistency: fleshy • stringy • brittle • leathery • cartilaginous •
woody
Surface: fibrillose • dry • viscid • scaly • smooth
Characters of stipe base (e.g., swollen, rooting, etc.)_____

_____

CHARACTERISTICS FOR THE IDENTIFICATION OF AGARICS
Page 2

VOLVA, if present: sheathing stem base • scurfy rings

RING, if present: single • double • membranous • filamentous
• persistent • fugacious • moveable • thick • thin • apical • median
• hanging (skirt-like)

FLESH: colour: inside cap: when wet_____when dry_____
in stem: when wet_____when dry_____
Colour changes when exposed to air:_____
Milk-like latex: present • absent
colour when exuded_____after exposure to air_____
Smell: before cutting_____after cutting_____

MICROSCOPIC CHARACTERS
BASIDIOSPORES:
Colour: in mass (spore print)_____ under microscope_____
Shape: spherical • ovoid • elongate • angular • curved • size ___-___
x ___-___ µm
Ornamentation: none • warty • rounded • pointed (spiny) • ridged • striate • net-like
Size and shape of germ-pore, if present_____
Iodine reaction of spore-mass: red-purple (dextrinoid) •
blue-black to dark violet (amyloid) • yellow-brown or brown (non-amyloid)

BASIDIA: length/width ratio:
less than 4:1 • more than 5:1
number of sterigmata:_____

CAP TRAMA: types of cell present:_____
GILL-TISSUE (TRAMA): type and arrangement of cells
between adjacent hymenial faces (see Fig. 5.5 E-G):
divergent • parallel • convergent • interwoven

CAP-SURFACE (PILEIPELLIS): cells of outer layer:
filamentous • rounded

STERILE CELLS — CYSTIDIA: present on:
gill-face • gill-edge • cap • stipe
shape:
filiform • cylindrical • clavate • ventricose • branched
size_____ - _____ x _____ - _____ µm
thick-walled • thin-walled • hyaline • pigmented
• other features_____

Leucoagaricus and *Lepiota* are all saprobic. *Endoptychum* is a sequestrate derivative of *Agaricus*.

b) Family Amanitaceae. All members of the genus *Amanita* (Figs. 5.5 A, 22.1 A, 22.2 D) have white spore prints, and most have a ring and a volva, though in some (formerly grouped in the genus *Amanitopsis*) the partial veil is inconspicuous and hidden inside the volva. The tissue inside the gills (the **gill trama**) is divergent (Fig. 5.5 E). Because some *Amanita* species are deadly poisonous (see chapter 22), mushroom hunters should always make sure they get to the base of the stipe of any agaric they pick, so they can see whether or not there's a volva. The 'destroying angel,' *Amanita virosa* (Fig. 22.1 A), is pure white, with ring, volva and white spore print. Like most other members of the family, this lethal species is ectomycorrhizal, and so fruits only near tree species with which it is symbiotic—see chapter 17. *Termitomyces* (Fig. 16.3), a saprobic genus, is involved in another kind of mutualistic symbiosis: with mound-building termites in Africa and Asia, a relationship discussed in chapter 16.

c) Family Bolbitiaceae. Basidiomata of the genus *Bolbitius* are small and ephemeral, since their tissues autolyse (self-digest) at maturity. The surface layer of the cap (the **pileipellis**) is epithelial (the cells are swollen, and don't appear filamentous). The spore print is ochraceous to rusty brown, and the spores have a germ pore. Representative genera are *Agrocybe*, *Bolbitius*, and *Conocybe*. *Conocybe filaris* contains deadly amatoxins (see chapter 22). In addition to normal agaricoid species, this family has some sequestrate members with basidia that don't shoot their spores. The genus *Gastrocybe* still looks like an agaric, but its symmetrically mounted basidiospores, and its habit of falling over as soon as it comes up, show that it is even now actively evolving, and that its spores are not wind-dispersed.

d) Family Coprinaceae. This family also has a pileipellis of swollen cells, but the basidiospores are usually black and smooth, with a germ pore. Members of the advanced genus *Coprinus* have weed-like vigour and opportunism, pioneering the exploitation of such habitats as recently disturbed ground, and dung. The best-known species, *Coprinus comatus* (Figs. 5.5 C, 8.5), the 'shaggy mane' or 'shaggy ink cap,' has a complex set of physical arrangements, and a precisely timed sequence of events during spore liberation, that make it one of the most advanced of all agarics. Its behaviour is described in detail in chapter 8, but I must mention here that its gills self-digest or **autolyse** during spore-liberation, and that this behaviour is characteristic of most coprini. *Panaeolus* is also black-spored and grows on dung, but its gills don't liquefy. The spore print of *Psathyrella* species varies from black to brown or even brick red. *Podaxis*, which fruits in deserts in many parts of the world, and on termite mounds in southern Africa, looks superficially very like *Coprinus comatus*, and has black spores; but it has no recognizable gills, and generally doesn't autolyse. The spore mass is dry, and the spores are dispersed only when the fruit body disintegrates. Though some taxonomists have erected a special Gasteromycete order for *Podaxis* and similar fungi, I see no reason to treat it as anything other than a sequestrate member of the Coprinaceae.

e) Family Cortinariaceae. Here, the cells of the pileipellis are never swollen, and the basidiospores are rusty brown and often ornamented. *Cortinarius, Galerina, Gymnopilus, Hebeloma* and *Inocybe* are representative genera. The best known genus is *Cortinarius*, which isn't too surprising, since it may have as many as 2,000 species, mostly ectomycorrhizal. This genus is easily recognized by its unusual partial veil, which is called a **cortina** (curtain)—numerous individual filaments stretch between the stipe and the edge of the pileus as it expands. Many *Hebeloma* species are also ectomycorrhizal. *Galerina autumnalis* is a small but deadly poisonous, amatoxin-containing species that grows on rotten wood in North America. Most species of the ectomycorrhizal *Inocybe* are also poisonous because they contain muscarine, and *Gymnopilus spectabilis* contains the hallucinogen, psilocybin (see chapter 22). Some members of the Cortinariaceae have become sequestrate. The genus *Thaxterogaster* closely resembles *Cortinarius* in many ways, but its cap never expands, and its gills have become so convoluted that even if they were to be exposed, they could not successfully drop many spores into the air. One species I found in New Zealand had even lost its external stipe, and looked rather like a puffball, though a sagittal section (through the vertical axis) revealed a central column of stipe tissue—the transformation still isn't complete. *Hymenogaster* is another sequestrate derivative of the Cortinariaceae: one of its non-shooting basidia is illustrated in Fig. 5.6 A.

f) Family Entolomataceae. The spores are pink to salmon-coloured in mass, and extremely angular or sometimes longitudinally ridged; the gills are attached to the stipe. *Entoloma* and *Clitopilus* are representative genera of this mainly terricolous family. Most species of the mycorrhizal genus *Entoloma* contain gastro-intestinal irritants, and some can cause serious poisoning. *Entoloma abortivum* is a common species in which normal fruit bodies are often accompanied by lumpy, rounded, misshapen basidiomata. These are being attacked by another agaric, *Armillaria mellea* (Tricholomataceae), whose basidia can be found in them. The easily recognized parasitized basidiomata are edible. *Entoloma* has given rise to a sequestrate offshoot, *Richoniella*.

g) Family Pluteaceae. The spore print is pink, like that of the Entolomataceae, but the spores are ellipsoidal and smooth, the gills are free (not attached to the stipe), and the gill tissue or **trama** is convergent (Fig. 5.5 G). The lignicolous genus *Pluteus* has 100 species. *Volvariella* has only 20, but one of these is *V. volvacea*, the straw mushroom, which is widely cultivated in the Far East (see chapter 18). Next time you eat mushrooms at a Chinese restaurant, see if they are immature basidiomata of this species—you can easily recognize it by the conspicuous and persistent volva which almost encloses the whole basidioma.

h) Family Hygrophoraceae. The basidia are long, the spore print white, and the gill trama is divergent or parallel. Species of *Hygrocybe* have parallel gill trama (Fig. 5.5 F), are yellow, orange or red, and have a very characteristic waxy, translucent appearance. These are among the commonest and most widely distributed agarics. *Hygrophorus* species have divergent gill trama (Fig. 5.5 E), often a partial veil, and are white, grey or brown.

i) Family Strophariaceae. A saprobic family containing many 'magic' mushrooms. The spores are purple-black or brown, smooth-walled and with a germ pore; the pileipellis is filamentous; the gills are attached to the stipe and often bear accessory cells called **chrysocystidia**, which have contents that stain yellow in alkali. Some species of *Psilocybe* and *Stropharia* contain the hallucinogen, **psilocybin**, and their flesh often turns blue when bruised. The non-hallucinogenic genera *Pholiota* and *Naematoloma* usually fruit on wood.

j) Family Tricholomataceae. The largest and most diverse family of agarics, with over 75 genera. It isn't a very 'natural' family, so we can't make many safe generalizations about it. The spores, however, are white to pink in mass, and have no germ pore; the gill trama is parallel, and the gills are attached to the stipe. Representative genera are *Armillaria*, *Clitocybe*, *Collybia*, *Flammulina*, *Laccaria*, *Lentinus*, *Marasmius*, *Mycena*, *Pleurotus* and *Tricholoma*. 'Marasmus' is the medical term for starvation, and some species of *Marasmius*, such as *M. rotula*, common on decaying hardwood, definitely have an emaciated appearance, with a stipe reduced to a black thread. Others, like *M. oreades*, the 'fairy ring mushroom,' though small, are usually numerous enough to be worth eating. Species of *Laccaria* and *Tricholoma* are often ectomycorrhizal. *Clitocybe dealbata* contains the toxin **muscarine** (see chapter 22), while *Clitocybe nuda* is the 'blewit,' a choice edible agaric. Other famous edible species (see chapter 18) are *Tricholoma matsutake*, the 'matsu-take' or pine mushroom of Japan, and *Lentinus edodes*, the 'shii-take,' or oak mushroom (neither of these is native to North America). *Lentinellus* and the edible *Pleurotus* are unusual in having virtually no stipe, and often fruiting on standing trees. One of the mysteries attached to the Tricholomataceae is that despite the large number of taxa it encompasses, only two sequestrate forms are known: *Hydnangium* and *Podohydnangium*, both of which arose from *Laccaria*. Compare that with what happened in the next family.

k) Family Russulaceae. An entirely ectomycorrhizal group, with flesh that is distinctively brittle due to the presence of unique, turgid, spherical, thin-walled cells called **sphaerocysts**. The spores have elaborate amyloid ornamentation of ridges and warts; the spore print is white. This family contains two large agaric genera, *Russula* and *Lactarius*, and six much less common sequestrate derivatives (which of course do not give spore prints). Although the two main-line genera are similar in many respects, they are easily distinguished by the presence of a milky latex in *Lactarius* and its sequestrate relatives, which are called 'milky caps,' and by the bright colour of the pileus in most *Russula* species. From *Lactarius* have evolved two sequestrate forms: *Arcangeliella* (still mushroom-like [agaricoid], but with a cap that encloses the gills, and non-shooting basidia), and *Zelleromyces* (which has become hypogeous and truffle-like). As noted above, all three genera produce latex. *Russula* seems to have given rise to two separate sequestrate lines, the *Macowanites - Gymnomyces* sequence, and the *Elasmomyces - Martellia* sequence, both involving an agaricoid and a hypogeous form, and both retaining micro-anatomical characters, such as sphaerocysts and amyloid spore ornamentation, that reveal their origin in *Russula*.

l) Family Boletaceae. Substantial, almost exclusively ectomycorrhizal agarics, with the hymenium lining a layer of vertical fleshy tubes that can be easily separated from the flesh of the cap. The often swollen stipe frequently has net-like or warty ornamentation, and sometimes a partial veil. The spores are elongated, and yellowish-brown in mass. There are no clamp connections on the hyphae. *Boletus* (Fig. 5.5 D), *Leccinum* and *Suillus* are representative genera. *Boletus edulis* is the famous edible 'Steinpilz' or 'cep' of Europe, and fortunately also occurs in North America. Many other boletes are also eaten, though species with orange or reddish pore-mouths must be avoided, and those whose flesh turns blue when bruised should be treated with caution. *Gastroboletus* is alleged to be a sequestrate derivative of *Boletus*. The sequestrate *Gastroleccinum* is related to *Leccinum*, and *Rhizopogon*, *Truncocolumella* and *Alpova* are sequestrate, hypogeous offshoots of *Suillus* which, like the parent genus, are important ectomycorrhizal partners of western conifers.

m) Family Gomphidiaceae. This mycorrhizal family has viscid caps, decurrent gills, a dark grey to brownish-black spore print, and microscopic structure that shows it is closely related to the Boletaceae. *Gomphidius* has white flesh; that of *Chroogomphus* is pink to orange. Sequestrate forms have arisen from both genera.

n) Family Gyrodontaceae. This family superficially resembles the Boletaceae, but the tubes are shallow and not easily detached; the spore print is yellowish or olivaceous brown; the spores are subglobose to ellipsoid; and the hyphae have clamp connections. *Boletinus*, *Gyrodon* and *Gyroporus* are representative genera.

o) Family Paxillaceae. Like the Gomphidiaceae, this mycorrhizal family has gills, but these are easily separated from the flesh of the cap. The gill trama is divergent (Fig. 5.5 E), and gelatinized. The spore print is brown or white, and the spores are ovoid to ellipsoid. Members of the common genus *Paxillus* have caps with inrolled edges.

p) Family Strobilomycetaceae. The cap of *Strobilomyces floccopus* is greyish-black, with large, shaggy scales, and the tubes are grey, turning reddish when bruised. The spore print is black, and the spores are ornamented with a network of ridges. The genus *Boletellus* appears to have given rise to no fewer than four sequestrate forms: *Austrogautieria*, *Chamonixia*, *Gautieria* and *Protogautieria*.

The foregoing is no more than a gesture sketch of the world of the agarics. If you want to learn more about what many people consider the most fascinating of all fungi, you must buy or borrow one of the field guides listed under 'Further Reading' at the end of this chapter. The large tome by Pomerleau has all the minutiae a North-easterner needs (though the colour illustrations are poor), but the pocket-sized Audubon Guide by Lincoff, though less detailed, covers the whole continent, and can go anywhere with you. The larger-format 'Mushrooms of North America' by Roger Phillips, the most recently published of these field guides (1991), has over 1000 colour photographs, and includes many more species of, for example, *Cortinarius* (93), *Amanita* (41), *Lactarius* (64) and *Russula* (81), than other guides. 'Mushrooms Demystified' by Arora, though oriented toward western North America, is a mine of useful, and often amusing, information for all mushroom-pickers; it also covers a wide range of taxa (even dealing with many sequestrate forms). 'The New Savory Wild Mushroom' has excellent colour photographs, but is mainly useful to those in the Pacific North-west. In addition to agarics, all five books cover some of the more conspicuous Gasteromycetes, Ascomycetes and Aphyllophorales. The Lincoff and Phillips books provide a very large number of colour photographs, and have the added recommendation of being relatively inexpensive. Some of the larger and more difficult genera call for separate keys, and those to the north-eastern species of *Russula* by Kibby and Fatto are excellent examples.

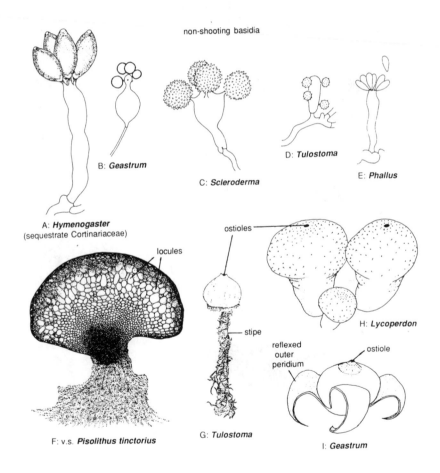

Fig. 5.6 Holobasidiomycetes which lack active spore discharge. A: Agaricales; B,H,I: Lycoperdales; C,F: Sclerodermatales; D,G: Tulostomatales; E: Phallales.

Although many kinds of sequestrate fungi can be clearly traced to their agaricoid origin, many others probably evolved so long ago that it is no longer possible to trace their ancestry with any degree of certainty. For these, which we call Gasteromycetes, we have erected special orders, based on the mode of passive spore dispersal into which they have evolved. I think you will agree that if these groups have any agaric ancestry, it is well concealed. All have non-shooting holobasidia, some of which are shown in Fig. 5.6 B-E.

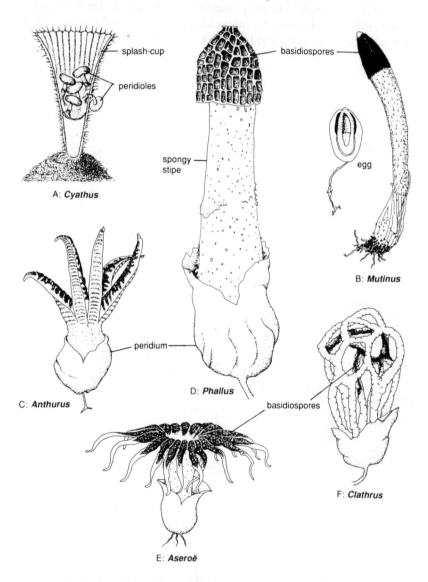

Fig. 5.7 Gasteromycetes. A: Nidulariales; B-F: Phallales.

(5) **Order Sclerodermatales**: 8 genera, 35 species. The earthballs. Here the spore mass (**gleba**) has small spore-containing cavities (locules) with no real hymenium, and is powdery at maturity, with no true stipe or capillitial threads. In the common genus *Scleroderma*, the spore mass is blackish at maturity, and the basidioma has no ostiole. The separate locules are clearly visible in *Pisolithus tinctorius* (Fig. 5.6 F), which is perhaps the most famous of all ectomycorrhizal fungi, since it helps conifers and eucalypts to thrive on particularly unfavourable sites. It has been the subject of many research projects, as you will read in chapter 17. *Sphaerobolus stellatus*, of the atypical family Sphaerobolaceae, has a six-layered peridium. At maturity, the innermost layer and part of the third layer liquefy, and the second layer takes up the free water, eventually everting suddenly and throwing the gleba up to 6 metres toward the light. This family contains the only gasteromycetes in which a form of active spore dispersal has been re-evolved. But notice that evolution did not actually reverse itself: the odds against that ever happening are astronomical, and I know of no documented cases.

(6) **Order Melanogastrales**: 9 genera, 46 species. A hypogeous group, in which the gleba has many locules, no true hymenium, and is mucilaginous at maturity. *Melanogaster* and *Leucogaster* are representative genera.

(7) **Order Tulostomatales**: 9 genera and 75 species of stalked puffballs, with dry, powdery gleba. Representative genera are *Tulostoma* (Fig. 5.6 D,G), *Calostoma* and *Battarraea*, which are often found in areas of warm, dry climate.

(8) **Order Lycoperdales**: 26 genera, 260 species. These are the common and well-known puffballs and earthstars, with powdery glebas. Though most are saprobic in soil and on rotten wood, some may be ectomycorrhizal. In contrast to the Sclerodermatales, the glebal cavities are lined by a hymenium when young. The mature spore mass is usually khaki-coloured, and mixed with capillitial filaments. The peridium has two or more layers, and usually develops an apical ostiole (Fig. 5.6 G-I). The papery inner peridium can be compressed by raindrops, expelling air and spores through the ostiole. Representative genera are *Lycoperdon* (most common puffballs: Fig. 5.6 H), *Bovista*, *Calvatia* (the giant puffball: Fig. 18.3), and *Geastrum* (the earthstar: Fig. 5.6 I). In the last, the thick outer peridium splits stellately as it dries out, and the segments fold back in order to raise the gleba, in its inner, papery peridium, above the dead leaves that might otherwise prevent the puffball mechanism from working.

(9) **Order Nidulariales**: 5 genera, 60 species. The bird's nest fungi, in which the basidioma has been modified to become a splash-cup spore dipersal mechanism. The gleba is divided up among several individual 'eggs' (more formally, **peridioles**). The kinetic energy of raindrops is focussed and reflected by the funnel-shaped basidioma, and the rebounding water carries the peridioles with it. *Crucibulum*, *Cyathus* and *Nidularia* are representative genera. In *Cyathus* (Fig. 5.7 A), the peridioles are attached to the wall of the basidioma by a long thread, most of which is folded up inside the stipe of the peridiole. When the peridiole is splashed out, the thread unwinds rapidly, trailing behind. At the end

of the thread is a sticky blob which acts to anchor the peridiole to whatever it strikes.

(10) **Order Phallales**: 25 genera, 45 species. The stinkhorns, whose spores are dispersed by animal vectors. The gleba is slimy and really does stink, so it attracts flies, which wallow in the mess, eating some spores and carrying others away on their feet. Although we have two well-known stinkhorns, representing the genera *Phallus* (Figs. 5.6 E, 5.7 D) and *Mutinus* (Fig. 5.7 B), the most bizarre genera are commoner in Australasia and the tropics. All stinkhorns develop in a gelatinous matrix within a membranous 'egg-shell' (peridium), but when they 'hatch,' their mature fruit bodies can be strikingly different. *Phallus* and *Mutinus* have the simplest morphology: the stipe elongates rapidly, carrying their respectively thimble-shaped and conical heads (often called receptacles), into the air, where they can release their effluvium and attract the flies more easily. In *Anthurus* (Fig. 5.7 C) the gleba covers the inner side of several octopus-like arms. In *Clathrus* (Fig. 5.7 F) the arms remain fused, and in some species form an open lattice, again with the gleba on the inside. *Aseroë* (Fig. 5.7 F) is surely one of the most flamboyant members of a spectacular order. Bright orange-red extensions of its receptacle radiate out like the petals of a flower, providing visual as well as olfactory clues to would-be vectors. *Hysterangium* is hypogeous, so the gelatinous layer is not well-developed, and there is no dramatic rupture of the peridium at maturity. But the affinities of this reclusive sequestrate genus with the otherwise exhibitionistic Phallales are accepted.

The two remaining classes in the subphylum Basidiomycotina are very different. One is of no economic importance, the other causes many serious crop diseases. Both have basidia that are divided into four compartments by septa, each compartment giving rise to a single basidiospore. In class Phragmobasidiomycetes, the basidia are borne on some kind of basidioma, but in class Teliomycetes, they arise from overwintering spores. Members of these classes often have the ability (1) to form secondary spores from their primary spores (2) and/or to produce yeast-like cells. Holobasidiomycetes can do neither.

Class Phragmobasidiomycetes

This group contains four orders: Tremellales, Auriculariales, Septobasidiales and Tulasnellales, which all have phragmobasidia.

(1) **Order Tremellales**: Jelly fungi found on dead wood. Long considered harmless saprobes, they have recently been unmasked as vicious mycoparasites of other wood-inhabiting fungi. The basidia (Fig. 5.8 A) are often described as 'cruciately septate,' being vertically divided into four compartments. Each of these develops a long outgrowth that extends to the surface of the gelatinous matrix and produces a ballistospore. The most recent interpretation of these "basidia" is that the vertical septation separates the nuclei into what can be called basidiospores, and that the long "epibasidia" which grow up to the surface of the jelly are actually germ tubes. This would mean that the "basidiospores" are actually secondary spores, results of a form of 'germination by repetition,' a phenomenon so common in the phragmobasidiomycetes that it is often used as

a diagnostic character. The basidiomata are often irregularly shaped (Fig. 5.8 A), but in *Pseudohydnum*, convergent evolution has produced a form reminiscent of certain holobasidiomycetes. *Pseudohydnum* has its hymenium on downward-pointing teeth like those of the Hydnaceae (Aphyllophorales), but the rubbery texture of its basidioma, and the cruciately septate basidia, give the game away. Other representative genera are *Tremella* (Fig. 5.8 A), *Tremellodon* and *Exidia*.

(2) **Order Auriculariales**: 4 genera, 15 species. Members of this order are easily identified by their gelatinous, ear-like basidiomata (Fig. 5.8 B) arising from wood. The elongated basidia are divided by transverse septa, and each of the four compartments develops a slender tubular outgrowth that produces a basidiospore when it reaches the surface of the gelatinous matrix. The Chinese

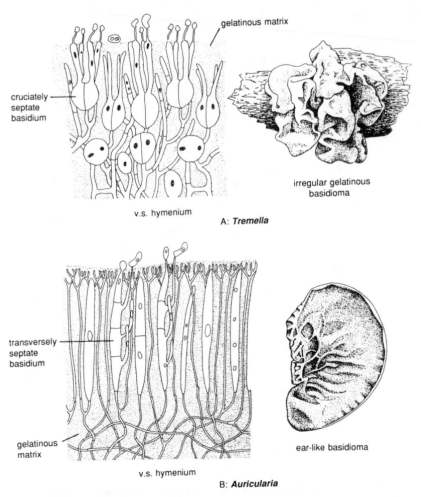

Fig. 5.8 Phragmobasidiomycetes. A: Tremellales; B: Auriculariales.

call members of the genus *Auricularia* 'cloud ears' or 'tree ears,' and use them in cooking, largely for their interesting texture. We have recently discovered that they contain a substance which reduces the clotting propensities of blood, and so may offer some protection against heart attacks.

(3) **Order Septobasidiales**: 2 genera, 175 species (mostly in *Septobasidium*). This order also has transversely septate basidia (Fig. 5.9 A), but its basidiomata are not gelatinous, and it parasitizes scale insects. These do not die, but become

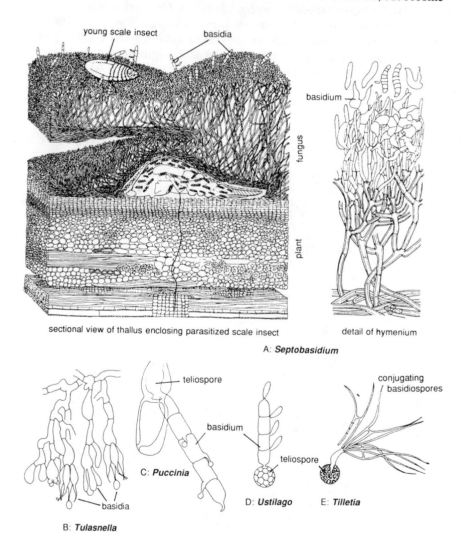

Fig. 5.9 Phragmobasidiomycetes and Teliomycetes. A: Septobasidiales; B: Tulasnellales; C: Uredinales; D, E: Ustilaginales.

sterile. They are buried in a weft of fungal hyphae that produces basidia on its surface, and provides shelter for other healthy scales.

(4) **Order Tulasnellales**: This small order is interesting to us mostly because it has yet another variation on the phragmobasidium. In *Tulasnella* the four developing sterigmata swell up and each becomes separated from the body of the cell by a septum (Fig. 5.9 B).

Class Teliomycetes

This group comprises two distantly related orders, Uredinales and Ustilaginales, which produce no basidiomata, and have simple septal pores with pulley-wheel occlusions (Fig. 5.1), rather than the dolipores characteristic of most other basidiomycetes.

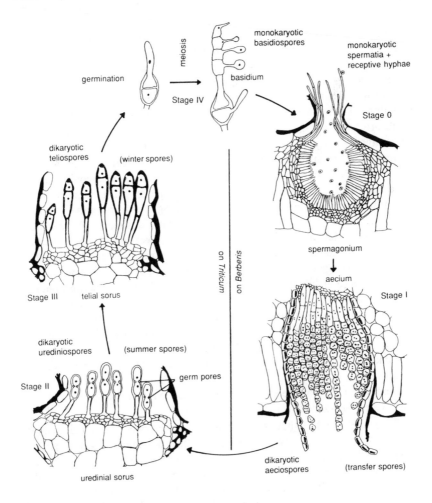

Fig. 5.10 Uredinales: life cycle of *Puccinia graminis*.

(1) **Order Uredinales**: 150 genera, 6000 species (3000 in *Puccinia*). The rust fungi are all obligately biotrophic on vascular plants, and often have very narrow host ranges, being restricted to a single family, a single genus, or even a single species. Although they have obviously co-evolved with their hosts for millions of years, and don't usually kill them, rust fungi can severely reduce yields of our domesticated plants, particularly the cereals on which we are so dependent. As I have already pointed out, the rust fungi produce basidia from overwintering spores (teliospores), so they don't form basidiomata. But they do produce five different kinds of spore, each specialized for a particular step or phase in the life cycle. And they often have two successive hosts, from taxonomically distant groups. This is important information, because as you will see in chapter 12, our efforts to control many diseases depend on our knowledge of the life history of the pathogens. In any case, these most complex of all fungal cycles are intrinsically fascinating.

Puccinia graminis subspecies *tritici* (Fig. 5.10), the fungus causing black stem rust of wheat, can exemplify **macrocyclic**, **heteroecious** rusts (those producing all five spore forms and moving back and forward between two different hosts). The basidiospores, which are of + and - mating types, land on a young leaf of barberry (*Berberis*) in spring, and initiate localized monokaryotic infections. The hyphae are intercellular, but they send haustoria into host cells to absorb food. Soon, these monokaryotic mycelia develop tiny flask-shaped **spermagonia** (stage 0) in the upper layers of the leaf. Each spermagonium forms innumerable tiny **spermatia** which ooze out in a sweet-smelling nectar. A tuft of **receptive hyphae** also grows out from the neck of the spermagonium. Insects are attracted by the nectar, and walk or fly from one spermagonium to another, unwittingly transferring spermatia of each mating type to receptive hyphae of the other type. This process, which is somewhat analogous to pollination, initiates the **dikaryophase**. This spreads to the lower surface of the barberry leaf, where the fungus has already produced the primordia of cup-like structures called **aecia** (stage I). The dikaryon now produces basipetal chains of dikaryotic **aeciospores** (transfer spores) which burst through the host epidermis, but can't infect the barberry. Only on wheat (*Triticum*) can they establish new dikaryotic infections. That is why I call them 'transfer spores.' The dikaryotic infections in the wheat plant soon produce pustules of reddish-brown, dikaryotic **urediniospores** (summer spores—stage II) which again burst through the host epidermis and are wind-dispersed to other wheat plants. The many new infections generated in this way soon produce further inoculum, and waves of urediniospores, borne on the prevailing winds, cause the massive epidemics of wheat rust that periodically sweep North America.

Toward the end of summer, the pustules switch over to producing another kind of spore, the dark, two-celled, thick-walled **teliospores** (winter spores — stage III). Each cell of the teliospore is binucleate at first, but karyogamy soon occurs and the spores overwinter in the genuinely diploid or zygotic condition. In spring, each cell germinates and gives rise to a short hypha which becomes a transversely septate basidium (Fig. 5.9 C)(rather like those of the Auriculariales and Septobasidiales). Each cell develops a short sterigma which in turn bears a basidiospore (stage IV). These are borne asymmetrically, and are shot away in typical basidiomycete manner. They must land on a barberry leaf if the cycle is to continue.

Some rust fungi don't produce all five spore forms, and are described as **microcyclic**. Some complete their cycle on a single host, and are called **autoecious**. *Puccinia poae-nemoralis*, a normally heteroecious rust fungus, persists in the Canadian arctic through the ability of its urediniospores to overwinter. It never forms teliospores, and so needs no alternate host. Some tropical rust fungi don't form teliospores either, but in this case it is because there is no need for an overwintering spore.

Stage I (aecia) and stage II (uredinia) may be regarded as the anamorphs of a rust fungus. Stage III, the teliospore, is regarded as the sexual state or teleomorph, so the host on which these spores develop is called the **primary host**. In the case of *Puccinia graminis* ssp. *tritici*, wheat is the primary host, and barberry the **alternate host**.

Because of the threat they pose to our food supplies, the cereal rusts have been intensively studied, and they have repaid that scrutiny with a rich harvest of taxonomic and genetic information. The species *Puccinia graminis* attacks many different grasses. Several subspecies have been recognized by their apparent restriction to individual grass genera, e.g. *P. graminis* ssp. *avenae* on oats (*Avena*), *P. graminis* ssp. *hordei* on barley (*Hordeum*), and, of course, *P. graminis* ssp. *tritici* on wheat (*Triticum*). Each of these subspecies is subdivided into many physiological races which differ in their ability to attack specified commercial varieties of the host genus. *Puccinia graminis* ssp. *tritici* has over 200 such races, and new ones are discovered every year. Wheat breeders have to work hard to stay one jump ahead of the pathogen. Breeding of resistant plants is discussed in chapter 12.

Some heteroecious rusts move between angiosperm and gymnosperm hosts, and sometimes it is the alternate host, rather than the primary host, that is economically important. This is true of *Cronartium ribicola*, which causes the destructive blister rust of 5-needled white pines (*Pinus strobus*, *P. monticola*) on which it produces its spermatia and aeciospores. Urediniospores and teliospores develop on wild currant (*Ribes*). The name of the disease, 'blister rust,' refers to the aecia, since it is the perennial aecial cankers on the pine that gradually spread and eventually girdle and kill the tree. *Cronartium fusiforme* alternates between various southern pines and oaks. *Gymnosporangium* species alternate between a rosaceous host like apple (*Malus*) or serviceberry (*Amelanchier*), and a conifer like juniper (*Juniperus*).

(2) **Order Ustilaginales**: 60 genera, 1000 species (300 in *Ustilago*). Like the rust fungi, the smut fungi are all parasites of vascular plants, and produce basidiospores on transversely septate basidia arising from overwintering teliospores (Fig. 5.9 D,E). But the two groups differ in many respects, as Table 5.1 shows.

Table 5.1 Differences Between Rust and Smut Fungi	
Uredinales	Ustilaginales
1) Teliospores terminal	Teliospores intercalary
2) Basidiospores 4, shot from sterigmata	Basidiospore number variable, not on sterigmata, not discharged
3) Spermagonia produced ('sex organs')	No 'sex organs,' any two compatible cells can fuse
4) Clamp connections absent	Clamp connections common
5) Often require 2 hosts	Never require 2 hosts
6) Obligately biotrophic	Facultatively biotrophic, yeast-like in culture
7) Infections usually localized	Infections usually systemic
8) Teliospores in telial sori, location unspecific	Teliospores replace host organ, e.g., ovary, anther
9) Attack ferns, gymnosperms, and angiosperms	Attack only angiosperms

a) Family Ustilaginaceae. In this group the teliospore is karyologically equivalent to that of a rust fungus, so the hypha arising from a germinating teliospore of a *Ustilago* becomes 3-septate, and buds off a yeast-like basidiospore from each compartment (Fig. 5.9 D). Compatible elements soon fuse to restore the dikaryon. In homothallic species this can rather conveniently involve basidiospores from the same basidium, or a basidiospore can fuse with a cell of the basidium, or two cells of the same basidium may fuse, or teliospores may germinate and form a mycelium between whose hyphae fusions can occur. Many smut fungi are heterothallic, so fusions must be between cells of different and compatible parents.

The teliospores of *Ustilago violacea* are present on the seeds of its host, *Silene* (Caryophyllaceae), and germinate when the seeds do. After the dikaryotization process described above, the newly dikaryotic mycelium infects the seedling. Although the mycelium becomes systemic, spreading throughout the host, it incites no pathological symptoms until the flowers develop. Then, the pollen is replaced by a mass of dikaryotic mycelium, which eventually disarticulates into teliospores. The disease is called anther smut. Many other smuts are also organ-specific: in corn smut, caused by *Ustilago maydis*, some kernels are replaced by grossly swollen masses of black teliospores. Note that the chosen organ is always one into which the plant directs high-energy resources.

b) Family Tilletiaceae. Here, events are physically more compressed: karyogamy, meiosis and mitosis all happen inside the teliospore. When this germinates, the resulting basidium produces a cluster of slender, parallel basidiospores from its apex. These soon copulate in pairs to restore the dikaryon (Fig. 5.9 E). *Tilletia caries*, the cause of 'bunt' or stinking smut of wheat, is just as important an economic problem as stem rust, because it has so far proved impossible to breed strains of wheat resistant to this fungus.

KEY TO SOME COMMON ORDERS OF BASIDIOMYCETES

1 No basidioma; basidia solitary (free), or on individual
   hyphae . . . . (see yeasts)

1 No basidioma; basidia arising from resting spores
   (class Teliomycetes) 2

1 No basidioma; basidia in a layer on surface of host
   plant . . . . **Exobasidiales**

1 Basidioma produced 3

  2 'Smut' fungi; autoecious, basidiospores not
   discharged, clamps common, resting spores
   intercalary; grow in culture . . . . **Ustilaginales**

  2 'Rust' fungi; often heteroecious, basidiospores
   discharged, clamps absent, resting spores terminal,
   obligately biotrophic . . . . **Uredinales**

3 Basidia divided vertically or transversely by septa
   (class Phragmobasidiomycetes) 4

3 Basidia not divided by septa (class
   Holobasidiomycetes) 5

  4 'Basidia' divided vertically into 4; each with a long
   apical extension, bearing one spore (jelly fungi) . . **Tremellales**

  4 Basidia divided transversely into 4; each cell with a
   lateral outgrowth bearing one spore (ear fungi) . . . **Auriculariales**

5 Basidiospores obliquely attached to sterigmata;
   hymenium exposed at maturity and spores forcibly
   discharged (give spore print)(series Hymenomycetae) 6

5 Basidiospores symmetrically attached to sterigmata,
   or sterigmata absent, spores not discharged (no spore
   print)(sequestrate Agaricales and series
   Gasteromycetae) 8

  6 Basidia slender, with two long extensions (tuning
   fork basidia), (jelly fungi) . . . . **Dacrymycetales**

  6 Basidia usually with 4 short sterigmata, no long
   extensions 7

7 Hymenium covering vertically oriented, radially
   arranged lamellae or lining vertically oriented fleshy
   tubes (agarics and boletes) . . . . **Agaricales**

7 Hymenium in other configurations . . . . **Aphyllophorales**

   8 Basidioma agaricoid, but not releasing spores; or
      micro-anatomical features establishing   sequestrate
      relationships to agarics or boletes . . . . **Agaricales**

   8 No clear derivation from Agaricales or other groups
      (series Gasteromycetae) . . . . 9 .

9 Basidiospore mass (gleba) slimy, stinking, exposed
   on receptacle (stinkhorns) . . . . **Phallales**

9 Gleba not evil-smelling . . . . 10.

   10 Gleba enclosed in several small, separate
      peridioles; basidiomata deeply funnel-shaped
      (bird's nest fungi) . . . . **Nidulariales**

   10 Not as above . . . . 11.

11 Spore mass powdery, drab or khaki coloured,
   peridium 2-layered, inner peridium papery, usually
   with ostiole (puffballs) . . . . 12.

11 Spore mass dark, 1-layered peridium, no ostiole
   (earth-balls) . . . . **Sclerodermatales**

12 Basidiomata more or less sessile . . . . **Lycoperdales**

12 Basidiomata prominently stalked . . . . **Tulostomatales**

Further Reading

Ainsworth, G.C., F.K. Sparrow and A.S. Sussman (Eds.) (1973) **The Fungi, an Advanced Treatise** Vol. 4B. Academic Press, New York.

Arora, D. (1986) **Mushrooms Demystified**. 2nd Edn. Ten Speed Press, Berkeley.

Bandoni, R.J. (1987) Taxonomic overview of the Tremellales. pp. 87-110 (in) **The Expanding Realm of Yeast-like Fungi**. (Eds.) G.S. de Hoog, M.Th. Smith and A.C.M. Weijman. Centraalbureau voor Schimmelcultures, Baarn.

Breitenbach, J. and F. Kränzlin (1986) **Fungi of Switzerland**. Vol. 2: Non-gilled Basidiomycetes. Verlag Mykologia, Lucerne.

Breitenbach, J. and F. Kränzlin (1991) **Fungi of Switzerland**. Vol. 3: Boletes and Agarics Part 1. Verlag Mykologia, Lucerne.

Coker, W.C. and Couch, J.N. (1928) **Gasteromycetes of the Eastern United States and Canada** University of North Carolina Press, Chapel Hill.

Corner, E.J.H. (1950) **A Monograph of *Clavaria* and Allied Genera**. Annals of Botany Memoirs 1.

Corner, E.J.H. (1968) **A Monograph of Cantharelloid Fungi**. Oxford University Press, London.

Corner, E.J.H. (1970) **Supplement to a Monograph of** *Clavaria* **and Allied Genera**. Beihefte Nova Hedwigia **33**.

Couch, J.N. (1938) **The Genus** *Septobasidium*. University of North Carolina Press, Chapel Hill.

Cummins, G.B. and Y. Hiratsuka (1983) **Illustrated Genera of Rust Fungi** (revised edition). American Phytopathological Society, Minneapolis.

Eriksson, J, K. Hjortstam and L. Ryvarden (1973-1988) **The Corticiaceae of North Europe**. Vols. 1-8. Fungiflora, Oslo.

Fischer, G.W. (1953) **Manual of the North American Smut Fungi**. Ronald, New York.

Jahn, H. (1979) **Pilze die an Holz wachsen**. Busse, Herford.

Kibby, G. and R. Fatto (1990) Keys to the species of *Russula* in north-eastern North America. (3rd Edn. Kibby Fatto Enterprises, 1187 Millstone River Rd., Somerville, N.J 08876.

Lincoff, G.H. (1981) **The Audubon Society Field Guide to North American Mushrooms**. Knopf, New York.

McKenny, M., D.E. Stuntz and J. Ammirati (1987) **The New Savory Wild Mushroom**. 3rd Edn. University of Washington Press, Seattle.

Miller, O.K. (1972) **Mushrooms of North America**. Dutton, New York.

Oberwinkler, F. (1982) The significance of the morphology of the basidium in the phylogeny of basidiomycetes. pp. 9-35 (in) **Basidium and Basidiocarp**. (Eds.) K. Wells and E.K. Wells. Springer-Verlag, New York.

Overholts, L.O. (1953) **The Polyporaceae of the United States, Alaska and Canada**. University of Michigan Press, Ann Arbor.

Petersen, R.H. (Ed.) (1971) **Evolution in the Higher Basidiomycetes**. University of Tennessee Press, Knoxville.

Phillips, R. (1991) **Mushrooms of North America**. Little, Brown & Co., Boston.

Pomerleau, R. (1980) **Flore des Champignons au Québec**. Les Editions La Presse, Ottawa.

Ramsbottom, J. (1953) **Mushrooms and Toadstools**. Collins, London.

Reijnders, A.F.M. (1963) **Les Problèmes du Developpement des Carpophores des Agaricales et de Quelques Voisins**. Junk, The Hague.

Singer, R. (1975) **The Agaricales in Modern Taxonomy**. 2nd Edn. Cramer, Weinheim.

Smith, A.H. and H.D. Thiers (1971) **The Boletes of Michigan**. University of Michigan Press, Ann Arbor.

Ziller, W.G. (1974) **The Tree Rusts of Western Canada**. Information Canada, Ottawa.

Chapter 6

Yeasts: Polyphyletic Fungi

Everyone knows the word 'yeast,' but very few people have much idea what a yeast really is, and fewer still are aware that the name is applied to organisms of very different origins. You are about to join that elite group. You probably know that yeasts are unicellular organisms which are important to us because they 'raise' bread, put the alcohol in beer and wine, are a high-protein food supplement and a rich source of B vitamins. But there is much more to them than that; and they have a darker side: since yeasts specialize in substrates of high osmotic pressure, some are implicated in food spoilage and others cause serious diseases of humans.

Yeasts used to be characterized as single-celled fungi that do not produce hyphae. They also supposedly reproduced by processes called budding or fission. As you will see, neither of these statements is true. Because of their economic importance, there was a need to identify microscopically similar but physiologically different yeasts. So zymologists (yeast experts) developed a taxonomic scheme based on physiological tests such as the ability of yeasts to ferment or assimilate a variety of sugars, their nitrogen and vitamin requirements, antibiotic resistance, etc. More recently, sophisticated techniques such as magnetic resonance analysis of cell wall components, electrophoretic enzyme analysis, cytochrome spectrophotometric analysis, serological tests, DNA reassociation, and DNA base composition, have all been pressed into service in the search for useful taxonomic characters in yeasts. One assumption underlying much of this activity was that yeasts had relatively few morphological characters to work on. But yeasts do in fact exhibit morphological and developmental features whose significance has only recently been appreciated: they even offer clues to the underlying phylogenetic diversity of the group. We now think of assimilative yeast cells as essentially **conidia** (Fig 6.1 A-E). Many of these unicellular anamorphs sometimes switch into the teleomorphic mode, and produce structures that would appear to place them among the Dikaryomycota, though since sex involves fusion of individual cells to form a zygote, there is never a dikaryon. Some yeasts form endogenous meiospores inside meiosporangia that are karyologically exactly comparable with asci, though the wall chemistry (a good indicator of phylogeny) is different. Others (e.g. *Sporobolomyces*) produce exogenous spores borne asymmetrically on pointed outgrowths of the cell: these spores are forcibly discharged, and the mechanism involved is obviously that of the basidium. But most yeasts (about 600 species in 22 genera) never develop a teleomorph, and are essentially conidial fungi.

I must also add that when members of the Ustilaginales (Teliomycetes) or Taphrinales (Ascomycetes) are grown in axenic culture, they become yeast-like. Basidiospores of Tremellales germinate to produce a haploid yeast phase. Several fungal pathogens of humans, while filamentous in culture, are yeast-like when growing inside us (e.g. *Histoplasma capsulatum*, *Blastomyces dermatitidis*—see chapter 23). Finally, a few fungi such as *Mucor rouxii* (Zygomycetes) can be changed from a hyphal to a yeast-like morphology, or vice versa, by varying specific factors, such as levels of carbon dioxide or of various nutrients.

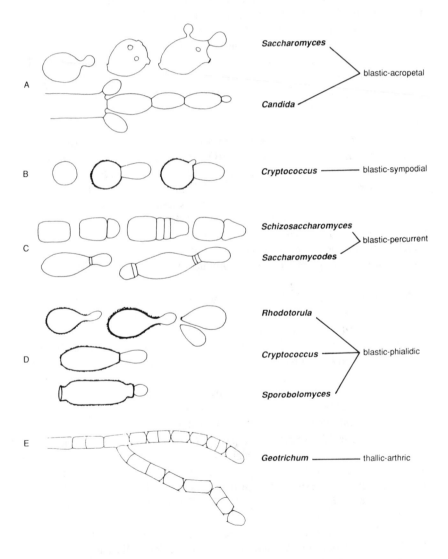

Fig. 6.1 Conidiogenesis in yeasts (compare with Figs. 4.5 - 4.8).

So 'yeast' morphology is sometimes a response to environmental factors such as osmotic stress, a response that has evolved many times in different groups (just as the lichenization process, and the change from agaric to sequestrate derivative, have occurred many times). As a final twist to this tale, mycologists have discovered that some fungi which consistently produce hyphae (e.g. *Arthroascus, Ashbya, Candida, Crebrothecium, Dipodascus, Eremothecium, Guilliermondiella, Saccharomycopsis*), are closely related to the unicellular yeasts. This conclusion is based on five kinds of evidence: (1) even in hyphal forms, there is never a dikaryophase; (2) they produce ascus-like meiosporangia in isolation, or singly, in clusters, or in chains, on individual somatic hyphae (Fig. 6.2 A), but never in any kind of ascoma; (3) their cell walls contain less chitin and more mannan than those of regular ascomycetes; (4) some of them produce yeast-like anamorphs (Fig. 6.2); (5) some of them have many extremely narrow **micropores** piercing each septum (Fig. 5.1 B), rather than a single central pore (Fig. 5.1 A). These features, among others, argue for the recognition of the 'ascus'-forming yeasts as a group distinct from the ascomycetes proper. I treat them as a separate class.

Class Saccharomycetes. Representative genera are *Dipodascus* with *Geotrichum* anamorphs (Fig. 6.2 B), *Hanseniaspora* with *Kloeckera* anamorphs, and *Saccharomycopsis* (Fig. 6.2 A) with *Candida* anamorphs. *Candida albicans*, which produces aerial hyphae (Fig. 6.2 C), and whose teleomorph (if any exists) is unknown, causes **candidiasis**, a disease which affects mucous membranes in various parts of the body, or may even become systemic. This is discussed in chapter 23. *Dipodascus* and *Saccharomycopsis*, which both produce hyphae, have septa with micropores (Fig. 5.1 B). The *Geotrichum* anamorph of *Dipodascus* produces thallic-arthric conidia (Fig. 6.1 E, 6.2 B).

Non-hyphal members of the Saccharomycetes have two kinds of conidium formation: (1) apiculate, bipolar budding yeasts have elongated cells that bud repeatedly from each end, extending percurrently in the process (e.g. *Saccharomycodes*: Fig. 6.1 C). Cells of what have been inaccurately termed 'fission' yeasts also extend percurrently, but on a much broader base (e.g. *Schizosaccharomyces*: Fig. 6.1 C). (2) multilateral budding yeasts bud from many different points on the cell, producing only one daughter cell (conidium) from each site, and leaving many scars (e.g. *Saccharomyces*: Fig. 6.1 A). Some members of each group produce ascus-like meiosporangia.

Class Holobasidiomycetes (pro parte). A second, very different group of yeasts have chitin-mannan walls which also contain some **xylose** or **fucose** (both absent from the Saccharomycetes). The anamorphs in this group also have two modes of conidiogenesis. Most are blastic-sympodial (e.g. the *Cryptococcus* anamorphs of *Filobasidiella*: Fig. 6.1 B). Others are blastic-phialidic (e.g. *Cryptococcus* anamorphs of *Filobasidium*: Fig. 6.1 D). The teleomorphs, where these are known, produce clamp connections and basidium-like structures (Fig. 6.2 D). These teleomorphs are placed in the family Filobasidiaceae, and regarded as belonging to the holobasidiomycetous order Aphyllophorales. *Cryptococcus* *neoformans*, the anamorph of *Filobasidiella neoformans*, causes a potentially serious lung disease, **cryptococcosis**, which is further discussed in chapter 23. Some other genera, such as *Phaffia* and *Bullera*, are known only as anamorphs. And although the teleomorph of *Trichosporon*, if one exists, is unknown, this anamorphic yeast probably belongs here, because its hyphae have dolipore septa (Fig. 6.2 E). This genus forms conidia sympodially, and the hyphae also tend to break up into thallic-arthric conidia.

Class Teliomycetes (pro parte). The third group are called the red yeasts, because they contain carotenoids (though some species of *Cryptococcus* and *Phaffia* also produce these compounds). *Rhodotorula* produces blastic-phialidic conidia from the attenuated ends of the yeast cells (Fig. 6.1 D). *Sporobolomyces* cells develop sterigmata from which asymmetrically borne spores are forcibly ejected. A series of such ballistospores is formed by sympodial extension of the

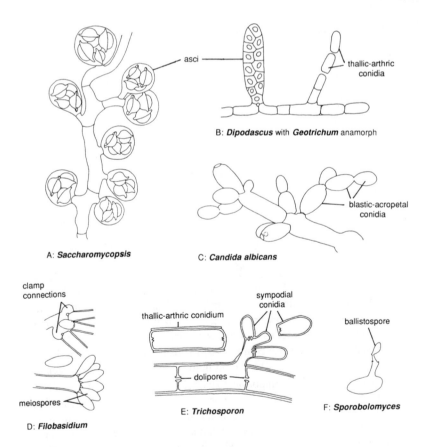

Fig. 6.2 Some unusual yeasts. A-C: Saccharomycetes; D,E: Holobasidiomycetes; F: Teliomycetes.

sterigma (Fig. 6.2 E). Note that although the spore-shooting technique being employed here is that of the basidium, the spores being formed are asexual mitospores (conidia). Yeasts of this group sometimes produce a teleomorph: a chlamydospore-like **teliospore**, which germinates to form an outgrowth from whose tip meiosporic ballistospores are formed and discharged. The red yeasts are now considered to belong in or near the order Ustilaginales of the class Teliomycetes (e.g. *Aessosporon* and *Sporidiobolus* with *Sporobolomyces* anamorphs; *Rhodosporidium* with *Rhodotorula* anamorphs).

The following brief table gives examples of anamorphs and teleomorphs in each of the three main groups of yeasts.

Major group	Teleomorph	Anamorph
Saccharomycetes		
Endomycetales		
Dipodascaceae	*Dipodascus*	*Geotrichum*
Ascoideaceae	*Saccharomycopsis*	*Candida*
Saccharomycetaceae	*Saccharomyces*	*Torulopsis*
Holobasidiomycetes		
Aphyllophorales		
Filobasidiaceae	*Filobasidium*	*Cryptococcus*
Filobasidiaceae	*Filobasidiella*	*Cryptococcus*
Teliomycetes		
Ustilaginales	*Aessosporon*	*Sporobolomyces*
Ustilaginales	*Sporobolomyces*	*Sporobolomyces*
Ustilaginales	*Rhodosporidium*	*Rhodotorula*

It is now possible to differentiate basidiomycetous yeasts from saccharomycetes by staining with buffered diazonium blue B. But in order to identify yeasts to genus and species, one now has to check such features as: (1) the minimum, optimum, and maximum temperatures for growth and sporulation; (2) growth in the presence of some toxic compounds; (3) osmotolerance (growth in high sugar or salt concentrations); (4) cell morphology and method of conidiogenesis.

Yeasts have always been important to us, primarily as the producers of bread and alcohol, which is still, despite competition from other fungal metabolites, our most widely used and accepted social drug (despite its manifest dangers). Accounts of the involvement of yeasts in human affairs can be found in chapters 10 (fungal genetics), 18 (fungi as food), 19 (fungi in food processing), and 23 (medical mycology).

Further Reading

Arx, J.A. von (1979) Propagation in the yeasts and yeast-like fungi. pp. 555-571 (in) **The Whole Fungus.** Vol. 2 (Ed.) B. Kendrick. National Museums of Canada, Ottawa.

Arx, J.A. von (1980) A mycologist's view of yeasts. pp. 53-61 (in) **Biology and Activities of Yeasts.** (Eds.) F.A. Skinner, M. Passmore and R.R. Davenport. Academic Press, London.

Arx, J.A. von (1981) Systematics of conidial yeasts. pp. 85-96 (in) **Biology of Conidial Fungi.** Vol. 1 (Eds.) G.T. Cole & B. Kendrick. Academic Press, New York.

Arx, J.A. von, L. Rodrigues de Miranda, M.T. Smith and D. Yarrow (1977) The Genera of Yeasts and the Yeast-like Fungi. Studies in Mycology **14.** Centraalbureau voor Schimmelcultures, Baarn.

Barnett, J.A., R.W. Payne and D. Yarrow (1990) **Yeasts: Characteristics and Identification.** 2nd Edn. Cambridge Unversity Press, Cambridge.

de Hoog, G.S., M.Th. Smith and A.C.M. Weijman (1987) **The Expanding Realm of Yeast-like Fungi.** Studies in Mycology **30.** Centraalbureau voor Schimmelcultures, Baarn.

Kreger-van Rij, N.J.W. (1984) **The Yeasts - a Taxonomic Study.** 3rd Edn. Elsevier Science Publishers, Amsterdam.

Samson, R.A., E.S. van Reenen-Hoekstra (with 12 others) (1988) **Introduction to Food-Borne Fungi.** 3rd Edn. Centraalbureau voor Schimmelcultures, Baarn.

Skinner, F.A., S.M. Passmore and R.R. Davenport (Eds.) (1980) **Biology and Activities of Yeasts.** Academic Press, New York.

Chapter 7

Lichens: Dual Organisms

These toughest of all organisms can grow on bare rock, in exposed situations where they are subjected to extremes of temperature, radiation and desiccation, from hot deserts to the arctic. What is their secret? They are **dual organisms**. Each lichen combines the talents and strengths of a fungus (the **mycobiont**) with those of an alga (the **phycobiont**). The fungus obtains water and minerals, builds a complex thallus, and produces sexual and asexual reproductive structures. The algae live and photosynthesize within the fungal thallus, and although they constitute only 5-10% of the total biomass (usually concentrated in a zone just below the upper surface of the thallus, as shown in Fig. 7.1M), they supply nourishment to the entire organism. In fact, the fungus has effectively 'captured' the alga, and the relationship is one of exploitation or balanced parasitism rather than of mutualistic symbiosis, since about 50% of the food synthesized by the alga is pirated by the fungal hyphae, which form tight little cages around the algal cells.

Although there are about 500 genera and 18,000 species of lichens, only 24 genera of algae are represented in lichens, and all are either eukaryotic green algae (**Chlorophyta**) or prokaryotic blue-green algae (**Cyanobacteria**). About 70% of all lichens contain the green alga *Trebouxia* (which has not been found free-living). The phycobionts of more than 90% of all lichens are drawn from only 3 genera of algae: the chlorophytes, *Trebouxia* and *Trentepohlia*, and the cyanobacterium, *Nostoc*. All of this means that lichen taxonomy is essentially fungal taxonomy.

Clearly, then, there are 18,000 lichenized fungi (about a quarter of all known fungi). About 10,000 produce only teleomorphic fructifications, while 8,000 produce conidial anamorphs as well, and there are 40 genera of lichens which produce only anamorphs or are sterile. Ascomycetes make up 98% of all lichenized fungi: 12 orders of ascomycetes are almost entirely lichenized, and 4 more have some lichenized members. There are 20 or so lichenized basidiomycetes. Unlike any other groups, lichens have no common ancestor: only a widely shared symbiotic process that has arisen time and time again as a result of natural affinity, opportunity, or need.

In nature, not one of the 18,000 lichenized fungi is ever found without its domesticated alga, though some of the algae can lead independent existences. The degree to which the association has led to physical as opposed to physiological integration varies. In the simplest case, that of the amazing cryptoendolithic associations of fungi and algae recently discovered beneath the surface of sandstones in the deserts of Antarctica and of Namibia, there are no special dual structures. In many other lichens, highly complex thalli have evolved, incorporating two or more partners. About 400 lichens with green phycobionts have areas on or in their thalli which contain blue-green algae instead. These anomalous areas are called **cephalodia**. The algal cells are evenly distributed throughout the thallus in a few lichens, but in most cases they are concentrated in a fairly narrow zone just below the upper surface.

Lichen thalli have four kinds of morphology: (1) **crustose** (Fig. 7.1 A,B)—so closely applied to the substrate that to collect them you often have to take

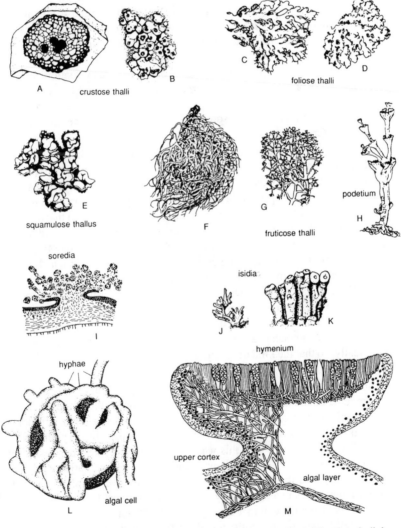

Fig. 7.1 Lichens. A-H: types of thalli; I-K: modes of asexual reproduction; L: lichen synthesis; M: v.s. apothecial ascoma of a discolichen; note algal layer and slowly maturing hymenium.

some of the rock or bark they are growing on as well; (2) **foliose** (Fig. 7.1 C,D) —having leafy or tongue-like lobes which are not so closely applied to the substrate; (3) **fruticose** (Fig. 7.1 F-H)—with upright or hanging, stalked, shrubby or hair-like thalli (fruticose means bushy, and has nothing to do with fruit); and (4) **squamulose** (Fig. 7.1 E)—the thallus is made up of small scales (in *Cladonia* the primary thallus is squamulose but there is also a secondary, reproductive thallus called a podetium (Fig. 7.1 H) which is much larger, more conspicuous, and often fruticose).

The obvious fruiting structure of most lichens is that of the fungal teleomorph —usually an apothecial ascoma (Fig. 7.1 M)—but in addition to this and its associated pycnidial anamorph, many lichens produce specialized vegetative propagules. The upper surface of the thallus ruptures, exposing a powdery mass of propagules called **soredia** (Fig. 7.1 I), which are small groups of algal cells entangled in fungal hyphae. Another kind of asexual reproduction involves small, finger-like or branched structures called **isidia** (Fig. 7.1 J,K), which grow up from the thallus, then break off. Some representatives of certain genera produce only isidia, others only soredia. Lichens that reproduce asexually are less likely to form ascomata.

Most common lichens found in the temperate zone are what we often call **discolichens**, the sexual fructifications of the mycobiont being recognizably apothecial, with a flat, exposed hymenium. But there are also many **pyreno-lichens** which produce pseudothecial ascomata. Some lichen asci are unituni-cate-inoperculate, others are bitunicate. Some have bitunicate asci that are of the 'jack-in-a-box' kind we have already seen in the Dothideales; but others, especially in the very large order Lecanorales (which has nearly 6,000 species), have a different kind of bitunicate asci that split at the tip, after which part of the inner wall sometimes emerges. Such asci are called, clumsily, **archaeas-ceous**. There is speculation that they may represent the ancestors of today's 'jack-in-a-box' asci, and have survived in lichens because the shooting of ascospores isn't as vital to them as it is to non-lichenized ascomycetes. Certainly, although lichen apothecia have exposed hymenia, their asci mature slowly and sporadically, so that the kind of 'puffing' so often seen in free-living apothecial fungi never happens in lichens.

The very existence of the ascospores is something of a puzzle, because when they are released, no algal cells go with them. This means that if the ascospores are to establish a new generation of lichens, they must encounter an appropriate alga, and this in turn implies that lichens must be constantly resynthesized in nature. The only problem with this was that for many years all our best efforts to synthesize lichens from their component fungi and algae failed. Only rela-tively recently was the trick finally mastered. It involves having each of the prospective partners in a thoroughly debilitated condition. Only then, it seems, will the fungus literally embrace the alga (Fig. 7.1 L), and only then will the alga permit itself to be co-opted without making the ultimate protest.

In a successful synthesis, the fungal hyphae grow around each algal cell and produce appressoria on its surface. It appears that, once the alga is in this situation, its physiology is subtly altered. While it metabolizes more or less normally, it becomes very 'leaky,' losing large quantities of soluble carbohydrates. *Trebouxia* leaks ribitol, *Trentepohlia* leaks erythritol, and *Nostoc* leaks glucose. All of these are quickly absorbed by the fungus, and converted into typical fungal carbohydrates such as trehalose. This is interesting in view of recent work suggesting that high levels of this sugar are one of the secrets of surviving extreme desiccation.

Since the sustaining alga usually makes up no more than 5% of the thallus, and since lichens in exposed situations will be dried out during much of the year, it is apparent that we can't expect lichens to grow very fast. And in fact, they don't: 1-4 mm per year is a respectable rate for many lichens, though some grow faster and some much slower than that. Their tough, resistant thalli, and their ability to sit out dry or cold conditions, resuming metabolism quickly when wetted, seem to have conferred on them great longevity: some lichen colonies are reputed to be 4,500 years old, giving the ancient bristlecone pines some inconspicuous competition for the title, 'world's oldest living thing.'

After building up a database of lichen colony measurements on gravestones, which allowed them to calculate past growth rates, lichenologists have been able to help glaciologists determine how long it has been since particular rock faces emerged from retreating glaciers. This study is called lichenometry. And lichens can tell even urbanites something important about their habitat. Since lichens have no roots or other specialized absorptive organs, and since they often live in soil-less habitats, they are dependent on the rain to bring them mineral nutrients. As we know, the rain over much of eastern North America contains dissolved pollutants—especially sulphur dioxide as sulphurous acid. Lichens are extremely susceptible to the deleterious effects of acid rain, and many cities are essentially lichen deserts. Fish, trees, lichens: all are like the canaries that miners used to take down the pit—ultrasensitive indicators of dangers to ourselves and to the entire biosphere.

Lichens produce about 230 unique compounds which are called lichen substances. These are mainly weak phenolic acids, derivatives of orcinol or beta-orcinol. They include depsides, depsidones, and dibenzonfuran derivatives such as usnic acid, which has antibiotic properties. The indicator, litmus, is obtained from depside-containing lichens. Some of these unique lichen substances are routinely used to identify the genera and species that produce them. Keys to lichens often call for chemical tests with 10% aqueous **potassium hydroxide, chlorine bleach** and 5% alcoholic **paraphenylenediamine**. These, when applied in various sequences, combine with depsides and depsidones to give characteristic yellow, orange or red colour reactions. Professional lichenologists can't stop at this level: accurate identification of many lichens calls for more refined techniques. (1) Recrystallization of lichen substances: these are first leached out of the thalli by acetone, then redissolved in a glycerine/alcohol mix with some water, orthotoluidine, aniline or quinoline added. Heating causes recrystallization, generating characteristic shapes, and colours observed under U/V. More precise identification can be attained by resorting to: (2) paper chromatography, or (3) thin layer chromatography. These procedures are necessitated by the existence of as many as six 'chemical strains' within some lichen species. These may look exactly alike, but their chemistry differs, and though they often have different distributions, these freqently overlap.

Although there are 12 almost entirely lichenized orders of ascomycetes, and 4 more with some lichenized members, I am going to mention only 8 of the larger or more common orders.

(1) **Order Arthoniales**: 17 genera, 650 species, with green (chlorophytan) phycobionts. Thalli mostly crustose, with apothecioid or lirellate (long and narrow) ascomata, producing bitunicate asci.

(2) **Order Graphidales**: 30 genera, 1700 species, with green phycobionts. Thalli crustose, with apothecioid or lirellate ascomata, containing unitunicate-inoperculate asci with a thickened apex rather like that of the Clavicipitales (Fig. 4.18).

(3) **Order Lecanorales**: 300 genera, 5700 species, with green phycobionts. Crustose, squamulose, foliose or fruticose thalli, with apothecioid ascomata producing archaeasceous asci (primitively bitunicate?). This huge order is home to many of our commonest lichen genera—*Cladonia* (including 'reindeer moss,' *C. rangiferina*, and 'British soldier,' *C. coccinea*), *Hypogymnia*, *Letharia*, *Parmelia*, and *Umbilicaria* ('rock tripe').

(4) **Order Opegraphales**: 35 genera, 900 species, with green phycobionts. Thalli are crustose or fruticose, with apothecioid or lirellate ascomata, and bitunicate asci.

(5) **Order Peltigerales**: 18 genera, 600 species, with blue-green phycobionts. Foliose thalli with apothecioid ascomata producing archaeasceous asci.

(6) **Order Pyrenulales**: 35 genera, 1150 species, with green phycobionts. Mainly crustose, with pseudothecial ascomata containing bitunicate asci.

(7) **Order Teloschistales**: 11 genera, 600 species, with green phycobionts. The thalli are of all four types, bearing apothecioid ascomata with archaeasceous asci, and also producing pycnidial anamorphs.

(8) **Order Verrucariales**: 25 genera, 700 species, with green phycobionts. Usually crustose, rock-inhabiting lichens with pseudothecial ascomata and bitunicate asci.

The discipline of lichenology has until fairly recently been conducted outside the mainstream of mycology, because the dual organisms were considered so radically different from non-lichenized fungi in nutrition, ecology and lifespan. But it is being increasingly realized that the life processes of lichens, including their biotrophic nutrition, are not really alien to those of many other fungi, and we can anticipate increased integration of this large minority group, as specialists in lichenized and non-lichenized fungi exchange information and ideas. At least one important reference work, the 'Dictionary of the Fungi,' now covers both groups.

Further Reading

Ahmadjian, V. and M.E. Hale (Eds.) (1973) **The Lichens**. Academic Press, New York.

Ahmadjian, V. and J.B. Jacobs (1981) Relationship between fungus and alga in the lichen *Cladonia cristatella*. Nature **289**: 169-171.

Brodo, I.M. (1981) **Lichens of the Ottawa Region**. Syllogeus **29**. National Museums of Canada, Ottawa.

Ferry, B.W., M.S. Baddeley and D.L. Hawksworth (1973) **Air Pollution and Lichens**. Athlone Press, University of London, London.

Friedmann, E.I. (1982) Endolithic microorganisms in the Antarctic cold desert. Science **215**: 1045-1053.

Hale, M.E. (1974) **The Biology of Lichens**. 2nd Edn. Arnold, London.

Hale, M.E. (1979) **How to Know the Lichens**. 2nd Edn. Wm. Brown, Dubuque.

Hawksworth, D.L. (1988) The variety of fungal-algal symbioses, their evolutionary significance, and the nature of lichens. Botanical Journal of the Linnaean Society **96**: 3-20

Hawksworth, D.L. (1988) Coevolution of fungi with algae and cyanobacteria in lichen symbioses. pp. 125-148 (in **Coevolution of Fungi with Plants and Animals**. (Eds.) K.A. Pirozynski and D.L. Hawksworth. Academic Press, London.

Hawksworth, D.L. and D.J. Hill (1984) **The Lichen-forming Fungi**. Blackie, London.

Kendrick, B. (1991) Fungal symbiosis and evolutionary innovations. pp. 249-261 (in **Symbiosis as a Source of Evolutionary Innovation**. (Eds.) L. Margulis and R. Fester. MIT Press, Cambridge.

Smith, D.C. (1973) **The Lichen Symbiosis**. Oxford University Press, Oxford.

Smith, D.C. (1978) What can lichens tell us about real fungi? Mycologia **70**: 915-934.

Chapter 8

Spore Dispersal in Fungi

Introduction

Fungi cannot walk or run, but some can swim, most can soar, a few can jump, and some must be carried. From your reading of the taxonomic survey in this book, you can probably put a few names in each of the categories I have just mentioned. At the beginning of the book, when I was defining the word 'fungus,' I concentrated on the unusual somatic morphology and the heterotrophic nutrition shared by most fungi. But perhaps I did not place enough emphasis on one of the main reasons for the success of the fungi, their ability to produce and disperse vast numbers of tiny, but often highly characteristic and specialized spores. By sheer fecundity the fungi make sure that, whenever and wherever a new food substrate becomes available, they will be on hand to exploit it. Many fungi are cosmopolitan—you could find them almost anywhere in the world. The air we breathe sometimes contains more than 10,000 spores per cubic metre. The soil contains astronomical numbers of spores, waiting for food. Why are there so many? How did they get there? This chapter will try to answer those questions.

Chemotaxis

The taxonomic survey recognized five Phyla of fungi. Each of these has solved the problems of dispersal in its own way, though some methods of dispersal have been invented more than once, and sometimes the parallelisms are striking, as you will see. The Phyla Chytridiomycota, Hyphochytriomycota and Oomycota are basically aquatic, so their spores are often, in true protoctistan style, equipped with flagella. In the Chytridiomycetes each zoospore has one, backwardly directed whiplash flagellum, and it swims like a sperm (Figs. 2.5, 2.6 A,B). In the Hyphochytriomycetes, the single tinsel flagellum is forwardly directed (Fig. 2.5). In the Oomycetes, each zoospore has two flagella, one whiplash and one tinsel (Fig. 2.8 A). These zoospores, once liberated from their mitosporangia, may embark on a random search for a new substrate, in which case their chances of survival aren't good: more fortunate spores are given a chance to use a special talent they possess for ascending a chemical gradient toward a food substrate. For example, the zoospores of *Pythium* and *Phytophthora*, many species of which parasitize the roots of plants, find their hosts by tracing the source of the sugars and other chemicals that leak out of root cells. Some chytrids that attack nematodes detect and swim toward substances emanating from the bodily orifices of the worms (see chapter 15).

Airborne Sporangia

Some oomycetes have become parasites of the aerial parts of plants (remember the downy mildews). Hopping from leaf to leaf is no job for a spore that's designed to swim. In response to this selection pressure, two completely new

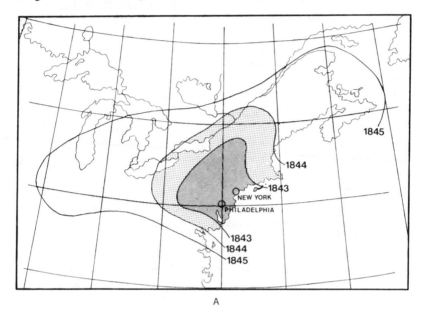

A

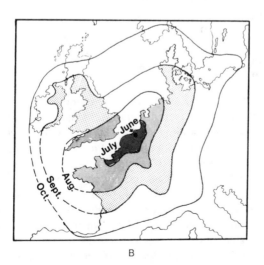

B

Fig. 8.1 Spread of **Phytophthora infestans**. A: in eastern North America 1843-1845. B: in Europe during 1845.

structures, the aerial sporangiophore and the detachable, wind-dispersed mito-sporangium, evolved (Fig. 2.8 B,C). The microscopic sporangia develop at the tips of the sporangiophore's branches, and are easily dislodged by wind or rain. Landing by chance on another leaf, those of most species revert to their ancestral behaviour, and require the presence of a film of free water so that they can release motile, biflagellate zoospores which swim off to infect the plant. In a few of the most highly evolved oomycetes, members of family Peronosporaceae, the airborne sporangia produce a germ tube. These fungi have cut their last link with the aquatic life of their ancestors. As I mentioned in chapter 2, the human species is probably the most important vector for many fungi. One important example of this is the oomycete, *Phytophthora infestans*, which causes late blight of potato. Human transoceanic commerce inadvertently carried this Central American fungus to north-eastern North America in 1843, and to Europe in 1845. I say 'inadvertently' because at that time no one even knew the fungus existed, or what it was capable of. The maps reproduced as Figs. 8.1 A and B show how, after these introductions, its natural spread proceeded. Airborne sporangia were obviously a successful invention.

The structures associated with sexual reproduction in zygomycetes are very conservative. Zygosporangia are basically tiny, look-alike, thick-walled, resistant capsules designed to survive hard times. But in a few cases they may also have some adaptations for dispersal. The antler-like outgrowths of the suspensors in *Phycomyces blakesleeanus* (Fig. 3.3) make the whole structure a 'micro-burr' that could be unknowingly picked up and carried away by a passing arthropod.

Non-motile Sporangiospores: Zygomycetous Anamorphs

When we look at the anamorphs of zygomycetes, we find a bewildering diversity of form and function. We can distinguish four main kinds of dispersal mechanism, and several sub-categories.

(1) Large, spherical, columellate mitosporangia each containing hundreds or thousands of spores (Fig. 3.4 A). But the generally similar form of these sporangia is not reflected in their dispersal techniques. (A) In some examples the spores are produced in a **slimy** matrix. This may be surrounded (i) by a thin but persistent membrane (peridium), as in *Phycomyces nitens*, or (ii) by an equally thin membrane that dissolves and exposes the spore drop. In many *Mucor* species the exposed mucilage imbibes water and swells to several times its original size, often supported by a collar-like remnant of the peridium. This is a stalked spore drop, and is often adapted for dispersal by small animal vectors. (B) In other cases the spores are **dry**, so that when the peridium ruptures, they can blow away on the wind, e.g. *Rhizopus stolonifer* (Fig. 3.4 A). (C) In the third group, the spore mass is violently discharged. This technique has been evolved by only one genus, *Pilobolus* (Fig. 3.6 A-C), a specialized inhabitant of the dung of herbivorous mammals. In order to survive, this fungus must get its spores away from the dung and onto the prospective diet of the animal concerned. The

subsporangial vesicle of this fungus ruptures when internal pressure reaches about 7 atmospheres, and expels the spore mass to a distance of up to 2 metres—far enough to get it away from even an Elephant's dung deposit.

(2) Small, few-spored sporangia (sometimes called **sporangioles**). In such genera as *Thamnidium* (Fig. 3.4D) and *Helicostylum*, large and small sporangia coexist. The small sporangia often break off and are wind dispersed, while the large sporangia remain in place and act as slimy spore drops. This fungus is unusual in this two-pronged allocation of reproductive resources. Other genera like *Blakeslea* (Fig. 3.4B) produce only the few-spored sporangia.

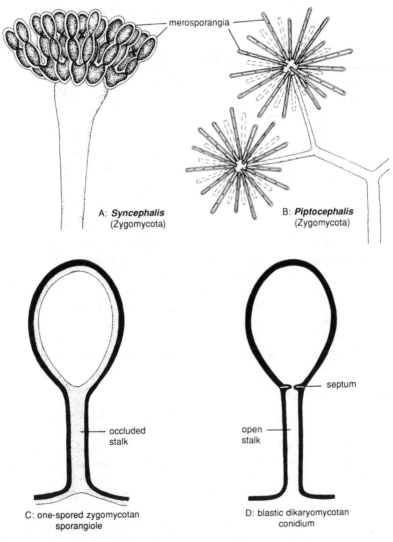

Fig. 8.2 Merosporangia, sporangioles and conidia.

(3) Specialized **merosporangia**. These are unusual small mitosporangia which often contain a row of spores, as in *Syncephalis* (Fig. 8.2 A) and *Piptocephalis* (Fig. 8.2 B). At maturity the sporangial wall breaks down and the spores are set free. Multiple merosporangia are usually formed on a special head cell, which may break off and carry the spores away with it. Merosporangia may be: (A) dry and their spores wind-dispersed, or (B) slimy and sticky.

(4) The logical end-point of this reductive process is a single-spored mitosporangium, which is in fact found in many genera. These are often virtually indistinguishable from the conidia of dikaryomycotan anamorphs under the light microscope, but they have an outer sporangial wall, and a complete inner spore wall which often also fills and occludes the stalk (Fig. 8.2 C), so release is often by rhexolytic rupture of the stalk. Dikaryomycotan conidia (the mitospores liberated by moulds), probably the most numerous and important fungal propagules of all, don't have separate inner and outer walls, and retain cytoplasmic continuity with their parent cell until release, which usually occurs by schizolytic separation of the components of the basal double septum (Fig. 8.2 D). (A) The one-spored sporangia of *Cunninghamella* (Fig. 3.4 C) are dry and wind-dispersed. (B) Those of *Kickxella* are slimy. (C) The sporangiophores of some dung-inhabiting genera are very tall, and elaborately branched or coiled, as in *Spirodactylon* (Fig. 3.4F). It is thought that these structures play an important part in spore dispersal, becoming tangled in the hair of the sedentary rodents on whose dung they grow, and being ingested during grooming activities.

In the Entomophthorales, one-spored mitosporangia are actively shot away by three different mechanisms: (A) In *Entomophthora muscae* (Fig. 3.6 E), the apex of the sporangiophore ruptures to expel the sporangium. Cytoplasm from the sporangiophore goes with the propagule, and may help it to adhere to the substrate when it lands. (B) Species of *Basidiobolus* have a line of weakness around the sporangiophore just below the apex. At maturity, the wall splits there, and the spore flies away with part of the sporangiophore attached. As in a two-stage rocket, the sporangiophore fragment falls away during flight. (C) In some species of *Entomophthora*, and in *Conidiobolus*, the mitosporangium is projected by the release of pressure built up between the sporangium and a tiny, intrusive columella.

Ascospores: Shot or Not

In the taxonomic section of this book it is made clear that ascomycetes and basidiomycetes, though they may look very different, appear to have arisen from a common ancestral group. Many of the superficial differences between their teleomorphic fructifications can be traced back to the different kinds of meiosporangia they produce: asci and basidia. It is worth comparing the mechanisms of these vital cells and the ways in which they have probably affected the evolution of their respective teleomorphs.

First, the ascus (Fig. 4.3) which seems originally to have evolved as a tubular spore gun: an elongated cell within which, once the spores have matured, turgor pressure builds up until the tip of the cell bursts and the ascospores fly out. You will remember the two basic lines of asci. First, the unitunicate ascus with either: an operculum or lid, opening around a built-in line of weakness at the moment of discharge; or an elastic apical ring, stretching enough to let the spores pop out through an apical pore, or everting. Second, the bitunicate ascus, in which the inner wall expands upward after the thin outer wall splits, then shoots the spores out of an apical canal. Three ways of achieving the same end. In each case, the basic function of the ascus is more or less the same. And most asci still conform to this norm. At least, those that have some access to the outside world do. Some are borne on apothecial ascomata in exposed layers (hymenia). They can 'shoot at will,' whenever they are mature. Anyone who spends much time looking for fungi will experience the phenomenon of 'puffing' in apothecial ascomata. This happens when atmospheric humidity changes suddenly and thousands of asci expel their ascospores simultaneously, producing a smoke-like cloud of ascospores. *Cookeina sulcipes* (Ascomycetes, Pezizales), a colourful tropical cup-fungus, produces 215,000 asci per cm^2, which liberate 1,720,000 ascospores. The asci in some apothecia have evolved light-sensitive mechanisms in their tips, so that they can aim their spores toward the light (e.g. *Ascobolus*: Fig. 4.2). *Cookeina* asci are straight, but their lids develop on the side toward the light, so the spores shoot in the right direction. The theory of puffing is that the many simultaneous jets of ascospores generate a general movement of the air above the hymenium, which carries the spores much further than if the asci fired individually.

Other asci develop inside ascomata that open to the outside world only by a narrow pore (an ostiole). These asci are more protected during development, but they can't all fire at once; they have to take turns. Each ascus, as it ripens, must stretch right up the neck of the ascoma to the ostiole before it can shoot its spores. Some ostiolate (perithecial or pseudothecial) ascomata have light-sensitive necks, making sure that their asci shoot toward the light. This is especially important to fungi growing on the dung of herbivores, (e.g. *Sordaria* and *Podospora*: Fig. 4.13A) which must get their spores away from the dung and onto the plants their host animal will eat.

The size of a projectile has a considerable influence on its range. In the dung-inhabiting *Saccobolus* the 8 ripe ascospores are glued together, and are expelled as a single projectile. Since *Saccobolus* is one of the commonest fungi found on dung, there must be some advantage to this strategy. *Podospora fimicola*, whose ascospores are large anyway (averaging 54 x 37µm), shoots all eight as a unit, and so achieves the phenomenal range (for an ascus) of 50 cm. Most asci, however, expel their spores separately, either in a single burst, or at short intervals. *Cordyceps militaris* (Fig. 4.18 D-F) has very long, narrow asci, with a very fine pore in their thickened tip. The ascospores are 400-500 µm long, 2µm thick, and arranged in a parallel bundle. A ripe ascus suddenly protrudes from the ostiole, the first ascospore flashes out after a second or two, followed at one-second intervals by the others. After the eighth spore has been shot, the tip of the ascus disappears, and is soon replaced by that of another ripe one. No one knows how this precise sequence is executed.

And then there are asci that **don't** shoot their spores. We believe that the shooting mechanism has been lost only in situations where it has become useless or inadaptive. This happens if the fungus adopts a cryptic habitat: if it fruits under bark or underground, for example. The known teleomorphs of the common moulds, *Penicillium* (e.g. *Talaromyces*) and *Aspergillus* (e.g. *Eurotium*: Fig. 4.21 A) produce closed (cleistothecial) ascomata, and their asci are spherical and have no shooting mechanism. Truffles fruit underground, so their ascomata are closed, and their asci are spherical (Fig. 4.10 G). Their spores are dispersed by mammalian vectors, which can find and dig up the buried ascomata only because these emit uniquely attractive aromas. For many years, the French hunted truffles with the aid of female pigs, because these had such good noses for truffles, and were so enthusiastic. We did not know until recently that the pigs were literally 'turned on' by a chemical they normally encounter only when it emanates from rutting boars. In some strange way, truffles have evolved a spore-dispersal mechanism that involves a mammalian pheromone.

It is easy to understand why asci that develop in closed ascomata don't shoot their spores. But quite a few ascomycetes with ostiolate ascomata have adopted the same habit. In the cellulolytic genus, *Chaetomium* (Fig. 4.13 B), the walls of the asci break down as the spores mature, liberating them into the cavity of the ascoma in a mucilaginous matrix. As the mucilage imbibes water and expands, it oozes out through the ostiole, and forms a long tendril or a gooey mass. *Chaetomium* species typically have a mass of coiled or branched hairs growing from the upper part of the ascoma: these hairs act as a natural holder for the spore drop. It seems likely that these spores are set up for arthropod or rain dispersal, rather than the original airborne route. The genus *Ophiostoma* (Fig. 4.21 B) follows a very similar pattern, but here the ascoma usually has a long, tubular neck. When the mucilage expands, it can escape only by moving up the neck, carrying the ascospores with it and forming a spore drop at the top which sits on a fringe of specialized supporting hyphae. These fungi often fruit in the tunnels of bark beetles, which pick up the ascospores (or the conidia of anamorph, another stalked spore drop) as they crawl along the tunnels, then fly off to other trees. This is the devastating secret of Dutch elm disease. Again, human vectors brought the fungus to North America, but flying beetle vectors have spread it very effectively within this continent. First found in Ohio in 1930, it reached Tennessee by 1946, California by 1975. In Canada it was first detected in Quebec in 1946. In fifteen years it had killed more than 600,000 trees in an area of 25,000 square miles. It has since spread to the maritime provinces, to Ontario, and as far west as Manitoba, though the discontinuous distribution of the elm in Canada suggests that the fungus reached Manitoba by human agency, or from the south.

The ascomata of the powdery mildew fungi (Erysiphales: Fig. 4.19) are closed, and might easily be described as cleistothecial. But their asci are elongate, often grow in a radially oriented cluster, and can shoot their spores.

So we must assume that the ascomata open at some point. How this happens in the genus *Phyllactinia* is a strange story with some interesting twists. The ascomata of this fungus have two unusual features: a ring of radiating, tapered, needle-like appendages; and a tuft of secretory hairs on top of the ascoma, that produce a blob of mucilage (Fig. 8.3 A). When the ascoma is mature, the appendages all bend downward and lever it upward, breaking its hyphal connections with the leaf (Fig. 8.3 B). It is now free to be dispersed by wind or water. When the ascoma lands on a new substrate, the blob of mucilage will hold it there—in the upside-down position, so that the business end of each ascus now points futilely at the substrate (Fig. 8.3 C). Fortunately, there is a line of weakness around the equator of the ascoma. This now splits open, and the lower

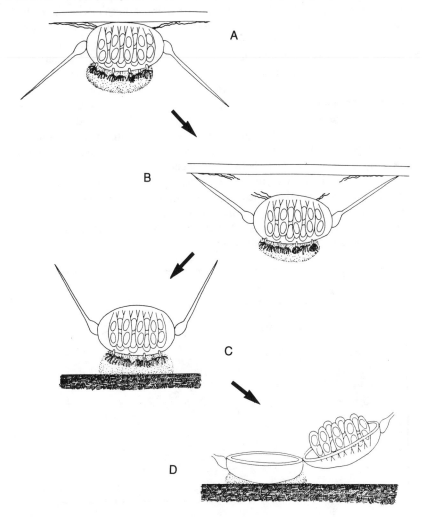

Fig. 8.3 Adventures of **Phyllactinia** (Erysiphales) (see text).

half of the ascoma swings over through 180 degrees (Fig. 8.3 D). Lo and behold, the asci now point outward, and the spores can finally be shot away into the air.

The dramatic spread of some fungi causing powdery mildews has been well-documented, since they affect economically important crops. Fig. 8.4 shows the way in which the powdery mildew of grapes, caused by *Uncinula necator*, spread in Europe after its introduction to England (from America or Japan) in 1845. By 1851/2 its airborne conidia had carried it throughout the wine-producing countries of the Mediterranean.

Basidiospores

The distances to which ascospores are projected ranges from less than a millimetre to 50 cm. Basidiospores are much more uniform in size and ballistic mechanism, and are projected for much smaller distances: 0.005-0.1 cm. Let us explore the reasons for that. Everyone is familiar with the appearance of a mushroom, but is probably much less aware of how it works. As a basidioma develops, its primordium is at first negatively geotropic, as the stipe grows upward; then as the cap (pileus) spreads out sideways, it is diageotropic; finally, the gills grow downward, and are positively geotropic. Once the structure is mature, we can see some of its potential and some of its limitations. The gills represent a huge area of hymenium, capable of producing millions of basidiospores. But gills are usually very closely packed. If a basidiospore was shot further than the distance between adjacent gills, it would simply hit the next gill, and probably lodge there. To take advantage of their enormous fertile area, agaric evolution has fine-tuned their spore-shooting mechanism. The spores must be launched delicately from their basidia and then allowed to free-fall straight down between the gills until they reach the open air below the cap, when natural turbulence will carry them away.

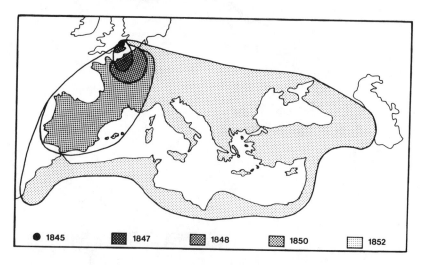

● 1845   ▓ 1847   ▒ 1848   ░ 1850   □ 1852

Fig. 8.4 Spread of powdery mildew of grapes in Europe, 1845-1852.

But how does the basidium forcibly discharge its spores? The spores develop individually and asymmetrically at the ends of sterigmata—fine, tapering projections from the apex of the basidium. The whole morphogenetic process, although under tight genetic control, and involving localized wall-softening enzymes, is clearly driven by turgor pressure. Just before the spore is discharged, a membrane-enclosed drop of fluid (the so-called 'Buller' drop) develops at one side of the base of the spore. A few seconds later, the spore is gently flipped into space. Although what happens at the moment of separation is not clear, I am inclined to accept the hypothesis that hydrostatic pressure is instrumental, as it is in so many other fungal discharge mechanisms. Certainly, if the basidium loses its turgor pressure, it becomes non-functional. High-speed photomicrography may help to clarify the details.

There are perhaps 10,000 species of agaric, and all, within fairly broad limits, share a similar design—they tend to look like open umbrellas. This is because they are in fact biological umbrellas. If the hymenia of most basidiomycetes get wet, they are ruined: the delicate mechanism of basidiospore discharge, which although largely driven by turgor pressure, may be at least partly operated by electrostatic charges, is disrupted. The umbrella form is so effective that it has evolved over and over again. Basidiomata that look rather like umbrellas, (or in some cases, half-umbrellas) are found among the Aphyllophorales (in the Cantharellaceae, stipitate Hydnaceae and Polyporaceae), the Tremellales (*Pseudohydnum, Phlogiotis*), and the Auriculariales, as well as the well-known agarics and boletes.

The annual weeds are among the most successful and most recently evolved of the flowering plants. They have an equivalent among the agarics: the genus *Coprinus*. Members of this genus have many unique and sophisticated features that earn them a place of honour in this chapter. *Coprinus comatus* (the shaggy mane: Fig. 8.5) is a large and common agaric that fruits on disturbed ground in late Fall, the first frosts triggering formation of basidiomata before it is too late. Almost everything about this mushroom increases its efficiency as a producer of spores. The stipe, though tall, is hollow, economizing on material. The cap does not spread out like those of most other agarics, but is very deep and almost cylindrical (Fig. 8.5). Most of the basidioma is made up of a tightly packed array of extremely thin gills. These gills are so close together that each has to produce a sprinkling of large, specialized cells called **cystidia** to keep its neighbours from touching it (Fig. 8.5). In addition, the gills are not rigorously kept vertical, as they are in most agarics. There is no way that spores could be fired from the surface of these gills and reach the world outside. No way, that is, except one.

In most agarics, any area of a gill will have basidia at various stages of development. But in *Coprinus* the process is highly regimented. Only the basidia at the bottom edge of a gill are permitted to mature. Their exposed position allows them to shoot their spores. But what about all the other basidia higher up? In order to expose them, the tissue at the lower edge of the gill undergoes self-digestion (autolysis). The process resolves into a beautifully orchestrated sequence. A perfectly timed wave of spore maturation, followed immediately by a wave of autolysis, sweeps up the gills. The cystidia near the gill-edge autolyze first, so that they will not be in the way of the spores. As spore-shooting proceeds, the entire cylinder of gills gradually melts away, as shown in Fig. 8.5.

The basidia of agarics may differ in size and shape, and even in the number of spores they produce, but they are remarkably uniform in the way they carry their spores. These always develop at the ends of tapering outgrowths of the basidium. And in functional agarics they always sit asymmetrically (Fig 5.2 B).

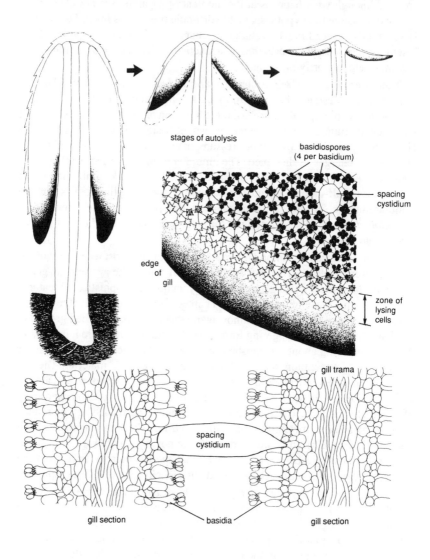

Fig. 8.5 Agaricales: *Coprinus comatus* showing gill-spacing and autolysis.

This asymmetry seems to be absolutely diagnostic of basidiospores that are actively shot away. If you find a basidium with spores symmetrically mounted on their sterigmata, as in Fig. 5.6 A-E, you can say definitely that those spores will not be actively propelled from their perches. Why should that matter? Well, it is an indicator of many other things that have happened to the fungus during the course of evolution. It marks a radical change in the biology of the organism.

As we saw in chapter 5, most families of agarics have produced what we call **sequestrate** offshoots which have lost their ability to shoot basidiospores, a loss that has gone hand in hand with changes in the development and morphology of the mature basidioma. In general, gills become crumpled, or even indistinguishable, as the hymenium-bearing tissues assume a loculate or spongy aspect, and in many cases the edge of the pileus, or the partial veil, encloses the spore-bearing tissues even at maturity. Stipes may be lost, and basidiomata may adopt a hypogeous habit.

We believe that these forms represent some of the most recent evolutionary developments in the fungi. Sequestrate forms seem to have arisen independently in no fewer than **14** families of agarics, probably as a response to exceptionally dry conditions which would damage the exposed hymenia of normal agarics. Spore dispersal must now be delayed until the basidioma breaks up, or may be carried out by insects or mammals. In fact, the California red-backed vole *Clethrionomys californicus* lives almost exclusively on false truffles such as *Rhizopogon*, which is a sequestrate derivative of *Suillus* (Boletaceae).

Some of the orders of Gasteromycetes have colourful common names—puffballs, earthstars, bird's-nest fungi, earthballs, stinkhorns—that suggest their specialized methods of spore dispersal. Puffballs (Lycoperdales) produce a mass of dry basidiospores (the **gleba**) inside a papery shell with a hole in the top. Raindrops cause this thin **peridium** to dimple, forcing a small puff of air mixed with spores out through the opening. Wind blowing across the opening can also suck out spores. Earthstars are just puffballs with an outer, fleshy peridium that develops several splits running radially outward from the centre. The segments thus formed open by bending backward, and as they reflex further and further, they lift the gleba above the surrounding leaf litter, exposing it to the rain and wind.

In the bird's-nest fungi (Nidulariales), the basidiospores of most genera form inside several small seed-like packets called peridioles or, more colloquially, eggs. These sit in a deeply funnel-shaped splash-cup receptacle, which focusses and reflects the kinetic energy of falling raindrops. Some of that energy is transferred to the peridioles, which are thrown for some distance.

In the earthballs (Sclerodermatales), a group otherwise extremely passive in its spore dispersal, there is one aberrant family, the Sphaerobolaceae, which has rather surprisingly evolved a new kind of active spore dispersal. The positively phototropic basidioma of *Sphaerobolus stellatus* is only 2mm in diameter, but can catapult its 1mm gleba up to 7 metres. The peridium in this fungus has several different layers. At maturity, the top splits and reflexes to expose the spherical gleba. The lower part of the peridium separates into two nesting cups which touch each other only at the rims. Glycogen in the cells of the inner cup is converted to glucose, and turgor pressure builds up until the inner cup abruptly turns inside out and flings the gleba into space. *Sphaerobolus* often occurs on old dung, and the evolutionary rationale for its explosive spore dispersal is clearly similar to those for the very different mechanisms we examined earlier in *Pilobolus*, *Saccobolus* and *Podospora*.

The stinkhorns (Phallales) are perhaps the most bizarre members of this strange menagerie. The young fruit body is called an egg. In *Phallus* (Fig. 5.7 D), the soft shell splits in the morning, as a dense mass of specialized tissue inside takes up water from the mucilage that surrounds the embryonic basidioma, and elongates quickly to produce a tall, spongy stalk. At the top is a receptacle, covered with a sugary but evil-smelling greenish slime in which the basidiospores are embedded. The smell attracts a procession of flying insects, particularly dipteran flies, which gorge excitedly on the slime, and also carry spores away on their feet. By evening, the green slime is gone, its mission accomplished. The most highly evolved phalloids seem to be those which, like *Aseroë* (Fig. 5.7 E), have basidiomata with long, bright red, radiating rays that can only be intended to supplement their olfactory message with a visual one. As a passing vector might say: "It's a flower. No, it's rotting meat. No, it's faeces!" Strange fungi indeed, that in the name of dispersal combine the qualities of flowers and excrement.

Further Reading

Buller, A.H.R. (1909, 1922, 1924, 1931) **Researches on Fungi**. Vols. I-IV. Longmans, Green & Co., London.

Burnett, J.H. (1976) **Fundamentals of Mycology**. 2nd Edn. Edward Arnold, London.

Corner, E.J.H. (1991) The active basidium. The Mycologist **5**(2): 69.

Ingold, C.T. (1971) **Fungal Spores: their Liberation and Dispersal**. Clarendon Press, Oxford.

Chapter 9

Fungal Physiology

Fungi, being eukaryotic organisms, have many physiological processes in common with other eukaryotes. But just as they have unique sets of morphological and behavioural features, so some aspects of their cellular chemistry differ from those of other organisms. If you already know all about basic cell chemistry, you can skip the next section and go directly to the rest of the chapter. But why not read through it anyway, just to refresh your memory?

Cell components

Proteins are large, complex molecules, made up of various mixtures and configurations of 20 different **amino acids**, held together by **peptide bonds**. Because of the essentially infinite number of structural possibilities that the building of a protein molecule presents, most organisms make many unique proteins. Fungal proteins are unique, yet function just like those of other organisms. Some are **enzymes** and **structural components**, others are associated with nucleic acids to form **nucleoproteins**, and a third group are conjugated with carbohydrates to form **glycoproteins**, which are found in membranes and the cell wall, as well as being secreted as extracellular enzymes.

Nucleic acids are of two kinds, commonly known as **DNA** and **RNA**. DNA is the central repository of genetic information. DNA incorporates the **genetic code**, in which sequences of 3 bases (**codons**) code for individual amino-acids, and thus specify the order in which these will be joined together to form the various proteins. DNA replicates itself, and also transcribes encoded information into RNA. Some RNA is associated with proteins in **ribosomes**, some occurs as **messenger RNA**, and some as **transfer RNA**. Ribosomes move along messenger RNA strands, reading the succession of 3-base codons, and stringing together amino acids brought in by transfer RNA. In this way, proteins are assembled.

DNA and RNA both have a sugar-phosphate spine, with **purines** and **pyrimidines** attached to the sugars. The sugar in DNA is **2-deoxyribose**, that in RNA is **ribose**. One of the pyrimidines of DNA, **thymine**, is replaced by **uracil** in RNA. DNA molecules are usually in pairs, helically intertwined: RNA is single-stranded. DNA is concentrated in the nuclei of eukaryotic cells, though some is also associated with the mitochondria (this is because these organelles were originally independent prokaryotes). One way of categorizing DNA is by its base ratio (percent guanine + cytosine). In the Eumycotan fungi, reported values range from 38% to 63%. The DNA content of fungi has been found to be very low, 0.15-0.3%. Their RNA content is much higher, 1-10% dry mass. Of this, the greater part is accounted for by ribosomal RNA, with a much smaller amount of transfer RNA, and even less messenger RNA.

Carbohydrates are **sugars, sugar alcohols**, and **polysaccharides** (polymers of sugars), all with the empirical formula $(CH_2O)_n$. Most fungal carbohydrates are polysaccharides, such as **chitin, chitosan, mannan, glucan, starch, glycogen**, and in the Oomycetes, something resembling **cellulose**. Chitin, a principal wall component in the Dikaryomycota, is a polymer of β-1,4 N-acetylglucosamine. Cellulose is a polymer of β-1,4 glucose. The main storage carbohydrate in true fungi is glycogen, but the disaccharide, **trehalose**, and sugar alcohols like **mannitol**, are also used.

Lipids all have an aliphatic hydrocarbon chain as part of their make-up. Their structure may be complicated by substitution with hydroxyl and carboxyl groups, they can be saturated or unsaturated, they may have aromatic moieties, and they can be combined with carbohydrates and amino-acids. All are soluble in non-polar solvents. They include the **fatty acids** (saturated and unsaturated), **fats** and **oils** (fatty acids combined with glycerol), **phospholipids**, and **sphingolipids**.

The main fatty acids found in fungi are **palmitic** (C16:0), **oleic** (C18:1) and **linoleic** (C18:2). The numbers in brackets indicate the number of carbon atoms in the molecule, and the number of double (unsaturated) bonds. Most fatty acids are combined with **glycerol** to form oils and fats, widely used as storage compounds. Phospholipids and sphingolipids are components of membranes, where they are often complexed with proteins. **Isoprenoid lipids** are based on isoprene, a 5-carbon branched chain molecule. **Terpenes** contain two isoprenes; sesquiterpenes, 3; diterpenes, 4; triterpenes, 6. **Carotenoids** are diterpenes, and **sterols** are triterpenes. Although **ergosterol** is the main fungal steroid, many other sterols are also present.

Metabolism

Metabolism may be defined as the sum total of all chemical reactions that support life. These may be divided into anabolic and catabolic functions. **Anabolic metabolism** converts food substrates into fungal biomass, **catabolic metabolism** extracts energy from various substrates, producing **adenosine triphosphate (ATP)**, **reduced nicotinamide-adenine dinucleotide (NADH)** and **NADPH**, as well as intermediates used in various anabolic processes.

All important reactions in biological systems are initiated and controlled by **enzymes**. In the absence of enzymes most reactions would go on too slowly (if they proceeded at all) to sustain life. Enzymes increase rates of reaction dramatically, by factors up to 10^7. An enzyme consists of a protein, often with a coenzyme such as a vitamin, and an activator such as Mg ions. Enzymes often work in sequence, each catalyzing a particular step in a metabolic pathway. Many fungi can produce enzymes that are rarely found in other organisms, e.g. ligninases and cellulases.

Glycolysis. Of the three pathways by which glucose can be converted to pyruvate before it is oxidized in the **citric acid cycle**, most fungi use two: the

Embden-Meyerhof (EM) and the **hexose monophosphate** (HM). The EM pathway yields **ATP** and **pyruvate**. The HM pathway yields **NADPH**, the main reducing agent in the biosynthesis of fatty acids and sugar alcohols, and **ribose**, used to make RNA, DNA and other nucleotides. Fungi respire aerobically, regenerating NAD by transfer of electrons from NADH to an external acceptor, oxygen. Fungal **fermentation** involves the regeneration of NAD by transfer of electrons to pyruvate, which is produced while the substrate is being metabolized. This kind of fermentation can produce alcohol or lactic acid. Everyone knows about the fermentation of pyruvate to **alcohol** and CO_2 by yeasts such as *Saccharomyces cerevisiae*, but species of *Aspergillus*, *Fusarium* and *Mucor* can do it too. Oomycetes and Zygomycetes carry out lactic acid fermentations.

Respiration involves three processes: the **citric acid cycle, electron transport**, and **oxidative phosphorylation**, all associated with the **mitochondria**, as they are in all eukaryotic organisms. The citric acid cycle accepts acetyl units, builds them into citrate, then oxidizes them to CO_2, reducing NAD as it does so. The electron transport mechanism transfers electrons to oxygen to make water, and along the way involves cytochromes in the phosphorylation of ADP to make ATP. Respiration can be inhibited in two ways: by uncoupling phosphorylation from electron transport, or by blocking electron transport. Many fungicides are unon the other or blockers.

Biosynthesis of amino acids. The average protein contains 20 or so different amino acids, but two of these amino acids, lysine and tryptophan, are of particular interest to students of the fungi. Eumycotan fungi and chytridiomycetes make **lysine** by a pathway that is different from that used by all other organisms, except the euglenids (unicellular, wall-less, flagellated algae). Eumycotan fungi, chytridiomycetes and euglenids synthesize lysine via 8 steps, one of which involves a unique intermediate, α-**amino adipic acid** (AAA). All other eukaryotic organisms that can make their own lysine (oomycetes, green algae and vascular plants) do so by a pathway involving 7 steps, and a unique intermediate called **diaminopimelic acid** (DAP). The two pathways have nothing in common: every step and every intermediate is different. (Animals are lysine auxotrophs— they can't make it at all, and must get it in their diet). Apart from anything else, the two radically different synthetic pathways suggest that the eumycotan fungi, chytridiomycetes and euglenids may have evolved from a common ancestral group, a group different from that which gave rise to the oomycetes, green algae and higher plants, and different from that which produced the animals.

Only one synthetic pathway is known for **tryptophan**, but genetic analysis of the loci controlling the sequence of enzymes has shown that while in two mycelial fungi (*Neurospora* and *Aspergillus*) four genes are involved, the yeast *Saccharomyces* requires five genes. The sedimentation of the various enzymes on sucrose gradients shows four patterns of enzyme aggregation, which are taxonomically distributed as follows: (1) chytridiomycetes, ascomycetes, holobasidiomycetes; (2) yeasts; (3) zygomycetes, teliomycetes; (4) oomycetes. Although we can't draw firm phylogenetic conclusions from such data, we can suggest that groups with different enzyme aggregation patterns are unlikely to be closely related.

Polysaccharide synthesis. I need hardly emphasize the importance of the hyphal wall to most fungi: it is simply the main skeletal component of the mycelium, imparting mechanical strength to the hyphae and protecting the living contents from deleterious outside influences just as the cellulose wall of the average plant cell does. The principal components of most fungal walls are polysaccharides, such as chitin (in the eumycotan fungi and chytridiomycetes) and a cellulose-like compound (in oomycetes). The sugar monomers from which these polysaccharides are built (N-acetyl glucosamine and glucose, respectively) are linked with a nucleotide, then enzymically added to the end of a growing chain. The spores of many fungi are embedded in slimy mucopolysaccharides, which may be important in dispersal.

Little need be said about the metabolism of specific elements, except to mention that fungi are **carbon** and **nitrogen** heterotrophs, so must be supplied with both in some combined form. A further restriction in the case of carbon is that the carbon source must be an energy-rich substance previously synthesized by another organism. Common carbon sources are sugars, hemicellulose, cellulose and lignin: the last two are relatively recalcitrant polymers that few other organisms can metabolize, presumably because they lack the necessary enzymes. Nitrogen can often be assimilated in the form of nitrate or ammonia, but amino acids, polypeptides and proteins can also be digested by many fungi. Again, some rather resistant structural proteins such as keratin can be attacked by certain groups of fungi (see chapter 23).

Secondary metabolism is a strange phrase. Surely the one word, metabolism, describes the total spectrum of chemical activities going on inside a living organism? But on close inspection, it becomes apparent that some organisms produce quantities of certain substances that do not seem to be part of the ordinary, ongoing business of existence (which is called 'primary metabolism'). These substances are now called 'secondary metabolites,' and may be defined as: natural products that are not necessary for growth, are often produced only by specific groups of organisms, during part only of their life cycle, and are derived from a few precursors formed during primary metabolism. Why then are we so conscious of these substances? Although they occur only sporadically, secondary metabolites tend to accumulate, since organisms usually produce them steadily, but do not degrade them. In addition, they are often biologically active. **Penicillin, griseofulvin, cyclosporine, aflatoxin, ergot alkaloids**, and **psilocybin**: all are secondary metabolites of fungi, and all are famous for their effects on other organisms.

Although secondary metabolites are rare in animals, they are common in plants, bacteria and fungi. Many are formed only after the requirements of cell growth have been satisfied. When growth stops, it seems that some biochemical pathways are not shut off, and things like fatty acids and amino acids accumulate, while the tricarboxylic acid cycle keeps on cycling. The organism now uses these raw materials, and a few others, to manufacture new end-products. For example, fatty acids give rise to polyacetylenes, amino acids to ergot alkaloids and penicillin. We now have a large catalogue of secondary metabolites, all derived from a relatively small number of precursors.

Secondary metabolites can be placed in five groups, according to the area of primary metabolism from which they are derived. (1) Glucose-derived substances like polysaccharides, peptidopolysaccharides, and sugar alcohols. (2) Condensation products of acetate derived from the acetate-malonate pathway of fatty acid synthesis, e.g. polyketides and phenolics. (3) Condensation products of acetate derived from the mevalonic acid pathway, e.g. terpenes. (4) Phenolics derived from the shikimic acid pathway of aromatic amino acid synthesis. (5) Derivatives of other amino acid syntheses.

Acetate is the raw material from which polyacetylenes, polyketides, steroids and terpenes are synthesized. **Polyacetylenes** are straight-chain compounds containing conjugated acetylenic systems. These compounds fluoresce brightly in UV, and so are easily detected. Of the 400 polyacetylenes known, about 80 are fungal, and found exclusively in basidiomycetes. **Polyketides** are produced by many ascomycetes and conidial anamorphs by condensation of acetyl units with malonyl units, with simultaneous decarboxylation. Examples are the antifungal antibiotic, **griseofulvin** (see chapter 23), and the mycotoxins, **ochratoxin** and **aflatoxin** (see chapter 21). **Terpenes** and **steroids** are biosynthesized from isopentenyl pyrophosphate, which is itself an acetate derivative. The **trichothecene** mycotoxins are sesquiterpenoids. **Gibberellic acid** is another fungal terpene that has also been found to be an important plant growth regulator. The mycotoxin, **zearalenone**, is a steroid. Though it produces profound sexual dysfunctions in young pigs, it is now widely used in the form of implants to promote growth of beef cattle.

Amino acids are the building blocks of proteins, but they are also the raw materials for many fungal secondary metabolites. Four groups stand out: (1) **cyclic oligopeptides**, which may be death-dealing toxins like the **amanitins** (8 amino acids), or lifesaving immunosuppressants like **cyclosporine** (11 amino acids); (2) **indole alkaloids** such as the hallucinogen, **psilocybin**, and the dangerous ergot alkaloids; (3) the **β-lactam antibiotics**, **penicillin** and **cephalosporin**; (4) plant growth regulators such as **auxin**, **cytokinin** and **ethylene**, which are formed by many fungi.

So far, I have taken the usual anthropocentric attitude in this brief survey of fungal secondary metabolites, concerning myself only with those that are of some direct importance to humans. In the interests of the impartial intellectual approach, it might now be a good idea to consider briefly the possible roles of these substances in the lives of the organisms that produce them. What value can a highly poisonous and extremely carcinogenic substance like aflatoxin have for *Aspergillus flavus*? What good, if any, is penicillin to *Penicillium chrysogenum*, or zearalenone to *Fusarium graminearum*?

It seems highly probable that these substances are not just waste products. Aflatoxin may well give *A. flavus* an advantage when it is competing with animals for food. Small mammals may learn to avoid mouldy nuts or seeds: and if they don't, they may be poisoned. Either way, the fungus wins. Penicillin, with its powerful bacteriostatic activity, may be presumed to give *P. chrysogenum* an edge over competing bacteria. Zearalenone, a mycotoxin that acts like a steroid sex hormone in pigs, is now believed to play a role in the development of the *Gibberella zeae* teleomorph of *Fusarium graminearum*.

Regulatory mechanisms. On reflection, it must be obvious that all of the thousands of reactions and cycles that make up the metabolic activity of an organism must be under some kind of control. Genes are turned on and off by environmental and inherent, developmental factors, but many processes have to go on all the time, or at least be constantly ready for action. Obviously, there isn't an overseer in the nucleus, turning all these switches on and off as needs are perceived and fulfilled. Most processes investigated have built-in controls, often simple but elegant feed-back mechanisms, which affect the enzymes that drive most reactions. For example, a different enzyme catalyzes each step in the production of leucine. If the raw material for this synthesis is in good supply, the pathway could churn out far more leucine than is needed: so, in a breathtakingly simple solution, the synthesis of the first enzyme in the series is inhibited by increased concentrations of the end-product, leucine. The pathway effectively turns itself off when it isn't needed.

Growth

Growth is often defined as irreversible increase in volume, but usually implies some other kinds of change as well: changes in components, metabolism, shape, function. A mycelial fungus will extend in all directions as its hyphae grow at their tips. The hyphae become longer, they often branch repeatedly, a lot of wall material is laid down, the amount of protoplasm and the number of nuclei in the colony increase. If the fungus is lucky, it will find more food than it uses up in the search, so it can both grow and accumulate reserves that will enable it to sporulate. Fungal growth is usually measured as increase in fresh weight (unreliable because of variations in water content), or in dry mass (which for obvious reasons can be measured only once for any particular colony), or by increase in the diameter or radius of the colony (which can be measured repeatedly). In unicellular yeasts, growth is measured by counting cells, or by measuring the increase in turbidity of the culture medium. If we were trying to produce conidial inoculum for use in a program of biological control (see chapter 14), we might express the success of the organism in terms of the numbers of propagules it formed in a certain time, at a certain temperature, or on a particular substrate. A mushroom-grower would be interested only in the mass of basidiomata produced.

Beginning from the spore, growth proceeds in stages, which can be categorized as: germination, assimilative growth, and sporulation. Each stage may require conditions very different from the others. I will examine them in turn. Much of our information about the early stages of growth has been obtained by plant pathologists, who are very interested in how pathogens get into their host plants, and in how they can be killed at their most vulnerable point, which is often the germ tube.

Other groups of organisms produce spores, but none produce them with such single-minded dedication, in such prodigal abundance, or in such an exuberant variety of forms, as the fungi (Fig. 3.2). The spore, almost as much as the hypha, is a fungal trademark. Spores may be single cells, or may be divided up in various ways into tens or even hundreds of compartments. Some live for a few hours; others for years. But all have two characteristics in common: they ensure the survival of the fungus through time, or space, or both; and sooner or later they germinate.

A **dormancy** phase usually precedes germination. Spores are often formed when conditions are deteriorating for the fungus. Temperatures may be falling, water drying up, food running out. If the spores germinated immediately, they would face the very problems they were produced to circumvent. Many spores have a built-in timer, an endogenous constraint that will not allow them to germinate until a certain time has elapsed. Many require prolonged cold treatment. Spores of many coprophilous fungi won't germinate until they have been exposed to high temperatures or to a specific chemical treatment: things that mimic what happens to them inside the gut of an animal. The signals they receive while passing through the gut prepare them to germinate in the dung as soon as it has been deposited, and so to have first access to the abundant nutrients it contains. Spores of some rust fungi won't germinate if they land too close to the parent mycelium or to sibling spores: this is called **self-inhibition**. However, spores of less specialized fungi often have no such built-in inhibitions, and will germinate as soon as appropriate conditions arise. In these cases, any dormancy must be regarded as exogenous: imposed from outside by lack of environmental encouragement.

Germination of powdery mildew conidia requires only oxygen, and the spores of some other obligately parasitic fungi need only oxygen and water. Most saprobic fungi need other factors, ranging from inorganic salts to various organic carbon sources. If a spore is to produce an extension of itself in the form of a germ tube (the first hypha), it must increase in volume. The only way to do this in the absence of an external food supply is to imbibe water or to produce it metabolically. Of course, the food reserves of the spore permit some synthesis of cytoplasm and wall material, but this is a limited resource and is soon exhausted. If the young hypha is to survive, it must find food.

The walls of resting spores are often chemically different from those of hyphae, and are relatively impermeable; but when they are ready to germinate, enzymes render the walls permeable, so that the spore can receive chemical stimuli from outside. When germination begins, enzyme action intensifies, softening the wall, often at a preformed thin area called a **germ pore** or **germ slit**. A germ tube emerges, the constituents of its cytoplasm, nuclei and wall material supplied by a renascent metabolism.

Once germination has happened, **growth** and **differentiation** are the next phases. Growth involves elongation of the young hypha at its tip, often with concurrent migration of cytoplasm and nuclei in the direction of growth. Growth implies increase in volume and increase in dry weight. These increases may be achieved by absorption of soluble nutrients already available in the environment. More usually, exoenzymes have to be secreted from the hyphal tip: they degrade the substrate into smaller, water-soluble molecules which can be absorbed and metabolized. However, if a hypha simply grew in a straight line, it could not effectively explore or exploit the substrate, and no appreciable biomass could ever be accumulated. This is where differentiation comes in. Soon after a germ tube appears, it branches. Then each of the two resulting hyphae branch; and so on, and so on (see Fig. 3.1). Soon, hyphae are growing in all directions possible, minutely exploring the substrate and forming the typical fungal colony, which will be spherical if the fungus can grow in three dimensions, as it does in a liquid medium; or circular if it is growing mainly in two dimensions, as it does when it spreads across the thin film of nutrient agar in a petri dish.

Growth rate. Since more and more fungi are being used for industrial or biotechnological purposes, it is important that fermentations be carried out under the best possible conditions of temperature, pH, and nutrition. Fungal physiologists have laid the groundwork for such applications. If we want to find out the best temperature to grow our fungus at, we set up a series of experiments in which conditions are the same in all replicates, except for the temperature. The two common measures of growth rate are: (1) increase in radius of colony over time; and (2) increase in dry mass of colony over time. The first has the advantage that sequential records can be obtained from each colony. The second is a more absolute measurement, but can be performed only once for each colony. If we are growing the fungus on a solid substrate like cellulose, it is difficult to separate the mycelium from the substrate at the end of the experiment, so we have to measure growth in another way: (3) by determining protein content. Such studies show that growth can be divided into several phases: (A) the **lag phase**, when growth begins slowly, then gradually accelerates; (B) the **exponential phase**, when growth continues at a high and steady rate; (C) the **decline phase**, as growth slows down and finally stops; (D) **death**, often accompanied by various degrees of **autolysis**.

This is the kind of picture we get when we study fungi in what is sometimes called **batch culture**. The fungus is grown in a flask or a fermenter, with a limited amount of food and space. When growth slows down, it might be because the fungus is running out of food. But the decline often comes long before the food is exhausted. This deterioration is often called **staling**, and is attributed to the accumulation of waste products that inhibit metabolism. If a fungus is inoculated at one end of a very long horizontal tube with a bed of nutrient medium along its length, it can remain in the exponential growth phase for as long as there is fresh medium to explore. Needless to say, this cannot happen often in Nature, so staling must be accepted as the norm. It may even be the switch that shifts some fungi into the reproductive mode.

Different fungi may grow at widely differing rates during their exponential phase, as may the same fungus grown under different conditions. One measure of growth rate is the time it takes a fungus to double its dry mass. A more easily determined measure is the **specific growth rate**, which is derived from measurements of a colony's mass at one-hour intervals. A fungus which increases in mass by 20% in an hour is said to have a specific growth rate of 0.2. Fungi have a wide range of specific growth rates. *Chaetomium virescens* has given a specific growth rate of 0.4 on glucose, and a value of 0.6 has been recorded for *Neurospora crassa* (or rather, for its *Chrysonilia* anamorph). These examples have much higher specific growth rates than most fungi. Yet some other fungi, including some common saprobic zygomycetes (e.g. *Rhizopus oligosporus*), and some yeasts, also have growth rates high enough to lead to their commercial exploitation, or to their denunciation as 'weeds.' Clearly, if we could understand and perhaps circumvent the mechanisms that limit the growth rate of many potentially useful fungi, biotechnological applications of these organisms would multiply.

Localization of growth. The walls of assimilative hyphae are not impermeable: they have pores similar in size to those in higher plant cell walls. Hyphal walls reduce but do not prevent the outward movement of water in dry conditions (desiccation), and the inward movement of deleterious substances from the environment. They do prevent the passage of most enzymes (large, proteinaceous molecules), and the exoenzymes on which fungi depend are in fact secreted almost entirely at or near the hyphal tip. This suggests that most hyphal wall material must be laid down just behind the hyphal tip. And experiments indicate that this actually happens. What kind of experiments? Early observations showed that the distances between septa, and between the origins of successive hyphal branches, did not change with time. Exposing growing hyphae to osmotic shock produced abnormalities only at their tips. Fluorescent antibodies have been used to distinguish between old and new wall material, and the resulting pattern of fluorescence showed that new material was introduced only at the hyphal tip. Tritiated N-acetylglucosamine was fed to growing hyphae and its incorporation pinpointed by autoradiography: again, incorporation was largely restricted to the apical micrometre. These are very significant observations. We can now see why a fungus needs so many hyphal tips, and how every fungal colony is essentially similar to the 'fairy ring,' driven to ever-expanding radial growth by its need for food, and by the exhaustion or staling of the substrate left behind.

Since **branching** is so vital to the success of the fungus in exploring its substrate, the mechanisms that control branching are of great interest. The phenomenon of apical dominance is well known in, for example, coniferous trees. It appears that a similar dominance can be detected in the hyphal tips of many fungi. Fungi growing in culture often have a characteristic distance from the hyphal tip to the first branch. Different metabolic inhibitors affect this relationship in different ways. Mitomycin C inhibits branch formation but not hyphal elongation: sodium fluoride has the opposite effect. (Mitomycin is known to inhibit DNA synthesis, NaF to inhibit metal-activated enzymes, but this knowledge hardly helps us to explain their differential effects on hyphal growth). In most fungi, the leader and the first one or two branches grow faster than the others: if the faster growing tips are cut off, the subordinate ones are 'released,' and grow faster. If inhibited branches are severed at their base, they proceed to grow faster, showing that the inhibition originated within the fungal thallus. The amount and kind of some nutrients, such as sulphur and nitrogen, available to the fungus also influence apical dominance. The complexity of the growth regulation system is indicated by the mapping of no fewer than 90 genes that control some aspect of colony morphology in *Neurospora*.

Septa (cross-walls) are a diagnostic feature of the hyphae of most true fungi. A septum is not usually laid down as a thin membrane, but rather begins as a ring of material around the inside of the hypha. The ring grows inward, eventually becoming an almost complete bulkhead which physically reinforces the intrinsically strong tubular configuration of the hypha. If we could watch a septum form, the process would resemble the closing of an iris diaphragm in a camera or a microscope condenser. In some fungal hyphae there is a clear relationship between septum formation and nuclear distribution: for example, in dikaryotic hyphae there is a septum for every two nuclei. But in many fungi there is no such relationship, nuclei pass through the septal pore between compartments with relative ease, and the mechanism that decides where septa will be laid down is obscure. Of course, many fungi are not restricted to the formation of individual hyphae, even during the assimilative phase. Various stimuli trigger the development of mycelial strands, rhizomorphs and sclerotia. But the true capacity for differentiation that is innate in most fungi is expressed only in the reproductive phase.

Media. In Nature, fungi grow on just about any organic substrate. When we grow them in pure culture, in the laboratory, we usually provide them with a special nutritive medium. This may be liquid (a broth), or solid (a gel). Most identification is done on solid media, but most fermentations and many physiological experiments are carried out in liquid media. Liquid media are based on water, and may contain a variety of nutrients, buffers, etc. The fungus is usually grown submerged, and its oxygen requirements are met by shaking (small flasks), or stirring and aerating (large fermenters). In solid media, the water and other components are held in a gel by agar. This complex polysaccharide, derived from a red alga, melts at 100°C but does not solidify until it cools to 45°C, and is not metabolized by most fungi. As little as 1-2% agar solidifies most media. Agar media are usually used to form thin layers covering the bottom of petri plates, or to fill the bottom third or so of test tubes (called 'slants' because they are placed at an angle while the agar is setting. Plates are used to grow cultures for identification. Typically, a small inoculum will be placed in the middle of the plate, then incubated. The colony which develops, growing partly above the surface of the medium, and partly below it, will often show diagnostic features (colour, texture, sporulation, etc.) Living cultures are often stored in slants, or may be **lyophilized** (freeze-dried and sealed in a high vacuum) for long-term storage.

If the culture is to be **axenic**, or as we say, uncontaminated, the medium, which is attractive and accessible to many microorganisms, must first be sterilized. This has usually involved pressure-cooking the medium in an autoclave at a steam pressure of 15 pounds/square inch (2 atmospheres) for 15 minutes. The temperature reaches 120°C, effectively killing all microooorganisms. But it also tends to caramelize sugars, and to destroy thermolabile substances like thiamin (a vitamin) and some antibiotics. Autoclaving is acceptable for routine work, but for critical physiological studies, it is better to filter the medium through membrane filters that effectively remove bacteria and fungal spores.

Nutritional Requirements

Carbon nutrition. One of the principal distinguishing features of most fungi is their inability to fix inorganic carbon. The simplest compound most fungi can use as a source of energy is the monosaccharide, **glucose**. Unlike most other carbon sources, this doesn't need to be enzymically broken down to anything simpler before it can be absorbed. Virtually all fungi are ready to metabolize glucose at a moment's notice: they already have all the necessary enzymes, which are thus described as **constitutive**. Fructose, mannose and galactose are also readily used, but there is often a delay before assimilation begins. This is because the enzymes involved in processing these sugars aren't necessarily ready and waiting. The fungus takes a little while to recognize the nature of the substrate, and to synthesize the proper enzymes. This process is called **induction**, and produces **adaptive** enzymes. If a lot of glucose is present, it may actually suppress the production of the enzymes that deal with other substrates: the fungus takes the easy route. A little glucose, on the other hand, may fuel the induction process, and shorten the lag phase on many substrates.

Although many experiments have been done to compare the ability of fungi to use different single carbon sources, these may not tell the whole story. In Nature, fungi usually have to deal with mixtures, and their behaviour in this situation can't always be forecast from single-substrate tests. We've already seen that the presence of glucose can suppress the utilization of other substrates. Perhaps the most important example of the mixed substrate situation involves **lignin**. Although the ability to degrade lignin to carbon dioxide is one of the things for which many basidiomycetes (the white rot fungi) are most notorious, they can't use lignin as sole carbon source, and will break it down only in the presence of another accessible carbon source, such as cellulose, cellobiose or glucose. Fungi may deal with lignin only to gain better access to the cellulose, or in order to release available nitrogen.

Culture media must also contain a source of **nitrogen**. No fungus (in fact, no eukaryote) can fix atmospheric nitrogen. Many fungi can use nitrate, though ammonium nitrogen is even more universally metabolized. Urea, amino acids, and various polypeptides and proteins, are accessible to some, but not all, fungi. A good nitrogen source for many fungi is hydrolysed casein, a mixture of amino-acids. **Sulphur** requirements can almost always be met by incorporating sulphate in the medium, though some chytridiomycetes require sulphur-containing amino-acids such as methionine.

Vitamins are coenzymes that are required in minute amounts. Although some fungi can make many of their own vitamins, many are deficient for **thiamin** (vitamin B1, involved in carboxylation), **biotin** (B7, carboxylation), **riboflavin** (B2, dehydrogenation), **pyridoxine** (B6, transamination), **nicotinic acid** (B3, dehydrogenation), and others. Vitamin deficiency is sometimes absolute, in which case the fungus can be described as auxotrophic in this respect, and won't grow unless one or more vitamins are supplied. In other cases it is only partial, so that additions of vitamins may merely increase growth, rather than making it possible. Vitamin deficiency may be temporary: *Myrothecium* needs biotin for spore germination, but not for mycelial growth. While many fungi require vitamins, others can synthesize them from precursors. Thiamin, for example, consists of a pyrimidine ring and a thiazole ring, linked by methylene. Some fungi, if provided with the two rings, can link them and complete the molecule; other fungi need only the pyrimidine ring; yet others need only the thiazole ring.

Fungi also need a range of elements, which can be divided into two groups according to the amounts required for normal growth. The **macronutrients** include: **potassium (K)**, which is used in carbohydrate metabolism, enzyme activity, and to maintain ionic balance; **phosphorus (P)**, an essential component of nucleic acids, and of energy transfer mechanisms; **magnesium (Mg)**, an enzyme activator required in ATP metabolism; **sulphur (S)**, a component of some amino acids, vitamins and other sulfhydryl compounds; and **calcium (Ca)**, an enzyme activator that is also often found in membranes. **Micronutrients**, sometimes called trace elements, include: **iron (Fe)**, found in cytochromes, haem apoenzymes, and pigments; **copper (Cu)** an enzyme activator also involved in pigments; **manganese (Mn)**, **zinc (Zn)**, and **molybdenum (Mo)**, all enzyme activators. Fungi get along without boron, chlorine, fluorine, iodine and silicon, though these elements are apparently essential to many other organisms. Incorporating iron in a growth medium can be a problem, since ferric iron is extremely insoluble at pH values above 4, and ferrous iron is quickly oxidized to ferric by the free oxygen most fungi need. Fortunately, a chelating agent such as EDTA (ethylenediamine tetraacetic acid) which acts as a metal ion buffer, will increase the biological availability of iron.

Although culture media must contain some available **water**, some conidial fungi and yeasts are the most xerotolerant organisms known, able to grow at water activities (a_w) as low as 0.70. If we consider that most animals grow only above a_w 0.99, most green plants wilt irreversibly at a_w 0.97, and most bacteria will grow only at a_w 0.95 or higher, this must be recognized as a truly remarkable talent, though for us it is an expensive nuisance, as you will read in chapter 20. Fungi that grow at low external water activities have comparably low internal a_w as well. Yeasts control their internal osmotic pressure by interconverting sugars and polyhydric alcohols such as glycerol and mannitol, and it seems probable that mycelial fungi may well do this too, though that has not yet been established. Most enzymes normally operate in an aqueous medium, and if a fungus is to function at low internal a_w, some enzyme-compatible water substitute must be present. It has been found that glycerol can play this role.

Using the information given above, you should be able to concoct a culture medium on which many fungi would grow well. By combining many individual chemicals, you could make specific provision for their basic metabolic needs. The medium you produced would be a 'defined' or even possibly a 'minimal' medium. But many fungi would grow even better on very complex substrates: things such as extracts of malt, or of potatoes, or of yeast. These rich mixtures, though 'undefined,' appear to be nutritionally optimal, and it is much easier to use one of them than to painstakingly measure out increasingly minute amounts of a long list of trace elements and expensive purified growth factors. Unless you are doing critical physiological experiments, you would probably grow most fungi on potato dextrose agar (PDA), malt extract agar (MEA), or some other undefined medium. Recipes of media suitable for a wide range of applications can be found in 'Methods In Microbiology' Vol. 4 (Ed: Booth 1966) and 'The Mycology Guidebook' (Ed: Stevens 1974). Also, remember that your best efforts to culture many groups of fungi are doomed to frustration. The physiology of many obligately parasitic fungi is intimately linked with that of their hosts, so no ordinary medium will support growth of members of the Uredinales, Peronosporaceae, Erysiphales, Laboulbeniales, Glomales, and others. The simplest system in which most of these organisms can be studied is a 'dual' culture: fungus + host.

Transport. Fungi can absorb food only in the form of relatively small molecules like glucose. Water moves into hyphae by passive diffusion, driven by osmotic differentials. Although the cell wall is more or less permeable in either direction to the kind of molecules the cell seeks to accumulate, it limits the inflow of water by offering a physical resistance (wall pressure) to expansion. The plasmalemma is semipermeable, and controls the movements of solutes. The membrane itself is largely lipid—actually a double layer of phospholipid molecules—which tends to keep water-soluble compounds out. Transport can be passive or active. In passive transport, the substrate moves along a concentration gradient or an electropotential gradient. Active transport requires an investment of energy, usually ATP, by the organism. Desirable substances may be carried in, or unwanted material expelled. In active transport, the substance being moved is believed to be pumped through special channels lined with proteins called permeases, or to become bound to a specific carrier protein, which is responsible for transporting it across the membrane. Carrier proteins also aid in passive 'facilitated diffusion.'

Cations such as: potassium, ammonium, magnesium, calcium, manganese and iron are all accumulated against high concentration gradients, showing that active, carrier-mediated transport mechanisms are involved. If a fungus is loaded with sodium, then supplied with potassium, sodium will be expelled as potassium is taken up. This kind of behaviour is called countertransport. The divalent cations, Mg^{++}, Ca^{++} and Mn^{++}, will be taken up only if phosphate is also available, and Fe^{+++} is chelated with siderochromes before being transported.

The transport of ions such as phosphate and sulphate is also carrier-mediated. Once phosphate is inside the cell, it is converted to polyphosphate, and internal concentrations of orthophosphate don't change. The study of nitrate uptake has been hindered by the lack of a really sensitive measuring technique, so it isn't certain that carriers are involved.

Glucose and other sugars move across the plasmalemma of fungi by facilitated diffusion, or by active transport, or by a combination of the two. A single fungus may have several different mechanisms. Some of the active mechanisms are constitutive (always present and ready), while some are inducible. Amino acids are also transported actively. *Neurospora crassa* has been shown to have at least five different amino acid transport systems: one carries only methionine; another, only acidic amino acids; a third, only basic amino acids; the fourth, aromatic and aliphatic amino acids; the fifth, aromatic, aliphatic and basic amino acids. Amino acid transport systems differ from those for sugars and ions in that no counter-transport has been detected.

Cellulose and Lignin Decomposition. Fungi produce an extraordinary spectrum of enzymes, and can degrade just about any organic substrate. Perhaps the most important of these substrates are cellulose and lignin. Billions of tonnes of **cellulose** is produced by the higher plants every year. It forms the greater part of their cell walls, and, being apparently unable to recycle it themselves, they discard it in vast quantities every year. Autumn-shed leaves, the entire biomass of annual plants, and eventually the corpses of the much longer-lived trees: all are bequeathed to the fungi, because no other organisms can initially unlock the energy they contain. The key to this wealth is the complex of fungal **cellulases** (some bacteria produce cellulases, but generally operate under wetter, more alkaline conditions). *Trichoderma viride* is a well known cellulolytic fungus that is commonly isolated from some forest soils, and from decaying plant material. It produces three distinct cellulolytic enzymes: **cellulase**, which hydrolyzes all kinds of cellulose; **glucan cellobiohydrolase**, which degrades crystalline cellulose to cellobiose; and the **glucanases**, which hydrolyze amorphous cellulose. There are two kinds of glucanase: the endoglucanases, which produce cellulose oligomers, and the exoglucanases, which attack those oligomers, cleaving off one glucose unit at a time. Exoglucanases and cellobiases digest cellobiose, releasing glucose. The enzymes of the cellulase complex are all glycoproteins, and are resistant to thermal denaturation.

Plants also produce vast quantities of **lignin**. This recalcitrant polymer strengthens the walls of many plant tissues, especially those involved in secondary thickening. Their deposition in wood tends to mask the cellulose content of the cell walls. Some fungi (the white rot Basidiomycetes) are the only organisms we know that can unequivocally degrade lignin; and even they cannot use it as their sole source of carbon. Ligninases are oxidative rather than hydrolytic enzymes. Many white rot organisms produce an extracellular **polyphenol oxidase** called **laccase**, which must play a critical role in lignin breakdown, since organisms that don't have it, can't attack lignin. Other, as yet undiscovered, enzymes are also almost certain to be involved.

Protein digestion. Although some proteins are water-soluble, they cannot cross the plasmalemma into the fungal cell unless they are broken down into small oligopeptide fragments containing no more than 3-5 amino acid molecules. Hence the need for extracellular proteases. Fungi like *Saccharomyces cerevisiae*, which produce only intracellular proteases, cannot assimilate proteins. At the other end of the scale are organisms like *Trichophyton* and other dermatophytes, which can attack **keratin**, a tough structural protein. There are two main kinds of protease: exohydrolases, which nibble individual amino acids from the ends of peptide chains; and endohydrolases, which will cleave a chain into two large fragments, doubling the number of ends on which the exohydrolases can operate.

Environmental Effects

Physical parameters like temperature, light, and gravity have profound effects on many fungi, but generalizations are dangerous. Some psychrophilic fungi grow at temperatures below 0°C; some thermophiles can function at temperatures above 50°C. Some fungi need light in order to fruit; others seem indifferent to illumination. Many macrofungi are extremely sensitive to gravity; many microfungi are totally oblivious to it.

It is helpful to know the **cardinal temperatures** of any fungus we want to work with. These are its minimum, optimum and maximum temperatures for

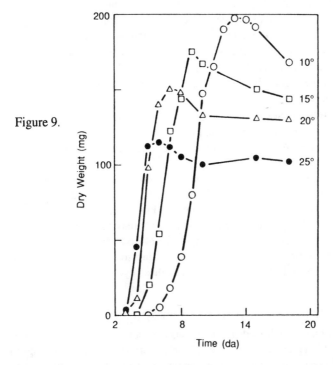

Figure 9.

Fig. 9.1 Effect of time and temperature on growth of **Phycomyces** in a defined medium (Robbins and Kavanagh, 1944).

growth. Most researchers find it convenient to grow a fungus at its optimum temperature, but this ignores the fluctuating and often extreme temperatures the organism must face in much of North America. I have already pointed out that falling temperatures in Autumn may induce fruiting in some fungi (such as *Coprinus comatus*), dormancy in others; that resting stages of many fungi (such as *Monilinia*) must be chilled before they will germinate; and that heat treatment produces the same effect in others. From study of their assimilative growth, fungi can generally be categorized as **psychrophilic**, **mesophilic** or **thermophilic**. Psychrophiles have minimum growth temperatures below 0°C, maxima below 20°C, and optima in the range 0-17°C. Mesophiles (the great majority of fungi) have minima above 0°C, maxima below 50°C, and optima between 15 and 40°C. Thermophiles have minima above 20°C, maxima above 50°C, and optima between 35 and 50°C. Establishing true optima may not be simple, as Fig. 9.1 shows. If a complete growth curve is not plotted at each of the chosen temperatures, incorrect conclusions could be drawn. Compare the answer you would get if you harvested the experiment detailed in Fig. 9.1 at day 7 with that you would get at day 14. Also note that the quickest start-up does not necessarily eventually produce the most dry mass.

Some of the most spectacular effects of **light** on fungi are documented in chapter 8 (dispersal) and chapter 11 (ecology). *Pilobolus* aims its explosive sporangial mechanism at the light; *Podospora* points the neck of its perithecial ascoma toward the light; the individual asci of *Ascobolus* point toward the light. Each of these mechanisms involves positive **phototropism**. Phototropism implies the existence of a photoreceptor. Most phototropic fungi respond best to blue light, and this is strongly absorbed by β-carotene, which is usually present in the photosensitive organs, but the true nature of the photoreceptor has not yet been established.

Circadian rhythms. Some fungi in culture display daily rhythms of growth, pigment production, or sporulation, which seem to be responses to the alternation of light and darkness. Although *Pilobolus sphaerosporus* (Mucorales) didn't need light in order to produce sporangia, establishment of a regular 12-hr light/12-hr dark regime increased the number of sporangia produced, and led to a peak of discharge 6 hours after the lights were turned on. Continuous light destroyed this synchrony, but in continuous darkness the cyclical discharge continued for several days, though with gradually decreasing intensity. Raising or lowering the temperature did not change this 24-hour rhythm. Many other such circadian rhythms have been recorded, including some 'clock' mutants of *Neurospora*, but the underlying mechanisms of these cycles are not yet understood.

Reproduction: the Formation of Propagules

The foregoing paragraph leads me to a consideration of reproductive physiology in fungi. If hyphae are the secret of the remarkable success of fungi in exploiting their myriad substrates, spores are the secret of their ubiquity. Spores are omnipresent, ensuring that whenever a new substrate becomes available, fungi will always be there to colonize it. We can express the strategy of many fungi quite simply: in the **assimilative mode**, fungi produce hyphae; as long as there is food to be had, the fungus concentrates on accumulating reserves of energy, some to be invested in producing more hyphae, some to be stored. When food runs out, or staling factors build up, or reserves reach an appropriate level, or specific environmental signals are received, the fungus switches into the **reproductive mode** and produces spores.

Some fungi produce spores directly on the assimilative hyphae; others form specialized but simple, one- or few-celled spore-bearing structures. In these cases, the onset of reproduction can be very rapid. In hyphomycetes like *Penicillium*, while assimilative hyphae at the margin of the colony are still advancing, the older hyphae are producing simple conidiophores and conidia. This situation can be recognized at a glance: the margin is white, while the rest of the colony is covered by a mass of green conidia. In other fungi, such as the agarics, the spore-bearing structure is large and complex. It takes longer for these fungi to prepare for the actual production of spores; though, once again, they are eventually liberated in astronomical numbers.

Careful physiological work on the hyphomycete, *Aspergillus niger*, has established that several stages lead up to sporulation. These can be recognized by their differing nutritional requirements. (1) Low levels of nitrogen, with adequate glucose and aeration, permitted the development of foot cells and the subsequent elongation of conidiophores. Addition of ammonium ion would prevent this. (2) Addition of ammonium nitrogen and a TCA cycle acid permitted development of the apical vesicle and the phialidic conidiogenous cells. (3) Glucose and nitrate were required for the formation of conidia. We cannot assume that exactly the same process operates in other fungi.

I have already mentioned the period of endogenous dormancy that is apparently built-in to spores. The hyphae arising from spores also seem to have a minimum growth period before they will sporulate. Hyphae which have not emerged from this phase will not sporulate, even in conditions that normally induce fruiting. Toward the end of this refractory period, the fungus becomes less able to take up glucose and other nutrients. This suggests some kind of membrane control as part of the induction process.

The range of temperature which permits sporulation is narrower than that over which assimilative growth can occur. For example, mycelia of *Penicillium* species grow at temperatures ranging from 2 to 43°C; conidia are formed between 3 and 40°C. *Gnomonia vulgaris* grows between 5 and 30°C, but produces ascomata only between 10 and 25°C.

Since fungi grow in so many different habitats, and have such varied ecological requirements, it isn't surprising that we can't generalize on the link between light and sporulation. Light may inhibit; it may stimulate; or it may have opposite effects at different points in development. It stimulates the production of conidia in the *Aspergillus* anamorph of a *Eurotium* species, while inhibiting development of ascomata of the teleomorph. The effects of light have been investigated from two angles: which wavelengths are active (the action spectrum); and how much light is needed (the dosage response). I noted earlier that blue light and near-UV stimulated phototropic responses in *Phycomyces* (Mucorales), and the same wavelengths (420-485 and 350-390 nm) induce formation of perithecial ascomata in *Gelasinospora*. Some ascomycetes and conidial fungi respond to UV, but not to visible light.

Although many fungi fruit only after exposure to light, the actual amount of light energy needed can be very small. Initiation of *Coprinus lagopus* basidiomata is triggered by only 8 joules (J) per square metre (5 seconds at 0.1 foot candle). To induce pseudothecial ascomata of *Leptosphaerulina* requires even less light (0.64 J m^{-2}). Most fungal responses need only 0.5-20 J m^{-2}; remarkably little, considering the magnitude of the induced effect.

The development of reproductive structures obviously necessitates changes in morphology and development, but the nature of the physiological and biochemical changes involved is not immediately apparent. Detailed comparisons of the mycelia and conidia of the *Chrysonilia* anamorph of *Neurospora crassa* show that some substances such as trehalose, glutamic acid, glutathione, carotenoids and phospholipid, which are present at low levels in mycelium, are found at much higher levels in conidia. Others, such as arginine, ornithine, and adenine nucleotides, are more plentiful in mycelium.

The Physiology of Sex

Reproduction in fungi frequently involves sex: though their sexual behaviour is sometimes obscure, and one mode of sexuality evolved by fungi is unique and extremely prolonged. Diffusible chemical substances that trigger sexual activity are found in many organisms. A differentiation has usually been made between **hormones**, which act on the organism that produces them, and **pheromones**, which act on other sexually compatible organisms. This differentiation is harder to make in the fungi. Closely related taxa may be homothallic and heterothallic, respectively, so a shared sexually active substance could be referred to as a hormone in the first case, and as a pheromone in the second. In the fungi it is simpler to call them all hormones.

The chytridiomycete, *Allomyces*, has a water-diffusible sex hormone called **sirenin**. This is released into the water by the female gametes, and the smaller, more motile male gametes swim toward them by detecting the concentration gradient. In vitro experiments with *Allomyces* showed that response decreased at hormone concentrations above 10^{-6}M. Presumably at this concentration the receptor sites on the male gametes were saturated, and they could no longer find their way up the concentration gradient. Male gametes normally maintain their sensitivity by breaking down the sirenin they intercept.

The oomycete, *Achlya ambisexualis*, produces sex hormones in a ping-pong sequence, to coordinate the development of the male and female sex organs. A potentially female mycelium secretes hormone A, which causes any nearby potentially male mycelium to develop antheridial branches. The male strain then releases hormone B, which triggers the development of oogonia on the female mycelium. The developing oogonia then release hormone C, which attracts the antheridial initials. These initials produce hormone D, which causes the oogonial initials to mature. The antheridia mature when they touch the oogonia, but hormone E might also be hypothesized. Two of these hormones have been isolated and characterized. Hormone A is called **antheridiol**, and hormone B, **oogoniol**. Pure antheridiol will also induce chemotropism and maturation of antheridia, so it may also represent hormones C and E.

The zygomycetes provide classic laboratory demonstrations of fungal sexuality. We plant a '+' strain of *Phycomyces* or *Mucor* on one side of an agar plate, and the corresponding '-' strain on the other. When the two meet, gametangia are formed, then zygosporangia. Because these events seem to happen when the mycelia touch, we don't necessarily think of diffusible hormones. Yet there is chemistry here, too. Sixty years ago, it was demonstrated that compatible strains of *Mucor* would form gametangia, even when separated by a semipermeable membrane. Much later, it was found that both mycelia produce a sex hormone called trisporic acid when grown close together. This induces the formation of gametangia. The final rendezvous of the gametangia is guided by volatile, mating-type specific substances which, though demonstrably present, have not yet been characterized.

The conjugation of yeast cells is governed by diffusible hormones, and by agglutination factors that are bound to the cell walls. Each mating type of *Saccharomyces cerevisiae* has its own hormone. One consists of oligopeptides of 12 and 13 amino acids. The other has a molecular weight of about 600,000, and contains protein and polysaccharide. Though they are so different, these substances have similar effects on the appropriate mating type: they inhibit the initiation of DNA synthesis, effectively locking the cell into interphase. Budding stops, and cells of opposite mating type become mutually adhesive. Since isolated protoplasts won't stick together unless they manage to regenerate walls, the agglutination factor must be wall-bound. Cells of opposite mating type have distinct but complementary peptidopolysaccharide agglutination factors. Conjugation follows agglutination. Sometimes the zygote multiplies to form a generation of diploid cells, sometimes it develops into an ascus-like meiosporangium.

Among the ascomycetes proper, sex hormones have been partially purified for *Neurospora* (Sordariales), and there is evidence for the existence of comparable hormones in *Ascobolus* (Pezizales) and *Bombardia* (Sordariales). The well-known mycotoxin, zearalenone, produced by the hyphomycete *Fusarium graminearum*, apparently stimulates the development of perithecial ascomata of its teleomorph, *Gibberella zeae* (Hypocreales).

Among the basidiomycetes, it has been shown that opposite mating types of *Tremella* (Phragmobasidiomycetes) have individual, constitutive sex hormones. One of them has been partially characterized. Tremerogen, as it is called, is a 12-amino acid lipopeptide with an isoprenoid conjugated to the sulphur of the cysteine at one end. When the yeast-like basidiospores are exposed to this, they stop budding and produce a conjugation tube. The red yeast, *Rhodotorula*, has similar hormones. One of these, named rhodotorucine, inhibits budding and induces formation of conjugation tubes in the opposite mating type. The resultant teleomorph is *Rhodosporidium* (Ustilaginales).

The situation in many basidiomycetes is complicated by the fact that although the first prerequisite for sexual reproduction, the bringing together of compatible nuclei, happens at the moment of dikaryotization, the ultimate sexual fusion of nuclei may be long delayed, and happens only to distant descendants of the original nuclear pair. Although sex hormones may facilitate the meeting of monokaryotic mycelia, other factors, nutritional and environmental, probably determine the timing of nuclear fusion and meiosis.

Although very few fungi have been investigated for the presence of sex hormones, it seems likely that their secretion is the norm rather than the exception. If ascomycete and basidiomycete sex hormones are shown to have some uniformity of structure and action, it would be fascinating to apply them to the vast number of dikaryomycotan anamorphs for which no teleomorph is known, to see if sexual development could be initiated, and many longstanding mysteries solved.

Antifungal Compounds

The chemical industry synthesizes thousands of new compounds every year. Many are routinely screened for various possible uses. Two questions commonly asked are: Are they antibiotic? Are they fungicidal? So, by empirical testing, new fungicides are found. Until recently it was only after a compound had been discovered to be fungicidal that its mode of action was investigated, though enough is now known about fungicidal action that new fungicides can be designed at the molecular level, with appropriate prosthetic groups. Here are some groups of fungicides and their sites of action. (1) **Copper, mercury, dithiocarbamates, phthalimides** and **quinones** tend to be non-specific enzyme poisons that bind to functional groups that normally maintain the secondary structure of proteins. (2) The anti-fungal **polyene antibiotics, nystatin** and **amphotericin B**, form complexes with sterols, and thus disrupt membrane formation. Oomycetes and bacteria, which have no sterols in their membranes, are unaffected. (3) The **sterol-inhibitors**, such as **bitertanol, triadimefon**, and **triforine**, prevent the biosynthesis of ergosterol, the major sterol in many fungi, and so might logically be expected to interfere with membrane synthesis, though whether this actually happens has not yet been established. (4) **Polyoxins** interfere with chitin synthesis in vitro by competing with chitin synthetase for its monomer substrate, but have a disappointingly limited range of activity in vivo. (5) **Cycloheximide** is a pyrimidine analogue, and blocks protein synthesis by binding to ribosomes. (6) **Benzimidazoles** (e.g. **benomyl**) bind to the tubulin that normally forms the mitotic spindle, and so disrupt nuclear division. Once again, oomycetes are not sensitive to benomyl, though their division is inhibited in a similar way by colchicine. (7) **Carboxins** interfere with the metabolism of mitochondria in many dikaryomycotan fungi, causing succinate accumulation.

As we learn more about the physiology and biochemistry of fungi we should be able to design molecules that will interfere in aspects of metabolism that are specific to fungi, leaving non-target organisms unaffected. We will also find new uses for many fungal metabolites.

Further Reading

Aronson, J.M. (1981) Cell wall chemistry, ultrastructure and metabolism. pp. 459-507 (in) **Biology of Conidial Fungi**. Vol. 2. (Eds.) G.T. Cole and B. Kendrick. Academic Press, New York.

Bartnicki-Garcia, S. (1966) Cell wall chemistry, morphogenesis, and taxonomy of fungi. Annual Review of Microbiology **22**: 87-108.

Berry, D.R. (1975) The environmental control of the physiology of filamentous fungi. pp. 16-32 (in) **The Filamentous Fungi**. Vol. 1 (Eds.) J.E. Smith and D.R. Berry. Arnold, London.

Burnett, J.H. (1976) **Fundamentals of Mycology**. Arnold, London.

Carlile, M.J. (1970) The photoresponses of fungi. pp. 309-344 (in) **Photobiology of Microorganisms**. (Ed.) P. Halldal. Wiley, New York.

Cochrane, V.W. (1958) **Physiology of Fungi**. Wiley, New York.

Garraway, M.O. and R.C. Evans (1984) **Fungal Nutrition and Physiology.** Wiley, New York.

Griffin, D.H. (1981) **Fungal Physiology**. Wiley, New York.

Hall, R. (1981) Physiology of conidial fungi. pp. 417-457 (in) **Biology of Conidial Fungi**. Vol. 2. (Eds.) G.T. Cole and B. Kendrick. Academic Press, New York.

Hawker, L.E. (1957) **The Physiology of Reproduction in Fungi**. Cambridge University Press, London.

Lowe, D.A. and R.P. Elander (1983) Contribution of mycology to the antibiotic industry. Mycologia **75**: 361-373.

Mueller, E. (1971) Imperfect-perfect connections in ascomycetes. pp. 184-201 (in) **Taxonomy of Fungi Imperfecti**. (Ed. B. Kendrick). University of Toronto Press, Toronto.

Robinson, P.M. (1978) **Practical Fungal Physiology**. Wiley, New York.

Smith, J.E. and D.R. Berry (Eds.) (1975, 1976, 1978) **The Filamentous Fungi**. Vols. 1-3. Arnold, London.

Smith, J.E., D.R. Berry and B. Kristiansen (Eds.) (1983) **The Filamentous Fungi**. Vol. 4. Arnold, London.

Turian, G. (1966) Morphogenesis in ascomycetes. pp. 339-385 (in) **The Fungi**. Vol. 2. (Eds:) G.C. Ainsworth and A.S. Sussman. Academic Press, New York.

Turian, G. (1969) **Differenciation Fongique**. Masson, Paris.

Chapter 10

Fungal Genetics

Introduction

Genetics is the discipline that seeks to understand the ways in which the information needed to reproduce an organism is stored within it, and how that information may change and be reassorted before it is passed on to the next generation. In recent years, we have also become concerned with how this information can be changed in a directed way by human intervention. This chapter attempts to show how fungi are useful tools in some areas of both Mendelian and molecular genetics. If your background in this area is sparse, you will find some useful introductory information in chapters 1 and 9. If you still have trouble with what follows, I recommend that you consult an elementary genetics text such as 'Principles of Genetics' 7th Edition, by E.J. Gardner and D.P. Snustad, published by John Wiley and Sons, New York.

In the simplest terms, genetic information (the genome) is maintained in the cell as long, linear sequences of nucleotide base pairs which make up DNA molecules. The order in which these bases occur constitutes the genetic code, and this code specifies the sequences of amino acids required to build all the proteins necessary for the construction and operation of the living organism. DNA molecules can be very long, incorporating many thousands of base pairs, and are called chromosomes. The genome of prokaryotes is contained in a single, usually circular chromosome found in the cytoplasm. The genome of eukaryotes is contained in two or more (often many more) chromosomes, which are contained in a nucleus, a special command module separated from the cytoplasm by a membrane.

The eukaryotic plants and animals differ from each other in many ways, but both are basically diploid. This means that their nuclei contain two matched sets of chromosomes: (usually one set originally derived from a male gamete, one set from a female gamete). So each chromosome has a 'double.' Most genes on each chromosome have a counterpart, called an **allele**, on the 'double.' This allele affects the same characters, though not necessarily in the same way. For example, the two alleles of one particular gene make pea plants tall and dwarf, respectively. If a tall plant is crossed with a dwarf plant, there will be more tall offspring than dwarf offspring. Plants will be dwarf only if both alleles are of the dwarfing kind. This shows that one allele can mask another: we say that the 'tall' allele is **dominant**, the 'dwarf' allele, **recessive.** This makes genetic analysis difficult, and also makes it hard to breed pure lines of many diploid organisms, because it is almost impossible to eradicate recessive genes, since you can't tell whether they are present or not (though it is easy to purebreed for recessive colour genes such as those expressed in white rats and mice.)

The vast majority of fungi are haploid, which means that their nuclei contain only a single set of chromosomes. This gives them certain advantages over diploid organisms for genetic studies, since there are no competing alleles, and every gene is potentially capable of being expressed in the **phenotype** (the physical manifestation or incarnation of the organism). This absence of masking makes genetic analysis much easier. The advantages of using fungi in genetic studies are as follows:

(1) The mycelia of almost all fungi are populated with haploid nuclei (oomycetes are atypically diploid), and many fungi form large numbers of uninucleate, haploid spores. These can be used to study naturally occurring or induced mutations.

(2) The hyphae of closely related eumycotan fungi can fuse with one another locally during normal assimilative growth (anastomosis), exchanging nuclei and thereby producing **heterokaryons** (mycelia containing genetically different nuclei).

The heterokaryotic condition confers great flexibility on many conidial fungi, helping them to cope with different substrates and conditions. Heterokaryons can be investigated under controlled conditions by isolating spores or hyphal fragments, and are used by geneticists in the complementation test (see below). The production of heterokaryons may also be an essential step toward a long- delayed sexual fusion, as when basidiomycetes initiate dikaryotization by anastomosis between sexually compatible mycelia.

3) Hyphal fusions also lead to exchange of cytoplasm, producing heteroplasmons. These make it possible to study extranuclear genetic phenomena, and the fungi are particularly valuable for the investigation of cytoplasmic inheritance.

(4) The phenomenon of **crossing-over**, a vital part of the process of genetic recombination, can be most elegantly studied in ascomycetes like *Neurospora* or *Sordaria*. These fungi have very short life cycles, and conveniently arrange the 8 nuclei resulting from meiosis and the subsequent mitosis in a linear sequence within the ascus. One nucleus goes into each ascospore, and the ascospores are arranged in single file within the narrowly cylindrical ascus. The ascospores in this 'ordered tetrad' can be individually cultured and tested in various ways. Using appropriate marker genes: (a) first-division segregation can be distinguished from second-division segregation; (b) reciprocal and non-reciprocal chromosomal exchanges can be detected; (c) chromosomes can be mapped; (d) interference can be studied. (All the terms just mentioned are discussed in more detail below).

(5) The phenomenon of **somatic crossing-over** was first seen in the fruit fly, *Drosophila*, but it can be much more easily studied in fungi. Somatic nuclear fusions occur, with low but predictable frequency in fungal heterokaryons. The resulting diploid nuclei occasionally undergo mitotic crossover. Some of the somatic diploid nuclei which have undergone mitotic crossover can revert to the

haploid condition through irregular forms of mitosis. These haploid nuclei have thus undergone genetic recombination without benefit of sex. The process is called **parasexuality**. Thanks to their production of large numbers of uninucleate spores expressing specific genetic markers (e.g. colour, or nutritional deficiencies), conidial fungi such as *Aspergillus nidulans* are especially well suited for investigations of this phenomenon.

(6) Fungi can be handled rather like bacteria—many pure cultures can be stored in a small space, and the generation time is short—yet fungi are eukaryotic, so results are much more applicable to the other major kingdoms, animals and plants.

Fungal genetics is not without its difficulties. Fungal nuclei are often very small, and we cannot do the kind of analysis of chromosomal arrangement at the metaphase stage of nuclear division that is possible in many plants and animals. The small size of conidia, ascospores and basidiospores makes them difficult to handle individually, and the necessity for sterile technique to avoid contamination doesn't make things any easier. But with practice, all these handling difficulties can be overcome. Fungi have been widely used to study recombination and gene action. But they have been little exploited in studies of population genetics. This may be partly because it is often hard to decide what a fungal individual is: it has such a diffuse 'body,' and through anastomosis the mycelia of eumycotan fungi often become heterokaryotic, containing nuclear material from several different genomes. Nevertheless, the potential for such studies remains, and is beginning to be exploited in studies of biological species complexes such as that represented by the binomial '*Armillaria mellea.*'

Investigating Crossing-over in a Fungus using Marker Genes

Crossing-over is a normal part of the major process called meiosis. As meiosis begins, the diploid cell has two sets of chromosomes. Each chromosome has already replicated itself, and so is composed of two parallel strands or **chromatids**. Each chromosome comes to lie parallel to the same (homologous) chromosome from the other set: in Fig. 10.1 the two 'white' chromatids represent one homologous chromosome, and the two 'black' ones, the other. If we assume that the 'black' chromatids carry a gene for dark-coloured ascospores, and the 'white' chromatids carry a different allele of the same gene, one that will produce light-coloured ascospores, then Fig. 10.1 A shows what happens in the absence of crossing-over, and Fig 10.1 B shows what transpires when a crossover occurs.

In the simplest crossover, shown in Fig. 10.1 B, a break occurs at the same place in one of the 'white' chromatids and one of the 'black' chromatids. The ends rejoin, but in a new arrangement: the part of the 'black' chromatid carrying the dark ascospore gene is now joined to part of a 'white' chromatid and vice versa. When the four chromatids separate, they will represent new combinations of genes. As you can see in Fig. 10.2, multiple crossovers can happen between the two homologous chromosomes. This strange but vitally important process of genetic recombination accounts for the unpredictable mixes of parental genes that occur in the offspring of sexual eukaryotes. Crossing-over ensures that sexually reproducing organisms vary in many ways, and so remain physiologically flexible. Crossing-over is one of the main mechanisms involved in providing the pool of variability on which natural selection acts.

If we have appropriate marker genes, like the ascospore colour gene just mentioned, we can use the incidence of crossing-over to find out roughly where these genes are in relation to the **centromere** (the point at which the chromatids are functionally joined, and the last thing to separate at mitosis). How can we do this? We begin by assuming that a chromosome is equally likely to break anywhere along its length. If this is true, then the further away from the centromere a marker gene is, the more likely it is to be involved in a crossover. Also, if we have two linked marker genes, the further apart they are on a chromosome, the more likely they are to be separated by a crossover. This kind of information allows us to make chromosome maps showing the relative (though not the absolute) locations of our marker genes.

Our map-making rests on the assumption that we can keep track of the products of meiosis. In most organisms we simply cannot recover and analyze all the nuclei arising from one meiosis. But this useful trick is possible in some ascomycetes, because their meiosis takes place in a long, narrow tube called an ascus. Fig. 10.1 shows how the products of the divisions lie in a linear sequence, so that their exact origin can be traced. The example I gave above involving light and dark coloured ascospores is in fact a real one. In *Sordaria fimicola*, ascospore colour is determined by a single gene. Wild-type ascospores are dark, but there is a mutant strain with pale spores. Since *Sordaria fimicola* is heterothallic (outbreeding), the mating of a normal dark-spored strain with a mutant pale-spored strain can be used to demonstrate some features of crossing-over. In this particular mating, if no crossover involving the ascospore colour gene has happened, there will be four dark ascospores at one end of the ascus, four light ones at the other end, as in Fig. 10.1 A. But if the segment of chromosome bearing the colour gene has been crossed-over, then each half of the ascus will contain a pair of light spores and a pair of dark ones, as shown in Fig. 10.1 B. These pairs can appear in several different sequences, depending on which of the chromatids undergo crossing-over. Crossovers can take place between any two of the homologous chromatids, so there are four possibilities for single crossovers: 1-3, 1-4, 2-3, 2-4.

In fact, crossing-over can be even more complex than I have just described, because it can happen twice between a particular pair of chromatids; or one chromatid can exchange segments with both of its homologues. Some of these possibilities are shown in Fig. 10.2. Of course, we can't watch these events, but we can explain the ascospore arrangements resulting from crosses between strains with two marker genes by diagrams like Fig. 10.2. Not all genes express themselves so immediately and unequivocally as that determining ascospore colour, but the process of segregation works just the same for any gene. In order to analyze other kinds of markers which don't express themselves visibly in the ascospore, we have to physically pick out the ascospores (this calls for great dexterity and lots of practice), and grow them individually in culture. The sequence of the spores inside the ascus is recorded, and helps in the interpretation of the subsequent genetic analysis.

As we have already seen, if no crossing-over happens between a particular gene and the centromere, the four ascospores at one end of the ascus will all be of one genotype, and the four at the other end will all be of the other genotype. This arrangement is called the first division segregation pattern because the two versions of the gene separate at first division meiosis (see Fig. 10.1 A). But if crossing-over has happened between the gene and the centromere, the two different versions of the gene are not separated until the second division of meiosis, as can be seen in Fig. 10.1 B. This arrangement is called a second division segregation pattern, and, as I have shown, there can be four such patterns, which occur with about equal frequency. Any particular gene will show a definite frequency of crossing-over, which naturally increases as its distance from the centromere increases. The recombination frequency for any gene will equal half of its frequency of crossing-over. This is because only two of the four chromatids are involved in any particular crossover. If we observe a squashed perithecium, and find that of 20 asci, 8 show evidence of crossing-over in the ascospore colour gene, we can say that the frequency of crossing-over for our marker gene is 40%, and the recombination frequency is 20%. That figure is also a useful way of placing the marker gene on a chromosome map. One map unit is arbitrarily defined as the distance between linked genes (genes on the same chromatid) that will give 1% recombination. The gene mentioned above is 20 map units from the centromere. If a second marker gene has a recombination frequency of 30%, this

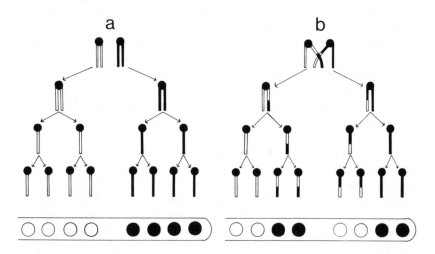

Fig. 10.1 (a) no crossing-over = first division segregation pattern; (b) crossing-over between ascospore colour gene and centromere = second division segregation pattern (see text).

means that it is 10 map units further from the centromere than the first marker. It could be only 10 map units from that first marker, but it could also be 50 map units away, on the other side of the centromere.

With patience and dexterity, a two-factor cross can be done with the ascomycete, *Neurospora crassa* (Sordariales), using two linked marker genes (with alleles A and a, B and b). Three main ascospore patterns will emerge. (1) The parental ditype, AB AB AB AB ab ab ab ab: if there is no crossing-over between the two marker genes, the two tetrads of ascospores will reflect the characteristics of the respective parents. (2) The tetratype pattern, e.g. AB AB Ab Ab aB aB ab ab: when a single crossover happens somewhere between the two marker genes, four kinds of ascospore result, two parental types and two recombinants. (3) The non-parental ditype, Ab Ab Ab Ab aB aB aB aB: if two crossovers occur between the marker genes, all the products will be reciprocal recombinants, arranged in two tetrads. None of the products have the same combination of genes as either of the parents. The relative frequencies of these three patterns can be used to calculate the linkage distance between the two marker genes, and to deduce their positions relative to each other and the centromere.

It can also be used to discover which of the two markers is closer to the centromere, and whether the markers are on the same or opposite sides of the centromere. For example, we analyze the ascospore arrangements resulting from a two-factor cross, and find that there are 56 parental ditype asci, 44 tetratype asci, and 0 non-parental ditype asci. What can we deduce from these data? If the marker genes were unlinked (i.e. not on the same chromosome), the frequency of parental ditype and non-parental ditype asci would be expected to be the same. Since no non-parental ditype asci are recorded, we can assume that the two markers are linked (i.e., on the same chromosome). In order to be able to place the markers in their correct relationship to each other and the centromere, we need to analyze the 44 tetratype asci further. We note that there are three arrangements:

> (i) 24 are AB AB Ab Ab aB aB ab ab
>
> (ii) 19 are AB AB ab ab AB AB ab ab
>
> (iii) 1 is AB AB aB aB Ab Ab ab ab

The marker genes could theoretically be arranged in one of three ways with respect to the centromere:

> (*I*) Centromere—Aa—Bb
>
> (*II*) Centromere—Bb—Aa
>
> (*III*) Aa—Centromere—Bb

Ascospore pattern (i) above is a result of first-division segregation of the Aa marker, and second-division segregation of the Bb marker (the B and b alleles have been exchanged, the A and a alleles haven't). The crossover that produced this arrangement must have happened between the Bb gene and the centromere, but not between the Aa gene and the centromere. If the two markers are on the same side of the centromere, Aa must be closer to the centromere than is Bb (gene arrangement *I*). But ascospore pattern (i) could also be explained by gene arrangement (///), in which the marker genes are on opposite sides of the centromere. So far, only gene arrangement (//) can be ruled out. However, if we now look at ascospore pattern (ii), it is clear that both Aa and Bb segregated at second division. If we assume there was only a single crossover, this means that it must have taken place nearer to the centromere than either Aa or Bb, and between the centromere and both markers. So both marker genes must be on the same side of the centromere, and gene arrangement (///) can be excluded.

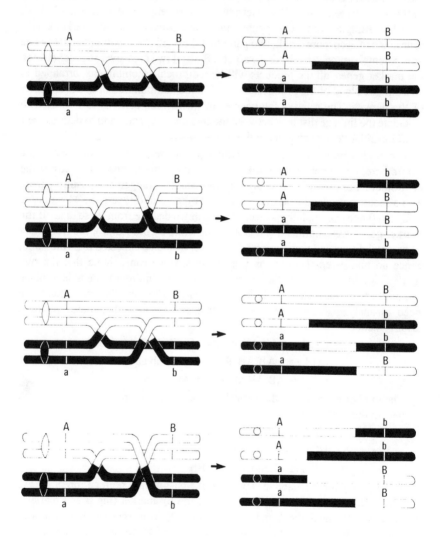

Fig. 10.2 Consequences of various double crossovers between two marker genes.

So, by a process of elimination, we have shown that only one of the three possible gene arrangements, (i) Centromere—Aa—Bb, fits all the observed facts. Even the 'oddball' ascospore pattern (iii) can be explained by a two-chromatid double crossover, between Aa and the centromere, and between Aa and Bb (you can easily work this out on paper: it is not one of the examples shown in Fig. 10.2, but can be visualized if the uppermost example is revamped with the crossover nearest the centromere happening between Aa and the centromere, rather than between Aa and Bb).

We can now calculate the 'map distances' of the marker genes from each other and from the centromere. Of the 100 asci examined, 25 (patterns i + iii) had a crossover between Aa and Bb, while 20 (patterns ii + iii) had a crossover between the centromere and Aa. Applying the appropriate formula (half the number of recombinants, divided by the total asci observed, multiplied by 100), we find that the distance between Aa and Bb is 12.5 map units, and the distance between the centromere and Aa is 10 map units.

Interference occurs when crossing-over at one point reduces the chance of another crossover in nearby regions of the chromosome. This phenomenon is detected by studying crossovers of three or more linked genes. Since the centromere itself acts as a marker, we have essentially a three-gene system in tetrad analysis, which is therefore a good way of studying interference.

The events discussed above involved truly reciprocal crossovers, in which exactly equivalent segments of chromatids are exchanged. But sometimes the exchange is not exactly equal. This is called non-reciprocal recombination, or gene conversion, and if very closely linked marker genes are studied, it is found that crossovers are actually more often non-reciprocal than reciprocal. This phenomenon is explained by the breakdown or excision of short lengths of DNA during recombination, and their replacement by replication from another chromatid. Once again, fungi like *Neurospora* have been very useful in elucidating gene conversion.

Mutant genes can act as markers enabling us to investigate the genetics of fungi. The kinds of mutant genes available affect such features as morphology, colour, mating type, and nutritional requirements. In some morphological mutants, the growth rate or branching pattern of hyphae is altered, with various effects on colony morphology. *Neurospora crassa* has 'button' and 'ropy' mutants. Other morphological mutations affect reproductive structures: *Aspergillus nidulans* has 'stunted' conidiophore, and 'bristle,' in which the conidiophore has no conidium-producing apparatus at its apex. Colour mutants usually affect spore colour: *Aspergillus niger* has 'white,' 'fawn' and 'olive' mutants.

Biochemical mutants are perhaps the most useful markers. Biochemical mutants usually require some nutrient that is not needed by the wild type. Such mutants are called **auxotrophs**. A minimal medium is concocted for the wild type (for *Neurospora crassa* this contains only inorganic salts, including a nitrogen source, sucrose, biotin and agar). Samples of the fungus are exposed to a mutagenic agent such as ultraviolet light, then plated out on the minimal medium and also on a complete medium, which contains malt extract and yeast extract in addition to the ingredients listed for the minimal medium. If a strain is found that will grow on complete medium, but not on minimal medium, some biochemical deficiency is suspected. Now a little detective work is called for. This strain must be systematically tested to see what it needs, by attempting to grow it on minimal medium with additions of mixed vitamins, or mixed amino acids, or nucleic acids. If the minimal medium plus mixed vitamins keep it alive, then it is grown on minimal medium supplemented with individual vitamins. In this way the specific requirement of the auxotroph can be pinpointed.

Fermentation mutants arise spontaneously in yeasts, resulting in inability to ferment a particular sugar. Resistance mutants also arise spontaneously in wild populations, but their frequency of occurrence increases if the organisms are exposed to antibiotics, antimetabolites or other deleterious influences: such mutants are actively sought in the laboratory. The fungus is grown in a concentration of the deleterious substance high enough to inhibit normal growth: resistant mutants are the only ones to survive. Suppressor mutants overcome or compensate for any deficiency induced by an earlier mutation, and cause an apparent reversion to the wild-type. Physiological mutants apparently change the biochemistry of the fungus subtly, altering its reactions to some environmental influence, such as temperature or light. One mutant of the zygomycete, *Phycomyces blakesleeanus*, has normal morphology, but its sporangiophores no longer grow toward the light.

Another group of biochemical mutants are those which produce greater than normal amounts of particular substances. Although this kind of mutant hasn't been subjected to very much genetic analysis, it is sometimes economically important. The commercially exploited strains of *Penicillium chrysogenum* that produce such large amounts of penicillin are mutants of this kind.

One Sex, Two Sexes, Many Sexes

Sexual reproduction will introduce more genetic variation to a population if the genomes which meet, and are then reassorted during meiosis, come from different individuals. That statement may sound strange and even superfluous to you, since you belong to a species in which such behaviour is not only natural, but obligatory. But in many cases, an individual fungal mycelium can and does keep its sexuality to itself: its hyphae can produce sex organs of both kinds which go through the processes of sexual fusion and produce a viable zygote. This condition is described as **homothallism**. Homothallic taxa are very useful if we simply want to demonstrate sexual behaviour in fungi, since we don't have to worry about providing a suitable mate. The advantage of this system in Nature is probably two-fold: to permit sexual reproduction when no appropriate compatible mycelium can be found (the lonely spore hypothesis), and to perpetuate particularly successful genotypes, which would tend to be reassorted, and therefore diluted, by outbreeding.

Many fungi, however, have evolved some form of reproductive differentiation of individual mycelia: we call this phenomenon **heterothallism**, and it enforces outbreeding. One approach is sexual dimorphism: the production of two kinds of sexual structure which look and act differently, and are often developed on different mycelia. In some fungi, both kinds of sex organ can be formed by a single mycelium, but only gametes originating from different mycelia can fuse. This implies genetic control of sexual reproduction through the development of mating types that incorporate incompatibility genes. These make sex impossible between strains of the same mating type. In many fungi, mycelia may be morphologically indistinguishable, yet invisible incompatibility factors can prevent their mating. Incompatibility can prevent anastomosis, or prevent karyogamy. In fungi like the ascomycetes, where fusion of assimilative hyphae does not initiate the sexual process, vegetative incompatibility is not a barrier to sexual reproduction, and is often determined by entirely separate genes, so that a single species may be divided up into a number of vegetative compatibility groups (VCGs). Such ascomycetous taxa as *Cryphonectria parasitica* (Diaporthales), *Neurospora crassa* (Sordariales), and *Fusarium moniliforme* (anamorphic Hypocreales), contain many VCGs. In the basidiomycetes, where fusion of ordinary, undifferentiated assimilative hyphae is a prerequisite to the establishment of the dikaryophase, and dikaryotization a prerequisite of karyogamy, vegetative incompatibility can effectively prevent sexual reproduction.

Basically, heterothallism implies that a haploid nucleus can complete the life cycle only if it mates with another haploid nucleus carrying a different mating-type factor. Heterothallism is the fungal equivalent of the separate sexes found in many plants and animals. As we shall see, the fungi, despite their restricted genome and relatively consistent organization, have evolved many and complex variations on this sexual theme.

The simplest kind of genetic system that can ensure outbreeding consists of two different alleles, which we can label 'A' and 'a,' at the same locus. Pairs of mycelia carrying the same allele will be incompatible (A with A, or a with a), while pairs of mycelia with different alleles (A and a) will be compatible. This system effectively divides a population into two categories, and has the same effect as division into two sexes. This two-allele system is found in all groups of fungi other than the most highly evolved basidiomycetes. Examples are the zygomycetes, *Rhizopus* and *Phycomyces*, species of the ascomycete genera *Neurospora*, *Ascobolus* and *Sclerotinia*, and species of the teliomycete genera *Puccinia* and *Ustilago*.

In Aphyllophorales, Agaricales and gasteromycetous basidiomycetes, compatibility is determined by one or two genes, each of which may have many different alleles. Only two or four alleles are present in any given dikaryon, at a single locus or at two loci. If all compatibility alleles occur interchangeably at one locus, the mating system of the fungus is called **bipolar**; if they are found at two loci, the mating system is called **tetrapolar**. If the alleles occur at a single locus, the offspring of a single basidioma will be of two different mating types. If the alleles are at two loci, offspring of a single basidioma will be of four mating types. Although the products of meiosis in the basidiomycetes are not an ordered tetrad, as they are in the cylindrical asci of some ascomycetes, it is still possible to culture the four basidiospores arising from an individual meiosis, and use them in compatibility trials.

In bipolar fungi (most smuts, some gasteromycetes, *Coprinus comatus*), the single locus at which all compatibility alleles occur can be called A. Now we can label the alleles in a given dikaryon: A1 A2 (they must be different, or the dikaryon wouldn't form in the first place). Other dikaryons will probably have different alleles, which we can call A3 A4, A5 A6, etc. Random matings in populations with such diverse mating-type alleles can be almost 100% successful. Remember that random matings in populations of 2-allele organisms would be only 50% successful. Now we can see why a multiple-allele system may be more desirable than a two-allele system.

In tetrapolar fungi (most Aphyllophorales, Agaricales and gasteromycetes), we can label the two loci A and B. For a dikaryon to be fertile, the alleles at each of the loci must be different—we can label them A1 B1 A2 B2. The haploid (monokaryotic) mycelia derived from this dikaryon will be of four kinds: A1 B1, A2 B2, A1 B2, and A2 B1. You can easily work out that only 25% of random matings among these siblings will be successful. Of course, matings of non-sibling monokaryons will again work much better: if we match up the four genotypes just listed with monokaryons derived from a dikaryon that is A3 B3 A4 B4, success should be complete. But what if the allele at one of the loci is the same as in our original strain, so that its alleles can be listed as A1 B3 A4 B4? What should be the percentage success of matings between this and the products of this and the original strain (A1 B1 A2 B2)? Work it out on paper. Your answer (which should be 50%) represents the number of fertile dikaryons that will result. But if you did this experiment, you would probably find that you finished up with many more dikaryons than you expected. This is because dikaryons can form between partially incompatible monokaryons, though such dikaryons will not be able to produce fruit bodies. In the example I just gave, there could be as many as 87.5% dikaryons (37.5% of them sterile), and only 12.5% total incompatibility.

It has been found that the genes at the two loci often control different parts of the dikaryotization process. In the basidiomycetes, *Coprinus lagopus* and *Schizophyllum commune*, clamp connections develop only if the dikaryon is heterozygous (has different alleles) for the A locus. For example, A1 B1 A2 B1 would have hyphae with clamps, A1 B1 A1 B2 would not. Nuclear migration is controlled by the B locus, and would fail in A1 B1 A2 B1.

Of 230 species of Aphyllophorales, Agaricales and gasteromycetes examined, 10-15% were homothallic, about 35% were bipolar heterothallic, and about 55% tetrapolar heterothallic. It has been estimated that *Schizophyllum commune* probably has about 340 + 120 different A alleles, and 64 + 12 different B alleles. Estimates in some other basidiomycetes are of the order of 100 different alleles for each locus, though the bird's-nest fungi, *Cyathus striatus* and *Crucibulum vulgare*, are believed to have only about 10 alleles for each locus.

Secondary homothallism can occur in heterothallic fungi. If an ascus contains only four spores, as in *Neurospora tetrasperma*, instead of eight, there can be a compatible pair of nuclei in each spore. Similarly, if a basidium bears only two spores, as in *Agaricus brunnescens*, each of these may also contain two compatible nuclei. Homothallism is possible, even in species with four-spored basidia. If an extra mitosis happens in the basidia, two compatible nuclei may find their way into some of the basidiospores.

Homothallism can also be introduced in what would otherwise be a heterothallic fungus by mating-type switching. In addition to the functional mating type allele at the active locus, *Saccharomyces cerevisiae* has 'silent' copies of mating-type alleles at two other loci. A site-specific endonuclease cuts the double stranded DNA at the active locus. The resulting gap is then repaired by splicing in DNA from one of the loci at which the silent copies reside. This often means that one allele is replaced by the other, so the mating-type of the organism is switched. Similar switching occurs in another yeast, *Schizosaccharomyces pombe*, and in the filamentous ascomycetes, *Sclerotinia trifoliorum*, *Chromocrea spinulosa*, and *Glomerella cingulata*, though the mechanism is still obscure in those fungi. The switching in *Chromocrea* and *Sclerotinia* happens in only one direction. If the mechanisms involved are like that found in *Saccharomyces*, it is likely that only one of the mating-type alleles is present in a silent form. We do not yet know how much fungal homothallism can be accounted for by mating-type switching. In some fungi, self-sterile spores with a single nucleus, and self-fertile spores with two nuclei, are both developed in the same fruit body. This kind of mating behaviour is called amphithallism.

Recognizing the existence of compatibility genes is one thing, understanding how they work is another. The best-documented compatibility system is that of the yeast, *Saccharomyces cerevisiae*. Here there is a single locus with two alleles. Each mating type secretes a constitutive polypeptide pheromone which causes cells of the opposite mating type to become arrested in the G1 stage of the cell cycle. Such arrested cells agglutinate and undergo plasmogamy and karyogamy. If the resultant diploid cells are starved, they will undergo meiosis and produce haploid meiospores. Each stage of this process is apparently under the control of mating-type genes. These genes are regulated by DNA binding proteins encoded by the mating-type alleles. One of the alleles contains a unique sequence of 747 base pairs, and encodes two regulatory polypeptides. The other allele has a unique sequence of 642 base pairs, and encodes two polypeptides, of which only one is known to be regulatory. The mating-type genes of other fungi are currently being isolated and characterized, and we should soon know how representative *S. cerevisiae* really is. It will be a tremendous challenge to explain how the hundreds of separate alleles we know to exist in some individual basidiomycete taxa differ, and are regulated.

Intersterility

Compatible mating-types are not always enough to ensure successful sex. Sometimes, mating fails despite apparent compatibility. There is therefore another genetic system, which we can call an intersterility system, that can override the usual incompatibility system. Unfortunately, we don't know nearly as much about the basis of this system as we do about incompatibility. The kinds of barriers involved are either prezygotic, preventing fertilization, or postzygotic, resulting in hybrids of reduced fertility or meiotic offspring less fit than the parents.

Prezygotic barriers exist between closely related populations of many well-known basidiomycetes, including *Armillaria, Collybia, Coprinus, Laccaria, Paxillus, Pleurotus, Ganoderma* and *Heterobasidion*. Since intersterility is usually complete, particularly in sympatric populations, the intersterile groups are equivalent to biological species. In some of these fungi, DNA reassociation or DNA restriction fragment patterns have shown that the intersterile groups are also genomically divergent. Sometimes two entirely intersterile sympatric populations are partly interfertile with a third population from another area. We do not yet know whether this third population could act as bridge between the other two solitudes. In *Ustilago cynodontis* intersterile populations and partly interfertile 'bridging' strains coexist within what appears to be a single complex species.

Postzygotic barriers are present when mating occurs, but most of the resulting spores are not viable. In closely related heterothallic *Neurospora* species, the reproductive barriers appear to be mostly postzygotic. Intraspecific crosses yield viable ascospores, but interspecific crosses produce largely non-viable ascospores.

Parasexuality

Ascomycetes and basidiomycetes can be easily distinguished when they reproduce sexually. In this phase (the teleomorph) they form characteristic fruiting bodies (ascomata and basidiomata) bearing unique meiosporangia (asci and basidia) from which, as we have seen, the products of a single meiotic event can be isolated and analyzed. Many of these fungi reproduce asexually as well, producing what are called anamorphs, which form mitospores called conidia, and often occur well separated in time and space from the teleomorph. In fact, we know thousands of anamorphs which have not yet been persuaded to metamorphose into a teleomorph. Many of these go on, generation after generation, in the asexual condition, and it now appears highly probable that many of them have entirely lost the ability to produce a teleomorph, thus becoming anamorphic holomorphs.

We know that one of the most vital functions performed by the teleomorph is genetic recombination. This reassortment of the gene pool during meiosis broadens the ability of the population to cope with the stresses imposed by changing environments. Conidial fungi, which are often highly opportunistic, and grow on a wide range of substrates, might seem to be especially in need of the flexibility conferred by genetic recombination. One of their responses to this perceived need for genetic diversification is to become heterokaryotic: to acquire more than one kind of nucleus as a result of one or more anastomoses. But we now know that they have also evolved a special mechanism for generating some genetic recombination without sex. We call this process, parasexuality. The parasexual cycle has three stages. (1) Fusion (anastomosis) of adjacent somatic hyphae, and exchange of nuclei, establishing a heterokaryon. (2) Fusion of different nuclei in the vegetative hyphae, to form somatic diploids. (3) Somatic recombination (mitotic crossing-over). (4) non-meiotic reduction of the altered nuclei via aneuploidy (loss of individual chromosomes) to the haploid condition. This sequence of events is rare, happening in fewer than one conidium in a million, but the number of conidia produced by most conidial anamorphs is astronomical, so parasexuality is a practical means for producing genetic variation. We don't yet know how widespread this phenomenon is among the conidial fungi, but it has been detected in species of *Aspergillus, Acremonium, Fusarium* and *Verticillium*, and is probably common.

It is worthwhile to compare sexuality and parasexuality. (1) Sexual reproduction is a highly organized, often precisely timed process, which is genetically programmed. Parasexuality involves a rare sequence of uncommon events which seems to operate by chance, rather than by design. (2) In sexual reproduction, nuclear fusion is often mediated by genetic factors, expressed as 'mating types,' happens in highly specific structures, and often involves many pairs of compatible nuclei. In the parasexual cycle, nuclear fusion is an isolated event, not mediated by mating-type factors, not found in specialized structures, and involving only individual nuclei. (3) During meiosis, crossing-over probably takes place in every homologous pair of chromosomes, and multiple crossovers are common. During somatic recombination, crossing-over commonly involves only one or a few chromosomes, and never happens as often as during meiosis. (4) In meiosis, segregation happens in a highly organized way during two specialized nuclear divisions. Somatic haploidization probably occurs as a result of successive chromosome losses from an aneuploid nucleus (2n-1) over several mitotic divisions until the stable haploid is reached.

The factors that initiate sexual reproduction vary enormously from one fungus to the next, presumably because of their diverse ecological adaptations, so it is very difficult to make generalizations, though special media have been concocted to persuade such important genetic tools as *Neurospora* to undergo sexual reproduction on demand. The parasexual cycle can be encouraged in various ways. Camphor vapour selects for somatic diploids in some fungi. In species with uninucleate conidia, the best approach is to produce a heterokaryon between two auxotrophic mutants (each of which has a different biochemical deficiency), then grow its conidia on minimal medium. Neither of the original auxotrophs will be able to grow, but diploid conidia will grow, since the chromosomes from one parent compensate for the deficiency in the other set, and vice versa (this is called complementation, and the diploid is described as being prototrophic). This technique has been used in *Verticillium albo-atrum, Aspergillus niger*, and *Aspergillus nidulans*, and yields about one diploid conidium in 10^6-10^7 conidia. The subsequent frequency of mitotic recombination can be increased by X-rays, U/V, mitomycin and nitrous acid. Finally, to complete the cycle, low concentrations of p-fluorophenylalanine or benlate stimulate haploidization.

We can see the potential advantages of the parasexual cycle to an asexual fungus, but is it of any use to the geneticist? As it happens, it can be used to determine linkage groups, the order of genes, and the position of the centromere. The genetic recombination achieved is on a much smaller scale than in meiosis: only one or two chromosomes are involved, and the possibility of multiple crossovers is so low that it can be ignored. This means that linkage analysis is much easier. The original diploids are heterozygous for the various marker genes. Those in which crossing-over subsequently occurs will become homozygous for any marker genes that are distal to the point of crossover. The relative frequencies with which such markers become homozygous is an indication of their relative distances from the centromere.

Extranuclear Inheritance

Some genetic phenomena can't be explained by reference to nuclear or chromosomal events. The logical corollary of this is that the determinants may be transmitted in cytoplasm rather than in nuclei. In some heterothallic fungi, the volume of cytoplasm that accompanies one of the nuclei during a sexual fusion may be much greater than that associated with the other nucleus. Alternatively, if one side of the fusion involves a microconidium or a spermatium, this must inevitably bring much less cytoplasm to the union than does the receiving partner. This sometimes results in the offspring resembling the parent that contributed more cytoplasm, and implies the existence of cytoplasmic genes. It has been shown that in *Aspergillus glaucus*, attributes such as spore germination, growth rate, pigmentation, and density of perithecia, are under cytoplasmic control. A well-known example of cytoplasmic control is the 'poky' mutant of *Neurospora crassa*. This grows more slowly than the wild-type, and cannot be speeded up by dietary supplements. If 'poky' is crossed with the wild-type, the poky condition is transmitted only when the 'poky' strain forms the perithecium initial, which means that it is essentially the maternal parent.

Another well-known example of extranuclear inheritance is the petite strain of *Saccharomyces cerevisiae*, which arises with a frequency of about 1 cell in 500. Such cells give rise to smaller than normal colonies, which can respire only anaerobically, even when oxygen is present. This deficiency is due to the absence of important respiratory enzymes such as cytochrome oxidase and succinic dehydrogenase. The mitochondria are defective. Whole colonies can be converted to 'petite' cells by growing them on medium containing 3 ppm acriflavine. Diploid petite cells don't reproduce sexually, but diploid hybrids derived from petite and normal haploid cells respire aerobically and can form ascus-like meiosporangia. If the meiospores are cultured, all are normal, and petite cells arise among their offspring only in the ordinary 1:500 ratio. Normal yeast cells contain cytoplasmic genes (in mitochondria) controlling the synthesis of respiratory enzymes. Petites arise by mutations in the mitochondrial DNA. When a cell containing this cytoplasmic mutant fuses with a normal haploid cell, the extranuclear genes from the normal cell render the resulting diploid normal again, and normal mitochondria find their way into any resultant haploid cells, which will all therefore be normal.

Genetics and Plant Pathology

Plant breeders try to produce, not only higher-yielding varieties of crop and garden plants, but also new disease-resistant strains. This is done by finding natural defence mechanisms that are present in wild relatives of the economically important host plant. Painstakingly, the plant breeders introduce the resistance genes to the crop plants. Although such new cultivars may be immune to a particular fungal disease for a few years, eventually a new race of the fungal pathogen appears which can overcome the resistance of the plant. Analysis of this endlessly repetitive cycle of resistance and susceptibility led to the theory of the gene-for-gene relationship between host and pathogen. This suggests that the evolutionary paths of host and pathogen have been so closely linked for so long, that for every gene in the host that is capable of mutating to give resistance, there is a corresponding gene in the pathogen which can mutate to overcome that resistance.

Table 10.1
Interactions of races of *Cladosporium fulvum* with three tomato varieties

Tomato with resistance gene	*Cladosporium* races							
	0	1	2	3	1+2	1+3	2+3	1+2+3
1	R	S	R	R	S	S	R	S
2	R	R	S	R	S	R	S	S
3	R	R	R	S	R	S	S	S

Cladosporium (Fulvia) fulvum, a hyphomycete, causes leaf mould of tomato. Three genes that confer resistance to this fungus are known, and tomato varieties exist which carry none, one, two, or all three of these genes. With the aid of these host varieties, eight races of *Cladosporium fulvum* can be discriminated. The most efficient way to differentiate these races is with three tomato varieties which have, respectively, resistance genes 1, 2 and 3, as can be seen from Table 10.1. If you examine the eight columns which give the responses of the three tomato varieties to the different fungal races, you will see that each column differs from all the others. This means that any of the eight races can be identified by testing it against only three tomato varieties. That is how prevalence and spread of many important plant pathogenic fungi is monitored. It is also the mechanism by which the existence of new physiologic races of pathogens is discovered. The more genes for resistance we recognize, the more pathogenic races can be distinguished. Almost 200 races of the flax rust fungus, *Melampsora lini*, have been identified by their reactions with 18 host varieties. *Puccinia graminis* subsp.

tritici, which causes wheat rust, has well over 200 races, and the number is growing steadily in response to the efforts of the plant breeders.

The genetics of resistance have also been explored in *Venturia inaequalis*, the apple scab fungus, which is a bitunicate ascomycete. It was found that the genes controlling virulence exist in virulent and avirulent alleles, which segregate regularly in the ascus. Seven of these genes were discovered, and seven apple varieties were found that would enable their presence to be recognized. For example, the avirulent allele of gene 1 didn't affect MacIntosh apples (which might simply mean that MacIntosh carried a corresponding gene for resistance to that allele). Yellow Transparent apple was resistant, not only to avirulent 1, but also to the avirulent alleles of genes 3 and 4. Each of the seven apple varieties had a different resistance gene or genes, which could be identified by exposing the host to various races of *V. inaequalis*.

The natural testing ground for resistance of potatoes to the late blight fungus, *Phytophthora infestans* (Oomycota) is central Mexico, where both sexes of the fungus are present, and new physiologic races can arise more readily than elsewhere. Working in this environment, potato breeders have found it more useful to aim for 'field resistance,' which is mediated by many genes with small individual effects, rather than concentrating on a few major resistance genes with all-or-none effects. The war goes on.

Recombinant DNA and Gene Cloning in Fungi

Since fungi have not been among the most important contributors to our knowledge of DNA and how it works, I will not burden you with the usual spiel on DNA, its functions and its replication: you can get that from any first year Biology text book. In addition, for an overview of recombinant DNA technology, you should refer to 'Gene Cloning: an Introduction' Second Edition, by T.A. Brown, published by Chapman and Hall (1990). However, although fungal DNA is essentially the same as that of animals and plants, it is present in relatively much smaller quantities: the fungal genome is only about six to ten times larger than that of the bacterium, *Escherichia coli*, having about 2.6-4.3 X 10^4 kilobases (kb). Repetitive DNA makes up less than 20% of the nuclear genome. Most fungal DNA is found in normal eukaryotic chromosomes, but there is also a circular mitochondrial chromosome of about 30-200 kb, mitochondrial plasmids, and often some small, supernumerary chromosomes in the nucleus, which do not appear to be essential for survival.

The techniques of molecular biology have not only given us a great deal of detailed information about the genetic material, and even the actual sequence of base pairs which make up parts of the genomic DNA, but also permit the movement of genetic material from one organism to another, and the expression of certain genes from one organism in another. I will set the scene by outlining the processes involved in moving genes from one organism to another. Recombinant DNA technology usually involves the following steps. (1) Cells of a host (often the bacterium *Escherichia coli*) are broken, and their DNA extracted. (2) This DNA includes **plasmids**, small closed rings of extrachromosomal DNA, which may be used as vectors for the introduction of foreign DNA. The vectors are separated from the other DNA by ultracentrifugation. (3) Special enzymes called restriction endonucleases cleave the plasmid vectors, and leave them as linear sequences of DNA with 'sticky' ends (unpaired bases). (4) DNA from the donor organism (the source of the desired gene) is isolated and then treated with the same restriction endonucleases, producing additional linear sequences with sticky ends that match those of the cleaved plasmids. (5) Vector DNA and donor DNA are mixed: sticky ends rejoin, by complementary base pairing, in various configurations—vector ends re-join, vector joins donor, donor joins donor. In a few cases the desired joinings happen, producing a closed loop, which is part vector DNA, part donor DNA. (6) The sugar-phosphate backbone of the DNA is then properly repaired by an enzyme called a DNA ligase. (7) The modified vectors are mixed with *E. coli* made permeable by treatment with a calcium salt. This allows some of the bacteria to pick up modified vectors, and so be transformed. (8) The transformed cells that bear the desired donor gene can now be isolated, with the help of selectable marker genes previously incorporated in the vector, and can subsequently be propagated on a large scale.

Why are yeasts and filamentous fungi now being used in gene cloning, if bacteria are such suitable hosts? Fungi are valuable because: (1) Many of the donor genes we want to clone are eukaryotic. Bacteria aren't ideal hosts for this job, because their mechanisms of gene transcription and translation are so different from those in eukaryotes. In fact, even if suitably modified plasmids are successfully introduced to *Escherichia coli*, relatively few eukaryotic genes will be expressed by this prokaryote. This is obviously not a problem in the fungi, which are all eukaryotes. The yeast *Saccharomyces cerevisiae* bypasses some of the roadblocks encountered when *E. coli* was the principal host available. *S. cerevisiae* can, for example, glycosylate proteins, fold them, or carry out other post-translational modifications which must be made if some eukaryotic proteins are to become functional. (2) *S. cerevisiae* and such filamentous fungi as *Aspergillus nidulans* are genetically well-explored, and useful mutations are available in many of their biochemical pathways. (3) Yeasts can be grown and handled in very much the same way as *E. coli*: simplicity itself compared to the tissue culturing of animal cells.

Two techniques are commonly used to transform yeast cells; one requires the removal of the cell walls, the other uses entire cells. The first technique is carried out as follows. (1) The yeast cells are treated with β-mercaptoethanol, a reducing agent, which facilitates subsequent digestion of the cell wall. (2) The wall is digested by mixtures of glucanases derived from snails or bacteria. (3) The resulting **protoplasts** (often called **spheroplasts**) are washed and suspended in a stabilizing solution (0.6 M KCl or 0.8 M sorbitol) to which is added the foreign DNA (vector incorporating the desired sequences). (4) Uptake of the plasmid DNA during protoplast fusion is promoted by adding polyethylene glycol. (5) The transformed protoplasts are then allowed to regenerate a wall, and are grown on a selective medium (one containing a specific antibiotic, or with a particular food substrate, depending on which marker genes were used) which will allow only appropriately transformed cells to grow (because only they carry the appropriate marker gene, which came with the vector, and confers resistance to that antibiotic or the ability to metabolize that particular substrate).

The alkali salt method permits transformation of intact cells. Cells are incubated in lithium acetate to make them competent, i.e. receptive to exogenous DNA. The DNA is then incorporated in the presence of polyetheylene glycol 4000. Although transformation is less efficient than with protoplasts, the procedure is simple and quick, cells can be stored for weeks without loss of competence, and the problem of diploid formation during protoplast fusion is avoided.

The first demonstration that yeast could be transformed with exogenous DNA was made in 1978, using a recombinant bacterial plasmid carrying the *Saccharomyces cerevisiae* gene for an enzyme needed in the synthesis of leucine (LEU 2). This gene had earlier been recognized in *E. coli* because it complemented a mutation in the bacterium that had caused the loss of the same enzyme. Several other yeast genes have now been cloned in *E. coli* by complementation of other bacterial mutants. These are useful markers which can be incorporated in the exogenous DNA along with the desired gene: their uptake and subsequent expression in yeast cells allows recognition and selection of yeast cells which have been appropriately transformed; that is, which now carry the desired donor gene.

Most strains of *S. cerevisiae* contain up to a hundred '2μm plasmids' per cell. Each plasmid has about 6300 base pairs. Hybrid plasmids made up of the entire 2μm sequence, plus the LEU 2 yeast gene, plus a bacterial vector sequence, efficiently transform yeast cells that lack the LEU 2 gene (As a consequence of the bacterial vector sequence DNA having been replicated in a bacterium, the 2μm plasmid also works in *E. coli*, so it can serve as a 'shuttle vector'). The complementation of the LEU 2 gene means that those cells which have been properly transformed can be selectively isolated on leucine-free medium, and subsequently multiplied. It has also been demonstrated that the hybrid plasmid replicates in transformed cells. However, it appears that smaller plasmids containing only a fragment of 2μm DNA are more versatile, giving higher frequencies of transformation, and more copies of the plasmid in each transformed cell (up to 300). All stages of gene-cloning can now be carried out in yeast, but it is usually more efficient to amplify recombinant plasmids in *E. coli*. The most important aim of the cloning exercise may be to obtain gene products, but cloning also lets us produce a lot of homogeneous DNA, which can then be used in the sequencing of genes.

Expression of genes in yeast

Yeast genes generally have the following components: (1) upstream promoter elements which include constitutive or regulated promoters (positive or negative); (2) 20-400 bp downstream, a TATA promoter element (so named because it incorporates the base sequence, thymine-adenine-thymine-adenine); (3) 30-90 bp downstream, a transcription initiating site which initiates production of mRNA; (4) protein-coding sequences; (5) transcription termination signals (Fig. 10.3). Transcription of the inserted DNA depends on the presence of a promoter sequence that is recognized by the host RNA polymerase.

Highly expressed yeast genes such as alcohol dehydrogenase I (ADH1) or glyceraldehyde-3-phosphate dehydrogenase (G3PDH) usually have very high mRNA levels, so most methods of expressing exogenous genes in yeast have concentrated on the production of high mRNA levels. This involves using multiple copy plasmids to boost the number of gene sequences per cell, and fusing coding sequences to efficient yeast promoters to increase transcription.

Yeast genes may contain both constitutive and regulated promoters, which serve to initiate transcription. Where both are present, the constitutive sequences are active at all times during cell growth, and may produce a base level of gene expression which can be modified by other upstream sequences. Regulated promoters need to be activated before they will initiate transcription, but will in some cases produce much higher levels of gene expression. Researchers initially tended to use constitutive promoters with high mRNA levels, especially those from the genes mentioned above (ADH1 and G3PDH), but found that while these gave high yields of homologous proteins, they produced much lower amounts of heterologous (donor) proteins. If large amounts of the desired protein are deleterious to the host cell, it is better to use regulated promoters, which are not derepressed until required. Good examples are those involved in galactose metabolism, such as GAL1, GAL7 and GAL10, which are repressed by glucose and derepressed by the addition of galactose to the medium. If cultures are grown with glucose or glycerol as carbon source, these promoters will remain repressed until almost all the glucose has been metabolised. If glucose is absent, and galactose is added to the medium, these promoters can be induced about 1,000-fold. Galactose induction is controlled by the GAL4 and GAL80 proteins. The GAL4 protein is a positive promoter that binds to specific DNA sequences upstream of the coding sequences of genes regulated by galactose. The GAL80 protein is a negative regulator which binds to the GAL4 protein, preventing it from activating transcription. If galactose is added, it binds to the GAL80 protein, stopping this from interfering with the GAL4 protein, which can then go about its business of promoting transcription. Recently, hybrid promoters have been developed, combining strong constitutive promoters with upstream sequences of regulated genes. One of these has been used in the controlled expression of human interferon.

Brewer's yeast must be provided with sugars if it is to produce alcohol. If yeast could be transformed so that it possessed an amylase (a starch-degrading enzyme), production of ethanol would be simpler and cheaper. Various amylase genes from bacteria, yeasts and filamentous fungi have now been cloned and expressed in *Saccharomyces cerevisiae*: commercial exploitation of these should soon be possible.

The cellulose and hemicellulose in wood represent almost limitless potential substrates for the fermentation industry. Complete degradation of cellulose to glucose requires the activities of three successive enzymes: endoglucanase, exocellobiohydrolase and β-glucosidase. *Trichoderma reesei* secretes all three cellulolytic enzymes, but normal cultures of the fungus aren't used to produce these enzymes commercially because all three enzymes are inhibited by their end-products. The strategy has been to isolate mutant, highly cellulolytic strains of *Trichoderma reesei*, then isolate the genes for the three enzymes and place them in vectors with control sequences appropriate for their expression in a suitable host. In 1987 the *T. reesei* gene for endoglucanase was cloned, characterized and expressed in *S. cerevisiae*. Endoglucanase and exoglucanase from the bacterium, *Cellulomonas fimi*, have been cloned, expressed and secreted in yeast in a regulated manner by attaching their coding sequences to the melibiase promoter and signal sequences from *Saccharomyces carlsbergensis*. Although yields are still too low for commercial exploitation, there is optimism that higher-yielding strains will be developed, and that cellulolytic brewer's yeast will be able to clarify beer, and provide cheaper fuel alcohol.

It appears that recipient yeast strains can take up and maintain exogenous DNA even without the mediation of vectors. The brewing industry has achieved this in two ways. Beer normally contains dextrins that are not degraded by brewing yeasts. These dextrins give a beer greater body, and a higher caloric content. The light beers which are so popular today (for reasons that escape me) have had these dextrins removed by an exogenous enzyme, glucoamylase. This enzyme is produced naturally by some non-brewing yeasts (for example, *Saccharomyces diastaticus*). Brewers have therefore tried to get the ability to make this enzyme into their brewing strains, so that these could produce a light beer without assistance. One approach has been to incubate the protoplasts of the brewing yeast with partially purified high molecular weight DNA from the donor yeast. A second approach has been to fuse entire protoplasts of the two yeasts. Unfortunately for this second method, the *S. diastaticus* brought with it, not only the glucoamylase, but also 4-vinyl guaiacol, which ruined the flavour of the beer. Classical hybridization techniques were then used to segregate the glucoamylase gene from the 4-vinyl guaiacol gene.

The flavour of Brazilian wines is often spoiled by an excess of 1-malic acid. Fusion of the wine yeast protoplasts with those of *Schizosaccharomyces pombe*, which metabolizes 1-malic acid, produced a hybrid that successfully reduced 1-malic acid levels in the wine. Protoplast fusion has some potential, because some characters important in baking, brewing and distilling are polygenic (controlled by many different genes), or are not well understood genetically. Such characters aren't suitable for enhancement by gene cloning or transformation. In addition, protoplast fusion combines whole genomes, and it is known that increases in ploidy may increase productivity. Intergeneric fusions are often unstable, but if one 'petite' parent (which has non-functional mitochondria) is used, more stable hybrids are produced, probably because the hybrid contains functional mitochondria from only one parent.

Expression of Eukaryotic Genes in Filamentous Fungi

Although for several years yeasts were the hosts favoured by gene-cloners seeking to express heterologous eukaryotic genes, they cannot secrete enzymes in the quantities produced by bacteria. But mycelial conidial fungi such as *Aspergillus niger* can secrete enzymes more efficiently than either yeasts or bacteria, and are therefore becoming the hosts of choice for expression and secretion of many enzymes, antibiotics and even mammalian pharmaceutical proteins. Transformation in filamentous fungi was first reported for *Neurospora crassa* in 1979, and transformation systems have now been developed for many other filamentous fungi.

Genes in filamentous fungi are composed of a promoter, a translation initiation region, DNA encoding a secretory signal peptide (where necessary), DNA encoding for the gene product, and DNA sequences for terminating transcription and for polyadenylation (Fig. 10.3). When a gene is to be moved to a new host, it is first assembled in a vector plasmid which can replicate in *E. coli*. A selectable marker may also be incorporated in the plasmid. As mentioned earlier, markers may be selectable because they compensate for some auxotrophic deficiency in the host, or (preferably, since in many cases we are not dealing with auxotrophic hosts) because they confer upon the host resistance to an antibiotic, or the ability to metabolize a particular food substrate. The hyphae of the host fungus are enzymically stripped of their walls, and the transformation of the protoplasts proceeds much as it does in yeasts. Following transformation, the protoplasts convalesce on a regenerative medium which lets them reconstitute their hyphal walls. In fungal transformations, the vector DNA usually becomes integrated into the host genome.

Bovine chymosin, a mammalian protease used in cheese-making, has been successfully expressed and secreted in *Aspergillus nidulans*. The cDNA sequence encoding the chymosin was attached to transcriptional, translational and secretory control elements of the glucoamylase gene from *Aspergillus niger*. All four units were incorporated into a suitable vector, which was used to transform *Aspergillus nidulans*. Active human interferon α2 and a bacterial endoglucanase have also been cloned in *A. nidulans*, this time using promoters from the *A. niger* glucoamylase gene and the *A. nidulans* alcohol dehydrogenase gene. Human tissue plasminogen activator (tPA, a protease used to dissolve blood clots) has been expressed and secreted in *A. nidulans*. One of the vectors constructed for this purpose is illustrated in Fig. 10.4.

Molecular Taxonomy

Fungal identification is often difficult, even with good, mature specimens of the usual reproductive structures in hand. If all we have are sterile mycelia, or fungus-inhabited substrates, identification can be virtually impossible. But now, with the advent of a variety of molecular techniques, the impossible just takes a little longer. We can detect the activity of specific enzymes. We can use probes to identify particular base sequences in the DNA. We can do immunoassays, using antibodies raised in a mammal against unique components of the organism.

Or we can use sodium dodecylsulphate polyacrylamide gel electrophoresis (more succinctly known as SDS-PAGE). This technique separates the proteins in any mixture by their molecular weight. An electrical field is used to draw the protein molecules through a porous gel. Smaller molecules move more quickly and so travel further in a given time. Eventually, the concentrations of the various protein molecules are made visible by staining with dyes or silver-based reagents, and the resulting spatial and intensity pattern of bands compared, often by computer, with those derived from known organisms. References describing these techniques are given at the end of the chapter.

It has also become possible to compare parts of the DNA or RNA sequences in the genome of different organisms with a view to establishing their degrees of biological relatedness. *Rhizopogon* is a false truffle, a hypogeous, mycorrhizal basidiomycete with a closed basidioma, a convoluted hymenium, and non-shooting basidia. For anatomical reasons, this fungus has been thought to be related (although nobody knew how closely) to 'normal' epigeous members of the Boletaceae, which produce basidiomata with a stipe, a cap, hymenium-lined tubes, and spore-shooting basidia. In recent molecular studies of these fungi, a number of fragments of *Suillus* mitochondrial DNA (mtDNA) were cloned and hybridized with mtDNA from other members of the Boletaceae. This showed that 15 different regions of the mitochondrial genome of *Rhizopogon subcaerulescens* are virtually identical to those of fourteen species of the 'normal' bolete genus, *Suillus*. This is surprising because not only does the order of these 15 regions differ among species of *Suillus*, but *Rhizopogon* and *Suillus* have traditionally been placed in different families or even different orders. Their molecular similarity, at least as far as this has been explored, is in striking contrast to their morphological divergence.

Using the polymerase chain reaction (PCR) technique, researchers were able to replicate very small samples of DNA thousands of times, and ultimately produce enough DNA to permit analysis of its base pairs. Base sequences from the mitochondrial large subunit of the ribosomal RNA gene show that *Rhizopo-*

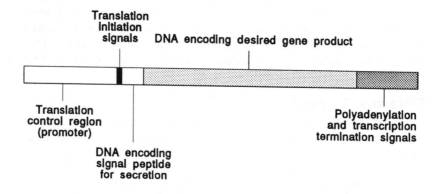

Fig. 10.3 Components of a fungal gene.

gon and *Suillus* are very closely related, and that both genera have diverged sharply from other boletes tested. In defence of classical taxonomy, I must point out that many mycologists have long believed that *Rhizopogon* is a secondarily reduced or sequestrate (non-spore-shooting) derivative of the genus *Suillus*. It is encouraging that this relationship has now been dramatically affirmed. This work also demonstrates either that major morphological changes may not be reflected by corresponding changes in the genome, or that we have not been looking in the right places to find the genetic reflection of those differences. It also emphasizes that our concepts of fungal relationships must be based on as many kinds of information as possible (not just morphological, and not just molecular).

Armillaria mellea, the only truly diploid basidiomycete, produces assimilative mycelial clones up to 400 metres in diameter, and up to several hundred years old, infecting many trees, and several different clones may be present. When homokaryons anastomose, nuclei migrate but mitochondria do not, so the resulting mycelium is uniform in its nuclear component, but has at least two sectors with different mitochondrial genotypes. Therefore, an examination of mitochondrial DNA polymorphisms can now help us discover the history of those clones.

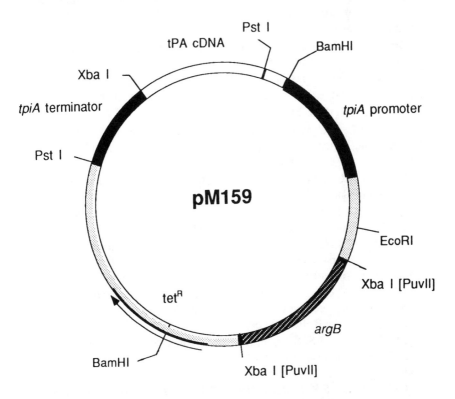

Fig. 10.4 A plasmid vector, pM 159, constructed for the expression of the human tissue plasminogen activator gene in **Aspergillus nidulans**.

In the years ahead we can look forward to molecular help with some of our more difficult taxonomic problems, although I do not foresee a day when our taxonomic concepts are based entirely on DNA sequencing. A fungus is much more than the sum of its base pairs!

Further Reading

Beggs, J.D. (1981) Gene cloning in yeast. pp. 175-203 (in) **Genetic Engineering** 2. (Ed.) R. Williamson. Academic Press, New York.

Bennett, J.W. and L.L. Lasure (Eds) (1985) **Gene Manipulations in Fungi**. Academic Press, Orlando.

Bennett, J.W. and L.L. Lasure (1991) **More Gene Manipulations in Fungi**. Academic Press, New York.

Berka, R.M. and C.C. Barnett (1989) The development of gene expression systems for filamentous fungi. Biotechnology Advances **7**: 127-154.

Blum, H., H. Beier and H.J. Gross (1987) Improved silver staining of plant proteins, RNA and DNA in polyacrylamide gels. Electrophoresis **8**: 93-99.

Brasier, C.M. (1987) The dynamics of fungal speciation (in) **Evolutionary Biology of the Fungi**. (Eds) A.D.M. Rayner, C.M. Brasier and D. Moore. Cambridge University Press, Cambridge.

Bruns, T.D., R. Fogel, T.J. White and J.D. Palmer (1989) Accelerated evolution of a false-truffle from a mushroom ancestor. Nature **339**: 140-142.

Bruns, T.D. and J.D. Palmer (1989) Evolution of mushroom mitochondrial DNA: *Suillus* and related genera. Journal of Molecular Evolution **28**: 349-362.

Burnett, J.H. (1975) **Mycogenetics**. Wiley, London.

Burnie, J.P., R.C. Matthews, I. Clark and L.J.R. Milne (1989) Immunoblot fingerprinting of *Aspergillus fumigatus*. Journal of Immunological Methods **118**: 179-186.

Fincham, J.R.S., P.R. Day and A. Radford (1979) **Fungal Genetics**. 4th Edn. University of California Press.

Herskowitz, I. (1988) Life cycle of the budding yeast *Saccharomyces cerevisiae*. Microbiological Reviews **52**: 536-553.

Jackman, P.J.H. (1985) Characterisation of microorganisms by electrophoretic protein patterns (in) **New Methods for the Detection and Characterisation of Micro-organisms**. (Ed.) C.S. Gutteridge. Wiley, U.K.

Jahnke, K-D., G. Bahnweg and J.J. Worral (1987) Species delimitation in the *Armillaria mellea* complex by analysis of nuclear and mitochondrial DNAs. Transactions of the British Mycological Society **88**: 572-575.

Martin, C.E. and S. Scheinbach (1989) Expression of proteins encoded by foreign genes in *Saccharomyces cerevisiae*. Biotechnology Advances **7**: 155-185.

Old, R.W. and S.B. Primrose (1985) **Principles of Gene Manipulation: an Introduction to Genetic Engineering**. 3rd Edn. Blackwell Scientific, Oxford.

Perkins, D.D. (1987) Mating-type switching in filamentous ascomycetes. Genetics **115**: 215-216.

Scheinbach, S. (1983) Protoplast fusion as a means of producing new industrial yeast strains. Biotechnology Advances **1**: 289-300.

Strathern, J.N., E.W. Jones, and J.R. Broach (Eds.) (1981) **The Molecular Biology of the Yeast** *Saccharomyces*, **Life Cycle and Inheritance**. Cold Spring Harbor Monograph Series. Vol. 11A. Cold Spring Harbor, New York.

Strathern, J.N., E.W. Jones, and J.R. Broach (Eds.) (1982) **The Molecular Biology of the Yeast** *Saccharomyces*, **Metabolism and Gene Expression**. Cold Spring Harbor Monograph Series. Vol. 11B. Cold Spring Harbor, New York.

Taylor, J.W. (1986) Fungal evolutionary biology and the mitochondrial DNA. Experimental Mycology **10**: 259-269.

Van Brunt, J. (1986) Fungi: the perfect hosts? Biotechnology **4**: 1057-1062.

Chapter 11

Fungal Ecology

Ecology is the study of organisms as they relate to each other and their environment. It must be apparent that even in the taxonomic chapters I gave a lot of ecological information. Think of the effects that fungi have had on people: the potato famine, the downy mildew of the French grape vines, the blue mould of Canadian tobacco, the way chestnut blight removed an important species from the forests of eastern North America, and the more recent loss of our beautiful ornamental elm trees to Dutch elm disease. Fungi may alter the ecology of our gardens, as their depredations persuade some people to give up growing roses (because of the black spot disease) or phlox (because of its susceptibility to powdery mildew); or the early leaf drop inflicted on horse chestnut trees by *Guignardia* blight may persuade us to plant other shade trees. But in this chapter I want to explore some other areas of fungal ecology: some of the ways in which fungi influence the course of events in a variety of natural, as opposed to Man-made habitats. I will explore their roles in three natural habitats I and my graduate students have personally examined in some detail, and then give a few more general comments.

The Succession of Coprophilous Fungi

The first habitat is dung. We may turn up our noses, but to some other organisms, dung is a considerable resource, which is constantly being produced in large quantities by billions of animals all over the world. You may think that because it has passed through an animal's digestive tract, every bit of nutritional value will have been extracted from it. This is an entirely false impression. There may not be a lot of high quality protein, but there is a great deal of microbial biomass, as well as many food components, for example, cellulose, that neither the animal nor its gut flora managed to digest. There are also excretory products which, though they are of no further value to the animal, are high in nitrogen: herbivore dung may contain 4% nitrogen; more, in fact, than the plant material originally eaten by the animal. So, at frequent intervals throughout its life, every mammal evacuates from its gut a mass of first class fungal substrate, simply asking to be exploited.

Are there fungi which specialize in exploiting dung? And if there are, how do they gain access to this substrate when it becomes available? The answers may surprise you. About 175 genera of ascomycetes are largely or exclusively found on dung. The extremely advanced and successful agaric genus *Coprinus* has many species that occur exclusively on dung. There are also many specialized dung-inhabiting zygomycetes, among which *Pilobolus* and some of the elaborate anamorphs in the Kickxellales are perhaps the most spectacular. So there is no doubt that a specialized mycota of dung-inhabiting (**coprophilous**) fungi exists.

But how do they compete successfully for this substrate? The answer here may be a little unexpected, but it is nevertheless perfectly logical. These fungi contrive to be first to exploit the dung by the simple expedient of being **in** it when it is deposited. The only way to achieve that is to be eaten by the animal. This the coprophilous fungi arrange in several ingenious ways. They must take into account some immutable logic. 1) The fungi are growing in the dung and will therefore have to fruit on it. 2) Animals do not, in general, eat their own dung (Rabbits do, and that raises interesting questions about the coprophilous fungi associated with them). 3) Therefore, the spores must be somehow distanced from the dung in such a way as to increase their likelihood of being eaten. You have already read about how several fungi of herbivore dung achieve this trick. How *Pilobolus* aims and shoots its sporangia up to 2 metres toward the light. How the ascus tips of *Ascobolus* protrude from the hymenium and bend toward the light before shooting their spores. How the necks of the perithecial ascomata of *Podospora* bend toward the light before their spores are expelled. Each of these independently evolved **phototropic** mechanisms is obviously designed to direct the spores away from any other adjacent dung, and to increase the efficiency with which spores are deposited on nearby vegetation that has a good chance of being eaten by the animal.

Some of the Kickxellales, zygomycetes often found on the dung of sedentary mammals (those with a defined home base, a small territory, and habitually used paths) produce extremely complex and convoluted anamorphs. *Spirodactylon*, possibly the most complex of all, was illustrated in Fig 3.4 F. It produces tall, branched sporangiophores that bear tiny coils within which develop innumerable one-spored sporangia. The whole structure must be designed to catch on the hairs of the rat or mouse as it passes by. This is made possible by the habits of the animal which, although it doesn't eat its own dung, at least deposits it somewhere along one of the trails it follows every day in its journeys to and from its den or burrow. The final step, the ingestion of the spores, is presumably taken when the animal grooms itself, as mammals (other than human children) habitually do. Some coprophilous hyphomycetes (e.g. *Graphium*: Fig. 4.21 B) produce slimy droplets of conidia at the top of tall conidiophores or synnematal conidiomata. These spores are presumably dispersed by arthropods which may themselves specialize in seeking out dung, and may thus act as specific, and very efficient, **vectors** for the slimy-spored fungi.

Many other dung-inhabiting fungi are less specialized than those I have just mentioned, or have specializations so subtle that we have not yet detected them. Nevertheless, the fact remains that with patient and repeated examination, we can find a large number of fungi representing most of the major fungal groups on the dung of many herbivorous mammals. Repeated observations will show that the various fungi tend to sporulate in a sequence. First the zygomycetes will appear; then the ascomycetes and conidial fungi, and finally the basidiomycetes.

It has been suggested that this is a true ecological succession, albeit a miniature and condensed one. Initially it was postulated that the sequence was a nutritional one. Zygomycetes can generally assimilate only fairly accessible carbon sources, such as sugars. Their fast growth was assumed to give them an advantage in finding these, and their early disappearance was thought to be due to the exhaustion of this substrate. The ascomycetes and conidial anamorphs that appeared next were assumed to be able to assimilate more complex carbon sources such as hemicellulose and cellulose; while the basidiomycetes, appearing last and persisting longest, were able to exploit both cellulose and lignin.

But when this hypothesis was scrutinized more carefully and tested by experiment and further observation, it did not hold up. The growth rates of the various fungi were found to be relatively similar, and the various carbon sources were not exhausted as quickly as had been assumed. So a second hypothesis was advanced. This one was based on the time it took for each kind of fungus to accumulate enough food reserves to permit it to fruit. It was argued that the simple sporangiophores of the zygomycetes could be developed after only a short period, while the more elaborate fruit bodies of the ascomycetes would require a longer build-up, and the even larger basidiomata of the Coprini would need the longest preparation of all. This is a more reasonable hypothesis, because if we grow some of the dung fungi on laboratory media, we find that it takes *Mucor hiemalis* 2-3 days to sporulate, while *Sordaria fimicola* needs 9-10 days, and *Coprinus heptemerus* 7-13 days.

So we can assume that an assortment of spores of coprophilous fungi will be present in dung when it is deposited, and that these will all have been triggered to germinate by some aspect of passage through the mammalian gut. While *Pilobolus* is producing its miniature artillery extravaganza (see chapter 3), the other fungi are growing and assimilating steadily within the dung, preparing for their own appearance at the surface. The new hypothesis had neglected only one important factor: competition. After a few weeks, almost the only fungi still sporulating on the dung will be species of *Coprinus*. These can go on producing a sequence of ephemeral basidiomata for months. We now know that the various components of the substrate are far from exhausted after the initial flushes of growth and sporulation. What has really happened is that *Coprinus* has seized control by suppressing most of the other fungi. Hyphae of *Coprinus* are actually extremely antagonistic to those of many other coprophilous fungi. If a *Coprinus* hypha touches one belonging to *Ascobolus*, the *Ascobolus* hypha collapses within minutes. We don't understand exactly how this trick is done, but it is extremely effective, and turns out to be a fairly common stratagem among the fungi, whose main competitors for many substrates are other fungi.

Another interesting and important gambit used by *Coprinus* involves repeated anastomoses. If spores are more or less evenly dispersed throughout the dung when it is deposited (Fig. 11.1 A), they all germinate more or less simultaneously and produce small mycelia within the dung (Fig. 11.1 B). When vegetatively compatible mycelia meet (Fig. 11.1 C), they anastomose, and soon the entire dung deposit is permeated by what amounts to a single mycelium (Fig.

11.1 D), which can then pool its resources and produce more and larger basidiomata. Obviously, cooperation pays off.

There are also some interesting subplots that run concurrently with the main story. Several of the zygomycetes that usually appear (e.g. *Piptocephalis*) are actually parasitic on other zygomycetes. One common zygomycete, *Rhopalomyces elegans*, parasitizes nematode eggs. Nematode-trapping fungi such as *Arthrobotrys* often sporulate, and develop their characteristic rings and nets (see chapter 15). Keratinolytic hyphomycetes such as *Microsporum* (Fig. 4.8 C) may appear on hair that the animal has accidentally eaten during grooming. Occasionally, an undescribed species of fungus may be seen. For many years the third year mycology class at Waterloo has followed the dung succession as a laboratory exercise. These undergraduates saw the zygomycete *Stylopage anomala* on horse dung several years before it was formally described in 1983. They have also found an undescribed species of *Podospora* (Ascomycetes), which is perhaps the 102nd species of this genus. Their most recent find was the rare zygomycete, *Helicocephalum*. And I expect more novelties to turn up in the years ahead.

Horse dung is easy to obtain in most areas, comes in discrete units, and can be handled and observed without creating much distress. As many as 40 species of fungi representing most major groups of eumycotan fungi are commonly recorded from a single collection of horse dung. Most of them can be identified fairly easily with the help of the specialized taxonomic literature that is now readily available: though I admit that some of the zygomycetes are not easily recognized as such by beginners. Many of the fungi can be isolated in pure culture without too much difficulty, and with a little imagination, many interesting experiments can be devised to investigate various aspects of their behaviour. Perhaps now you can understand why I and many other teaching mycologists ask our classes to put their culturally determined attitudes on hold, adopt an objective scientific approach, and study the succession of fungi on horse dung, then think about the biological mechanisms and manoeuvring that lie behind the visible manifestations.

Amphibious Fungi in Streams

The second area of fungal ecology I want to examine is a stream flowing through a woodland, somewhere in the temperate zone. We already know that the tiny chytrids and oomycetes live here, but we might not expect to find many of the typically terrestrial dikaryomycotan fungi. However, if you pass a litre of stream water through a filter, then stain the filter in cotton blue and examine it through the microscope, you will see some fairly large and strikingly shaped fungal spores. Most will have four or more arms sticking out in different directions (Fig. 11.2). Some others will be long, thin and sinuate or sigmoid. They are all produced by conidial anamorphs that are specially adapted for living in streams. Where do these spores come from, and how do the fungi that produce them make a living?

The first clue came when limnologists (biologists specializing in freshwater systems) began to examine the energy budgets of streams. Because some streams flow through forests, they are heavily shaded during the growing season. This means that few green plants (primary producers) can grow in them. It was found that more than half, and sometimes nearly all, of the energy supporting organisms that live in streams comes from autumn-shed leaves.

When they first fall into the water, these leaves are extremely unpalatable to stream invertebrates, but as they are colonized and 'conditioned' by microorganisms, their acceptability increases. Experiments in which batches of leaves were treated with antifungal or antibacterial antibiotics showed that the fungi were chiefly instrumental in making leaves palatable to animals living in the stream. Later experiments with leaves conditioned by individual stream fungi showed that not only were some of the fungi that produce tetraradiate or sigmoid conidia most active in conditioning leaves, but their mycelia and sporulating structures were also highly nutritious food for detritivorous stream animals such as *Gammarus* (Crustacea, Amphipoda). An important ecological role had been established for these fungi.

But many questions remained. Were those fungi with tetraradiate spores related to one another? Did they have teleomorphs? (which would help to answer the first question). Since streams always flow the same way, and have a natural tendency to carry small things like spores downstream, where did the inoculum

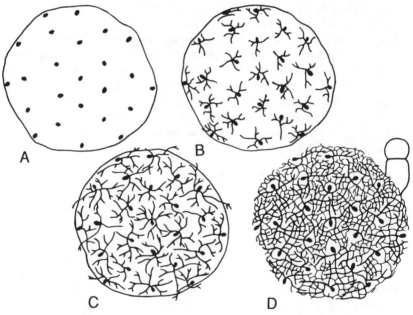

Fig. 11.1 Behaviour of **Coprinus** in dung. A: spores present when dung is deposited; B: spores germinate synchronously; C: mycelia anastomose; D: composite mycelium can exploit the entire substrate and produce large basidiomata.

for the upper reaches come from? What were the advantages of the tetraradiate and sigmoid spore shapes? The information we needed was gradually accumulated over several years of experiments, until eventually we were in a position to give some answers. Many of the tetraradiate spores, though similar in configuration at maturity, developed in rather different ways. I will describe just two of these. In some, three arms grew upward and outward from the top of the first-formed arm. In others, one arm grew upward, the other three or four outward and downward at the same time from a central cell. Some of these conidia were thallic, some blastic. A few had clamp connections; most didn't. This impression of diversity was confirmed when some of the teleomorphs were

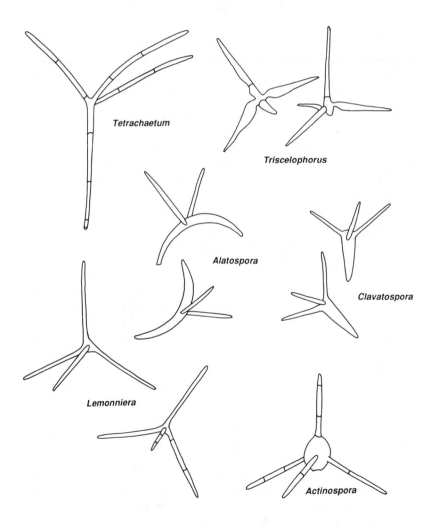

Fig. 11.2 Tetraradiate conidia of stream-inhabiting amphibious hyphomycetes.

discovered. Some were unitunicate ascomycetes, both operculate and inoperculate, producing apothecial and perithecial ascomata. Some were bitunicate ascomycetes. Some were basidiomycetes. It became clear that the morphologically similar anamorphs were actually a mixed bunch: fungi of very different origins that had undergone convergent evolution, molded by selection pressure into similar shapes. The teleomorphs also provided one answer to the question of how these fungi got upstream: ascomata and basidiomata, unlike the anamorphs, were not submerged in streams, and they liberated airborne ascospores or basidiospores. The group has been christened the **amphibious fungi**, because of its immersed anamorphs and emergent teleomorphs.

But why did so many of these taxonomically diverse amphibious fungi evolve conidia with similar shapes? It was found that as they were carried along by the water, tetraradiate spores sometimes entered the layer of still water just above the surface of submerged leaves, and then made three-point landings on these leaves. We know that a tripod is the most stable configuration, able to stand firm on irregular surfaces. The spores formed microscopic tripods that gave them a foothold on the dead leaves for long enough to germinate from the ends of the three arms, and attach themselves to the substrate before being swept away. The reason for the sigmoid shape has not yet been fully established.

After colonizing the leaves, the amphibious fungi sporulate again, and it was found that they would do this only in highly oxygenated conditions, and with the physical stimulus provide by flowing water. If the spore numbers are charted over the entire year, it will be seen that their numbers peak in Fall and Spring. In the first place, the massive new input of autumn-shed leaves provides the necessary substrate. In the second case, spring run-off will also carry plant debris into the stream. The entire process is diagrammatically summarized in Fig. 11.3.

Aero-Aquatic Fungi in Ponds

One good aquatic habitat deserves another, so after sorting out the role of fungi in streams, we switched our attention to woodland ponds. Again, primary production within the pond was limited by the forest canopy. Again, there was a specialized group of fungi living in the pond, though no-one knew if these fungi played an important role in the ecology of the pond. In this case the fungal propagules commonly found were hollow, and floated. Again, this end was achieved in several different ways, of which I will describe only two. (1) A conidiophore emerges from the water, and branches like a tree (Fig. 11.4). Eventually, the ends of the fine branches all swell up and fuse with their neighbours to form an air-filled, watertight structure. This is the propagule of *Beverwykella*. (2) Another conidiophore emerges from the surface of the water, and its tip begins to grow in circles (Fig. 11.5). Coiling repeatedly on itself in wider and wider, then narrower and narrower gyres, it eventually builds a barrel-shaped, air-filled, watertight structure. This is the propagule of *Helicoon*. Because these fungi live and grow under water, but produce conidia only above the surface, they are called the **aero-aquatic fungi**. It's obvious that the two structures I have just described, though functionally equivalent, are not closely related. Again, convergent evolution has been at work, the selection pressure applied by some ecological imperative.

We finally discovered that this was the need to be first on the scene when new substrate appears. When a dead leaf falls into a pond, it does not sink

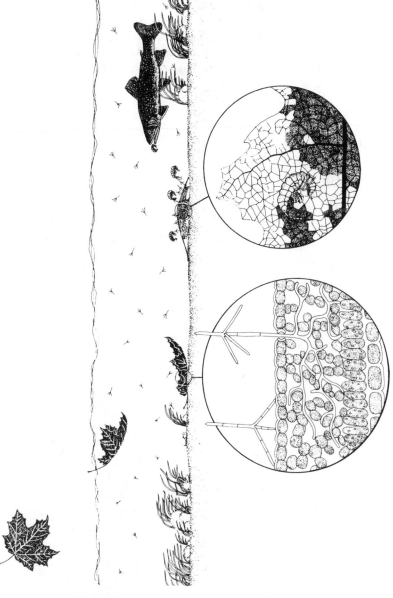

Fig. 11.3 Energy flow in streams: leaf→fungus→*Gammarus*→trout.

immediately. It may actually fall on top of some of the floating propagules illustrated in Figs. 11.4 and 11.5, or the propagules may be drawn to the floating leaves by surface tension. In either case, these fungi will be the first pond-adapted species to enter this new substrate. They also have the ability to grow at low oxygen levels, and to survive the virtually anaerobic conditions that prevail at the bottom of a pond for extended periods. Sporulation will happen again when the pond begins to dry out, the following summer, and the water level subsides until the colonized leaves are once more just below the surface. We found that these aero-aquatic hyphomycetes play an ecological role parallel to that of the amphibious fungi in streams: conditioning the dead leaves, and making them palatable to the detritus-eating invertebrates that live in the pond.

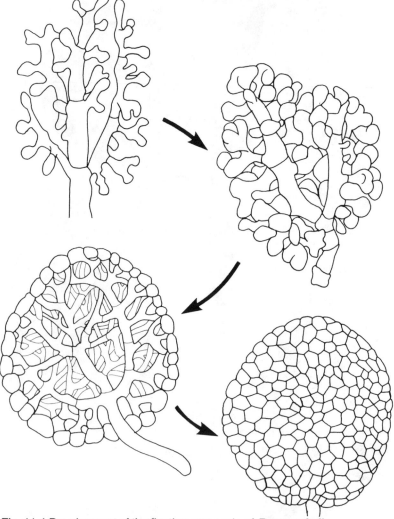

Fig. 11.4 Development of the floating propagule of **Beverwykella**.

Other Habitats

The biosphere has myriads of other habitats, each unique in various ways, and each making special demands of the organisms that live in it. The roots of plants create special conditions around themselves, and have established especially intimate relations with hundreds of endotrophic and thousands of ectotrophic mycorrhizal fungi (which have chapter 17 to themselves). Other rather

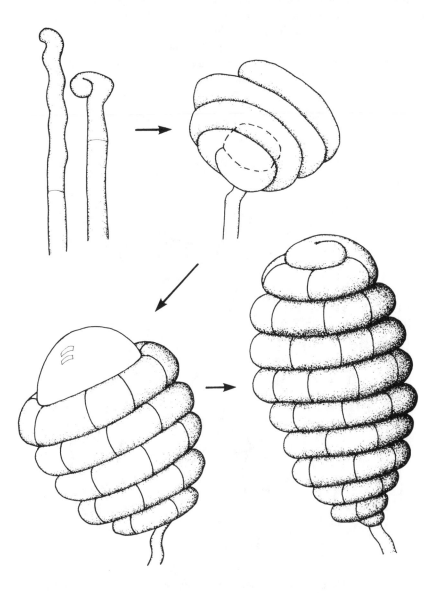

Fig. 11.5 Development of the floating propagule of *Helicoon*.

less specialized saprobic and parasitic fungi also abound on and near roots. The surface of living leaves is inhabited by a specialized mycota, while dead and decaying leaves are substrates for a succession of other species. The soil, into which most leaf remains are incorporated, is itself a mass of microhabitats, and is the richest reservoir of fungal diversity. And of course the leaves of different plants, and the various soil types, will have different subsets of the total mycota.

Not all fungi can be parcelled out neatly into successive steps of a succession. Often, fungi compete for access to a substrate. Sometimes a natural phenomenon will give us an unexpected insight into this struggle. Fig. 11.6 shows a block of wood which has been colonized by many different mycelia. The boundaries between the 'territories' of different mycelia can be clearly seen as black lines or zones. The black material is melanin-like, oxidized and polymerized phenolics deposited by wood-rotting fungi, and although the biological function of the

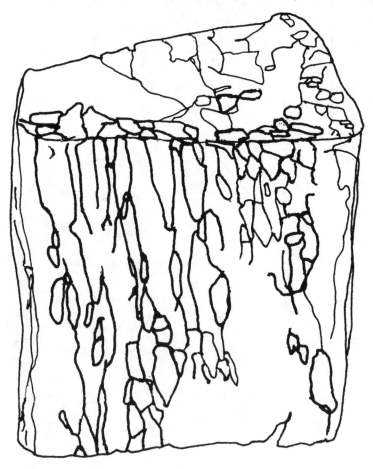

Fig. 11.6 Melanized boundaries between 'territories' of different mycelia in a block of rotting wood.

zones isn't entirely clear, melanins are the precursors of the humic acids: long-lived and important determinants of soil fertility.

Special substrates have evoked specialized fungi: keratin is attacked by some of the Onygenales and their anamorphs; wood by many Aphyllophorales. Extreme physical conditions have selected specialist fungi which, by evolving the ability to cope with high or low temperatures, or low water activity, have essentially escaped from competition, and gained access to untapped food supplies. Some fungi are the most osmotolerant organisms known (see chapter 20). The cycling of anamorph and teleomorph, which I mention many times in connection with plant disease fungi in chapters 4 and 12, is often largely a matter of their response to specific ecological conditions, which turn on and off large segments of the genome. The fungal ecology of sewage, compost, mushroom beds, agricultural and forest soils, naturally decomposing plant remains, some cheeses, bread, wine and beer, crops in the field and after harvest, the air, the space between your toes, and the tissues of immune-deficient or immune-suppressed people: all can be the subjects of worthwhile, and even important, studies of fungal ecology.

Many of the food webs illustrated in ecology textbooks miss out more than half of the organisms involved in the transfer of energy and nutrients. They often stress macroscopic organisms, while omitting microscopic organisms such as the saprobic and mycorrhizal fungi. This neglect is unfortunate, especially since we now appreciate that microorganisms, being at the base of food webs, provide nutrients and mutualistic symbionts for almost all plants and animals. The basic links in terrestrial food webs lie in the soil which is, of course, where a very large number of fungi still live. Every attempt to understand trophic systems must start and finish with soil organisms. And surely the fungi are among the most important of those.

Further Reading

Baerlocher, F. (Ed.) (1992) **The Ecology of Aquatic Hyphomycetes.** Ecological Studies Vol. 94. Springer, Berlin.

Baerlocher, F. and B. Kendrick (1974) Dynamics of the fungal population on leaves in a stream. Journal of Ecology **62**: 761-791.

Baerlocher, F. and B. Kendrick (1981) The role of aquatic hyphomycetes in the trophic structure of streams. pp. 743-760 (in) **The Fungal Community: its Organization and Role in the Ecosystem**. (Eds.) E.T. Wicklow and G.C. Carroll. Marcel Dekker, New York.

Bell, A. (1983) **Dung Fungi: an illustrated guide to coprophilous fungi in New Zealand**. Victoria University Press, Wellington.

Hudson, H.J. (1980) **Fungal Saprophytism**. 2nd Edn. Arnold, London.

Michaelides, J. and B. Kendrick (1982) The bubble-trap propagules of *Beverwykella, Helicoon* and other aero-aquatic fungi. Mycotaxon **14**: 247-260.

Price, P.W. (1988) An overview of organismal interactions in ecosystems in evolutionary and ecological time. Agriculture, Ecosystems and Environment **24**: 369-377.

Richardson, M.J. and R. Watling (1974) **Keys to fungi on dung**. British Mycological Society, Cambridge.

Seifert, K., B. Kendrick and G. Murase (1983) **A Key to Hyphomycetes on Dung**. University of Waterloo Biology Series, Number 27. Department of Biology, University of Waterloo, Waterloo.

Webster, J. (1970) Coprophilous fungi. Transactions of the British Mycological Society **54**: 161-180.

Webster, J. and E. Descals (1981) Morphology, distribution, and ecology of conidial fungi in freshwater habitats. pp. 295-355 (in) **Biology of Conidial Fungi**. Vol. 1 (Eds.) G.T. Cole and B. Kendrick. Academic Press, New York.

Chapter 12

Fungal Plant Pathology in Agriculture and Forestry

Introduction

We are utterly dependent on plants. Directly or indirectly they supply all our food. So it is an extremely serious matter if something prevents our domesticated plants from living up to their genetic potential in terms of growth and yield. Outside influences that do this are said to cause disease, and are dealt with by a broad collection of disciplines grouped under the heading of Plant Pathology. At many Universities, whole academic Departments are devoted to it; entire Government laboratories do nothing else. This is because our crops, in field or forest, are threatened by thousands of diseases. Plant Pathology concerns itself both with non-infectious or physiological diseases caused by factors such as mineral deficiencies, climate or pollutants, and with infectious diseases caused by a horde of different organisms: nematodes, bacteria, mycoplasmas, viruses—and fungi. This chapter, as you might expect, will be concerned only with diseases caused by fungi.

Although insects are our chief competitors for food, fungi are a good second. Crops in Ohio are attacked by about 50 bacterial diseases, 100 viral diseases, and 1,000 fungal diseases. About 60% of all plant disease literature concerns fungal diseases. You have already read about some of these in the taxonomic chapters at the beginning of this book: rusts, smuts, blights, downy mildews, powdery mildews, etc. I am not going to repeat myself: you should refresh your memory of the organisms involved by looking back into that section. You could even glance through it now, before you go on with the rest of this chapter. That's the great thing about a book; it's a very flexible teaching machine. But I will mention some additional diseases here, just to broaden your perspective.

Ever since people became farmers, they have had problems with fungal diseases of plants. These diseases weren't visited upon them by the Gods, as the ancient Romans thought, but were a natural consequence of growing plants in extensive pure stands, or **monocultures**. Whether the fungi grow, swim, float, ride or blow from one host plant to the next, they will find a new home much more readily in a monoculture than in most natural plant communities. This is because most plant disease fungi have a limited host range, and the very diversity of the community means that individuals of a particular host species are often well separated, so may escape infection emanating from their relatives.

Although fungal diseases have been recognized for thousands of years, they were not connected with the organisms that caused them until the mid-nineteenth century. Fortunately, the scientific revolution was in full swing when the potato famine caused by *Phytophthora infestans* (Oomycota, Peronosporales) struck Europe (Fig. 12.1), and it was not many years before the relationship between fungus and disease was firmly established. This knowledge has not prevented many subsequent disastrous episodes when particular fungi have ravaged field or forest. A few examples may help to establish this. The **downy mildew of grape**, caused by *Plasmopara viticola* (Oomycota, Peronosporales), that almost destroyed the French wine industry. The **chestnut blight** caused by *Cryphonec-*

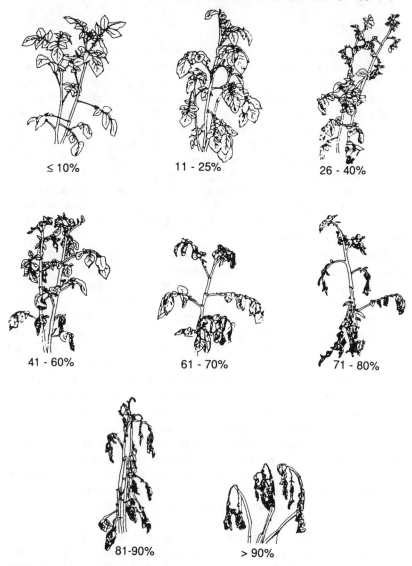

≤ 10%   11 - 25%   26 - 40%

41 - 60%   61 - 70%   71 - 80%

81-90%   > 90%

Fig. 12.1 Progressive attack of *Phytophthora infestans* on potato plants.

tria (Endothia) parasitica (Ascomycetes, Diaporthales), which has killed almost all mature sweet chestnut trees in North America. The **wheat rust** epidemics of the 'dirty thirties,' caused by *Puccinia graminis* (Teliomycetes, Uredinales), which made the depression an all the more bitter experience for prairie farmers. The **southern corn blight** epidemic of 1970, caused by *Drechslera maydis* (Hyphomycetes), which destroyed up to 70% of the crop in several corn-growing States. The **Dutch elm disease**, caused by *Ophiostoma ulmi* (Ascomycetes, Ophiostomatales), which continues to decimate our beautiful native American elm over much of the continent. **Blue mould** of tobacco, caused by *Peronospora tabacina* (Oomycota, Peronosporales), which destroyed $100 million worth of Ontario tobacco in 1979. The 'bayoud' fungus, which is killing the date palms in the oases of Morocco and Algeria and speeding up desertification. The whimsically named but incurable 'brewer's droop' of hops, caused by a *Verticillium* (Hyphomycetes), which is now spreading through the hop-growing areas of Britain.

And there will be more surprises, more defeats, and many ongoing battles against the army of fungi that encroach on our chosen plants. Why are fungi such a threat? Why can't we breed totally resistant plants, or synthesize ultimate fungicides? The answer lies in the remarkable genetic flexibility of the fungi, some aspects of which are discussed in chapter 10. Why, to ask an even more basic question, do the fungi attack living plants in the first place? The answer may well be hidden in the distant past, but it seems to me that once there is a division between autotrophic and heterotrophic organisms, it will only be a matter of time before some of the heterotrophs seize the advantage by attacking the autotrophs before they die, rather than respectfully waiting until afterward. This calls for the development of new talents: ways of overcoming the natural defence mechanisms of the target organisms, of penetrating their cell walls, of ensuring dispersal from one host to the next. The fungi have responded nobly to this challenge.

I've already pointed out that for thousands of years we didn't know that fungi caused plant diseases; but even now, pinning the blame on the pathogen isn't always easy. Finding a fungus fruiting on a diseased plant isn't enough to allow us to blame that fungus for the disease. Pre-existing disease, and the necrotic tissue that often results, may open the way for exploitation of that tissue by secondary colonizers, which may or may not be parasites themselves. We can't hope to deal with a disease until we know exactly which organism is causing it. Fungi can be unequivocally labelled as pathogens only after a number of conditions, known as **Koch's postulates**, have been satisfied. (1) The fungus must be consistently associated with the disease. (2) The fungus must be isolated in pure, axenic culture (a culture on a susceptible host has to suffice for obligate biotrophs). (3) When the fungus is re-inoculated onto healthy host plants, it must produce the original disease. (4) The fungus must then be re-isolated from the diseased plant. If you have been through all those steps, there won't be much doubt in your mind about the pathogenicity of the fungus in question. Actually, even Koch relaxed these postulates a little because they were so difficult to meet in their entirety.

Classification of Plant Diseases

There are many possible approaches to an understanding of plant disease and its control. We need to know the precise identity of the organism causing the disease. But before we can hope to control the disease, we need to know much more than that. We have to establish the nature of the relationship between the fungus and its host, how and where and when it gets into the plant; the kind of symptoms it causes, the parts of the plant it attacks; and above all, its life history, which may reveal a weak point at which it may be attacked. This kind of information can be treated systematically in several different ways, each of which can materially assist us in our planning.

Host-Pathogen Relationships. To kill one's host is not the ideal strategy. Just as the parasite is settling in comfortably to enjoy the amenities of its new home, the host collapses and dies. It is almost axiomatic that a host and a parasite that have been associated for a long time have co-evolved to produce a balanced relationship in which the host doesn't expel the parasite, and the parasite doesn't kill the host. There is a finely tuned genetic equilibrium between pathogenicity and resistance (or tolerance). When a pathogen is introduced to a new host (generally one related to its usual host, but lacking the accumulated genes for resistance), the results are likely to be catastrophic. See if you can pick out these fateful meetings in the examples discussed below.

The adoption of a parasitic existence necessitated many specialized adaptations. Some fungi evolved new enzymes: **cellulases** that could dissolve the substance of plant cell walls, and **pectinases** to dissolve the cement that holds plant cells together. At one extreme, some fungi evolved diffusible **toxins** that killed host cells at long range, and circumvented the problems inherent in exploiting living cells. At the other extreme, some fungi became so intimate with their hosts that they ultimately became dependent upon the living host cytoplasm for many things: not just food, but also a variety of vital enzymes, or even whole biochemical pathways. Some fungi produced **plant growth regulators** that either increased or decreased the ability of host cells to grow and divide.

In this way, three different kinds of pathogen evolved. (1) Some are **facultative parasites**: these versatile organisms can live either saprobically or parasitically. Many of these are pathogens of annual herbaceous crop plants, and must survive between growing seasons as members of the normal soil mycota. This ability makes them particularly difficult to control, and virtually impossible to eradicate: *Fusarium oxysporum* var. *cubense*, which causes Panama disease of bananas, can survive in the soil for at least 40 years in the absence of the host. (2) Other fungi are **necrotrophs**: basically saprobic, but producing toxins specific to susceptible host cells. The *Monilia* anamorphs of *Monilinia* species causing brown rot of peaches and other stone fruits, belong to this category. (3) The last group are called **obligate parasites** or **obligate biotrophs**, because they have long since lost their independence, and cannot grow at all except on or in a suitable host. In fact, the dependence is often so complete that only one host species, or a few cultivars of that species, will support a particular race of such a pathogen. The rust fungi, for example the genus *Puccinia*, are good examples of this third category.

Life cycle studies. Often we can't decide on the best way to tackle a fungal disease until we know a great deal about the life cycle of the fungus. For example, many of the obligately biotrophic rust fungi have evolved complex patterns of existence that require two hosts (such rust fungi are called heteroecious), with an obligatory annual migration from one to the other. We may be able to control the fungus by eradicating one of the hosts (assuming that it is neither of economic importance, or rare, of course) wherever it grows too close to the other. Perhaps the best-known example of this practice is the widespread eradication of barberry (*Berberis* spp.) in North America to break the life cycle of the wheat rust fungus, *Puccinia graminis* (Teliomycetes, Uredinales), or at least reduce its opportunities for genetic recombination, since dikaryotization happens on the barberry.

The *Spilocaea* anamorph of *Venturia inaequalis* (Ascomycetes, Bitunicatae) is a virulent parasite which attacks the leaves and fruit of apple trees and causes the unsightly scab disease. But it can also live saprobically, because the ascomata of the teleomorph develop in the dead apple leaves over the winter, releasing ascospores (the primary inoculum) in spring. To control the anamorph requires repeated spraying throughout the growing season and, as the chapter on fungicides clearly shows, the fungus quickly develops resistance to each new fungicide. Removal of dead leaves from the orchard floor, and spraying with disinfectants while the trees are dormant, are valuable ways of reducing the amount of ascospore inoculum released in spring.

Phytophthora infestans (Oomycota, Peronosporales) produces easily detached and subsequently airborne mitosporangia; but when these land on a new potato plant, they still release swimming spores. These are delicate, short-lived, and can function only when free water is present on the potato leaf. This stage might be described as the Achilles' heel of the fungus, since minute quantities of fungicide in the water will kill the zoospores. But once the fungus is inside the host plant, control becomes much more difficult (Fig. 12.1). It is clear that we must have detailed knowledge of the life cycles of pathogenic fungi if we want to develop optimal disease control strategies.

Stage of host development affected. Diseases can strike a crop at any point in its development. Some important diseases, such as loose smut of wheat (*Ustilago tritici*: Teliomycetes, Ustilaginales) are seed-borne. Others, such as damping off (*Pythium* spp.: Oomycota, Peronosporales) devastate tender seedlings. Yet others attack the growing or mature plant (the hyphomycete, *Alternaria solani*, causes early blight of potato; the oomycete, *Phytophthora infestans*, late blight). Finally, some diseases cause serious losses after harvest (the hyphomycetes, *Monilia* and *Botrytis*, cause soft rot of peaches and grey mould of strawberries, respectively). And many root disease organisms simply sit in the soil and wait for an appropriate host to appear. Their propagules are so long-lived that it isn't critical which year the host returns.

Some infections, notably those caused by smut fungi, some rust fungi, and some members of the Clavicipitales, spread throughout the plant, and are described as **systemic**. Others, such as vascular wilts and heart-rots, are restricted to a single tissue. Yet others attack a single organ, as in fruit or seed diseases, or anther smut. Finally, individual infections of some, like the wheat rust just mentioned, are extremely localized, and may form only a tiny leaf spot.

As a systemic infection spreads, or as the number of small, individual infections increases, the host will usually develop physical symptoms, such as reduction in growth, necrotic or discoloured areas, hypertrophied tissues, etc. Each disease has its own trademark, producing a particular set of symptoms, though some diseases (such as smuts) can remain asymptomatic for long periods, and in others, such as the heart-rots of trees, the symptoms are cryptic. But sooner or later, the fungus will reproduce, making it much easier to name the culprit. It will be sooner in wheat rust, where the anamorphic uredinia produce spores that can infect only wheat, and pass through several 8-day generations as an epidemic grows. It will be later in the case of smuts or woodrotting fungi. But always the spores are produced in astronomical numbers, because the odds are so heavily against their individual survival.

It is interesting to consider just how diseases damage their hosts. Damping-off (*Pythium* spp.: Oomycota, Peronosporales) causes breakdown of seedling tissue by enzymically dissolving the pectic middle lamella between cells, and also produces toxins. This fungus can obviously derive its food from dead cells. The vascular wilts caused by species of *Fusarium* and *Verticillium* (Hyphomycetes), and *Ophiostoma* (Ascomycetes) drastically reduce the upward movement of water in the xylem. The vessels become blocked with hyphae and spores, fungal polysaccharides, or tyloses (outgrowths developed by the plant into the lumen of the vessels in an attempt to stop the spread of the fungus). The transpiration stream is reduced to 2-4% of normal, and wilting and death inevitably follow. The damping-off and wilt fungi don't strike me as particularly well-adapted to their hosts.

Rust fungi (Teliomycetes, Uredinales) are obligately biotrophic, so they don't kill the cells of their hosts; and the combined biomass of many tiny rust infections is probably not large enough to cause a serious drain on the plant. So why are yields often so drastically reduced by these fungi? The answer becomes clear when they rupture the host epidermis to release their urediniospores. The plant's waterproof skin is broken in so many places that in a dry prairie summer it can no longer maintain turgor pressure, and its physiology is disrupted. Some other highly adapted pathogens don't kill, or even seriously damage, the vegetative organs of the plant. But they do subvert the energy the plant normally accumulates for reproductive purposes. Smut fungi (Teliomycetes, Ustilaginales) enter the plant when the seed germinates, or may already be present as mycelium in the grain. The ergot fungus (*Claviceps*: Ascomycetes, Clavicipitales) gains access through the stigma of the flower. But both fungi eventually home in on the developing ovary, and ultimately replace it with their own reproductive structures. If we grew corn and rye as we do lettuce, just for the leaves, these diseases wouldn't be so serious. And if carrot leaf blight didn't reduce the efficiency of the harvesting machinery (the leaves are weakened, and break off, leaving the carrot in the ground), it might not be taken nearly so seriously by the growers, since it doesn't drastically reduce the actual carrot crop.

Host organs attacked. Diseases can be described as root rots, vascular wilts, leaf spots, etc. When a disease is first noticed, the fungus causing it will not usually be producing diagnostic structures. Symptoms may well develop in parts of the plant that aren't being directly attacked: symptoms of root disease will often manifest themselves in the shoot system. Consequently, many plant disease manuals concentrate on describing and illustrating sets of symptoms by which diseases can be diagnosed early. Although positive identification of the fungus may not be possible until it eventually fruits, or is isolated and identified in pure culture, treatment must begin as early as possible, to prevent the build-up of an epidemic. It is easy to talk about such diseases as *Alternaria* blight and *Cercospora* blight of carrots, as if these were easily recognizable entities like mushrooms or mice, but the truth is that the early symptoms are often very inconspicuous, that they change continuously as the condition develops, and that it takes a very practised eye to make an early diagnosis of most diseases. Plant diseases can be classified according to the symptoms they elicit.

(1) **Necrosis**, generalized cell death, is the most extreme reaction. It can affect the base of the shoot, as in **damping off** (caused by *Pythium* species: Oomycota, Peronosporales); or the leaves, as in late blight of potato (*Phytophthora infestans*: Oomycota, Peronosporales); or storage tissues, as in soft rot of peaches. Necrosis goes by many names: anthracnose, blight, canker, scab, leaf spot, shot-hole.

(2) **Permanent wilting**, caused by blockage of the xylem by hyphae or as a reaction to a fungal toxin, as in wilt of tomato (caused by *Verticillium*: Hyphomycetes), Panama disease of banana (*Fusarium oxysporum* f.sp. *cubense*: Hyphomycetes), and Dutch elm disease (*Ophiostoma ulmi*: Ascomycetes, Ophiostomatales).

(3) **Hypertrophy** or **hyperplasia**, caused by growth hormones (auxins) liberated by the pathogen, as in white rust of crucifers (caused by *Albugo candida*: Oomycota, Peronosporales), corn smut (*Ustilago maydis*: Teliomycetes, Ustilaginales), and peach leaf curl (*Taphrina deformans*: Ascomycetes, Taphrinales).

(4) **Leaf abscission**, caused by hormones produced or stimulated by the pathogen, as in powdery mildew of gooseberry (*Sphaerotheca*: Ascomycetes, Erysiphales), and coffee rust (*Hemileia vastatrix*: Teliomycetes, Uredinales).

(5) **Etiolation**, excessive extension growth, caused by a growth hormone (gibberellic acid) produced by the pathogen, as in 'foolish seedling' disease of rice (caused by *Gibberella fujikuroi*: Ascomycetes, Hypocreales).

(6) **Prevention of reproduction**, caused in various ways: choke of grasses (*Epichloë typhina*: Ascomycetes, Clavicipitales) prevents flowering; ergot of grasses (*Claviceps purpurea*: Ascomycetes, Clavicipitales) replaces the grain with a fungal sclerotium; and anther smut (*Ustilago violacea*: Teliomycetes, Ustilaginales) replaces the pollen with fungal spores.

Irrespective of how we classify and diagnose fungal plant diseases, the prime objective of plant pathology is to thwart the game plan of the pathogens, and many disciplines now contribute to this end. The **meteorologist** provides data which will allow the plant pathologist to forecast outbreaks of certain diseases, and prescribe appropriate preventive measures: this technique is particularly valuable in dealing with late blight of potato. Some plant pathologists have delved into micrometeorology and aerodynamics to probe the way conditions within the canopy of a forest or of a field crop affect spore dispersal and germination. The **chemist** synthesizes new and ever more sophisticated fungicides. The **plant breeder** produces cultivars with built-in resistance to specific diseases.

The plant pathologist is dealing, not simply with an isolated interaction between a **fungus** and a **plant**, but with the overriding effects of **climate** and **microclimate** on how that interaction develops through **time**. Most imponderable of all is the fungus itself which, with its endless genetic flexibility, is never more than one jump behind the plant breeders and the fungicide formulators. Sometimes there are other complicating factors: the mysterious wanderings of animal **vectors** such as the bark beetle that carries Dutch elm disease from tree to tree; and since Dutch elm disease was brought, albeit accidentally, by **people** from Europe to North America, the control of all plant imports assumes tremendous importance. Although some diseases are almost ubiquitous, many are still relatively localized, and governments try, with mixed success, to exclude exotic pathogens by quarantine regulations, employing plant pathologists to inspect incoming shipments of plant products. Much of what we know about long-range dispersal of fungi (see chapter 8) concerns the spread of crop diseases, which will make themselves felt, and hence be documented, wherever they appear. It must be clear by now that there is no simple formula for dealing with plant diseases. Each is a special case; and each outbreak will differ from all others in various ways. Plant pathologists will never put themselves out of a job.

Establishment of Disease

When pathogen meets plant, a number of factors determine whether disease will develop. The plant may be entirely resistant, extremely susceptible, or somewhere between those extremes. The fungus may be extremely virulent, almost avirulent, or somewhere between the two. The stage of development of the host may be important: damping-off attacks only young seedlings; ergot ascospores can infect only grasses in flower. The weather may be critical: many downy mildews have an absolute requirement for free water.

Perhaps the most crucial phase in the development of any disease is the initial **penetration** of the host. A microscopic spore (One in a hundred? One in a million?), lands on a leaf. If the spore is initiating the first infection of the growing season, it is called a **primary inoculum**, and causes a primary infection. Spores produced by primary infections are called **secondary inocula**. So an ascospore of *Venturia inaequalis*, liberated from the overwintered dead leaves, is a primary inoculum, while the conidia of the *Spilocaea* anamorph, produced on the new season's growth, are secondary inocula. In smuts, there is only primary inoculum, since the fungus doesn't form any further spores until the end of the season. In either case, the more primary inoculum there is, the more serious the disease is likely to be.

But all this assumes that the spore successfully infects the host, and we mustn't take that for granted. Many things can go wrong. Does the leaf belong to a susceptible host? Is the temperature suitable for spore germination? Is free water available, or is the relative humidity high enough? And will it stay that way long enough for the spore to germinate and penetrate the plant? If our spore is typical, it will die, before or after germination. But one in a hundred, or one in a million, go on to establish themselves. Some germ tubes, and the zoospores of some downy mildews, find their way to a stomate, but other fungi make a frontal assault (Fig. 12.2 A,B). The germ tube establishes an **appressorium**, a small swelling of the hypha, that adheres very tightly to the plant surface. This gives the fungus the physical leverage it needs in order to go ahead with the actual penetration. Now a very narrow hypha partly digests, partly forces, its way through the cuticle and then the cell wall. Some pathogens always enter a cell, others just as regularly grow between host cells.

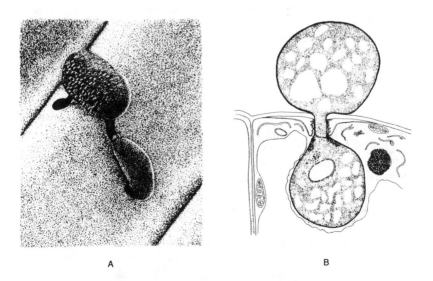

A   B

Fig. 12.2 Penetration of host by fungus. Drawings derived from A: scanning electronmicrograph; B: transmission electronmicrograph.

Once inside, the hypha broadens out, extends, branches, and establishes an infection if the plant is susceptible. Plant resistance may take a number of forms: the cuticle and/or the epidermal cell wall may be thick and tough enough to resist penetration. In hypersensitive plants, the penetrated cell dies almost at once. This is enough to discourage many parasites. Obligately biotrophic fungi, deprived of the kind of nutrients living cells provide, will certainly die (of course, if the fungus is a necrotroph, the hypersensitive reaction won't faze it). The host may lay down a sheath of material around the invader, and this encapsulation sometimes starves the fungus out. Specially produced cork layers or abscission layers can effectively isolate the pathogen at a later stage: in shot-hole disease of leaves, the infected part simply drops out. Many defences are biochemical. Most pathogens, although their spores obviously land on an enormous number of different plants, can infect relatively few of them (sometimes only one). All the others must in some way deter or resist the fungus: this is what we call non-host resistance. Some plants contain substances like **phenolics**, which inhibit the development of many fungi. Others produce special antifungal compounds called **phytoalexins**, also often phenolic, only when attacked. The genetic aspects of disease resistance are discussed in chapter 10.

Epidemiology

Epidemics of different diseases develop in different ways. The incidence of smuts is predetermined by the level of infection or spore contamination of the seed when the crop is planted. But the severity of most other diseases depends on their success, not only in producing primary infection, but in multiplying their secondary inoculum during the growing season. This success, of course, is a product of the interaction of many factors: virulence in the fungus, suscepti-bility in the host, favourable weather, lack of action by laissez-faire farmers. Conditions for the development of major epidemics of many diseases do not happen every year, but some crops are always threatened. For example, if apple growers did not spray 8-20 times per season to control apple scab (the *Spilocaea pomi* anamorph of *Venturia inaequalis*), between 70% and 100% of their crop would be unsaleable. If peanut growers didn't spray 8-10 times a season for foliar diseases, they would lose 20-75% of their crop. Peaches need foliar and post-harvest treatments if 80% of the crop is not to be lost. Strawberry growers stand to lose 70% of their crop if it is not sprayed several times. Grains, on the other hand, can often be protected against their worst diseases by a single seed treatment, which prevents losses of up to 35%.

Let's see how some of those diseases develop. Apple scab begins the season with ascospores, primary inoculum shot into the air from ascomata developed in last year's dead leaves. But it immediately switches into anamorph mode: each infection derived from a single ascospore soon produces many conidia on the current season's leaves. These spread the infection to new leaves, and the new infections soon produce even more conidia. The number of conidia in-creases in a geometric progression, and unless this cycle of infection and conidium production is interrupted, the outlook is bad. You will find a detailed discussion of the difficulties involved in controlling apple scab in chapter 13. It is an interesting story, with no end in sight.

Other crops are threatened by more than one serious disease. Potatoes, for example, suffer from an early blight caused by *Alternaria* (Hyphomycetes), then from late blight caused by *Phytophthora* (Oomycetes). No single fungicide will effectively control both fungi. **Mancozeb** is commonly used for the *Alternaria*, and **Ridomil** for the *Phytophthora*, and a close watch is kept on the weather to determine when it is necessary to spray for late blight.

Experienced plant pathologists perform an invaluable service when they go out into a field and diagnose a disease, but they cannot keep track of every disease on every crop. And if the development of epidemics, and the results of control measures, are to be documented, we need some objective ways of deciding how much disease is present, and how serious it is. Sometimes these take the form of descriptions, as in the following excerpts from a key for assessing potato blight: 'Up to 10 spots per plant = 1% of crop diseased.' 'Every plant affected and about one-half of leaf area destroyed by blight; field looks green flecked with brown = 50% of crop diseased'. In other cases, visual aids are provided, which allow farmers to assess the severity of attack for themselves. Figure 12.1 shows a chart for assessing damage caused to potato plants by late blight. Fig. 12.3 A shows a chart used with *Septoria* glume blotch of wheat, and Fig. 12.3 B one used with powdery mildew of cereals.

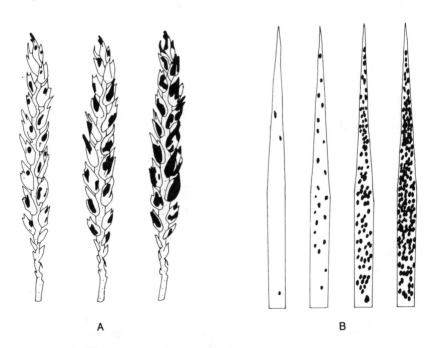

A   B

Fig. 12.3 Diagrams used to assess severity of disease. A: *Septoria* glume blotch of wheat; B: *Erysiphe* powdery mildew of cereals.

Some diseases begin very inconspicuously. The ergot fungus, *Claviceps purpurea*, can gain entry to its host only through the stigma of the open flower. This indicates considerable co-evolution of plant and fungus. If the fungus did not shoot its ascospores during the relatively brief time that the grass flowers are receptive, it would miss the boat. The very precision of this timing may be turned against the fungus if we can develop rye cultivars that flower earlier or later than normal. The disease remains virtually asymptomatic until the fruit begins to develop, when it soon becomes apparent that the resources allocated for that purpose have been misappropriated. At the other extreme are diseases which manifest themselves as soon as infection occurs. The soft rot of peach becomes visible as a spot of necrotic tissue within hours of fungal penetration. This is caused by a specific phytotoxin produced by the *Monilia* anamorph of *Monilinia fructicola*.

Some fungal diseases kill plants—*Phytophthora infestans* can turn a field of thriving potato plants into a mass of rotting vegetation (cf. the sequence shown in Fig. 12.1); repeated defoliation by the coffee rust fungus, *Hemileia vastatrix* (Teliomycetes, Uredinales), can kill a coffee tree; *Cryphonectria parasitica* and *Ophiostoma ulmi* (both Ascomycetes) have killed millions of chestnut and elm trees, respectively but many diseases do no more than significantly reduce the photosynthetic activity of the plant. So why are they taken so seriously? The answer lies in the economics of the situation. Does the disease attack one of our crop plants? Does it significantly reduce crop yield? If the answer to both questions is yes, the disease automatically enters the province of the plant pathologist. But even after a disease has been recognized as a problem, it is by no means certain that anything will be done about it. Economic considerations are again paramount in matters of disease control. Some diseases are easy and cheap to control. It would be possible to suppress many others with an appropriate regime of sanitation and prophylaxis, but the return in increased yield would not cover the cost of the program. This is particularly true of many forest diseases. At the other end of the scale, greenhouse crops are often so valuable that expensive control programs (from soil fumigation to repeated applications of fungicide) are routine.

Control of Plant Diseases

Control measures range from hot water treatment of seeds to kill hitch-hiking spores of *Ustilago tritici*, to chilling of fruit to retard spoilage by *Monilia*. We try to control fungal plant diseases in four ways: by **exclusion**, by **eradication**, by **protection**, and by **immunization**. I'll discuss these in turn.

(1) We can **exclude** pathogens from susceptible hosts in a variety of ways. (a) By keeping them out of the country: this involves quarantine regulations and careful inspection of all incoming plant material and soil. The price of freedom from introduced diseases is ceaseless vigilance. The potato blight fungus crossed the atlantic to Europe before anyone knew that fungi caused plant disease. But even now, fully aware as we are of the threat, pathogens are still carried inadvertently from continent to continent as an unfortunate side-effect of inter-

national trade. *Ophiostoma ulmi* entered the U.S. from Europe in 1930, on elm burl logs imported for veneer. Regulations to prevent the import of elm products to Canada were introduced in 1928 and 1934, but the disease was seen in Quebec in 1944, having probably been introduced on crates made of diseased elm wood. The contents of the crates not having anything to do with elm trees, the crates themselves probably escaped scrutiny. This shows how difficult it is for bureaucracies to cope with microscopic fungi. Other ways of excluding pathogens include: (b) growing susceptible plants in conditions that are inimical to the development of the fungus, and (c) in the case of some obligate parasites which cannot survive without the host, using disease-free seed or stock.

(2) It is worth trying to control some pathogens by **eradicating** them. (a) By rigorously destroying all diseased plants: most of the magnificent old elms in Fredericton, New Brunswick, and along the Niagara Parkway in Southern Ontario, have been preserved by the consistent and immediate removal of any tree found to be infected by Dutch elm disease. (b) By pruning out affected branches (this wouldn't work for Dutch elm disease, because the pathogen spreads though the vascular system of the tree rather rapidly by means of microconidia). (c) By applying fungicides: systemic fungicides will kill the fungus both outside and inside the host plant, so eradication is sometimes possible.

(3) In some cases, it is worth protecting healthy plants from the predictable attacks of pathogens by dusting or spraying them with protectant fungicides. Through much of the growing season the leaves of French grape vines look blue because they are covered with a residue of a copper-containing spray which is repeatedly applied to discourage the ingress of the downy mildew fungus, *Plasmopara viticola*.

(4) The use of cultivars which are immune or resistant to specific pathogens is now very common, but actual immunization the induction of antibodies to particular disease organisms by challenging the host organism with a dead or attenuated pathogen which is so important in dealing with many diseases of animals and people, is impractical in plants: they simply don't have the sort of immune system found in animals. Nevertheless, the hypersensitive reaction, in which the host cell dies as soon as it is penetrated by a pathogen, can deny some parasites, especially biotrophic ones, a foothold. This reaction, and the production of specifically antifungal substances, called **phytoalexins**, by many plants, may be regarded as analogous responses.

To give you some idea of what practising plant pathologists are expected to know, I will list the fungal diseases to which a few crops are susceptible.

Onions are attacked by: (1) purple blotch (*Alternaria porri*: Hyphomycetes); (2) neck rot and grey mould rot (*Botrytis allii*, *Botrytis squamosa* and *Botrytis cinerea*: Hyphomycetes); (3) leaf blight (*Botrytis squamosa*), (4) smudge or anthracnose (*Colletotrichum circinans*: Coelomycetes); (5) *Fusarium* bulb rot (*Fusarium oxysporum* f.sp. *cepae*: Hyphomycetes); (6) downy mildew (*Peronospora destructor*: Oomycota); (7) pink root (*Pyrenochaeta terrestris*: Coelomycetes); (8) white rot (*Sclerotium cepivorum*: sterile anamorphs); (9) smut

(*Urocystis magica*: Teliomycetes). Of course, a given crop will not develop all of these diseases at once, but the control strategies used by farmers are sufficiently diverse to be worth outlining.

Four main strategies are adopted. (1) **Crop sanitation**. Since many pathogens overwinter and complete their life cycle on the decaying remains of their host plant, it makes sense to destroy crop debris by burning it or ploughing it under. (2) **Crop rotation**. Another way of reducing the populations of pathogenic organisms is to alternate susceptible with non-susceptible crops. The length of rotation depends on how long the pathogen can survive without the host. Sometimes a 2- or 3-year rotation will do, but since *Sclerotium*, *Colletotrichum*, *Pyrenochaeta*, and *Urocystis* can survive in the soil for a long time, rotations of at least 5 years would be necessary to reduce their inoculum potential to a reasonable level. Such long rotations are often impractical. (3) **Fungicide treatments**. Seeds are treated with fungicides to prevent damping-off and smut, because the inoculum for these diseases is seed-borne. Leaf diseases are difficult to treat once they have appeared, and require repeated, and therefore expensive, sprayings. So a protectant spray is often applied before any disease symptoms appear. Preventive spraying may be repeated if weather conditions or disease forecasts call for it. (4) **Resistant cultivars** are under constant development by plant breeders. When available, they are the most effective and the cheapest way of avoiding losses.

More specifically, in onion fields, purple blotch, neck rot and leaf blight are controlled during the growing season by fungicides, and their inoculum potential reduced after harvest by removing and destroying plant residues. Neck rot is basically a storage rot, and can be minimized by harvesting the onions in dry weather, air-drying them before storing, then keeping them at 0°C and a relative humidity (R.H.) below 70%. Smudge occurs at harvest time and in storage, so drying onions properly, and keeping them at 0°C and 70% R.H., is recommended. *Fusarium* bulb rot is difficult to eliminate, since *Fusarium* species commonly survive in the soil as chlamydospores, or grow saprobically on crop residues. A 3-year rotation is required to keep this disease in check, and use of resistant cultivars is recommended. To become established, the downy mildew fungus, *Peronospora*, needs cool temperatures and rain or dew on the leaves (just like potato blight, and for the same reasons). A few hours of dry, sunny weather will slow *Peronospora* down considerably. The farmer can help by avoiding mildew-contaminated sets, practising a 2-year rotation, spraying regularly with fungicide, and destroying infected crop debris. If pink root becomes a problem, a long rotation will be necessary. White rot also necessitates a long rotation, though soil treatment with fungicide may deal with small problem areas. Control of smut is achieved by coating the onion seed with a systemic fungicide, practising rotation, and using onion transplants if the soil is already contaminated: established plants will not be affected by the disease.

It is instructive to compare the fungal diseases attacking onions with those found on carrots. **Carrots** are prone to *Alternaria* blight (*Alternaria dauci*: Hyphomycetes); *Cercospora* blight (*Cercospora carotae*: Hyphomycetes); rusty root (*Pythium* spp.: Oomycota); violet root rot (*Rhizoctonia crocorum* anamorph of *Helicobasidium purpureum*: Basidiomycetes); *Rhizoctonia* crown rot (*Rhizoctonia solani* anamorph of *Thanatephorus cucumeris*: Basidiomycetes); *Sclerotinia* rot (sclerotial anamorph of *Sclerotinia sclerotiorum*: Ascomycetes); and black rot (*Stemphylium radicinum*: Hyphomycetes). Are any genera common to both lists? Only *Alternaria*: this gives you some hint of the diversity of pathogenic fungi, and the difficulties faced by the plant pathologist. Which group of fungi is most prominent in both lists? Dikaryomycotan anamorphs, mainly those we call Hyphomycetes. This is a generalization that holds across the entire spectrum of plant disease fungi. Of course, the diseases vary in distribution and in their economic impact. *Cercospora* blight is favoured by hot, humid weather, and develops in high summer, while *Alternaria* blight and *Sclerotinia* rot like it cooler, and develop later. Rusty root is most severe in wet soils, *Rhizoctonia* crown rot in organic soils after repeated carrot crops. *Sclerotinia* rot probably causes the greatest losses.

Since the range of control measures available to us is much more restricted than the variety of fungi involved, I don't need to elaborate on this except to say that the measures used will reflect such features of the fungus as its longevity in the soil, the part of the plant it attacks, and economics. In the case of the two *Rhizoctonia* diseases, no effective control is possible at present, so the only possible recourse is to grow carrots in uninfected soil. It is hoped that resistant varieties will eventually be developed.

Plant Disease Forecasting

Plant disease forecasting is not, of course, designed simply to tell the farmer when to expect an outbreak of a particular disease; it is meant to give him a chance to apply preventive measures that will effectively stop the development of the epidemic. But how does it work? In some areas, potato growers can now telephone computerized systems, supply specific weather data, and receive advice on the necessity or otherwise for crop spraying to prevent late blight. Simpler programs call for the grower to use a hygrothermograph and a plastic rain gauge to keep track of the daily maximum, minimum and mean temperature, and daily rainfall on a standardized record sheet. A blight-favourable day is recorded as a '+', and the first spray is dictated by 10 successive '+' days. Every 7 days after this, the need for spraying is reassessed, using humidity, temperature and rainfall data.

A weather-timed spray program has been devized to keep *Alternaria* and *Cercospora* leaf blights of carrot from killing more than 15% of the leaf area. If this level is exceeded, harvesting machinery tends to tear off the weakened leaves, leaving the carrot in the ground. No fungicide is applied until the blight covers 1-2% of the leaf area. Then fungicide is applied before the next forecast rain, or before the next night with a forecast minimum temperature of 16°C or higher. At least 7-10 days are allowed between subsequent sprays, which are applied in conditions similar to those for the first spraying. Sprays are not needed before forecast rains when the night temperature will be below 9°C, because the fungal spores infect the leaves only when these are both warm and wet for an extended period.

Although wetness is vital for the successful establishment of most leaf diseases, the xerotolerant powdery mildew fungi are less affected by moisture, and more by the availability of inoculum: levels of airborne conidia. A third factor is the increasing susceptibility of some crops as they age. Programs have now been worked out to determine the critical date for a single application of fungicide to forestall powdery mildew of barley, the date of the first spray to control powdery mildew of rubber, and the timing of successive sprays against powdery mildew of apple.

The value of plant disease forecasting is, as one might expect, economic. In the carrot blight situation, an average of 2-5 sprayings were saved by following the program. The saving resulted from delaying the first spraying, and making subsequent spraying contingent upon the existence of conditions favourable to infection, rather than ritually spraying every so many days. Each program must be designed or modified to take into account conditions prevailing in the area where it will be applied.

Forest Pathology

The American sweet chestnut, *Castanea dentata*, once grew from Maine to Alabama. It was a fine tree that thrived even in poor soil and on steep hillsides. Some specimens in the Great Smoky Mountains were 4 metres in diameter and 40 metres high. Chestnut wood was extensively used for fencing and roofing, to make furniture and to build barns. During the burgeoning industrial revolution of the 19th century it was used for lining mine shafts and in mine roof supports, as railroad ties, as telegraph poles, and as fuel. Chestnut trees shared pride of place with elms as street and shade trees. Appalachian farmers fattened their hogs on chestnuts, which were also roasted and used in meat stuffings. The chestnut was the most economically important tree in the eastern hardwood forests.

Near the end of the 19th century, chestnut seedlings imported from the Orient to New York brought with them the fungus *Cryphonectria (Endothia) parasitica* (Ascomycetes, Dothiorales). This introduction found a defenceless host in the american chestnut. The first diseased trees were noticed in 1904 in the New York Zoo, and from then on, the epidemic mounted and spread remorselessly. The early issues of 'Mycologia,' the Journal of the Mycological Society of America, contain repeated rather plaintive references to the advancing plague. Despite their agonizing concern, mycologists and foresters could only watch helplessly as millions of chestnut trees died, and the face of the forests in eastern North America changed. By the 1940s or 1950s practically all the mature American chestnut trees had died, though living roots are still sending up sprouts that reach a fair size before being killed by the fungus, and some large trees still survive, because they are apparently infected by a hypovirulent strain of the pathogen (apparently the result of its becoming infected by a virus).

All that is history now, and it's too late to do much about it, except to slowly reintroduce scions of surviving trees to areas in which the species used to grow.

What of current concerns in forestry? The lumber industry is a mainstay of the economy in many areas of North America, but until recent years forests were 'mined' with little thought to replacement, since the resource was assumed to be virtually infinite, or at least entirely self-renewing. In Canada, a combination of depletion of first-growth forests by clearcutting, heavy tree mortality due to insects and diseases (which together cause an annual loss of almost 130 million cubic metres of wood), and extensive forest fires, combined to produce a potential wood shortage. Even if only 20 million cubic metres could be saved, this would provide 39,000 jobs, $800 million in wages and salaries, and forest products worth $2.9 billion. All this makes fungal diseases important, because they are one of the main factors contributing to the losses.

Tree diseases are often distinctly unspectacular in appearance, and their effects are insidious rather than dramatic. Trunk decays and root rots progress steadily, year in, year out. Once established in a tree, they cannot be eradicated. In Canada alone, the various rots cause a combined loss estimated at 30 million cubic metres of wood each year.

Root-rot caused by *Phellinus (Poria) weirii* (Basidiomycetes, Aphyllophorales) is widespread in west coast forests, and is especially destructive in Douglas fir (*Pseudotsuga menziesii*). Despite extensive studies, we still have no cost-effective way of preventing or eliminating this problem. Nevertheless, it appears that losses could be reduced by earlier cutting of infected stands, selective cutting to favour the establishment of less susceptible tree species, and the use of red alder in rotation to reduce the amount of *Phellinus* inoculum in the soil. Other silvicultural practices that would be helpful include: stump removal, fumigation, prescribed burning, fertilization, interplanting, sanitation, biological control, and host tolerance or resistance.

Heart-rot caused by *Fomes pini* (Basidiomycetes, Aphyllophorales) is also a severe problem in western forests. Trees with signs of internal decay should be cut because *Fomes pini*, unlike many other rot fungi, doesn't cause further decay after harvest. Root-rot caused by *Heterobasidion annosum* (Basidiomycetes, Aphyllophorales), an aggressive parasite that infects cut stumps, spreads from root system to root system, and kills many different conifers, was the subject of nearly 600 publications between 1960 and 1970. Recommended management procedures include: wide spacing in new plantations; preventing stump infection by applying inoculum of *Peniophora gigantea* (Basidiomycetes, Aphyllophorales) (biological control by a saprobic competitor); decreasing the number of thinnings per rotation; removing as much of the stump and taproot as possible during logging; regenerating by seeding instead of planting; and using resistant species. At present, the single best way to reduce losses caused by decay fungi appears to be to shorten the rotation time: in the southern U.S., heart-rot losses in pines have been reduced from 30% to below 1% simply by decreasing the age at which trees are harvested.

A survey of forest pathologists across Canada showed that root-rot caused by *Armillaria mellea* (Holobasidiomycetes, Agaricales) was the only disease placed in the ten most important diseases for all six forest regions, and was among the top three for all except the Quebec region. White pine blister rust, caused by *Cronartium ribicola* (Teliomycetes, Uredinales), was among the top ten diseases in all regions of Canada but one. This disease produces spreading cankers on branches or main trunk that may eventually girdle and kill the tree, meanwhile producing the aecial stage of the fungus. This fungus, like many others causing rust diseases, has two hosts, so eradication of the alternate host, *Ribes* spp., has been widely practised. *Cronartium comandrae*, cause of the similar *Comandra* rust on lodgepole pine and other 2- and 3-needled pines, is not susceptible to this form of control, because its alternate host is a common and inconspicuous herbaceous plant.

In the southern United States, another stem rust called fusiform rust, caused by *Cronartium fusiforme*, is responsible for losses of about $30 million a year. This disease is on the increase as a result of: (1) the use of infected nursery stock; (2) widespread monoculture of susceptible tree species; and (3) an increase in the alternate host, red oak, following improved fire prevention. The only practical control measures are the use of fungicides in nurseries, and the breeding of resistant tree cultivars.

Gremmeniella abietina (Ascomycetes, Leotiales) causes a serious canker of conifers, especially pines, in north-eastern North America. The fungus has two races. The American race is very widespread in Ontario north of latitude 45, and kills many young trees in their first decade. Once more than 2 metres tall, they seem able to survive the depredations of this race. But since 1975 the European race has been found killing mature pines in New York State, and at a few locations in Quebec, New Brunswick, and Newfoundland. All infected material discovered has been destroyed, and the situation is being closely monitored.

Integrated Pest Management

Integrated pest management (IPM) is now a concept to be reckoned with. Although the idea hasn't yet been fully incorporated into agricultural and forestry practice, it is the next logical step for plant pathology. This approach considers all the pests and pathogens which attack a particular crop, and develops an overall plan to control them. The crop is considered as an ecosystem, and all factors influencing that system are taken into account. Instead of simply applying chemical sprays at regular intervals, all possible control measures are considered. Sanitation, crop rotation, cultivation practices, sowing date, plant spacing, use of resistant cultivars, disease forecasting, and biological control, as well as chemical control. Sprays may be fewer but more complex, with components aimed at widely differing organisms, such as fungi and insects. Obviously, integrated pest management calls for a lot of preliminary analysis, and detailed but flexible planning; processes that are facilitated by computers. We can expect to see a lot more IPM in future, because its sophistication will result in less expensive pest control, and will reduce our use of, and dependence on, chemical pesticides.

Table 12.1 Some Important Fungal Diseases of Plants			
Pathogen	Host(s)	Disease	Control
Alternaria solani (Hyphomycetes)	potato, tomato	early blight	Mancozeb
Armillaria mellea (Agaricales)	forest trees	root-rot, butt-rot	?
Botrytis cinerea (Hyphomycetes)	lettuce, tomato, strawberry, etc.	grey mould	Captan, Benomyl
Bremia lactucae (Oomycetes)	lettuce	downy mildew	Dithiocarb
Ceratocystis fimbriata (Ascomycetes)	sweet potato	black rot	?
Cercosporella herpotrichoides (Hyphomycetes)	wheat, barley	eye-spot	cultivar
Claviceps purpurea (Ascomycetes)	rye, other grasses	ergot	clean seed
Colletotrichum lindemuthianum (Coelomycetes)	beans	anthracnose	clean seed
Diplocarpon rosae (Ascomycetes)	roses	black spot	Captan
Erysiphe graminis + Oidium (Ascomycetes)	cereals (grasses)	powdery mildew	cultivar, Tridemorph
Heterobasidion annosum (Aphyllophorales)	conifers	root-rot, butt-rot	shorten rotation

Further Reading

Agrios, G.N. (1978) **Plant Pathology**. 2nd Edn. Academic Press, New York.

Carefoot, G.L. and E.R. Sprott (1967) **Famine on the Wind**. Rand McNally, New York.

Dickinson, C.H. and J.A. Lucas (1977) **Plant Pathology and Plant Pathogens**. Blackwell Scientific Publishers, Oxford.

Disease Compendium Series (1977-1988) American Phytopathological Society, St. Paul. (Alfalfa, Barley, Beet, Citrus, Corn, Cotton, Elm, Grape, Ornamental foliage plants, Pea, Peanut, Potato, Rhododendron & Azalea, Rose, Sorghum, Soybean, Strawberry, Sweet potato, Turfgrass, Wheat).

Horsfall, J.G. and A.E. Dimond (Eds.) (1959-1960) **Plant Pathology**. Academic Press, New York.

James, C. (1971) A manual of assessment keys for plant diseases. Canada Department of Agriculture Publication No. 1458. American Phytopathological Society, St. Paul.

Johnston, A. and C. Booth (Eds.) (1983) **Plant Pathologists' Pocketbook**. 2nd Edn. Commonwealth Mycological Institute, Kew.

Kenaga, C.B., E.B. Williams and R.J. Green (1971) **Plant Disease Syllabus**. Balt Publishers, Lafayette.

Large, E.C. (1962) **The Advance of the Fungi**. Dover, New York.

Roane, M.K., G.J. Griffin and J.R. Elkins (1986) **Chestnut blight, other** *Endothia* **diseases, and the genus** *Endothia*. APS Press, St. Paul.

Roberts, D.A. and C.W. Boothroyd (1972) **Fundamentals of Plant Pathology**. Freeman, San Francisco.

Scopes, N. and Ledieu, M. (Eds.) (1979) **Pest and Disease Control Handbook**. BCPC Publishers, Croydon.

Chapter 13

Fungicides

Introduction

Fungi have ravaged our crops ever since we invented agriculture. As soon as we start to grow many of the same kind of plant close together (a **monoculture**), any other organisms that make a living from that plant will find life much easier, since the next meal (called a **host**) is sitting right beside the previous one. But until about 150 years ago, we had no idea what caused most plant diseases, and until we learned that pathogenic fungi were actually extraneous, spore-dispersed living organisms, rather than 'humours' or 'effluvia of the earth, or of thunder, or of snakes,' we couldn't do anything about it. So, for example, the destruction of the Irish potato crop by *Phytophthora infestans* (Oomycota) during the 1840's went completely unchecked, for all its terrible effects on the human population. The first practical fungicide wasn't devised until forty years later, by a University Professor in France.

Even today, over a third of all crop losses are due to fungal diseases. They cost American farmers alone more than $3.5 billion a year. Some pathogenic fungi (e.g. *Puccinia graminis*: Uredinales) can best be controlled by breeding resistant plant varieties. But all commercial apple varieties are susceptible to apple scab (caused by the *Spilocaea pomi* conidial anamorph of the bitunicate ascomycete, *Venturia inaequalis*). The conditions conducive to infection are precisely known, and occur up to 20 times each growing season. Unprotected orchards may produce no saleable fruit at all, so fungicide must be applied 6-15 times each year. Over $1.5 billion are now spent, world-wide, on fungicides of all kinds. This chapter is an exploration of our increasingly sophisticated efforts to combat pathogenic fungi with chemicals.

The First Generation: Inorganic Fungicides

In the 1880's, the famous vineyards of Bordeaux were being devastated by a recent accidental introduction from America, *Plasmopara viticola* (Oomycota), which causes downy mildew of grape. Strolling through a vineyard at St. Julien in the Medoc, Professor Millardet was surprised to see that the vines bordering the path looked much healthier than those further away. When he asked the vigneron how these plants had been treated, he was told that it was the custom to spatter the vines near the path with some conspicuous, poisonous-looking substance such as verdigris, to deter passers-by from eating the grapes. Millardet, who knew a lot about the fungus and its habits (much had been learned since the terrible potato blight epidemics), went away and concocted a variety of witches' brews, optimistic that he could poison the fungus when it was at its most vulnerable, just after the wind-dispersed mitosporangia had released their delicate zoospores on the wet surface of the plant. He finally settled on a blend of **copper sulphate** and **calcium hydroxide** (quicklime). This soon became famous as **Bordeaux mixture** (in French, 'Bouillie Bordelaise'). Other copper sulphate-based fungicides followed: Burgundy mixture, in which the lime was replaced by sodium carbonate, and Cheshunt mixture, in which it was replaced by ammonium carbonate. Although Bordeaux mixture is an efficient, wide-spectrum fungicide, it has now largely been replaced by formulations of **copper oxide, copper hydroxide**, and **copper oxychloride**.

Bordeaux mixture, and almost all other fungicides developed before 1960, are called **protectants**: they are toxic to pathogenic fungi, but only if they intercept the fungi outside the host plant. If the plant's exterior is not thoroughly coated with fungicide, the fungus can slip through the defence. Once inside its host, many pathogens can't be reached by the chemical, and have only the plant's internal defences to deal with. Inorganic fungicides also tend to damage the plant itself (they are **phytotoxic** as well as **fungitoxic**), and they can be washed off by rain. This necessitates repeated spraying during the growing season, and ultimately leads to a build-up of toxic substances in the soil. Long-term use of Bordeaux mixture on grape vines has produced concentrations of up to 130 ppm copper in the soil.

One early alternative to Bordeaux mixture was **sulphur**, applied as elemental sulphur or as lime-sulphur. It is not toxic to animals, and is still occasionally used to control powdery mildews, apple scab and peach leaf curl, but it may 'scorch' leaves, causing them to drop, and can have a dwarfing effect on plants.

Mercurous chloride was also found to be an excellent broad-spectrum fungicide (heavy metals denature a wide range of enzymes), but its residues can cause both **acute** and **chronic** toxicity in animals. Its LD_{50} to rats—the amount that will kill half of the animals exposed to it—is 1-5 mg/kg, and long-term exposure to even very low levels of mercury eventually causes severe brain damage (Minamata disease).

The Second Generation: Organic Fungicides

The **organo-mercurials** were the first of a new generation of fungicides that was developed in response to this problem. They retained the persistent fungi-toxicity of the mercury, but in compounds that were less poisonous to animals (their LD50 (rat) ranges from 30 to 200 mg/kg). The general formula for many organo-mercurials is RHgX, where R = aryl or alkyl, and X = chloride, acetate, etc. For example, the protectant organo-mercurial, **Ceresan**, is **2-methoxyethyl mercuric chloride**. It was obviously unwise to spray or broadcast such toxic compounds, and fungicides containing mercury were mostly used as seed dressings (though **phenyl-mercuric acetate** was used in orchards for 20 years until it was officially proscribed in 1971). Organo-mercurials successfully controlled many seed-borne and soil-borne diseases such as rots, seedling blights and damping off, but they have now been replaced by less toxic chemicals (see Thiram, Captan, Carboxin).

Organo-tin fungicides were similar in principle to the organo-mercurials. They were often relatively phytotoxic, but one of them, **triphenyl-tin hydroxide, (Du-ter)**, was widely used to control potato blight. Its LD_{50} (rat) is 108 mg/kg, and it is believed to act by uncoupling oxidative phosphorylation. An organo-copper, **copper naphthenate (Cuprinol)**, cannot be used as a plant spray or a seed treatment: it is a broad-spectrum biocide and is used as a wood preservative.

The **phenols**, another group of organic fungicides, are like copper naphthenate in that they are **disinfectants** (general biocides) rather than protectants. **Pentachlorophenol** is widely used as a wood preservative, and in the control of slime development during paper-making, though environmental concerns are now inhibiting some of its applications. Another phenol, **4,6-dinitro-o-cresol (DNOC)**, is used as a disinfectant spray for orchard floors. It is aimed at the saprobic overwintering stages of such pathogenic fungi as *Venturia inaequalis*, whose teleomorph develops in dead apple leaves, and provides the ascospore inoculum that reinfects the host in spring. DNOC is also used in 'dormant sprays' (sprays which would damage living leaves, so are applied to kill fungi and other pests while fruit trees are still dormant). Phenols apparently work by uncoupling oxidative phosphorylation. The LD_{50} (rat) of pentachlorophenol is 210 mg/kg, and that of DNOC is 25-40 mg/kg.

The 1930's saw the introduction of the **dithiocarbamates**, an important family of organic, protectant fungicides with very low phytotoxicity. There are **dimethyl-dithiocarbamates**, and **ethylene-bis-dithiocarbamates**. The dimethyl-dithiocarbamates include **Thiram, Ferbam,** and **Ziram**. Thiram is used as a seed treatment, to control damping-off diseases. It has an LD_{50} (rat) of 400-900 mg/kg.

Ferbam and Ziram are used to combat leaf pathogens, and have LD_{50}s (rat) of 17,000 and 1,400 mg/kg, respectively. The **ethylene-bis-dithiocarbamates** (EBDCs) include **Nabam, Maneb, Mancozeb** and **Zineb**. The LD_{50}s (rat) of these four fungicides are 400, 7,000, over 8,000, and 5,200 mg/kg, respectively. As you can see, the last three seem to be particularly non-threatening to animals. But the EBDC fungicides are not really safe: when they break down, ethylene thiourea, a carcinogen, is formed. This happens when EBDC-contaminated plant parts are cooked. Ethylene thiourea causes **teratological** effects (malformed offspring) in rats at a dosage of only 10 mg/kg. Despite this drawback, the dithiocarbamates are still the most important of the organic, protectant fungicides. This is because when copper compounds were replaced by dithiocarbamates, potato yields rose dramatically: the dithiocarbamates caused so much less damage to the plants. As you might expect, special precautions are now taken to avoid contamination of food with dithiocarbamate residues. What do you think the most important of these precautions might be?

Another important group of protectant, organic fungicides are the **phthalimides**. The best-known of these is **Captan**, though **Captafol (Difolatan)** and **Folpet (Phaltan)** are also widely used. Captan was registered in Canada in 1951 as a foliar treatment and a seed dressing, often in mixes with other fungicides. It has a very short half-life in soil or water, and has little toxicity to mammals: its LD$_{50}$ (rat) is 9,000 mg/kg. Like heavy metals, it acts on many sites in the target fungi, so resistance is unlikely to develop. Captan is widely used on fruit crops, especially apples, peaches and strawberries, to control many pathogens. It has been estimated that without this fungicide, 25% of the fruit crop would be lost. It is also used to protect conifer seedlings against grey mould (*Botrytis*) and powdery mildew. About 13 million kg of captan are used each year. It is the centre of some controversy, since it has been alleged to have some carcinogenic effects, and has been partially banned in Sweden. Recent North American studies find the accusations unproven, point out that no fully effective substitutes are available, and suggest that fruit growers go on using it, conservatively, and with strict precautions.

Some **quinones** are used as organic, protectant fungicides. **Dichlone (Phygon)** is one of the most effective treatments currently approved for use against apple scab. **Chloranil** and **Dichlorane** control downy mildews (Oomycota): Chloranil is so effective that $775,000 invested in it brought a return of $19,000,000 to the pea industry in 1951.

The Third Generation: Systemic Fungicides

A new generation of fungicides was born with the appearance of the **benzimidazoles** in the 1960's. **Benomyl (Benlate)** was the first **systemic** or **eradicant** fungicide—the first to get **inside** the plant and kill the fungus where it had previously been safe from attack. Benomyl is **apoplastic**—it accumulates mainly between, rather than in, living cells, and travels upward in the transpiration stream flowing through the dead xylem vessels. Since it is not retained in living cells, it does not move downward in the phloem. A benzimidazole fungicide applied near the ground may travel up to the growing tips of a plant, but not down into the roots. Benomyl is stable and non-toxic—its LD$_{50}$ (rat) is 10,000 mg/kg—and it was effective against many ascomycetes and their conidial anamorphs at extremely low doses. Whereas with Maneb it took 5.4 kg a.i./ha (kilograms of active ingredient per hectare) to control apple scab, a mere 0.3 kg a.i./ha of benomyl did the job. Better still, because benomyl is systemic and stable, fewer sprays were needed. Even benomyl's mode of action was new—it absorbed to the spindle fibres of dividing ascomycetous nuclei, disrupting microtubule assembly, and so aborting the division process.

But even benomyl was not a panacea. It became commercially available for use on apples in 1973, and was immediately widely adopted by apple farmers because it controlled all major fungal diseases of this crop. By 1975, some apple pathogens had begun to develop resistance to the new fungicide. Before very long, both *Venturia inaequalis* (the cause of apple scab) and *Penicillium expansum* (which causes a storage rot) had become rather resistant to Benomyl. However, this eradicant fungicide remains active against many other disease organisms, and is still widely used, especially in combination with other fungicides. Although benomyl acts on a wide range of fungi, basidiomycetes are relatively unaffected by it, and one possible future large-scale use of Benomyl is as a treatment for the roots of outplanted conifer seedlings: it should give their basidiomycetous ectomycorrhizal fungi (see chapter 17) a head start by suppressing the competition.

Some of the new ambimobile systemic fungicides are also **selective**—they kill certain groups of fungi and not others. This should enable us to treat certain diseases without totally disrupting the soil mycota, or discouraging the vital mycorrhizal fungi. Some of the newer fungicides, for example **Fosetyl-Al (Aliette, aluminum ethyl phosphite)** and the **acylalanine, Metalaxyl, (Ridomil, Subdue, Apron)**, act selectively on members of Phylum Oomycota: genera such as *Phytophthora, Pythium, Plasmopara,* and *Peronospora,* which cause root rots, damping-off and downy mildews. Metalaxyl has been shown to control many of these fungi, including *Pythium* and *Phytophthora* on soybeans, *Phytophthora* on strawberries, and *Plasmopara* on grape. After the very destructive epidemic of blue mould (*Peronospora tabacina*) which rocked the tobacco farmers of Ontario in 1979, Metalaxyl was quickly registered for soil application to control this disease. Aliette is registered in California and Hawaii to control similar pythiaceous fungi on avocado and various tropical fruits. As a bonus, it has been shown to stimulate the growth of certain endomycorrhizal fungi.

Another new family of systemic but non-selective fungicides are the **sterol-inhibitors**. These act by preventing the biosynthesis of ergosterol, the major sterol in many fungi. Since ergosterol is a basic component of fungal membranes, any shortage will severely curtail fungal growth. Examples of this new group are **Bitertanol (Baycor), Triadimefon (Bayleton), Fenarimol (Rubigan, Bloc), Triforine (Funginox, Saprol), Etaconazole (Vangard), Triarimol (Trimidal), Prochloraz (Sportak),** and **Fendapanil.**

On apple, sterol-inhibitors give good control of scab (*Spilocaea* anamorph of *Venturia inaequalis*: Ascomycetes), powdery mildew (*Oidium* anamorph of *Podosphaera leucotricha*: Ascomycetes), and cedar-apple rust (*Gymnosporangium juniperi-virginianae*: Teliomycetes), if applied weekly—they lack long-term residual activity. On stone fruits, sterol-inhibitors control brown rot (*Monilia* anamorphs of *Monilinia* spp.: Ascomycetes), leaf curl (*Taphrina* spp.: Ascomycetes), shot-hole (*Coryneum* sp.: Coelomycetes), and cherry leaf-spot (*Coccomyces hiemalis*: Ascomycetes). In other words, they inhibit the development of a wide range of unitunicate and bitunicate ascomycetes, ascomycetous anamorphs, and some basidiomycetes as well. Earlier, I mentioned that the dithiocarbamate protectant, maneb, used to control apple scab at 5.4 kg/ha, could be replaced by the benzimidazole systemic, benomyl, at 0.28 kg/ha. The sterol-inhibitor systemic, **Fenarimol,** will do the same job at an even lower dosage: only 0.065 kg/ha.

But as you probably suspect, sterol-inhibitors aren't perfect, either. On stone fruits they don't work well against peach scab (*Cladosporium carpophilum*: Hyphomycetes), *Rhizopus* (Zygomycota) fruit rot, or *Alternaria* (Hyphomycetes) fruit rot. And some resistance has already developed in certain pathogens, such as powdery mildews (Ascomycetes).

Resistance to Fungicides

As you read through the earlier sections of this chapter, you probably noticed that the phenomenon of target resistance to fungicides became troublesome only after the introduction of the systemic fungicides. It transpired that the resistance was developing, not because these fungicides were systemic, but because they acted on very specific sites within the fungus. A broad-spectrum fungicide like mercury poisons so many enzyme systems—it is a multi-site fungicide—that only an absolutely inconceivable number of simultaneous genetic alterations could confer resistance on a pathogen. But benomyl operates by interfering specifically with microtubule assembly in ascomycetes, and it has become apparent that some target organisms, when repeatedly exposed to benomyl, rapidly evolve strains that are resistant to this and other benzimidazole fungicides. This story has been repeated with each new family of systemics. Resistance has been reported to the acylalanines (Metalaxyl), to the carboxamides, and even to some of the sterol-inhibitors.

Dodine is a protectant/eradicant (LD_{50} (rat) = 1,000 mg/kg) used against apple scab. Resistance was reported in 1969, after this fungicide had been used exclusively in some orchards for 10 years. Resistance to Benomyl was noted in 1975, after that fungicide had been used exclusively and repeatedly for only 2 years. Orchardists who used Benomyl + Dodine began to experience resistance to the combination in 1978. We now realize that it is often best to ring the changes: to use mixtures of unrelated fungicides, or to apply a sequence of different fungicides, as part of an Integrated Pest Management scheme. Had this been done initially with Benomyl, we would probably be experiencing fewer resistance problems with this fungicide today.

Choice, Formulation and Application of Fungicides

The many different diseases to which single crops are subject often call for a variety of fungicides. Metalaxyl, a systemic acylalanine, is very effective against an oomycete like *Phytophthora infestans*, which causes late blight of potato, but not against an ascomycetous anamorph like *Alternaria solani*, which causes early blight. So the farmer has to use something like Mancozeb, an ethylene-bis-dithiocarbamate (EBDC), as well, to control the *Alternaria*. Interestingly enough, the *Phytophthora* has also developed some resistance to metalaxyl, and a metalaxyl/mancozeb mix works better than either fungicide alone. Ridomil, a commercial formulation of Metalaxyl, is now sold with a 48% Mancozeb content, and some other acylalanines are now sold only mixed with protectant, residual fungicides. Recent stone-fruit fungicide trials have involved mixing or alternating sterol-inhibitors with other fungicides such as Benomyl, Captafol, Captan, Chlorothalonil (Bravo), Dichlone, Dichloran, Dodine and Thiophanate-methyl.

Tomato powdery mildew (*Leveillula taurica*) is well controlled by Propiconazol (Tilt), or Triadimefon (Bayleton), both sterol-inhibitors, while Benomyl is ineffective. However, because Propiconazol and another sterol-inhibitor,

Etaconazole (Vangard), have undesirable growth-regulator effects on plants of the family Solanaceae, they aren't suitable for use on potatoes and tomatoes.

Perhaps I can place the development of fungicides and our attitudes toward them in perspective by giving a case history. Hops (*Humulus lupulus*), which are an invaluable flavour ingredient in beer (they add the bitterness), suffer from a destructive downy mildew caused by *Pseudoperonospora humuli* (Oomycota). At the beginning of the 20th century this was treated with Bordeaux mixture. More recently, Zineb, an EBDC, was the fungicide of choice. But this breaks down to the carcinogenic ethylene thiourea, so the brewing industry asked that it be abandoned. Metalaxyl is an excellent substitute, but signs of resistance have appeared, so this ambimobile systemic is now often mixed with a protectant such as copper oxychloride. Satisfactory control involves using (1) resistant hop cultivars, (2) sanitation—removing infected material, (3) timely application of fungicides.

Many systemic fungicides are almost insoluble in water, and the plant cuticle keeps water-borne substances out as well as in. So if these fungicides are dispensed as wettable powders (WP), after the spray droplet has dried, most of the fungicide will still be outside the plant. More fungicide gets in if it is supplied as an emulsifiable concentrate (EC), and if surfactants (to lower the surface tension of the spray and make it spread out over the surface of the plant), and humectants (to slow the drying of the droplets), are incorporated. These measures allow lower dosages to be used. New sprayers are now being developed which increase the efficiency of application by dispersing the fungicide in finer droplets than ever before, and by placing an electrostatic charge on the droplets, so that they will be drawn directly to the plant.

The most efficient use of fungicides is obviously as seed dressings. Corn is grown on over 40 million hectares in the U.S., and over 90% of the seed is treated with fungicide. Without this treatment, it is estimated that yield would be reduced by 10-12% in most years. Seed treatment involves some contamination of the soil, but since the newer fungicides are not very persistent, and the amounts applied per hectare are minute, this is not a serious problem. Seed and root dips are also sometimes employed.

Many crops need more than seed dressings if disease is to be adequately controlled. Cotton receives seed treatment, in-furrow treatments, and some foliar sprays for cotton rust. Without fungicides, it is estimated that 20% of the cotton crop would be lost. Peanut leaf spot (*Cercospora*: Hyphomycetes) is potentially devastating. No resistant cultivars exist; crop rotation doesn't help in controlling leaf diseases; and the conditions for infection (leaves wet for 4-6 hours, or near 100% R.H. at temperatures above 22°C) exist almost every day in the S.E. United States. Fungicides have to be applied every 2 weeks. Losses due to leaf spot diseases are now 2.5-15%. Without fungicide, this figure would soar to 20-75%, and peanuts would not be worth growing.

No discussion of fungicides would be complete without some mention of several other techniques for controlling or eradicating fungi. (1) Soil sterilization may involve steam or dry heat treatment, or chemicals such as **formalin**,

chloropicrin and **methyl bromide**. Some of the same chemicals are also used to control arthropods and fungi in stored food. The Canadian Government has recently banned five chemical fumigants, including **ethylene dibromide**, which has been identified as a carcinogen, and most other available fumigants are under investigation. (2) Anti-mould compounds are often added to paints, fabrics, paper, cosmetics, soaps, etc. Many modern fungicides are good candidates for such uses, because they have low solubility in water, are non-toxic to mammals, are biodegradable, and are not very persistent. (3) Mould inhibitors—weak acids such as sorbic, benzoic, acetic, or propionic acid, or their esters, which are fungus inhibitors rather than fungicides, are added to some foods. Calcium propionate, for example, is added to bread to extend its shelf-life.

Further Reading

Canadian Journal of Plant Pathology—recent issues.

Johnston, A. and C. Booth (Eds.) (1983) **Plant Pathologist's Pocketbook** 2nd Edn. Commonwealth Mycological Institute, Kew.

Marsh, R.W. (Ed.) (1977) **Systemic Fungicides**. 2nd Edn. Longman, London.

Phytopathology—recent issues.

Chapter 14

Fungi as Agents of Biological Control

Introduction

In recent years we have begun to understand the consequences of the widespread and repeated use of chemical biocides to control the host of organisms, such as insects, weeds and fungi, that threaten human interests. You probably know that while many pests became resistant to persistent pesticides like DDT (a chlorinated hydrocarbon), predatory birds such as the Peregrine falcon suffered population crashes as a result of the biological accumulation of DDT residues. Since we, too, are at the top of many food webs, this and other examples could hardly be ignored. We soon phased out the more persistent pesticides, at least in North America, and intensified the search for replacements.

Newer generations of pesticides are less persistent, but are often very toxic to many non-target organisms, including the natural enemies of the pests and, not too surprisingly, humans. The elimination of natural enemies may allow outbreaks of secondary pests, and rapid resurgence of the target species, once the pesticide loses its activity. To make things worse, some pests soon develop resistance to each new formulation. Nevertheless, many chemical pesticides give quick results and a high level of control, and no substitutes are yet available for most of them, so we will inevitably go on using them for many purposes; but it makes good sense to look for less dangerous alternatives. Biological control—often shortened to **biocontrol**—is one of these alternatives.

How does biocontrol work? We begin by looking for a natural predator, parasite, or competitor of the organism to be controlled, then we try to shift the ecological equilibrium in favour of this biocontrol agent so that it can drastically reduce the population of the target organism. These are simple principles, but their practical application is often difficult.

Natural enemies of pests and pathogens may be few, rare, or inconspicuous. They may be found only in restricted areas, or at specific times of year; they may have complex life histories involving two hosts, and they may attack friend as well as foe. They may even have been left behind when the pest 'migrated' to a new area or continent. It often takes patient detective work to bring them to light, then years to test their host range, develop techniques to mass-produce them, and learn the most effective ways and times to introduce them to the host population.

It is encouraging to know that biocontrol has already had several spectacular successes—you may already be aware of the moth (*Cactoblastis*: Lepidoptera) which was introduced to Australia to control the prickly pear (*Opuntia*: Cactaceae) which was taking over vast areas of grazing land; and the myxomatosis virus which was introduced to control the population explosion of rabbits. I will tell you about a few other famous victories (which naturally involve fungi), and about some promising or potential applications of fungi in this area.

Most early attempts at biocontrol pitted one arthropod against another, for example, ladybugs (Coleoptera, Coccinellidae) against aphids (Homoptera, Aphididae). But the fungi are, potentially at least, better biocontrol agents than any arthropod, because: (1) Fungi have an extremely high reproductive capacity. (2) Fungi have a very short generation time. (3) Fungi are often highly specific in their action, attacking only the host with which they have co-evolved. (4) Fungi often produce resting stages or saprobic phases that can survive for a long time when no host organism is available. If you will also compare these four features with the characteristics of chemical pesticides, you will understand the advantages of using fungal biocontrol whenever possible.

So why haven't the fungi cornered the market? The problem was partly one of perception, partly one of practice. Under natural conditions, the population of a fungal parasite may build up to very high levels, but not quickly enough to control the target organism during the period when it causes the most damage. There's not much advantage in a fungus killing off most of our houseflies in September, when the nuisance has been around all summer, and the frosts of October would have done the job anyway.

So fungi have several potential shortcomings as biocontrol agents. (1) They may only damage, rather than kill, their host. (2) They may only reduce, rather than eliminate, the target population. (3) They may do both of these things relatively slowly. These outcomes are not entirely satisfactory to humans, who are used to the quick action and high kill-rate of chemical biocides. But the non-toxic, target-specific, self-reproducing, self-perpetuating characteristics of fungi are persuasive incentives for considering them as alternatives, so we are making efforts to overcome their deficiencies.

Several critical factors must be manipulated before we can count on success. (1) It must be established that the biocontrol fungus is not pathogenic to any economically valuable organisms that might be exposed to it. (2) A large amount of inoculum must be available. (3) This must be properly distributed early enough to saturate the target population well before that reaches its peak. (4) Climatic conditions must favour growth, sporulation and dispersal of the fungus.

Where can we make effective use of fungi in biocontrol? Principally in three areas: (1) control of arthropod or other invertebrate pests, (2) control of weeds, and (3) control of fungi causing plant diseases or biodeterioration. I'll examine these areas in turn, and give some case histories. Even where fungi alone cannot give effective biocontrol, they may often be usefully combined with other agents, biological and/or chemical, in an integrated pest management program. (Integrated pest management, or IPM, is discussed in Chapter 12).

(1) Control of Animal Pests by Entomogenous Fungi

Arthropods, and particularly insects, are our greatest competitors. They damage or destroy our crops before and after harvest, and transmit many fatal or debilitating diseases. In the Third World, insect control is often a matter of life or death. A number of fungi are lethal parasites of arthropods; in most cases the fungal spores are released in enormous numbers, and can infect the host at any stage of its life cycle. The spores germinate on the host cuticle, the germ tube penetrates the chitinous exoskeleton, and branching hyphae riddle the viscera. Spore-bearing structures of the fungus eventually emerge from the corpse, liberating fresh inoculum. We are only now learning how to exploit entomogenous fungi in biocontrol.

Several of these fungi cause spectacular epidemics in natural insect populations, and are now being grown in large-scale artificial culture to produce inoculum with which we hope to induce epidemics on demand. I will mention examples from three fungal Phyla: these range from established success stories to promising newcomers, with one case of tantalizing, but as yet unfulfilled, potential. Most of my examples are illustrated in Fig. 14.1. Four hyphomycetes have proved so successful that spray concentrates containing their spores are now sold under trade names as **mycoinsecticides**—but don't look for them yet at your local hardware store or nursery.

(1) *Beauveria bassiana* (Hyphomycetes) has a fascinating history. In the early 1800's the so-called **muscardine disease** was ravaging the silkworm industries of Europe. Silkworms died, their corpses hardened, and a white bloom appeared on them. The disease spread rapidly through silkworm colonies, but no one knew what caused it, though there was some notion that it was probably 'environmental' in origin. Bassi, an Italian scientist, subjected the larvae to the most barbarous treatments: 'the poor creatures died by thousands and in a thousand ways.' Eventually he discovered that the disease was caused by an 'infectious principle' which he identified as the white powder on the mummified corpses. He even recognized that it was a parasitic fungus. So originated, in 1834, the **germ theory** of disease—a milestone in the history of biology. Conidia of the fungus around which the theory was conceived are now mass-produced as a preparation called **Boverin**, and have been used in Russia since 1965 to control the Colorado potato beetle (*Leptinotarsa*: Coleoptera). This pest, if left unchecked, will completely strip potato plants of their leaves. The Boverin, which contains 30 billion conidia/g, is sprayed onto the potato fields twice, at a rate of 1-1.5 kg/ha, with 15-21 days between applications. Boverin also controls codling moth (*Carpocapsa*: Lepidoptera), whose larvae cause enormous losses by tunnelling into young apples. In damp seasons, naturally occurring *B. bassiana* helps control chinch bugs (*Blissus leucopterus*) in lawns.

(2) *Metarhizium anisopliae* (Hyphomycetes), available as a commercial mycoinsecticide under the name **Metaquino**, is widely used in Brazil to control Cercopidae (Homoptera) (the nymphs are known as spittlebugs and suck large quantities of sap from their host plant; the adults are called froghoppers) on sugarcane and in pastures. The same hyphomycete has also been used with great

success as part of an integrated pest management program in the South Pacific islands of Tongatapu and Western Samoa. The Rhinoceros beetle (*Oryctes*) arrived on these islands about 1930. It subsequently killed all newly planted coconut palms by chewing up the young shoots, and similarly prevented most of the existing palms from reproducing. The introduction of *Metarhizium* and an entomopathogenic virus in 1968 soon controlled the beetle. Now, young trees survive, and old trees once again bear fruit. Mosquito larvae of the genera *Anopheles*, *Aedes*, and *Culex* are also attacked by *Metarhizium*, as are spruce budworm larvae.

(3) *Hirsutella thompsonii* (Hyphomycetes) causes spectacular epidemics each year among populations of citrus rust mite (*Phyllocoptruta*: Acarina) in

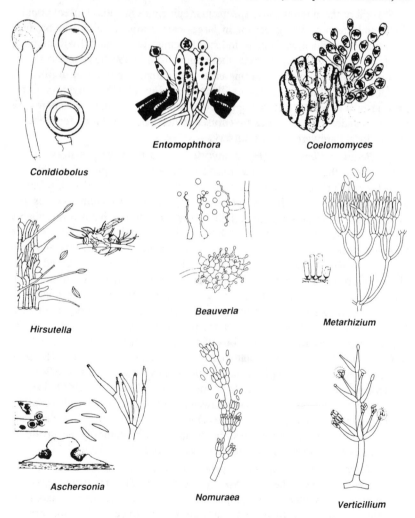

Conidiobolus

Entomophthora

Coelomomyces

Hirsutella

Beauveria

Metarhizium

Aschersonia

Nomuraea

Verticillium

Fig. 14.1 Genera of fungi used in biocontrol of arthropods.

Florida—but only after the fruit has been damaged. Mass-produced as a **mycoacaricide** under the trade name **Mycar**, it is now sprayed early in the season to prevent the build-up of mite populations.

(4) *Verticillium lecanii* (Hyphomycetes) causes natural epidemics in two groups of plant-sucking pests: aphids (Homoptera, Aphidoidea) which cause malformation and transmit viruses, and scale insects (Homoptera, Coccoidea) in the tropics and in greenhouses. Its conidia are now available commercially under the trade names **Vertalec** and **Mycotal**. Vertalec contains a strain which is highly pathogenic to aphids, while Mycotal incorporates another strain that is lethal to greenhouse whitefly.

(5) *Nomuraea rileyi* (Hyphomycetes) doesn't yet have a trade name, but is nevertheless an effective mycoinsecticide, causing high mortality in caterpillar pests (Lepidoptera, Noctuidae) on cabbage, clover and soybean. It is being intensively studied for potential large scale agricultural applications.

(6) My last example of a fungus being mass-produced for use in biocontrol of insects is *Entomophthora* (Zygomycota, Entomophthorales). This may well be the only entomogenous fungus that most people will ever see. It infects and kills houseflies, which for some reason usually crawl into an exposed location before dying. The cause of death can be ascertained from the masses of sporangiophores emerging through the insect's cuticle, or from the halo of discharged sporangia around the victim. Roland Thaxter, who made an incredibly productive life's work of exploring the fungi growing on insects, was drawn to this field when an epidemic of *Entomophthora* decimated the fly colony maintained at Harvard for experimental purposes.

Although species of *Entomophthora* attack aphids, houseflies, caterpillars, and grasshoppers, their use in biocontrol has been hindered by the short lifespan of their sporangia, and by the great dependence of the fungus on such factors as rainfall, temperature, and host density. The spotted alfalfa aphid (*Therioaphia*) was first detected in Australia in 1977. It had somehow contrived to arrive without the *Entomophthora* pathogens that often kill it in North America. *Entomophthora* was introduced into Australian populations of the aphid in 1979, and is apparently spreading. This theme, of a pest reaching a new country and leaving its parasites or predators behind, is a recurring one, and often presents an opportunity for biocontrol.

(7) Dutch elm disease is caused by an ascomycete, *Ophiostoma ulmi*, but is transmitted by bark beetles. In Britain it has recently been observed that a coelomycetous anamorph, *Phomopsis oblonga*, occurring naturally in the bark of the elms, discourages or disrupts the breeding of the local vectors, *Scolytus scolytus* and *Scolytus multistriatus* (Coleoptera). This may help control the spread of the disease.

(8) *Coelomomyces* (Chytridiomycota) is an obligate parasite of mosquito larvae, and sometimes causes heavy mortality in natural populations of such important disease-carrying mosquitoes as *Anopheles gambiae*, a notorious vector of malaria. Although natural epidemics are fairly common occurrences, attempts to infect larval mosquito populations were unsuccessful. The reason

for this became clear in the mid-1970's, when it was discovered that *Coelomomyces* requires a copepod or an ostracod as an obligate alternate host if it is to complete its life cycle. This problem may well prevent this fungus from being exploited in the biocontrol of mosquitoes. Yet since these insects are probably the most important pests in the world—there are seven million cases of malaria each year in Africa, and half a million deaths, almost all of them children— strenuous efforts are being made to overcome this impasse.

If you have sympathy to spare for insects, save it for larval scale insects (Homoptera, Coccoidea) and whiteflies (Homoptera, Aleyrodidae)—they are susceptible to the widest range of entomogenous fungi. They can be attacked by members of the Chytridiomycetes, Zygomycetes, unitunicate and bitunicate Ascomycetes, Phragmobasidiomycetes, and conidial fungi (Hyphomycetes and Coelomycetes). Since scales and whiteflies are difficult to control by chemical means, I think we may eventually use mycoinsecticides routinely to keep them in check. Another potential application for biocontrol is in the suppression of arthropods that infest stored food, where it is impossible, for obvious reasons, to use regular pesticides. Table 14.1 lists some of the actual and potential uses of fungi in biocontrol of arthropods.

Table 14.1 Some Fungal Pathogens of Arthropods

Genus	Trade name	Phylum	Principal target
Coelomomyces		Chytridiomycota	Mosquito larvae
Entomophthora		Zygomycota	Aphids
Conidiobolus		Zygomycota	Aphids
Beauveria	'Boverin'	Dikaryomycota (Hyphomycetes)	Colorado beetle, codling moth
Hirsutella	'Mycar'	Dikaryomycota (Hyphomycetes)	Citrus rust mite
Metarhizium	'Metaquino'	Dikaryomycota (Hyphomycetes)	Spittlebug, mosquito larvae, rhinoceros beetle lepidopteran larvae
Verticillium	'Vertalec'	Dikaryomycota (Hyphomycetes)	Aphids
Verticillium	'Mycotal'	Dikaryomycota (Hyphomycetes)	Whitefly
Nomuraea		Dikaryomycota (Hyphomycetes)	Lepidopteran larvae
Aschersonia		Dikaryomycota (Hyphomycetes)	Whitefly, scale insects

Nematodes, rotifers, copepods, tardigrades, collembola, soil amoebae and other microscopic animals are also parasitized or preyed upon by fungi. I use the latter phrase advisedly, because a number of microfungi (again from several major taxonomic groups) are actually predators of these animals: they have evolved special trapping devices with which they catch their prey, thereupon sending in hyphae to exploit the newly acquired substrate. Other parasitic fungi have small spores of unusual shapes, which when eaten by the unsuspecting animal, catch in its gullet and colonize its viscera. But these stories, the pictures that will help you to visualize this strange microcosm, and the possible roles of such fungi in biocontrol, can be found in chapter 15.

(2) Control of Weeds by Plant Pathogenic Fungi

Now for a look at the second major area of fungal involvement in biocontrol. The target organisms here are higher plants; pioneer species of remarkable vigour which compete only too well with our domesticated plants. Weeds: they have even spawned a strange verb, 'to weed' (which actually means 'to de-weed'), and every gardener pays tribute on his or her knees to their success. Until recently, farmers could control weeds only with various forms of cultivation, but now they can call on broad-spectrum herbicides like Paraquat, and selective weedkillers such as 2,4-D and 2,4,5-T. These control dicotyledonous weeds in monocotyledonous crops (fortunately, many of our staple food plants are grasses—wheat, corn, rice, millet, sorghum, oats, barley, rye). And, of course, they used to help us to keep marginally ahead of the dandelions which grow so well in our lawns. But these weedkillers, after being freely broadcast for years, were discovered to have ingredients that are toxic and teratogenic (causing developmental defects). And no herbicide is available to control annual grasses in small grains. Even at their best, chemical herbicides lack the finely tuned selectivity of many plant pathogenic fungi, which often restrict their attacks to a single host species. For a discussion of how fungi attack and damage or destroy plants, refer to chapter 12.

Of the more than 300,000 plants, a mere 200 species cause almost all of our weed problems. Two-thirds of the world's worst weeds are present in North America, and crop losses caused by weeds in the U.S. are estimated to cost $14 billion a year. Many weeds are plants which have been accidentally introduced to a new area without their natural enemies. Of 117 common weeds in Canada, more than three-quarters were introduced from other continents. The classical biocontrol strategy is to search in the weed's homeland for fungal pathogens that help to keep it in check there. This section details several examples of fungi (most of which are illustrated in Fig. 14.2) which are actual or potential biocontrol agents for weeds. Rust fungi (Teliomycetes, Uredinales) are often extremely host-specific, and it is fitting that my first two examples of fungal herbicides should be members of this group.

(1) When European blackberry (*Rubus* sp.) began to encroach on ranges and pastures in Chile, introduction of a European rust fungus, *Phragmidium violaceum*, successfully suppressed its spread. Unlike wheat rust, this species needs

only one host to complete its life cycle—we say it is **autoecious**—so no other plants were threatened by its introduction.

(2) A Mediterranean plant, *Chondrilla juncea* ('rush skeletonweed'), was accidentally introduced to Australia in the early 1900's, leaving its natural enemies behind. It spread rapidly, and infested hundreds of thousands of hectares of wheatlands, competing with the wheat for water and nitrogen, and clogging harvesting equipment. By the 1940's some farmers had given up

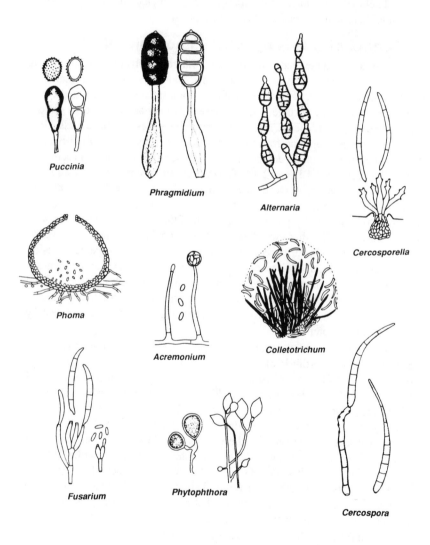

Puccinia

Phragmidium

Alternaria

Cercosporella

Phoma

Acremonium

Colletotrichum

Fusarium

Phytophthora

Cercospora

Fig. 14.2 Genera of fungi used in biocontrol of weeds.

growing wheat. Those who persevered were later able to spray with 2,4,5,-T to control it, though the cost of spraying vast areas, which in Australia give low yields anyway, was almost prohibitive. In 1966 a search for potential biocontrol agents was mounted in the Mediterranean region. By 1971 a rust fungus from Italy, *Puccinia chondrillina*, was being released in Australia. The introduction was so successful that almost half a million hectares no longer need to be sprayed. This program has already saved Australia 112 times its cost, in one of the most spectacular successes ever achieved with biocontrol. There is a footnote to this story: on its home territory in the Mediterranean region, *Puccinia chondrillina* itself has a fungal hyperparasite (*Eudarluca caricis*: Coelomycetes), and the material being introduced to Australia had to be carefully checked to make sure it was not contaminated by this hyperparasite, which might have reduced its effectiveness.

In each of the examples just given, the fungus is obligately biotrophic, so inoculum cannot be mass-produced in artificial culture. In these cases, small amounts of natural inoculum have been introduced to the area in which the host plant is growing, and further spread of the pathogen has been by natural spore dispersal. In other examples of fungal biocontrol of weeds, of which I will mention five, it has been necessary to mass-produce the fungal propagules and apply them as a **mycoherbicide** spray. This massive inoculum swamps any host resistance, and if conditions are right, initiates an epidemic.

(3) Northern joint vetch, *Aeschynomene virginica*, infests rice and soybeans in the United States. It is severely attacked and often killed by the coelomycete, *Colletotrichum gloeosporioides*, but in many areas low levels of natural inoculum seem to preclude development of an epidemic. Accordingly, plants were sprayed with a suspension containing 2-6 million conidia/mL, and 95-100% of the sprayed plants subsequently succumbed. This was the first practical mycoherbicide, which has now been patented and is being produced under the trade name **Collego**. The fungus overwinters on and in joint vetch seeds, but this natural inoculum must be augmented each year.

(4) Strangler vine, *Morrenia odorata*, is a weed of Florida citrus groves that can overgrow mature citrus trees. It is now controlled by a commercial mycoherbicide, **Devine**, which contains an oomycetous pathogen, *Phytophthora palmivora*. The fungus causes a root and stem rot, and can kill mature vines in 3-4 weeks. One pint of the liquid suspension contains nearly a million chlamydospores/mL, and treats an acre, when diluted in 50 gallons of water. The fungus, once established in the soil, persists well from year to year.

(5) A search has recently been made for potential biocontrol agents of water hyacinth (*Eichhornia crassipes*), a beautiful but prolific aquatic plant which has clogged waterways, lakes and reservoirs in many parts of the tropics. In 1976 a previously unknown species of hyphomycete, *Cercospora rodmanii*, was found causing a local epidemic on *Eichhornia* in Florida. This fungus has now been patented as a mycoherbicide, and is being produced commercially, following extensive research to ensure that it is not harmful to non-target plants or animals.

(6) Another hyphomycete, *Acremonium zonatum*, which is also pathogenic to water hyacinth, may yet be used along with the *Cercospora* and other agents in an integrated weed control programme, but there is still some concern about its host range, since it is known to attack two valuable crop plants: figs (*Ficus*) and coffee (*Coffea*). This demonstrates the care that must be taken to ensure that biocontrol agents are without unwanted side-effects. But since the potential for fungal control of many weeds exists, it is surely matter of time before this is developed, especially as the more insidious effects of chemical herbicides come to light.

(7) A species of *Colletotrichum* (Coelomycetes) is now used in some parts of China to control the parasitic flowering plant, *Cuscuta*, ('dodder') which can be a serious weed on certain crops.

(8) *Phomopsis convolvulus* is being tested in Canada as a potential biocontrol agent for field bindweed, *Convolvulus arvensis*. Other examples of actual or potential mycoherbicides are listed in Table 14.2.

Table 14.2
Actual (A) and potential (P) applications of fungi in weed control.

Fungal Biocontrol Agent	Weed Target	Crop infested & Area
(A) *Puccinia chondrillina* (Uredinales)	*Chondrilla juncea* (rush skeletonweed)	wheat, Australia
(A) *Phragmidium violaceum* (Uredinales)	*Rubus* sp. (blackberry)	pastures, Chile
(A) *Colletotrichum xanthii* (Coelomycetes)	*Xanthium spinosum* (bathurst burr)	rangeland, Australia
(A) *C. gloeosporioides* (Coelomycetes) **Collego**	*Aeschynomene virginica* (northern joint vetch)	rice, soybean, U.S.A.
(A) *Phytophthora palmivora* (Oomycota) **DeVine**	*Morrenia odorata* (strangler vine)	citrus, Florida
(P) *Ascochyta pteridium* (Coelomycetes)	*Pteridium aquilinum* (bracken fern)	pastures, Britain
(P) *Colletotrichum malvarum* (Coelomycetes)	*Sida spinosa* (prickly sida)	cotton, soybeans, U.S.A.
(P) *Colletotrichum dematium* (Coelomycetes)	*Cassia occidentalis* (coffee senna)	pastures, U.S.A.
(P) *C. dematium* (Coelomycetes)	*Convolvulus arvensis* (field bindweed)	sorghum, U.S.A.

(P) *C. coccodes* (Coelomycetes)	*Abutilon theophrasti* (velvetleaf)	lima beans, U.S.A.
(P) C. gloeosporioides (Coelomycetes)	*Jussiaea decurrens* (winged water primrose)	rice, U.S.A.
(P) *Acremonium* sp. (Hyphomycetes)	*Cassia surattensis* (kolomana)	pastures, Hawaii
(A) *Acremonium diospyri* (Hyphomycetes)	*Diospyros virginiana* (persimmon)	rangeland, U.S.A.
(P) *Cercospora lantanae* (Hyphomycetes)	*Lantana camara* (lantana)	rangeland, Hawaii
(A) *Cercospora eupatorii* (Hyphomycetes)	*Eupatorium adenophorum* (crofton weed)	Australia
(P) *Alternaria cassiae* (Hyphomycetes)	*Cassia obtusifolia* (sicklepod)	cotton, soybean, U.S.A.
(P) *Alternaria macrospora* (Hyphomycetes)	*Anoda cristata* (spurred anoda)	cotton, U.S.A.
(P) *Fusarium lateritium* (Hyphomycetes)	*Anoda cristata*	cotton, U.S.A.
(P) *Fusarium lateritium* (Hyphomycetes)	*Sida spinosa* (prickly sida)	cotton, soybean, U.S.A.
(P) *Fusarium solani* (Hyphomycetes)	*Cucurbita texana* (Texas gourd)	
(A) *Cercospora rodmanii* (Hyphomycetes)	*Eichornia crassipes* (water hyacinth)	water, tropics
(P) *Acremonium zonatum* (Hyphomycetes)	*Eichornia crassipes* (water hyacinth)	water, tropics
(P) *Cercospora piaropi* (Hyphomycetes)	*Eichornia crassipes* (water hyacinth)	water, tropics
(P) *Fusarium roseum* (Hyphomycetes)	*Eichornia crassipes* (water hyacinth)	water, tropics
(P) *Sclerotinia sclerotiorum* (Ascomycetes)	*Cirsium arvense* (Canada thistle)	many crops, Canada, U.S.A.
(P) *Phomopsis convolvulus* (Coelomycetes)	*Convolvulus arvensis* (field bindweed)	many crops, many countries.

(3) Fungi in Biocontrol of Other Fungi

This third area in which fungi have biocontrol potential may initially seem strange, but I'm sure you will quickly appreciate the logic of setting a fungus to control a fungus. The main reasons can be stated very briefly: (A) Some fungi are parasitic on other fungi—I've already mentioned one example in discussing the biocontrol of *Chondrilla* in Australia. (B) Fungi often compete strenuously with one another for substrate. (C) Preinoculation of a host plant with avirulent strains of some normally pathogenic fungi, or with close but non-pathogenic relatives of those fungi, can protect the plant from attack by virulent strains of the same fungi. I will discuss several examples of each approach.

(1) *Sphaerellopsis filum* (Coelomycetes), often discussed in the literature under an older name, *Darluca filum*, is parasitic on many rust fungi (Teliomycetes, Uredinales). It is credited with keeping some rust diseases down to low levels in natural host populations, and it has been proposed as a potential biocontrol agent against the heteroecious rusts, *Cronartium strobilinum* and *Cronartium fusiforme* (which cause serious blister rust diseases of pines), while they are growing on their other hosts, oak trees. The fungus can move from the oak to the pine only if teliospores are produced, so it is significant that in some natural populations of *Cronartium strobilinum* on oak, 93% of the rust sori were found to be infected with *Sphaerellopsis*, and only 0.8% formed teliospores. Researchers have concluded that the parasite was more likely to control *C. strobilinum*, which was growing actively in the oaks all summer, than *C. fusiforme*, whose few weeks of activity on the host did not give the *Sphaerellopsis* enough time to colonize the rust and control it. The future of *Sphaerellopsis* in rust control is still uncertain.

(2) *Tuberculina maxima* (Hyphomycetes) is another parasite of rust fungi that is active against *Cronartium ribicola* (Teliomycetes, Uredinales), the cause of white pine blister rust, but although its biocontrol potential has been hinted at by various forest pathologists, it has not yet been exploited.

(3) *Cicinnobolus cesatii* (Coelomycetes) parasitizes powdery mildews (Ascomycetes, Erysiphales), and is now being used as a spray to control *Sphaerotheca* on greenhouse cucumbers.

(4) *Cladobotryum amazonense* (Hyphomycetes) gives control of *Crinipellis perniciosa* (Holobasidiomycetes, Agaricales), which causes a serious disease of cocoa, called witches' broom.

Competition between fungi is the area in which biocontrol of fungal pathogens has achieved its greatest successes. Species of *Trichoderma* (Hyphomycetes), green moulds common in some forest soils, are powerful antagonists to many pathogens.

(5) *Trichoderma viride* both parasitizes the hyphae of many other fungi and produces an antibiotic. This double-barreled approach allows it to deal effectively with soil pathogens such as *Rhizoctonia solani* (a sterile basidiomycetous

anamorph that causes a variety of diseases on many hosts), and *Armillaria mellea* (Holobasidiomycetes, Agaricales), which kills many species of trees.

(6) *Trichoderma harzianum*, mass-produced in culture and applied to soil, controls *Sclerotium rolfsii* (another sterile fungus which causes diseases of many hosts) on tomatoes and peanuts. A pharmaceutical company is developing *T.*

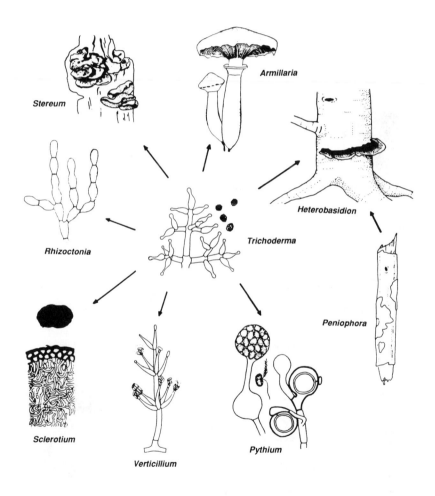

Fig. 14.3 Fungal pathogens controlled by ***Trichoderma*** and ***Peniophora*.**

harzianum as a commercial biocontrol for *Sclerotium rolfsii*. This could be indirectly frustrated by the fact that peanuts are very susceptible to attack by *Cercospora* (Hyphomycetes), which causes a serious leaf-spot disease. Repeated fungicidal sprays needed to control the *Cercospora* also reduce the population of *Trichoderma* and lead to an increase in stem blight caused by *Sclerotium rolfsii*.

(7) Nevertheless, in France, *Trichoderma* spray concentrate is competitive in price with the well-known systemic fungicide, Benomyl, and is used to control

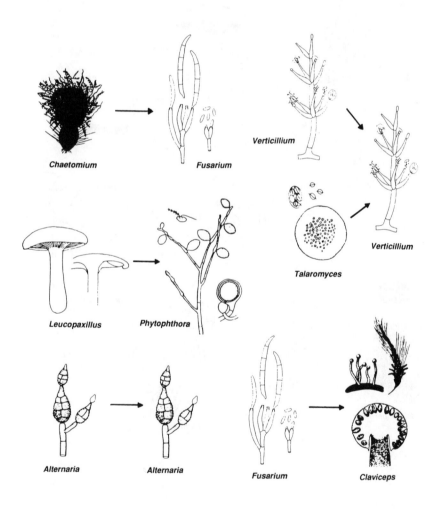

Fig. 14.4 Fungal biocontrol agents and their target pathogens (see text).

Verticillium fungicola (Hyphomycetes), a serious pathogen of the cultivated mushroom, *Agaricus brunnescens* (Agaricales).

(8) Some basidiomycetous pathogens of trees often gain entrance to their host through wounds. It has been found that application of *Trichoderma* spores to fresh wounds, such as those caused by pruning of plum trees, will prevent subsequent infection by *Stereum purpureum* (Holobasidiomycetes, Aphyllophorales), which causes silverleaf disease.

(9) Freshly cut tree stumps painted with a *Trichoderma* spore suspension will not be invaded by *Heterobasidion annosum* (Aphyllophorales), a very serious root pathogen that spreads from tree to tree through root contact.

(10) A commercial preparation of the saprobic *Peniophora gigantea* (Aphyllophorales) is available for treating newly cut pine stumps to protect them from invasion by *Heterobasidion*.

(11) Spraying apple leaves with spore suspensions of *Chaetomium globosum* (Ascomycetes, Sordariales) reduces infection by the apple scab fungus, the *Spilocaea* anamorph of *Venturia inaequalis*.

(12) Protection from some soil-borne diseases can be obtained by treating seeds with biocontrol fungi. For example, spores of *Chaetomium globosum* will protect corn against seedling biight caused by *Fusarium roseum* (Hyphomycetes). Spores of *Penicillium* spp. (Hyphomycetes) will confer similar protection on peas.

(13) Eggplant is started in pots before outplanting. Inoculation of the potting medium with spores of *Talaromyces flavus* (Ascomycetes, Eurotiales) has been found to reduce the incidence of wilt caused by *Verticillium dahliae* (Hyphomycetes) by 67-76%, and to increase yield by 18-54%.

Preinoculation or, as it is sometimes called, **cross-protection**, is now receiving serious attention from plant pathologists.

(14) Application of weakly pathogenic strains of *Verticillium alboatrum* (Hyphomycetes) protected cotton plants from more virulent strains of the same wilt-disease fungus. This protection appears to accrue from a kind of immunization process. The weak pathogen, while doing little damage, stimulates the host plant to produce **phytoalexins**—specifically antifungal compounds— which are then ready to repel subsequent attacks by more pathogenic strains. Sometimes different species, rather than different strains of the same species, are used to induce cross-protection.

(15) For example, the weakly pathogenic *Verticillium nigrescens* (Hyphomycetes) induces resistance in mint plants to the more pathogenic, wilt-producing, *Verticillium dahliae*.

In 1980, Ontario growers harvested 33,000 tonnes of peaches worth over $14 million. But another 57,000 tonnes had to be imported. Ontario should be growing more peaches, yet peach production is gradually declining. Why is this? It is largely due to a fungal disease called peach canker, caused by the coelomycetous *Cytospora* anamorph of *Leucostoma* (Ascomycetes). The *Cytospora* can't attack healthy trees: it can gain access only through wounds, such as those regularly caused by pruning. Infections begin and spread during fall and spring dormancy. Each year the cankers spread, yield declines, and eventually the tree dies. Because of the deep-seated nature of the disease, only limited chemical control has been possible, even with the newest fungicides. Fortunately, there is now some prospect of biological control of peach canker by species of *Trichoderma* and *Gliocladium* (Hyphomycetes), which are highly competitive saprobes, and also actively parasitize many fungi.

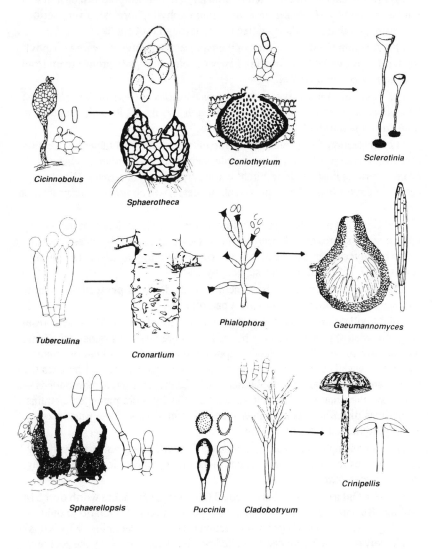

Fig. 14.5 More fungal biocontrol agents and their target pathogens (see text).

Grey mould of strawberries is caused by *Botrytis cinerea* (Hyphomycetes), and has usually been combatted with the fungicide, Captan. In recent years, the advisability of using Captan has been questioned. Fortunately, it has been established that the mycoparasite *Gliocladium roseum* (Hyphomycetes) can also control *Botrytis*. We know that the crucial stage in the development of the problem is during the flowering of the strawberry, well before the fruit forms. An ingenious delivery system has been designed, in which honey bees leaving the hive are automatically dusted with about 50,000 *Gliocladium* conidia, which they deliver directly to the flowers.

Table 14.3
Some actual and potential applications of fungi in the control of fungal plant diseases.

Target fungus	Disease & host(s)	Biocontrol fungus
Rhizoctonia solani (anamorphic Aphyllophorales)	damping-off, root rot, stem canker: many crops	*Trichoderma viride* (Hyphomycetes)
Armillaria mellea (Agaricales)	root disease: trees	*Trichoderma viride* (Hyphomycetes)
Stereum purpureum (Aphyllophorales)	silverleaf: plum	*Trichoderma viride* (Hyphomycetes)
Heterobasidion annosum (Aphyllophorales)	root disease: trees	*Trichoderma viride* (Hyphomycetes)
Heterobasidion annosum (Aphyllophorales)	root disease: trees	*Peniophora gigantea* (Aphyllophorales)
Pythium spp. (Oomycetes)	damping-off: seedlings	*Trichoderma hamatum* (Hyphomycetes)
Sclerotium rolfsii (sclerotial anamorph)	stem blight: peanuts	*Trichoderma harzianum* (Hyphomycetes)
Verticillium fungicola (Hyphomycetes)	dry bubble: mushrooms	*Trichoderma* sp. (Hyphomycetes)
Fusarium roseum (Hyphomycetes)	seedling blight: corn	*Chaetomium globosum* (Unitunicatae)
Phytophthora cinnamomi (Oomycetes)	root rot: trees & herbs (48 families)	*Leucopaxillus* sp. (Agaricales)
Verticillium alboatrum (Hyphomycetes)	wilt: cotton	*Verticillium alboatrum* (Hyphomycetes)

Verticillium dahliae (Hyphomycetes)	wilt: eggplant	*Talaromyces flavus* (Eurotiales)
Verticillium dahliae (Hyphomycetes)	wilt: mint	*Verticillium nigrescens* (Hyphomycetes)
Alternaria zinneae (Hyphomycetes)	leaf spot: beans	*Alternaria tenuissima* (Hyphomycetes)
Claviceps purpurea (Unitunicatae)	ergot: grasses	*Fusarium roseum* (Hyphomycetes)
Sphaerotheca fuliginea (Unitunicatae)	powdery mildew: cucumbers	*Cicinnobolus cesa*ii (Coelomycetes)
Cronartium ribicola (Uredinales)	blister rust: pines	*Tuberculina maxima* (Hyphomycetes)
Cronartium strobilinum (Uredinales)	blister rust: pines	*Sphaerellopsis filum* (Coelomycetes)
Puccinia spp. (Uredinales)	rust: many crops	*Sphaerellopsis filum* (Coelomycetes)
Sclerotinia sclerotiorum (Unitunicatae)	watery rot: many crops	*Coniothyrium minitans* (Coelomycetes)
Gaeumannomyces graminis (Unitunicatae)	take-all: wheat	*Phialophora radicicola* (Hyphomycetes)
Crinipellis perniciosa (Agaricales)	witches' broom: cocoa	*Cladobotryum amazonense* (Hyphomycetes)
Botrytis cinerea (Hyphomycetes)	grey mould of strawberry	*Gliocladium roseum* (Hyphomycetes)

The years ahead should see many advances in biocontrol by fungi: certainly our increasing knowledge of the adverse effects of chemical biocides on the biosphere and on ourselves car only accelerate the search for alternatives.

Further Reading

Anon. (1980) Proceedings of workshop on insect pest management with microbial agents. Boyce Thompson Institute, Ithaca.

Baker, K.F. and R.J. Cook (1974) **Biological Control of Plant Pathogens**. Freeman, San Francisco.

Baker, R., P. Hanchey and S.D. Dottarar (1978) Protection of carnation against Fusarium stem rot by fungi. Phytopathology **68**: 1495-1501.

Bastos, C.N., H.C. Evans and R.A. Samson (1981) A new hyperparasitic fungus, *Cladobotryum amazonense*, with potential for control of fungal pathogens of cocoa. Transactions of the British Mycological Society **77**: 273-278.

Burges, H.D. (Ed.) (1981) **Microbial Control of Pests and Plant Diseases 1970-1980**. Academic Press, New York.

Charudattan, R. and H.L. Walker (1982) **Biological Control of Weeds with Plant Pathogens**. Wiley, New York.

Cullen, D., F.M. Berbee and J.H. Andrews (1984) *Chaetomium globosum* antagonizes the apple scab pathogen, *Venturia inaequalis*, under field conditions. Canadian Journal of Botany **62**: 1814-1818.

Cullen, J.M., P.F. Kable and M. Catt (1973) Epidemic spread of a rust imported for biological control. Nature **244**: 462-464.

Ferron, P. (1978) Biological control of insect pests by entomogenous fungi. Annual Review of Entomology **23**: 409-442.

Freeman, T.E. (1981) Use of conidial fungi in biological control. pp. 143-165 (in) **Biology of Conidial Fungi**. Vol. 2. (Eds.) G.T. Cole & B. Kendrick. Academic Press, New York.

Gutteridge, R.J. and D.B. Slope (1978) Effect of inoculating soils with *Phialophora radicicola* var. *graminicola* on take-all disease of wheat. Plant Pathology **27**: 131-135.

Harman, G.E., I. Chet and R. Baker (1980) *Trichoderma hamatum* effects on seed and seedling disease induced in radish and pea by *Pythium* spp. or *Rhizoctonia solani*. Phytopathology **70**: 1167-1172.

Hasan, S. (1981) A new strain of the rust fungus *Puccinia chondrillina* for biological control of skeleton weed in Australia. Annals of Applied Biology **99**: 119-124.

Kelleher, J.S. and M.A. Hulme (Eds.) (1984) **Biological Control Programmes against Insects and Weeds in Canada 1969-1980**. Commonwealth Agricultural Bureaux, Farnham Royal.

Lee, B. (1981) Pests control pests: but at what price? New Scientist **89**(1236): 150-152.

Marois, J.J., S.A. Johnston, M.T. Dunn and G.C. Papavizas (1982) Biological control of *Verticillium* wilt of egg plant in the field. Plant Disease **66**: 1166-1168.

Roberts, D.W. and R.A. Humber (1981) Entomogenous fungi. pp. 201-236 (in) **Biology of Conidial Fungi** Vol. 2. (Eds.) G.T. Cole & B. Kendrick. Academic Press, New York.

TeBeest, D.O. and G.E. Templeton (1985) Mycoherbicides: progress in the biological control of weeds. Plant Disease **69**: 6-10.

TeBeest, D.O. (Ed.) (1991) **Microbial Control of Weeds**. Chapman and Hall, New York.

Templeton, G.E., D.O. TeBeest, and R.J. Smith, Jr. (1979) Biological control of weeds with mycoherbicides. Annual Review of Phytopathology **17**: 301-310.

Trutmann, P., P.J. Keane and P.R. Merriman (1982) Biological control of *Sclerotinia sclerotiorum* on aerial parts of plants by the hyperparasite *Coniothyrium minitans*. Transactions of the British Mycological Society **78**: 521-529.

Webber, J. (1981) A natural biological control of Dutch elm disease. Nature **292**: 449-451.

Chapter 15

Fungi Exploiting Microscopic Animals

Introduction

As a tiny soil nematode wriggles along, its head passes through a tiny hoop. Its body follows, sliding smoothly through. Just as it is about to clear the hoop, this suddenly inflates inward and grips the worm tightly. Thrash about as it will, the worm cannot escape. Soon its tail end triggers another ring-trap. It has been captured by a fungus, and it is doomed to die (Fig. 15.1).

Fungi are usually thought of as being slow and insidious in their lifestyle, insinuating themselves stealthily, silently penetrating and permeating the substrate with their hyphae and their enzymes. It comes as something of a shock to encounter fungi that set traps to catch animals, or have spores that instantaneously inject their contents into their unsuspecting target. Yet these fungi, and others almost equally bizarre, exist in the microcosms of the soil, the compost pile and the rotting log.

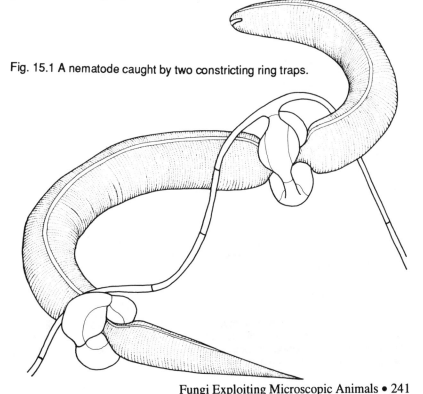

Fig. 15.1 A nematode caught by two constricting ring traps.

Relatively few fungi attack large animals, and those which do are often specialists with a taste for keratin, or opportunists able to grow at the body temperature of birds and mammals, or to attack injured fish. But as we descend the scale of size, we eventually reach a point where any physical confrontation between fungus and animal becomes a much more even contest. The tiny animals that roam through the soil make excellent proteinaceous dietary supplements, so perhaps it is not surprising that the 150 or so fungi that have adopted this 'carnivorous' lifestyle are drawn from four of the five major fungal groups (Chytridiomycota, Oomycota, Zygomycota and Dikaryomycota). The mechanisms they have evolved in order to exploit this resource are diverse and ingenious. We will consider eleven such mechanisms.

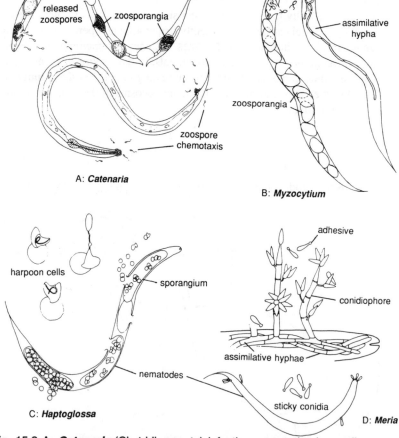

Fig. 15.2 A: **Catenaria** (Chytridiomycota) infecting nematodes by motile zoospores; B: **Myzocytium** (Oomycota) releasing infective motile zoospores; C: **Haptoglossa** (Oomycota) releasing infective harpoon cells (see Fig. 15.3); D: **Meria** (Hyphomycetes) producing infective sticky conidia.

Mechanisms for Infecting Nematodes and other Small Animals

(1) **Motile spores**: The chytridiomycetes and oomycetes have motile cells, and in carnivorous species these have taken on the responsibility of finding the prey. The uniflagellate spores of *Catenaria* (Chytridiomycota) (Fig. 15.2 A) swim to a nematode by **chemotaxis**, and encyst near its mouth or anus before penetrating the cuticle and attacking its internal organs. The biflagellate spores of some species of *Myzocytium* (Oomycota) (Fig. 15.2 B) do the same thing, encysting on the surface of a new host, then penetrating its cuticle. The zoospores of other species of *Myzocytium* disperse actively for a short while, but then conserve energy by encysting and developing a special adhesive bud, which can stick to a passing nematode. This makes these species a combination of categories 1 and 3 (see below).

(2) **Injected spores**: The oomycetous genus *Haptoglossa* (Fig. 15.2 C, 15.3) is unique among fungi. It produces spores which, though non-motile, are sophisticated 'harpoon cells.' A harpoon cell adheres to the substrate and sits with the 'barrel' pointing upward at a low angle (Fig. 15.3). It has a high turgor pressure, and is triggered by contact with prey: a built-in line of weakness ruptures, and an internal tube with a harpoon-like tip is rapidly everted with sufficient force to penetrate the integument of the prey and inject sufficient material into the animal to form a tiny infection unit. This is an extremely highly evolved mechanism: its considerable mechanical complexity can be clearly seen in Fig. 15.3. The only comparable mechanisms I can think of are: (a) that of the zoospore in *Plasmodiophora*, a colonial protoctistan, and (b) that of the nematocysts of the animal phylum, Cnidaria (corals, sea anemones and jellyfish): there is, of course, no suggestion of homology here.

After these protoctistan fungi get inside the animal, they grow through its internal organs, absorbing nourishment from them. This is not healthy for the animal, which soon expires. Its corpse eventually houses several to many mitosporangia, which liberate large numbers of flagellate or injective propagules to begin the cycle again. Sexual reproduction can also occur, and

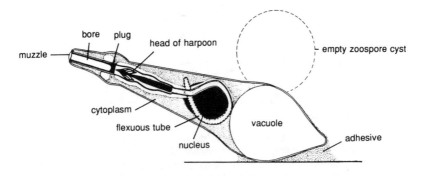

Fig. 15.3 Details of the harpoon cell of *Haptoglossa*.

Myzocytium, for example, sometimes fills its hosts with oogonia, each ultimately containing a thick-walled, resting zygote (oospore).

(3) **Adhesive spores**: *Meristacrum* is a common nematode-exploiting zygomycete. From a parasitized nematode arise tall sporangiophores with helically twisted apical regions. Sticky one-spored mitosporangia are produced on these, and are forcibly shot away. If they don't make contact with a nematode, they will germinate and form a small, adhesive-coated secondary spore at the top of a little stalk. These stick to nematodes: some cause infection, while others form secondary spores, and the host worm may thus spread the infection to other nematodes while it can still move about.

Hyphomycetes are well-represented among the nematode-exploiting fungi, and have evolved the widest range of techniques for gaining access to the interiors of nematodes. *Verticillium* and *Meria* (Fig. 15.2 D) use the sticky-spore technique already mentioned. Once penetrated by the germ tube arising from these conidia, the worm is doomed. After a few days, its body is riddled with assimilative hyphae. Then the fungus breaks out of this capsule and produces

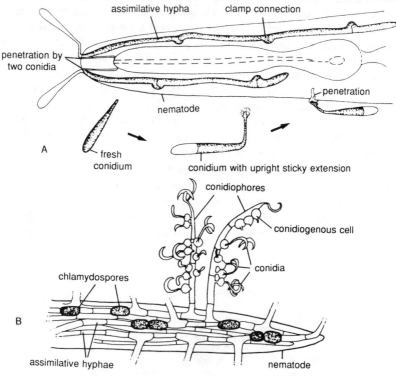

Fig. 15.4 A: ***Nematoctonus leiosporus*** (dikaryotic basidiomycetous anamorph) sticky conidia penetrating the host nematode and developing assimilative hyphae with clamp connections; B: ***Harposporium anguillulae*** (anamorph of ***Atricordyceps harposporifera***: Ascomycetes, Clavicipitales) producing chlamydospores and curved, pointed conidia that are ingested by the host worm.

characteristic conidiophores, bearing adhesive conidia. The conidia of *Nematoctonus leiosporus* (Fig. 15.4 A), after becoming detached, develop a vertical extension that ends in a sticky, infective swelling. The assimilative hyphae inside the host have clamp connections, showing that this is a dikaryotic basidiomycetous anamorph. Several species of *Nematoctonus* have been shown to be anamorphs of species of *Hohenbuehelia* (Holobasidiomycetes: Agaricales) (see also method 8, below).

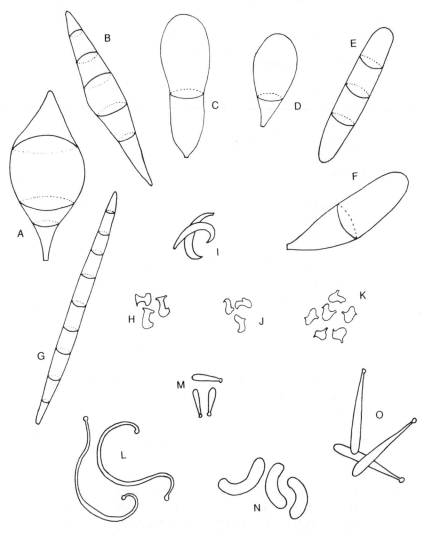

Fig. 15.5 Conidia of nematode-exploiting fungi; the large spores (A-G) are of trap-forming species, the small spores (H-O) either stick to nematodes or are eaten by them. A-G: *Arthrobotrys* spp.; H-L: *Harposporium* spp.—H: *H. bysmatosporum*; I: *H. anguillulae*; J: *H. diceraeum*; K: *H. rhynchosporum*; L: *H. helicoides*; M: *Meria conospora*; N,O: *Nematoctonus* spp.

(4) **Ingested spores**: Some hyphomycetes have evolved conidia that are designed to be eaten by their victims. The conidia of *Harposporium anguillulae* (Fig. 15.4 B) are crescent-shaped, with a sharp point at one end. These conidia literally stick in the craw (actually the oesophagus) of the worm, and from this initial bridgehead their hyphae soon permeate the host. Eventually, new conidiophores arise from the defunct nematode. It has recently been discovered that the teleomorph of *Harposporium anguillulae* is *Atricordyceps harposporifera* (Ascomycetes, Clavicipitales), which attacks millipedes. This is the only case I know of in which the anamorph exploits one group of animals, the teleomorph another. Other species of *Harposporium* also have 'edible' conidia. Those of *H. diceraeum* (Fig. 15.5 J) have a striking resemblance to a high-heeled shoe or clog: those of *H. rhynchosporum* (Fig. 15.5 K) look like cartoons of small birds minus legs. In each case there is a subtle asymmetry, and one or more sharp points, which undoubtedly combine to help the conidia lodge in the muscle of the worm's buccal cavity or oesophagus. The longer conidia of *H. helicoides* (Fig. 15.5 L) don't pierce the gut wall mechanically, but germinate in the intestine and infect the worm just as effectively from there.

Harposporium spirosporum has sinuate, twisted conidia which are very sharp at both ends. These conidia are eaten by rotifers, and lodge in the gullet or mastax to initiate an infection. At least twelve species of the hyphomycete genus *Diheterospora* parasitize rotifers after they ingest conidia. Although these conidia are not pointed, they still lodge in the mouth, gullet or mastax, and penetrate the body cavity of the animal in the usual way.

Mechanisms for Trapping Nematodes

The remaining fungi that exploit nematodes do so by trapping or snaring them. The traps are of six different kinds, but can initially be categorized as either adhesive or non-adhesive. Some fungi have evolved a very efficient nematode glue (or glues) to which the cuticle of nematodes adheres instantly and strongly. Others lack this feature, and have developed even more interesting alternatives.

(5) **Adhesive assimilative hyphae**: in some zygomycetes, the assimilative hyphae are covered with adhesive. *Cystopage* can be recognized by its thick-walled chlamydospores (it does not produce mitosporangia). *Stylopage* produces a few large spores on upright hyphae.

(6) **Adhesive side branches** (Fig. 15.6 D): a few species of *Dactylella* (Hyphomycetes) have specialized adhesive-coated side branches on their otherwise non-sticky assimilative hyphae. These branches project from the substrate just far enough to ensure proper contact with passing nematodes. We presume that this simple form of trap gave rise to the more elaborate and sophisticated types reported below. *Dactylella copepodii* manages to capture copepods with adhesive branches (it also uses adhesive knobs—see method 7).

(7) **Adhesive knobs** (Fig. 15.6 A-C, 15.7 A) are specialized, swollen cells, coated with nematode glue, and often situated at the ends of short side-branches. They are found in nearly twenty species of *Arthrobotrys*, *Dactylella* and *Nema-*

toctonus (all Hyphomycetes). Sometimes the knobs are firmly enough attached to prevent a nematode from leaving the scene, particularly if the animal has stuck to several of them at once. Often the nematode tears a knob loose from its moorings and makes good its escape. But the ensuing freedom is short-lived. The knob remains firmly attached to the worm's cuticle, and soon sends in an infective hypha. Game over.

Some species of *Nematoctonus* which are anamorphs of the gilled fungi *Hohenbuehelia* and *Resupinatus* (Holobasidiomycetes, Agaricales), produce unique adhesive knobs shaped like hour-glasses, enveloped in a drop of glue (Fig. 15.6 C). These knobs do not break off, but hold nematodes firmly while

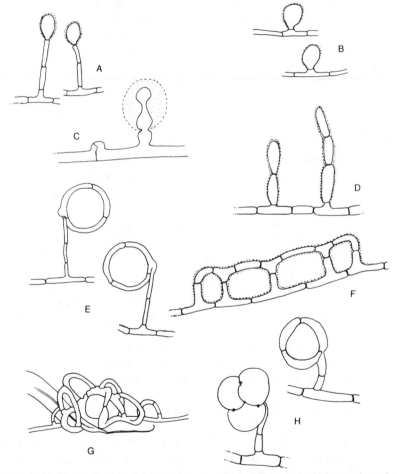

Fig. 15.6 Trapping devices of nematode-exploiting fungi. A-C: sticky knobs—A: **Arthrobotrys candida**; C: **Nematoctonus** sp. (anamorph of **Hohenbuehelia**: Basidiomycetes, Agaricales) D: sticky branches of **Dactylella cionopaga**; E: non-constricting rings of **Arthrobotrys candida**; F: net of **Dactylella gephyropaga**; G: net of **Arthrobotrys oligospora**; H: constricting rings of **Arthrobotrys anchonia**.

infection proceeds. The clamped hyphae of *Nematoctonus* also bear conidia (Fig. 15.5 N), but these are not infectious until they have germinated and formed a sticky knob at the end of the germ tube.

(8) **Adhesive nets** (Fig. 15.6 F,G) are probably the commonest trapping device, since they have been recorded in nearly 40 species of fungi. They may originally have evolved by anastomosis of adjacent adhesive branches (only Eumycotan fungi can do this), and some of them are still simple hoops. Others are more complex, ranging from two-dimensional ladder-like arrangements, to the contorted three-dimensional labyrinths of *Arthrobotrys oligospora*, the commonest nematode-trapping hyphomycete. These networks can arise only as a result of repeated anastomoses. The advantage of the more complex systems is not simply their greater extent, but also the fact that larger nematodes are likely to become stuck at more than one point, and are therefore less likely to escape. The adhesive works equally well on dry and wet nematodes (though not on other soil animals). The nematodes are not just blind, insensate victims: they often recoil violently when they touch an adhesive net—an aversive reaction that sometimes saves them from certain death. When the fungus is successful in establishing adhesion, an infective hypha soon penetrates the body of the prey, and the worm becomes comatose within an hour: so quickly, in fact, that the fungus is suspected of producing a toxin. After the prey has been riddled by absorptive hyphae, the converted biomass is exported—translocated to the external hyphae, which use the energy, spider-like, to spin new nets, and also to produce the distinctive conidiophores of *Arthrobotrys oligospora*, with their successive clusters of 2-celled, colourless conidia.

(9) **Non-constricting rings** (Fig. 15.6 E, 15.7 A), which could also be called detachable rings, are produced by four species of *Arthrobotrys* and *Dactylella* (Hyphomycetes). A single hypha grows around in a perfect circle, finally anastomosing with a new bud waiting at the top of the stalk-to-be. The 3-celled ring is stouter than the stalk. When a nematode crawls through the ring, this fits snugly around its body, and easily breaks away from the narrow stalk. The worm goes on its way wearing its newly-acquired collar. As you will have deduced, infection and assimilation soon follow. All species with non-constricting rings produce sticky knobs as well (Fig. 15.7 A). In terms of the spread of the pathogen, it is interesting to note that fungi producing sticky spores, or detachable knobs or loops, may be carried some distance by the animal before it becomes incapacitated.

(10) **Constricting rings** (Fig. 15.1, 15.6 H, 15.7 B-D) are the most sophisticated nematode traps of all. They are produced by twelve Hyphomycetes, especially species of *Arthrobotrys* and *Dactylella*. At first sight, these traps seem very similar to non-constricting rings: the ring is composed of three cells, borne on a stalk. But here the stalk is shorter and stronger: these traps are designed to stay put. Their true nature is revealed only when they are triggered. If a nematode passes through the loop, and touches the inside of one or more of the cells, all three cells simultaneously inflate inward, in about one-tenth of a second, and the nematode is held in a vice-like grip (Fig. 15.1, 15.7 D). The inflated cells

soon squeeze the worm so tightly that it is virtually garrotted. Rings can be triggered by mechanical stimulation or by heat, when no nematode is present, and in this case the three cells expand to three times their original volume: until they touch one another and the centre of the ring is completely occluded. Between the contact stimulus and the implosive response there is a delay of a few seconds. If a worm is lucky, it may retract during that period of grace, leaving a trap sprung but empty.

How do these traps work? A variety of experimental and observational techniques have now provided us with a reasonable hypothesis. The three cells

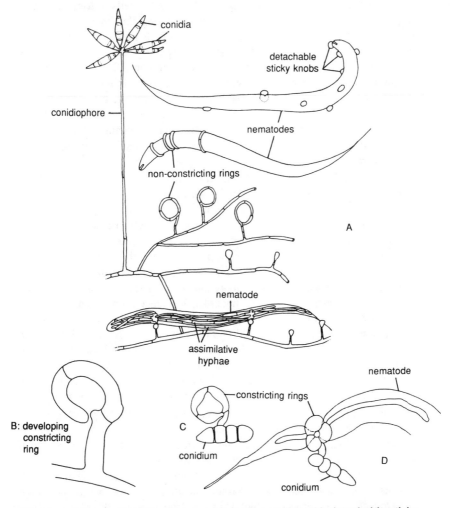

Fig. 15.7 **Arthrobotrys** (Hyphomycetes). A: **A. candida** with detachable sticky knobs, and detachable non-constricting rings; B-D: **A. brochopaga** — B: developing constricting ring trap; C: germinated conidium which has formed a constricting ring trap; D: conidium with a constricting ring trap which has caught a nematode.

of each constricting ring trap have a high turgor pressure, generated by a high internal osmotic pressure. The cell membranes are freely permeable to water, and the cytoplasm would take up more, but is prevented from doing so by the presence of the outer cell walls, which are exerting an equal and opposite wall pressure. The trap waits for its victim, in a state of hydrostatic tension. A clue to future events is given by the presence of two inconspicuous lines of weakness running around the inner faces of the ring cells. And if we look inside the cells, near the lines of weakness, we find folded reserves of wall material and membrane.

When a nematode enters the ring, and touches the cells, it triggers a rapid sequence of events. The outer walls rupture along the lines of weakness, removing the inhibiting wall pressure. The ring cells now take up water very quickly over their entire surface. The cells expand inward from the line of weakness, deploying the reserve wall and membrane. The three inwardly expanding cells grip the nematode, but do not crush it immediately, because their increase in volume has reduced their osmotic pressure to about a third of its former value. The osmotic pressure is quickly pumped up again, turgor pressure increases, and the worm is strangled. All that remains is for the fungus to send in assimilative hyphae which will extract the vital nitrogen supplement from the animal.

This is clearly an unusual kind of mechanism to find in a fungus. If we try to unravel the evolutionary steps that led to it, we begin with the ability of eumycotan hyphae to anastomose. Without that, no trap is possible. When hyphae anastomose repeatedly, they can produce a network: some nematode-trapping fungi have gone no further than this. But worms can wriggle out of passive networks, and there was obviously a selective advantage for the fungus to do something extra to detail the moving meal. As is usually the case, the various intermediate steps in the elaboration of the trap mechanism are nowhere to be seen. Like so many other missing links, they have inconveniently vanished in the mists of time. But we can draw some analogies with other fungal mechanisms that depend on a build-up of turgor pressure followed by its rapid release: the ascus, the basidium, the harpoon-cell of *Haptoglossa*, the subsporangial vesicle of *Pilobolus*. These show how a basic physical phenomenon like turgor pressure, teamed with an appropriately placed line of wall weakness, can be used for purposes as diverse as shooting spores and catching food.

Many of these fungi exploit nematodes only as a dietary nitrogen supplement, and they may often grow in places where an adequate supply of nematodes is not forthcoming. Here, the development of traps would be a pointless waste of energy. To avoid this possibility, the fungi will not produce traps unless they detect certain chemical trademarks that indicate the presence of nematodes. It has also been confirmed that the communication goes both ways. The fungi secrete a chemical attractant which lures nematodes to their doom. This attractant may be ammonia or carbon dioxide.

The conidia of some of the trap-forming fungi will sometimes produce a trap almost immediately after germinating (Fig. 15.7 C). This suggests that nematodes are a very important part of the diet of these particular fungi. It is also significant that the conidia of trap-formers are usually quite large, enabling them to carry enough reserves to build a trap (Fig. 15.5 A-G). Spores of species that rely on adhesive, mobile or ingested propagules are usually much smaller (Fig. 15.5 H-O).

Chemical Warfare

(11) **Toxins**: mycelia of the widely-eaten and cultivated 'oyster mushroom,' *Pleurotus ostreatus* and several other *Pleurotus* species, secrete a substance that rapidly inactivates nematodes, allowing the fungus to colonize their inert bodies. Since *Pleurotus* species are often primary colonizers of dead wood, a substrate notoriously deficient in nitrogen, the nematodes may be an important component of the fungal diet, as they appeared to be for the other agarics (*Hohenbuehelia* and *Resupinatus*) mentioned earlier.

A few fungi parasitize nematode eggs. *Rhopalomyces elegans*, a striking zygomycete commonly encountered on dung, is one of these. Nematode eggs appear to release some kind of attractant which causes hyphae of *Rhopalomyces* to grow toward them. On arrival, the hyphae establish appressoria, then penetrate the egg and assimilate its contents. *Rhopalomyces* hyphae also parasitize adult nematodes.

Exploitation of Other Animals and Protists

Nematodes, as you will already have noticed, are not the only animals preyed upon by fungi. **Amoebae, rotifers, tardigrades, copepods** and even **collembola** (springtails) are also exploited. The largest animal known to be captured by a predaceous fungus is a small springtail. *Arthrobotrys entomopaga* (Hyphomycetes) produces a prostrate hyphal network from which arise clusters of two-celled traps, the upper cell of each bearing a large droplet of glue. In a confrontation like that of Gulliver and the Lilliputians, the collembolan, which is up to 130 μm long, sticks to several microscopic droplets at once, and cannot escape their combined effect. Another hyphomycete, a species of *Harposporium*, has been found attacking tardigrades. *Zoophagus* (Oomycota) traps rotifers by means of 'lethal lollipops'—sticky knobs which the animals unwisely try to eat (Fig. 15.8).

Six hyphomycetes trap amoebae, usually testaceous rhizopods. These fungi are drawn from four genera: *Dactylella*, *Pedilospora*, *Tridentaria* and *Triposporina*. The amoeba *Geococcus vulgaris* normally feeds on fungi by attaching itself to the wall of a spore or hypha and sucking out the cytoplasm. But when it encounters *Dactylella passalopaga*, the tables are turned. The fungus responds to the attack of the amoeba by gagging it with a bulbous outgrowth that effectively prevents escape. Assimilative hyphae subsequently digest the amoeba. Most amoeba-trapping hyphomycetes rely on sticky knobs to catch their prey. The rarity of amoeba-trapping hyphomycetes can probably be explained by a difference of scale. A robust hyphomycete would need to exploit a large number of the tiny amoebae in order to accumulate enough energy to form conidiophores and conidia.

Some years ago, when we first became aware of the ubiquity of the nematode-exploiting fungi, it was suggested that they might be useful in controlling the populations of plant-parasitic nematodes in the soil. A number of attempts were made to obtain biological control of eelworms by boosting natural populations of the fungi, or by shifting ecological equilibria in their favour. Unfortunately, although small scale experiments often gave promising results, field trials were generally less successful. A combination of green manuring and additions of nematode-destroying fungi

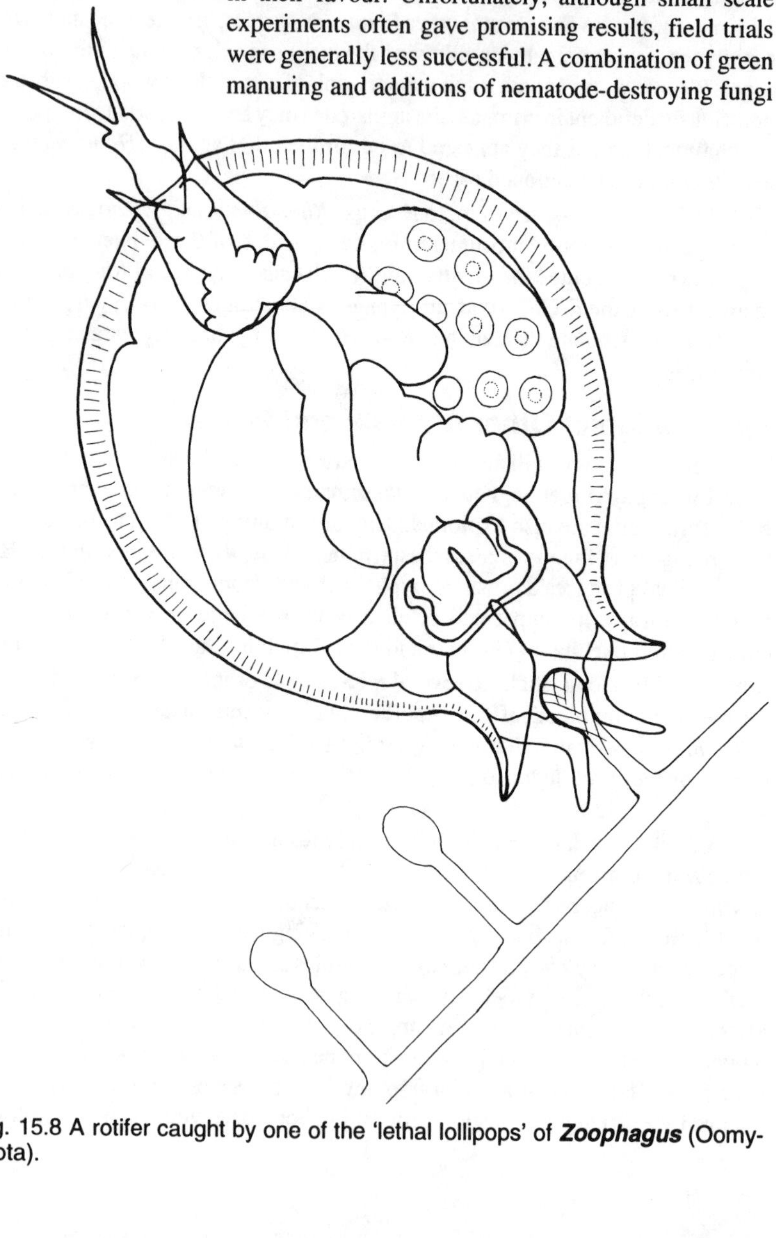

Fig. 15.8 A rotifer caught by one of the 'lethal lollipops' of **Zoophagus** (Oomycota).

gave the best results. Nematode-exploiting fungi are naturally present in all agricultural soils. If they are already actively exploiting nematode populations, the impact of adding more fungal inoculum might well be less than expected.

Further Reading

Barron, G.L. (1977) **The Nematode-Destroying Fungi**. Canadian Biological Publications, Guelph.

Barron, G.L. (1981) Predators and parasites of microscopic animals. pp. 167-200 (in) **Biology of Conidial Fungi**. Vol. 2. (Eds. G.T. Cole and B. Kendrick). Academic Press, New York.

Barron, G.L. (1985) Fungal parasites of bdelloid rotifers: *Diheterospora*. Canadian Journal of Botany **63**: 211-222.

Barron, G.L. (1986) A new *Harposporium* parasitic in bdelloid rotifers. Canadian Journal of Botany **64**: 2379-2382.

Barron, G.L. (1987) The gun cell of *Haptoglossa mirabilis*. Mycologia **79**: 877-883.

Barron, G.L. (1990) A new predatory Hyphomycete capturing copepods. Canadian Journal of Botany **68**: 691-696.

Duddington, C.L. (1962) Predacious fungi and the control of eelworms. Viewpoints in Biology **1**: 151-200.

Gray, N.F. (1987) Nematophagous fungi with particular reference to their ecology. Biological Reviews **62**: 245-304.

Nordbring-Hertz, B. (1988) Ecology and recognition in the nematode/nematophagous fungus system. Advances in Microbial Ecology **10**: 81-114.

Samuels, G.J. (1983) Ascomycetes of New Zealand 6. *Atricordyceps harposporifera* gen. et sp. nov. and its *Harposporium* anamorph. New Zealand Journal of Botany **21**: 171-176.

Thorn, R.G. and G.L. Barron (1984) Carnivorous mushrooms. Science **224**: 76-78.

Thorn, R.G. and G.L. Barron (1986) *Nematoctonus* and the tribe Resupinatae in Ontario, Canada. Mycotaxon **25**: 321-453.

Chapter 16

Mutualistic Symbioses Between Fungi and Animals

Introduction

At first sight, such relationships sound bizarre, even unlikely. What service could fungi render that would make it worthwhile for animals to modify their whole lifestyle to accommodate such aliens? And what could be in it for the fungi, which usually compete with animals for food?

The first and most important driving force is the inability of animals to digest cellulose and lignin. Some animals, like the detritivores in streams and ponds, wait until amphibious and aero-aquatic hyphomycetes have exploited the plant remains, then seek out and eat the hyphae and conidiophores of these fungi. Many other animals, including the herbivorous mammals and some termites, have overcome this deficiency in a more efficient and reliable way, by harbouring large populations of cellulolytic microorganisms in their gut. Then they can eat the cellulose and lignin directly, leaving their gut microbiota to digest these substrates for them. But certain social insects, the **mound-building termites** of Africa and Asia, and the **leaf-cutting ants** of Central and South America, have evolved a rather different strategy. They cultivate specific cellulolytic fungi in underground gardens. And I use the words 'cultivate' and 'garden' deliberately. The insects establish pure, axenic cultures of special coevolved fungi, keep them constantly supplied with food and moisture, and weed out any contaminants. The fungus, then, receives very special treatment, and there is no doubt that it benefits from the arrangement. How many other fungi have guardians that keep out the competition, and bring endless supplies of food? But then the ants and termites have their turn. As you have no doubt guessed, they are exclusively mycophagous. The fungi have transformed the wood brought by the termites, and the leaves supplied by the ants, into digestible and nutritious fungal biomass.

Leaf-cutting Ants, *Leucoagaricus* and *Lepiota*

The gardening ants of the New World make up the Tribe Attini. Now although you have probably never heard of them before, people in South America are only too familiar with them. Searching for leaves to feed to their tame fungus, these ants will defoliate trees and growing crops. In the 16th century, the invading Spaniards may have conquered the native peoples of South America, but the native ants got the better of them—their failure to grow cassava and citrus fruits was attributed to Attine ants, whose nests, at the base of the trees, were 'white as snow' (presumably with fungal mycelium). Leaf-cutting ants of the genera *Atta* and *Acromyrmex* have long been regarded as serious pests, and they still make farming difficult in some primitive areas. The native peoples eat the large females, but this, unfortunately, doesn't seem an adequate population control for the ants.

Nevertheless, in tropical rainforests, these insects and their fungi have an important ecological role to play. In these forests, the turnover of organic matter and mineral nutrients at the soil surface is very rapid, and few organisms, including the trees, penetrate far into the soil. Here, a large nest of *Atta*, with hundreds of fungus gardens, vastly increases the organic matter content of the soil, and opens it up for subsequent colonization by many other organisms. In some areas of Trinidad, small species of Attine ants achieve densities of one nest for every two square metres, and are a dominant feature in soil ecology and nutritional status.

Although the Attini comprise hundreds of species in more than 50 genera, *Atta sexdens* is the most economically important species, and therefore the most intensively studied. A winged female, carrying inoculum of the all-important fungus in a special pocket at the back of her mouth, and with her spermatheca stocked with perhaps 300 million sperm, establishes the colony. First she expels the fungal pellet from her mouth, and finds some plant material for it. As soon as the fungus starts growing, the queen lays eggs on it. Soon she is laying about 50 eggs a day, but eats most of them herself until the worker population is established, which takes about 3 months. A second entrance to the nest is added after another year, then entrances proliferate: there are about 75 by the end of the second year, and about 1,000 by the end of the third year. From now on, new females emerge each year to establish colonies elsewhere. In case you are

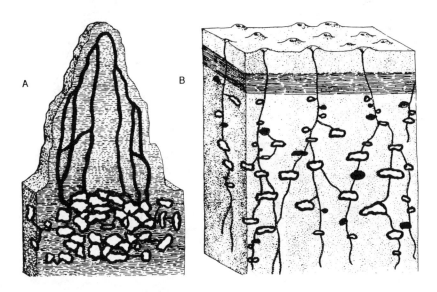

Fig. 16.1 Sectional views of — A: termite mound; B: attine ant nest. Fungal gardens or combs are shown in white.

wondering why these animals haven't taken over South America, it is worth pointing out that an estimated 99.7% of all new nests are destroyed in their first six months.

When a 4-year-old nest was excavated, it was found to contain 1027 subterranean chambers, of which 390 had fungus gardens. Another *Atta* nest, more than six years old, had 1,920 chambers, of which 248 contained fungus gardens, and 1,219 were empty. The gardens were usually 20-30 cm in diameter, and weighed about 300 g. It was calculated that this colony had consumed nearly

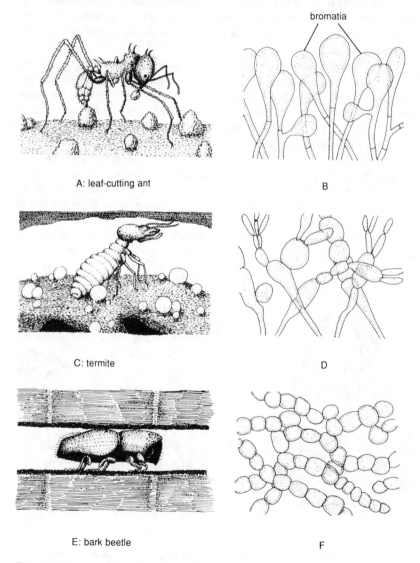

A: leaf-cutting ant

B

C: termite

D

E: bark beetle

F

Fig. 16.2 Mycophagous insects and the fungal structures they eat.

6,000 kg of vegetation. Fig. 16.1 B shows a section of a representative nest, with many entrances and many interconnected chambers: note that most of the larger chambers contain fungus gardens (shown in white).

In the early days of the colony, the queen and the first broods establish the first fungus garden, excavating a chamber, filling it with vegetation brought by workers, and inoculating the substrate with the fungus. Leaf-cutting ants forage for leaves along well-marked trails which often extend up into the crowns of trees. The ants have no difficulty in scissoring out large pieces of leaf, petal or twig with their formidable jaws, though they may have a little trouble manoeuvring on their way home. Back in the nest, they cut the material into smaller pieces, lick it all over, chew the edges, and often deposit an anal droplet on it. Then they wedge it into the garden, and put tufts of mycelium on it. Gardens have a sponge-like construction, containing many cavities. The ants walk all over the garden, probing the fungus with their antennae, licking and sometimes eating hyphae, and depositing anal droplets, as in Fig. 16.2 A. Some Attines are not leaf-cutters, but they nevertheless grow perfectly functional fungal gardens on such substrates as plant debris and insect excreta.

The gardens invariably contain only one species of fungus. This is surprising, because decaying organic substrates are usually competitively colonized by a wide range of different fungi. If a garden is removed from the colony, it soon becomes overgrown by extraneous fungi or bacteria. From this, we deduce that the ants must have some kind of chemical inhibitors that prevent the growth of unwanted microorganisms. It seems likely that these substances, and perhaps others that promote the growth of the proper fungus, are present in the ants' saliva and anal fluid, with which they constantly anoint their tame fungus. In return, it flourishes, and develops clusters of inflated hyphal tips (Fig. 16.2 B), which the ants eat. I must emphasize that although the insects cut up and chew up the leaves they bring to the nest, leaves are never eaten. The ants are exclusively **mycophagous**.

The fungi cultivated by the Attine ants never seem to fruit in or near the gardens, so various attempts have been made to isolate them in pure culture, and mature basidiomata have sometimes developed. These belonged to species of *Leucoagaricus* or *Lepiota* (Holobasidiomycetes, Agaricales). Species of *Xylaria* (Ascomycetes, Sphaeriales) and *Auricularia* (Phragmobasidiomycetes, Auriculariales) may also be involved.

Termites and *Termitomyces*

Across the South Atlantic Ocean from the territory of the leaf-cutting ants begins the realm of the fungus-growing termites. The subfamily Macrotermitinae is found in the Old World, its twelve genera being variously found in subsaharan Africa, Madagascar, the Indian subcontinent, and much of south-east Asia, including the Indonesian archipelago. Unlike many other termites, these have no cellulolytic protozoans in their gut, so, like the Attine ants, they have established a mutualistic symbiosis with fungi.

Each colony is founded by a winged male and female, which wall themselves up in an underground chamber. The queen lays eggs, and the resulting workers bring food to the sequestered couple, take eggs away for incubation, and build the nest. The fungus garden or comb surrounds the royal chamber. Above their nests, many fungus-growing termites construct mounds (termitaria), which can be an impressive 6 metres tall and 3 metres across at the base. The mounds are penetrated by air shafts leading to the nest below, particularly to the fungus garden, which may be a large, central structure, 50 cm in diameter and weighing as much as 25 kg, or a series of smaller combs (as in honeycomb: riddled with holes) in individual chambers (Fig. 16.1 A).

A large colony may contain a million termites, which forage for wood and other plant debris. Unlike the Attine ants, the termites eat this material on the spot, so their fungus gardens are made entirely from faecal material. The gardens have a sponge-like or deeply convoluted appearance, and at many points on their surface spherical sporodochial conidiomata develop (Fig. 16.2 C) with monilioid conidiophores bearing dikaryotic conidia (Fig. 16.2 D). The workers eat these, and nibble the garden itself, redepositing the resultant faecal material on the comb. The cellulases of the fungus remain active in the gut of the insect. The soldiers, nymphs, king and queen don't eat the fungus directly, but live on salivary secretions provided by the workers.

The taxonomy of the termite fungi is better understood than that of the ant fungi, for the simple reason that termite fungi fruit in nature (Fig. 16.3). When

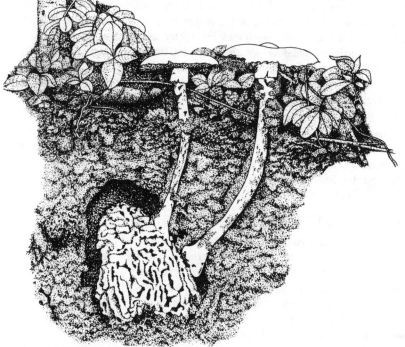

Fig. 16.3 *Termitomyces* basidiomata arising from a subterranean fungal comb.

termites of the genus *Pseudacanthotermes* desert a comb, the fungus produces basidiomatal primordia on its surface. When the rainy season starts, rainfall of more than 2 cm/day stimulates the primordia to develop long stipes, which grow up to the soil surface and produce a large pileus. These mushrooms are identifiable as *Termitomyces striatus* (Holobasidiomycetes, Agaricales). Interestingly, the combs of fungus-growing termites are often inhabited by an additional fungus, a species of *Xylaria*, which may also produce stromata on the comb. Although about 30 species of *Termitomyces* have been described, only two species of *Xylaria* have been found associated with termites.

Macrotermitinae are regarded as major pests of tropical agriculture, and they are destructive to wooden buildings. They take scarce organic matter underground, where its nutrients may remain locked up for years. However, there are a few minor compensations. Termites are food for many other animals, and many *Termitomyces* species are among the most highly prized, and the largest, edible tropical agarics: so much so that attempts have been made to domesticate them.

Beetles and Ambrosia Fungi

Although social insects like ants and termites are the most visible, the most dramatic, and probably the most highly evolved examples of animal-fungus mutualism, they are not the only such relationships. A similar bond exists between wood-boring beetles of the families Scolytidae, Platypodidae and Lymexylidae, and the ambrosia fungi they carry in special organs called **mycangia** as they travel from tree to tree, and on which their larvae feed exclusively. The fungus is introduced to weakened or freshly logged trees when a female beetle burrows into them to lay its eggs. By the time the larvae hatch, the fungus has colonized the surrounding wood and is sporulating all over the walls of the beetle tunnels. Since they cannot digest wood, the larvae eat the fungal biomass, which is called ambrosia. Before an adult female beetle leaves the tree to seek fresh habitat, it will rock back and forth to make sure that its mycangium is stocked with the fungus (Fig. 16.2 E,F). Many species of beetle have specific ambrosia fungi, though their larvae may feed on other fungi that are also found sporulating in the tunnels. The full spectrum of such fungi takes in some yeasts (Saccharomycetes: *Ascoidea, Dipodascus, Endomyces, Endomycopsis, Hansenula, Saccharomyces*), ascomycetous anamorphs (*Acremonium, Ambrosiella, Diplodia, Scopulariopsis*), and some basidiomycetes and their conidial anamorphs.

Scales and Septobasidiales

There are almost 200 species of the Phragmobasidiomycete order Septobasidiales. All grow on the surfaces of plants, and are associated with scale insects (Homoptera, Coccoidea). Some of the insects are parasitized by the fungus, but do not die. And although the infection renders them dwarfed and sterile, they continue to feed from the plant, supplying the enclosing fungus with a reliable flow of nutrients. The tough mat of fungal hyphae (150-1,000 µm thick) that develops around parasitized insects protects many other healthy scales from predators and parasitoid hymenoptera. The mutualism is not perfectly balanced, because the insects are occasionally seen to survive without the fungus.

Midges and *Macrophoma*

Some gall-midges (Diptera, Cecidomyiidae) have mutualistic relationships with members of the coelomycetous anamorph, *Macrophoma* (Teleomorph = *Botryosphaeria* [Ascomycetes, Dothideales]) which inhabit 'ambrosia galls.' The dipteran larvae must eat the fungal mycelium, and the fungus needs the adult midge as its vector. The female gall-midge carries the fungus away in a pair of specialized pouches called **mycangia**, and lays some conidia with her eggs.

Woodwasps and Wood-rotting Fungi

Woodwasps of the genus *Sirex* (Hymenoptera, Siricidae) often invade dead or dying trees, but may also be implicated in the death of healthy ones. They drill through the bark of the tree with a long ovipositor, and lay eggs in the xylem. A pair of mycangia associated with the ovipositor are full of thallic-arthric conidia of a basidiomycete, some of which are deposited with the eggs. Female larvae also have mycangia in which the fungus is maintained in a dormant condition, embedded in wax plates. The role of the fungus is not fully understood, and different workers have suggested that: (1) the fungus regulates moisture content and provides a suitable microclimate for egg incubation; (2) the fungus reduces the intensity of the tree's response to attack; (3) the fungus is eaten by the larvae. Whatever the relationship is based on, it is apparently an obligatory one, since it has been experimentally established that fungus-free females cannot reproduce successfully. The fungi associated with woodwasps have been identified as species of *Stereum* and *Amylostereum* (both Holobasidiomycetes, Aphyllophorales).

Anobiid Beetles and Endosymbiotic Yeasts

Anobiid beetles (Coleoptera, Anobiidae) live in wood. These beetles have pouches called **mycetomes** at the beginning of their midgut. These are full of yeast-like fungi of the genus *Symbiotaphrina*. Adult beetles transmit the symbionts to their offspring by smearing the eggs with fungal cells. The newly hatched larva eats some of the eggshell, and becomes 'infected.' The fungus apparently supplies vitamins and essential amino acids. Its role is mainly to recycle nitrogen in a rather nitrogen-deficient habitat. It has been demonstrated (by disinfecting the eggs) that beetles without endosymbionts cannot grow, even when given their normal diet.

Boletinellus and Root Aphids

A few years ago, another apparently mutualistic relationship between fungi and insects was discovered in the mycology laboratory here at Waterloo, this time between a bolete and a root-aphid. *Boletinellus merulioides* (Holobasidiomycetes, Agaricales) is commonly associated with ash trees (*Fraxinus*), and was once thought to be their ectomycorrhizal partner. We examined many ash roots closely, and found that they were exclusively endomycorrhizal. The *Boletinellus* was subsequently found to produce hollow black sclerotia near the roots, and within these sclerotia lived individuals of a root aphid, *Meliarhizophagus fraxinifolii* (Homoptera, Aphidae). From within this safe haven, the aphids pierced the roots and sucked sap at their leisure. We suggested that in exchange for housing and protecting the aphid, the fungus obtained nutrients, especially sugars, excreted by the aphid in its honeydew.

Red-backed Voles and False Truffles

My last example is perhaps less clear-cut than those above, since there isn't a true 'living with' involved. Nevertheless, the diet of the California red-backed vole (*Clethrionomys californicus*) consists almost exclusively of the hypogeous basidiomata of ectomycorrhizal fungi such as the genus *Rhizopogon* (Holobasidiomycetes, sequestrate Boletaceae). This establishes the dependence of the vole on the fungi, but although the fungal spores can survive passage through the vole gut, and are therefore spread by the animal, it is unlikely that the fungus depends entirely on this small mammal for dispersal.

Although that more or less exhausts the known examples of animal-fungus mutualistic symbiosis, there are almost certainly others out there waiting to be recognized. Perhaps you will discover and describe one of them.

Further Reading

Batra, L.R. (Ed.) (1979) **Insect-Fungus Symbiosis**. Allanheld, Osmun. Montclair.

Batra, L.R. and S.W.T. Batra (1967) The fungus gardens of insects. Scientific American **217**: 112-120.

Bissett, J. and A. Borkent (1988) Ambrosia galls: the significance of fungal nutrition in the evolution of the Cecidomyiidae (Diptera) (in) **Coevolution of Fungi with Plants and Animals** (Eds.) K.A. Pirozynski & D.L. Hawksworth pp. 203-225.

Brundrett, M.C. and B. Kendrick (1987) The relationship between the Ash Bolete (*Boletinellus merulioides*) and an aphid parasitic on ash tree roots. Symbiosis **3**: 315-320.

Buchner, P. (1965) **Endosymbiosis of Animals with Plant Microorganisms**. Wiley, New York.

Couch, J.N. (1938) **The Genus *Septobasidium***. University of North Carolina Press, Chapel Hill.

Pirozynski, K.A. and D.L. Hawksworth (Eds.)(1988) **Coevolution of Fungi with Plants and Animals**. Academic Press, New York.

Weber, N.A. (1972) **Gardening Ants: the Attines**. Memoir **92** American Philosophical Society, Philadelphia.

Chapter 17

Mycorrhizae:
Mutualistic Plant-Fungus Symbioses

Introduction

When green plants first colonized the land, more than four hundred million years ago, the invasion may have succeeded because they established an intimate alliance—a **mutualistic symbiosis**—with fungi. Early land plants could photosynthesize effectively, but hadn't yet developed extensive root systems and must have been hard-pressed to acquire water and mineral nutrients. The filamentous fungi, which had themselves only recently emerged from the water, were perfectly adapted for exploring the soil and finding those very things, but desperately needed energy-rich carbon compounds of the kind produced by the plants. Traces of sugars and amino-acids leak out of plants, and Devonian fungi were undoubtedly attracted by these. The relationships presumably developed in more than one direction: some fungi remained saprobic; others became destructive parasites, causing wilts and root rots; yet others evolved into a mutually beneficial symbiosis. Proof of this lies in the fact that fossils of some Devonian plants contain well-preserved fungal structures just like those we can find in the roots of more than 90% of healthy modern plant species.

About a century ago, several biologists noticed that some plant roots, though extensively invaded by fungi, were not diseased. The name **mycorrhiza** (fungus root) was coined in 1885. We now know that, especially in poor soils, mycorrhizal plants grow better than non-mycorrhizal plants. This is because the hyphae of the fungal symbionts permeate large volumes of soil and obtain scarce elements—especially phosphorus, which is often limiting for plant growth—which they pass on to the plant in exchange for photosynthates.

Interest in these symbioses has escalated dramatically in recent years, because of their potential benefits to agriculture, forestry, and the revegetation of ecosystems damaged by human activities such as mining. Some plants cannot become established or grow normally without an appropriate fungal partner (often called the **mycobiont**). Even when plants can survive without mycorrhizae, those with 'fungus roots' need less fertilizer, withstand heavy metal and acid rain pollution better, and grow better on the infertile soils of marginal lands, on mine spoils and other areas needing revegetation, and at high elevations. They also survive transplant shock better, are more resistant to soil-borne diseases, withstand higher soil temperatures, higher soil salinity, and wider extremes of soil pH. Mycorrhizal fungi are almost ubiquitous, and over 90% of all higher plant species are normally mycorrhizal, and can be called **phytobionts**.

Two main kinds of mycorrhizae are constantly found in association with our agricultural and forest crops. By far the commoner of the two is the **endotrophic mycorrhiza** in which specialized hyphae of the fungus enter the cells of the root cortex and set up finely branched, microscopic intracellular interfaces (Fig. 17.1). Although about 300,000 plant species are believed to have endotrophic mycorrhizae, only about 130 species of fungi have so far been described from such relationships. These fungi will grow only in association with plant roots (i.e. they are obligate biotrophs), and only one of them has ever been seen to reproduce sexually. They are placed in the phylum Zygomycota.

The second kind of mycorrhiza is the **ectotrophic mycorrhiza**, so called because the fungus grows around the root and between its cortical cells, but

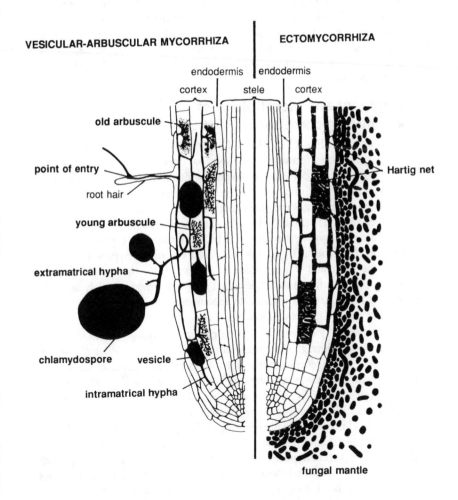

Fig. 17.1 Diagrams of endo- and ecto-mycorrhizal structures.

never actually penetrates the cells (Fig. 17.1). This kind of mycorrhiza is found in only about 2,000 species of plants, but these include some of the most important forest trees—e.g. Pinaceae (pine, spruce, fir, etc.), Fagaceae (beech, oak, southern beech), and Myrtaceae (eucalypts). These plants have about 5,000 fungal partners. Although these fungi are usually found only in association with tree roots, most of them can be grown in pure culture, and almost all produce sexual fructifications in their natural habitat. They are nearly all members of the phylum Dikaryomycota, mostly **basidiomycetes**, though a number are **ascomycetes**.

The mycorrhizal symbiosis, whether ectotrophic or endotrophic, must have three basic functioning components: (1) fungal mycelium exploring large volumes of soil and retrieving mineral nutrients; (2) a fungus-plant interface where the exchange of chemicals can go on; and (3) plant tissues which produce and store carbohydrates. Strangely enough, within each of the main groups of mycorrhizae, the root-associated fungal components look rather alike, and we have to refer to other components, (4) the reproductive structures before we can identify the fungus.

Development and Morphology of Ectotrophic Mycorrhizae

Ectomycorrhizae (Fig. 17.1, 17.2 A-C) normally develop 1-3 months after the tree seed germinates, forming on the 'short' or 'feeder' roots, near the surface of the soil. Roots may be colonized by hyphae which grow through the soil from another mycorrhizal root, or by airborne spores. When the latter germinate, they can subsist on root exudates until they reach the root. Colonization occurs only in the unsuberized zone behind the root tip. The process of colonization involves: (A) penetration of hyphae between the cells of the root cortex to form a characteristic **Hartig net**; (B) establishment of a **mantle** of hyphae around the outside of the root; and (C) extension of hyphae from the mantle into the surrounding soil. The fungus produces plant growth hormones which cause the short roots of the plant to grow faster, to become thicker, and often to branch in characteristic ways (e.g. dichotomously).

The Hartig net may be restricted to the outermost layer(s) of the root, or it may spread slowly through the cortex until it reaches the endodermis, which effectively bars any penetration of the stele. As the hyphae insinuate themselves between the cortical cells, these separate at the middle lamella, and an almost complete single layer of fungal hyphae eventually surrounds each cell, though plasmodesmata still connect many cortical cells. Far from being deleterious, the presence of the Hartig net actually seems to prolong the life of the cortical cells, and of the root as a whole. The fungal mantle surrounding the root varies from a relatively loose weft of hyphae to a thick, pseudoparenchymatous layer which accounts for nearly half the biomass of the mycorrhiza. The formation of root hairs by the plant is suppressed, since they have been rendered redundant by mycelial strands and/or individual hyphae radiating from the mantle. Compared to non-mycorrhizal roots, ectomycorrhizae are: (1) a different colour; (2)

thicker; and (3) much more often branched—pinnately and racemosely in *Abies*, *Fagus* and *Eucalyptus*, and dichotomously in *Pinus*. The truly diagnostic structure, however, is the **Hartig net**, the functional extracellular interface between the symbionts (Fig. 17.2 B,C).

Individual ectomycorrhizae remain active for up to 3 years. Roots and mantles often extend at the same rate, but the root sometimes breaks through and grows beyond the mantle. The root may then be colonized by other opportunistic ectomycorrhizal fungi, which may be better adapted than the original partner for the specific soil microhabitat being encountered. A tree may thus have a number of different fungal partners on its root system at the same

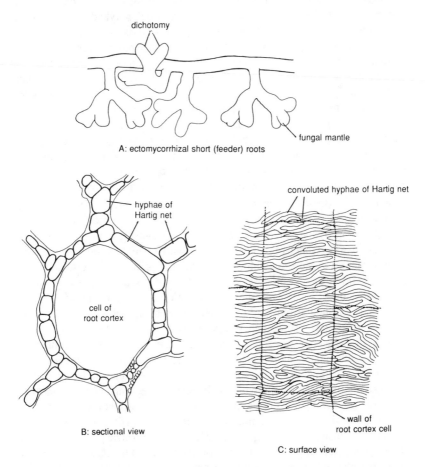

Fig. 17.2 Ectomycorrhizae. A: dichotomous mycorhizal short roots of *Pinus*; B: sectional view of part of Hartig net, note that cortical cell is completely surrounded by hyphae; C: surface view of part of Hartig net, showing convoluted, interlocking hyphae.

time. Many of the fungi responsible for ectotrophic mycorrhizae can be isolated in axenic culture without much difficulty, but most will not fruit in culture, grow slowly, and require vitamins like thiamine, some amino acids, and other normally root-derived substances, as well as simple carbohydrates. Most of them are completely incapable of degrading cellulose or lignin, although these substances are the principal diet of many other saprobic basidiomycetes. If we add to this picture the information that, when not associated with a tree, these fungi cannot compete with fungi of the saprobic soil mycota, and are adversely affected by toxins present in humus and leaf litter, we gain the impression that in nature, these fungi are more or less obligate root symbionts.

Sugars are translocated from the root to the fungal mantle, where they are converted into **trehalose** (a disaccharide), **mannitol** (a polyhydric alcohol), and **glycogen**—all typical fungal carbohydrates. The glycogen is insoluble, and therefore unavailable for possible reabsorption by the plant. More surprisingly, although the mannitol and trehalose remain in solution in the fungus, the plant is incapable of reabsorbing them. Thus the fungal sheath acts as a sink where reserves of carbohydrates derived from the plant are stored. This has some interesting consequences. (1) As autumn approaches, many of the fungi mobilize the stored carbohydrates and produce flushes of large mushrooms or hypogeous fruit bodies near the tree. (2) Carbohydrates can be translocated through mycelial strands from established trees to seedlings of the same species. This must help in the maintenance of pure stands. (3) The tree can reclaim some of the stored energy if conditions become appropriate for a new surge of growth.

How much does a tree invest in its mycorrhizal partners? If we add up the various organs of the fungus—the conspicuous fruit bodies, the extensive though inconspicuous mycelium ramifying through the soil, and the rootlet mantles—we find that trees often invest at least 10% of their total production of photosynthates in their mycobionts. The drain of photosynthates from the tree is clearly more than compensated for by the increased efficiency of mineral absorption, and by the fact that the fungal mantle can also store mineral nutrients, e.g. chloride, ammonium, and especially phosphate, that aren't immediately needed by the tree. These can subsequently be released to the plant during periods of deficiency or of active growth. Since the mycorrhizal rootlets are perennial, the mantle can repeatedly act as a storage organ when the root is not acting as a growing organ. This, and the ability of the fungus to fruit massively during a relatively short time-window, indicate that ectomycorrhizal plants and fungi are both adapted to grow in climates where seasonal changes are often dramatic, causing wide fluctuations in growth rate and in the supply of nutrients. This goes some way toward explaining why ectomycorrhizal plants are common in cool temperate climates, in boreal forests, in montane regions, and in other habitats subjected to environmental extremes.

Systematics of Ectomycorrhizal Fungi and their Hosts

Most EM (Ectotrophic Mycorrhizal) fungi are **holobasidiomycetes**: members of at least 73 genera in 9 orders. They are: (1) **agarics** (2) former agarics which have become **sequestrate** (closed, not shooting spores at maturity), sometimes fruiting above ground, sometimes underground (**false truffles**); (3) some **club fungi, chanterelles, tooth fungi**, and **resupinate hymenomycetes** (all Aphyllophorales). There are also ectomycorrhizal fungi in 16 **unitunicate ascomycete** genera from 2 orders. All but one of these ascomycete genera fruit underground. The principal EM fungal taxa are listed in Table 17.1, and many are illustrated in chapters 5 and 22.

Table 17.1
Taxonomic Distribution of Ectomycorrhizal Fungi

	Number of Genera
Division: **Dikaryomycota**	
Subphylum: **Basidiomycotina**	
Order: Agaricales	
Family: Amanitaceae	(2)
Hygrophoraceae	(1)
Tricholomataceae	(6)
Entolomataceae	(1)
Cortinariaceae	(5)
Paxillaceae	(2)
Gomphidiaceae	(5)
Boletaceae	(13)
Strobilomycetaceae	(3)
Russulaceae	(5)
Order: Gautieriales	(1)
Order: Hymenogastrales	(8)
Order: Phallales	(1)
Order: Lycoperdales	(1)
Order: Melanogastrales	(4)
Order: Sclerodermatales	(3)
Order: Aphyllophorales	(8)
Subphylum: **Ascomycotina**	
Order: Pezizales	
Family: Pezizaceae	(1)
Balsamiaceae	(3)
Geneaceae	(1)
Helvellaceae	(1)
Pyronemataceae	(3)
Terfeziaceae	(4)
Tuberaceae	(2)
Order: Elaphomycetales	(1)
Total genera	90

Most ectomycorrhizae (the actual fungus roots) are rather similar, so the 5,000 fungi involved must usually be identified from their macroscopic fruit bodies (**basidiomata** or **ascomata**), which are produced during a relatively short season each year. Many EM fungi belong to cosmopolitan agaric genera like *Russula, Lactarius, Cortinarius, Amanita, Tricholoma, Inocybe* and *Laccaria. Cortinarius* alone is estimated to have 2,000 species. Some families are almost entirely ectomycorrhizal—Boletaceae, Gomphidiaceae, Russulaceae, Strobilomycetaceae, and Cantharellaceae. So are all or most species of the genera *Amanita, Armillaria, Cortinarius, Hebeloma, Laccaria, Pisolithus, Scleroderma,* and *Tricholoma,* as well as almost all known hypogeous basidiomycetes (e.g. *Rhizopogon, Truncocolumella, Hymenogaster*). Among the ascomycetes, members of the hypogeous Tuberaceae (**truffles**) are probably all mycorrhizal. One Phylum-wide generalization may be in order: if a fungus produces sizeable underground fruit bodies, then it is very likely to be mycorrhizal, whether it is a basidiomycete or an ascomycete.

Some EM fungi have a wide host range, for example, *Amanita muscaria, Boletus edulis, Cantharellus cibarius, Cenococcum geophilum, Laccaria laccata, Pisolithus tinctorius,* and *Thelephora terrestris.* Others seem to be more selective, and some are virtually host-specific—*Suillus grevillei* associates only with *Larix* (larch or tamarack), *Suillus lakei* with *Pseudotsuga menziesii* (Douglas fir). As I have already pointed out, one tree may have several, or even many, different ectomycorrhizal partners on its roots at the same time, and these may be replaced by others as the tree ages. So a single tree species can have a large number of potential mycobionts. Douglas fir may be able to form ectomycorrhizae with as many as 2,000 different species of fungi. And different isolates of the same fungal species may relate differently to the same tree species.

The full host spectrum of the ectomycorrhizal fungi is: Gymnosperms—Pinaceae and some Cupressaceae. Angiosperms—only 4 monocots (including *Kobresia* of the Cyperaceae, *Festuca* of the Gramineae, and *Euterpe* of the Palmae); all or some members of 21 dicot families—all members of the Fagaceae, Betulaceae, Salicaceae, and Dipterocarpaceae subfamily Dipterocarpoideae, and most Myrtaceae; also the tribes Amherstieae and Detarieae of the family Caesalpinioideae, some Mimosoideae and Papilionoideae (all legumes), sea grape (*Coccoloba*) of the Polygonaceae, *Neea* and *Pisonia* of the Nyctaginaceae, and scattered representatives of the Aceraceae, Bignoniaceae, Cistaceae, Combretaceae, Euphorbiaceae, Juglandaceae, Rhamnaceae, Rosaceae, Sapindaceae, Sapotaceae, Tiliaceae and Ulmaceae (see Table 17.2 for a comparison between the hosts of the ectomycorrhizal and endomycorrhizal fungi).

Table 17.2
Comparison of the Phytobionts of Ecto- and Endo-Mycorrhizal Fungi

Ectomycorrhizal Fungi	Endomycorrhizal Fungi
2,000 spp. of plants — mainly trees.	300,000+ spp. of plants —herbaceous, woody.
Gymnosperms:	380 Families:
ALL Pinaceae & Cupressaceae Angiosperms: ALL Fagaceae, Betulaceae, Salicaceae, Dipterocarpoideae; MOST Myrtaceae; MANY legumes, SOME Aceraceae, Euphorbiaceae, Rosaceae, Tiliaceae, Ulmaceae, & seven other families.	(EXCLUDING: ALL Brassicaceae, Commelinaceae, Cyperaceae, Juncaceae, Proteaceae, SOME Amaranthaceae, Caryophyllaceae, Chenopodiaceae, Polygonaceae, members of 3 other families, and MOST ectomycorrhizal spp.)

The approximately 2,000 ectomycorrhizal plant species are almost all woody and perennial. Many of them grow in extensive pure stands. Many are indigenous to the Northern Hemisphere, and some are the main components of the boreal forest. The Pinaceae are the single most important ectomycorrhizal family, since they cover vast areas of the globe, and are harvested and replanted in astronomical numbers each year. Selection of appropriate mycorrhizal partners for our forest trees, and inoculation of seedlings before outplanting, or encouragement of ectomycorrhizal fungi indigenous to outplanting sites, could improve the survival and growth of tree seedlings, and therefore offers important economic benefits.

Evaluation and Selection of Ectomycorrhizal Fungi

The thousands of different species of ectomycorrhizal fungi probably evolved in response to the diverse needs of many hosts in many habitats. How many host-fungus-soil-climate combinations are there? No one knows, but for example, one 250 km transect running east from the coast of Oregon passes through 17 major forest zones, hundreds of kinds of habitat, and includes at least 10 genera of economically important ectomycorrhizal trees. So how can we select the best possible mycobiont for each combination? Fortunately for the decision-making process, one or two characteristics are often of overriding importance. For example, if a fungus cannot be grown in pure culture for the large-scale production of mycelial inoculum, it is in most cases effectively excluded, no matter how good a mycorrhizal partner it is.

All potential host-fungus pairs should ideally be tested for all of the following characteristics. (1) Rapidity and extent of mycorrhization. (2) Host response. (3) Efficiency of inorganic nutrient uptake. (4) Water relations (keeping in mind the conditions under which the pair must operate after outplanting). (5) Tolerance of temperature extremes, and (6) pH extremes that will be experienced after outplanting. (7) Tolerance of air pollution or soil toxicity. (8) Stability of the partnership (a measure of the competitive ability of the fungus). (9) Disease resistance (this need be tested only for diseases present at the outplanting site). (10) Mycelial strand formation by the fungus. (11) Ease of isolating the fungus in pure culture. (12) Ease and rapidity with which large quantities of inoculum can be produced. (13) Edibility of the fruit bodies of the fungus.

The potential range of mycobionts for a given tree in a given habitat may be estimated by listing the fungi found fruiting nearby, combined with estimations of the degree of mycorrhizal infection on the roots, though this should not rule out the possibility of introducing new and efficient EM partners to the area. Field observations showed that *Suillus plorans* was the predominant naturally occurring EM fungus associated with *Pinus cembra* at treeline in the Swiss Alps. But the choice is not usually so simple. The process of testing host-fungus pairs involves isolating the fungi in pure culture, and inoculating them onto seedlings grown individually and aseptically in tubes or soil pouches, where the development of mycorrhizae can be visually checked. I will discuss the thirteen criteria in sequence.

(1) Rate and extent of mycorrhization. Ectomycorrhizae can be seen with the naked eye, and can be readily quantified. Entire root systems of seedlings can be examined, but in older trees only a sample obtained by soil coring or local excavation can be studied. The percentage of mycorrhizal short roots can be determined visually, and the weights of these structures determined. Results may be expressed as number and weight of ectomycorrhizal structures per unit area, or per unit volume of soil.

(2) Host response. The reaction of a seedling or tree to mycorrhizal colonization can be measured in various ways. An easy, non-destructive method is to follow seedling survival, expressed as percentages of the initial uninoculated and inoculated populations. Such data can be gathered at various ages, before and after outplanting. Other non-destructive measures are plant height, thickness of stalk at ground level, number of leaves, leaf length and leaf area. More definitive measurements involve determining the dry weight of the whole plant, or of separate root and shoot systems. Measurements of stem height and stem diameter at soil line are eventually replaced by diameter at breast height (1.4 m) in older trees. A 'mycorrhizal influence value' (MIV) can be determined for any parameter by expressing the mean value for non-inoculated plants as 100, and calculating the value for mycorrhizal plants as an integer relative to that 100. Thus the MIV would be a percentage of the control value in each case (usually greater than 100%).

(3) Mineral nutrition. Phosphorus uptake, and levels achieved in the mantle and in the plant have been determined using radiotracer techniques, and are among the most important reflections of the effects of EM fungi on their hosts. Ectomycorrhizal plants also absorb many other minerals, e.g. calcium, potassium, copper, molybdenum, magnesium and zinc, from the soil more efficiently than non-mycorrhizal plants can. The fungal mantle can store inorganic nutrients, e.g. chloride, ammonium, and especially phosphate, and release them to

the plant during periods of deficiency or active growth. *Pisolithus tinctorius* thrives in soils of extremely low fertility, such as mine spoils, while *Paxillus involutus* does well only on sites with relatively abundant available nitrogen. But since it is in the uptake of phosphorus, often a limiting nutrient in poor soils, that EM fungi make their greatest contribution to the symbiosis, evaluation of rate and amount of P accumulation must be one of the most important criteria in selection.

(4) Water relations. The fungus *Cenococcum geophilum* is especially tolerant of low water potential, which correlates well with its propensity for forming ectomycorrhizae in dry areas. In fact, because *Cenococcum* grows best at a water potential of -15 bars, it can be difficult to establish in irrigated nurseries, where it may be replaced by *Thelephora terrestris*.

(5) Temperature. *Pinus cembra* destined for high-altitude outplanting is inoculated with a cold-adapted strain of *Suillus plorans*. Other fungi, especially *Pisolithus tinctorius*, have been found to be adapted to high temperatures. *Cenococcum geophilum* appears to tolerate both extremes relatively well.

(6) pH. Pine seedlings with *Pisolithus tinctorius* ectomycorrhizae survive and grow better on acid coal mine spoils than do non-mycorrhizal seedlings. This fungus can tolerate a pH range of 2.6-8.4. *Cenococcum geophilum* forms mycorrhizae from pH 3.4-7.5. Other ectomycorrhizal fungi improve the growth of pines in alkaline soil.

(7) Toxicity. EM fungi have been shown to destroy heat-formed phytotoxins in the soil. In view of the selective absorption of various ions by mycorrhizal fungi, and their capacity for storing ions in the mantle, they may be active in ameliorating marginal soil toxicities. There is still little published work in this area, but studies in progress on the spoils derived from nickel mining at Sudbury, Ontario, indicate that some EM fungi can tolerate fairly high levels of heavy metals in the substrate. When soil around pecan trees was treated with a variety of nematicides and fungicides, an increase in mycorrhiza formation by *Scleroderma bovista* (Sclerodermatales) was observed, due perhaps to a combination of toxin tolerance and reduced competition.

(8) Persistence. The stability of the partnership need be established only in the short term, since the choice of a mycorrhizal partner for a tree should probably be based on the immediate benefits it bestows. Although the initial mycobiont has in many cases been shown to be supplanted or supplemented by other EM fungi after the seedling has been outplanted, its presence in the early days may well make the difference between death and survival of very young seedlings. Selection of a mycobiont adapted to the conditions of the outplanting site, and preferably already established there, as determined by the occurrence of its basidiomata or ascomata, may produce the best results.

(9) Disease resistance. The presence of EM fungi on the roots of trees gives them some protection against the attacks of several serious root-pathogenic fungi. *Boletus bovinus* helped to protect *Picea abies* from *Heterobasidion annosum*. *Pisolithus tinctorius* increased the survival rate of *Pinus taeda* seedlings exposed to *Rhizoctonia solani*. Mycorrhizae formed by *Suillus granulatus*

seemed to protect seedlings of *Pinus excelsa* from a root-rotting *Rhizoctonia*. Seedlings of *Pinus clausa* were protected against *Phytophthora cinnamomi* by mycorrhizae of *Pisolithus tinctorius*. The effects of the pathogen, *Mycelium radicis atrovirens*, on *Picea mariana* and *Pinus resinosa*, were markedly reduced by the presence of *Suillus granulatus*. This effect is not fully explained, but may be due to competition between fungi for nutrients and for access to the root.

(10) Mycelial strand formation. These aggregations of parallel hyphae serve as effective agents for the spread of the fungi through the soil, and in the long-distance translocation of phosphate and other nutrients to the mycorrhizae. Different species, and different isolates of the same species of EM fungus, may have differing strand-forming tendencies. Other things being equal, it would seem reasonable to choose a strand-forming fungus, such as *Pisolithus tinctorius*, over one that did not produce these structures.

(11) Ease of isolation. Pure cultures of ectomycorrhizal fungi are usually derived from fruit body tissue, though they can also be obtained from surface-sterilized mycorrhizal roots, sclerotia, rhizomorphs or mycelial strands. It is difficult to germinate basidiospores, and this is rarely attempted. Isolation from fruit bodies allows precise identification of the fungus at the outset. Members of the following genera are often fairly easy to isolate: *Amanita*, *Boletus*, *Cortinarius*, *Hebeloma*, *Hysterangium*, *Laccaria*, *Lactarius*, *Leccinum*, *Paxillus*, *Pisolithus*, *Rhizopogon*, *Scleroderma*, *Suillus*, and *Tricholoma*. Happily, these include some of the better mycorrhizal partners with the broadest host ranges. But only a few species of *Russula* have yet been cultured. I think most EM fungi will eventually be grown in axenic culture when their rather stringent nutritional requirements have been worked out.

(12) Large scale inoculum production. Since *Pisolithus tinctorius* has been shown to establish mycorrhizae with almost 50 different tree species, thrives over a wide range of soil pH, tolerates high temperatures well, and can establish mycorrhizae in the poorest soils, it has been touted as a panacea for all our ectomycorrhizal problems. It was also the first EM fungus to be made available in the form of commercially produced mycelial inoculum. Nevertheless, it seems unlikely that *Pisolithus* can be all things to all EM trees. It is probably at its best coping with heat and drought stress. It has been collected only a few times in Canada, and I suspect that it will not turn out to be the perfect partner for boreal conifers. Some recent work suggests that when conifer seedlings with *Pisolithus* mycorrhizae are outplanted in Northern Quebec, *Pisolithus* is soon replaced by indigenous species. Attempts are being made to scale up production of mycelial inoculum of *Cenococcum geophilum*, *Rhizopogon* spp., *Suillus* spp., *Thelephora terrestris* and others.

(13) Edibility. If several potential partners seem more or less equivalent, the ultimate choice may be dictated by secondary, though not negligible, factors such as the edibility or otherwise of the fruit bodies of the fungi being considered. For example, if a hypothetical choice lay between a species of *Amanita* known to be highly toxic, and another agaric, such as *Boletus edulis*, that was

edible and choice, the decision would be straightforward. Less obvious, but also important, is the caution that species known to have toxic fruit bodies should not be introduced to new areas as mycorrhizal partners, even if they might seem otherwise desirable. One of the most toxic of all agarics, *Amanita phalloides*, was inadvertently introduced into South America as a mycobiont of oak seedlings imported from Europe early in this century. The cyclopeptide toxins (amatoxins) in this fungus have since caused many fatalities. The Australian government prevented a similar problem by refusing to allow the importation of cultures of *Amanita pantherina*, a good mycorrhizal partner, but producing basidiomata containing dangerous levels of ibotenic acid. At the other end of the scale are the French experiments with 'trufficulture'—the deliberate use of *Tuber melanosporum* as a mycorrhizal partner, with an eye to the production of truffles, an extremely valuable crop. The first steps toward the culture of other choice edible fungi have been made, again by the French. Using pure cultures of the famous 'cep' (*Boletus edulis*) and three other boletes, as well as *Lactarius deliciosus* and *Tricholoma flavovirens*, ectomycorrhizae have been established on *Pinus pinaster* and *Pinus radiata* in test tubes and in greenhouse pots. It remains to be seen whether outplanted seedlings bearing mycorrhizae of these species will ultimately produce basidiomata, thereby providing an interesting and perhaps valuable byproduct of afforestation.

Sources of Ectomycorrhizal Inoculum

Ectomycorrhizae may be initiated by several different kinds of inoculum. (1) Naturally dispersed spores. (2) Colonized soil. (3) Mycorrhizal seedlings. (4) Ascomata, basidiomata, spores or sclerotia specifically collected for the purpose. (5) Fungal mycelium produced in axenic culture. It is worth comparing the merits of these different kinds of inoculum.

(1) Natural spore inoculum is, of course, one of the prime dispersal mechanisms for fungi, but it can't always be relied on to infect nursery or outplanted seedlings because: (a) It is available only during a relatively short season, since most agarics fruit in late summer or early fall. (b) Even when spores are being released, they may not reach the seedlings in adequate numbers, especially if the seedlings are a long way from the nearest stand of ectomycorrhizal trees. (c) We have no control over the nature of the fungal partners being introduced. This is important because EM fungi vary widely in their efficiency. (d) If seedlings are being started at a low elevation nursery for high elevation outplanting, they may acquire local mycobionts unsuited to conditions at the intended growth site.

(2) In Western Australia, pine seeds planted at 14 new nurseries germinated, and grew relatively well for a few months, then began to decline and die. The few remaining healthy seedlings were found to have developed ectomycorrhizae. When soil from around the healthy seedlings was used to inoculate other seedbeds, the seedlings there recovered. Soil from beneath established ectomycorrhizal trees is a fairly reliable source of inoculum if 10% by volume is added to a new nursery bed. The mycobionts are often unknown, and there is some risk of introducing pests or pathogens, but this has rarely caused difficulty, because

the source location can be carefully checked in advance. Colonized soil has been used to establish exotic pines in many parts of the southern hemisphere, and soil transfer is a regular procedure in many developing countries.

(3) Introduced mycorrhizal seedlings carry the same risks as (2), but have also worked relatively well. This technique was first used on a large scale in Indonesia, and is still used there. Mycorrhizal seedlings are planted in seedbeds at 1-2 m intervals. At outplanting time, some seedlings are left to inoculate the next crop.

(4) The deliberate collection and introduction of spores, fruit bodies or sclerotia would seem to be an obvious way of improving upon nature, but there are some problems: (a) Naturally occurring fruit bodies of most EM fungi are available only during a small part of the year. (b) In most cases the amount of inoculum available will be limited, and will fluctuate from year to year. (c) Fruit bodies usually occur sporadically and scattered over large areas, so collection of in the amounts needed for large-scale forestry applications would be almost impossible. Only the particularly concentrated spore-source represented by gasteromycetes could be obtained in the necessary quantity. (d) Storage of the eminently perishable basidiomata would be difficult. (e) Initiation of mycorrhizae by basidiospore inoculum takes 3-4 weeks longer than when mycelial inoculum is used. This gives pathogens longer to attack the roots, and the later-developing mycorrhizae also provide less growth stimulation during the crucial early stages of seedling development.

One widespread mycobiont, *Cenococcum geophilum*, produces structures called **sclerotia** that are much less perishable than either spores or basidiomata, since they obviously evolved as a long-term survival mechanism. These sclerotia often occur naturally in the soil in huge numbers, and could probably be harvested and used as inoculum. Over 450 kg of *Pisolithus tinctorius* basidiomata were collected on coal mine spoils in Alabama in 75 person-days. Since less than 1 mg of spores is needed to inoculate a plant, this collection provided enough inoculum for hundreds of millions of pine seeds. The basidiospores were used in a seed-pelletizing mix, each seed being coated with 500,000 to 5 million spores which became dispersed around and below the seed after planting as a result of rain or irrigation, and colonized the roots as these developed.

(5) If mycelial inoculum derived from pure cultures of known mycobionts is used, the identity of the fungus will be known, pests and pathogens will be absent, inoculum will be compact and easily transported, and should be available year-round. However, it too has inherent problems, not the least of which is that it is by far the most expensive of the alternatives: (a) Some ectomycorrhizal fungi are difficult to isolate in pure culture. (b) Cultures are expensive to maintain, and grow slowly, taking a long time to produce enough biomass for large-scale applications. (c) We still do not know how well such inoculum survives in the soil in face of predation and competition from indigenous organisms. (d) We have not yet defined the best possible fungus-host combinations for many soil-climate combinations. It is hardly worth going to the expense

of mass-producing mycelium of many species until we are sure that the results will be economically worthwhile. However, some EM fungi, often those with relatively small basidiomata (e.g. *Thelephora, Laccaria*), are early colonizers, associated with young trees, while others, often with large fruit bodies (e.g. *Boletus*) are late colonizers, often associated with larger, older trees. It would seem appropriate to concentrate on early colonizers.

It is easy to grow enough mycelial inoculum for small-scale research projects, but experience has shown that it is much more difficult to generate enough to inoculate the many millions of seedlings produced each year. Various methods of producing mycelial inoculum of *Pisolithus tinctorius, Thelephora terrestris* and *Cenococcum geophilum* have been tried. It was found that peatmoss plus vermiculite moistened with modified Melin-Norkrans nutrient (MMN) solution gave good results. The MMN solution contained: 0.05 g $CaCl_2$, 0.025 g NaCl, 0.5 g KH_2PO_4, 0.25 g $(NH_4)_2PO_4$, 0.15 g $MgSO_4.7H_2O$, 1.2 mL 1% $FeCl_3$, 100 g thiamine HCl, 3 g malt extract, 10 g glucose, and distilled water to make 1 litre. Using starter mycelium grown in liquid culture and mixed throughout the substrate, *Thelephora terrestris* and *Pisolithus tinctorius* will thoroughly colonize the substrate in 1-2 months at room temperature. *Cenococcum geophilum* may take 4-5 months to achieve the same result. The inoculum is leached in tapwater for 2-3 minutes, then dried until its water content is 20-65%. Inoculum of *Pisolithus tinctorius* can be stored at 5°C for 9 weeks without much loss of activity, but the sooner it is used, the better. A commercial formulation of *Pisolithus tinctorius* mycelial inoculum has been developed, grown on a large scale in the vermiculite-peatmoss-MMN medium. Unfortunately, quality-control problems (read: contamination and low mycorrhiza-forming efficiency) caused this product to be withdrawn from the market in 1983. It is now being produced in 'breathable' plastic bags by another company.

Several methods of application have been tried: (A) **Broadcast inoculation**: a known quantity of inoculum is spread out over a given area of seedbed, and mixed into the top 10-20 cm of soil before the bed is seeded. Inoculum of *Pisolithus tinctorius*, broadcast at a rate of 1 litre/square metre, gave the same results as those obtained with higher levels of inoculum. Inoculum incorporated in container growth media at a rate of 6% by volume produced effective mycorrhization in many conifers. Here, inoculation and container filling processes can be combined. *Pinus taeda* nursery beds have been successfully inoculated with cultures of *Pisolithus tinctorius*. Laboratory grown inoculum was leached under running tapwater, cool-dried to about 20% moisture, and kept cold, but not frozen, until used. Nursery beds previously fumigated with methyl bromide-chlorpicrin were inoculated with the dried preparation, which was dug into the top 7-10 cm of soil, before seeding. (B) **Banding of inoculum below seeds**: this concentrates inoculum in a zone that will be penetrated by the growing roots. Seeds and inoculum can be dispensed at the same time. This method needs only about a third as much inoculum as the broadcast technique.

(C) **Slurry inoculum**: this has the advantage that bare-root or containerized seedlings can be rapidly inoculated by dipping before transplanting.

The production and field application of mycelial inoculum of EM fungi is still in its expensive, and at times unreliable, infancy. Yet many foresters believe that the inoculation of both bare-root and container-grown seedlings with appropriate EM fungi will eventually become routine practice. It is worth noting, however, that in many parts of the world it is not afforestation, but reforestation that is important. In this case, the soil of the site to be replanted will often contain good mycorrhizal fungi. It may be possible to give these indigenous fungi a competitive advantage by discouraging other components of the local mycota with selective fungicides such as Benomyl, which inhibits ascomycetes and their anamorphs without significantly affecting the basidiomycetes.

Morphology and Development of Vesicular-Arbuscular Mycorrhizae

The almost omnipresent endotrophic mycorrhiza, often known as the **vesicular-arbuscular mycorrhiza** or **VAM (though not all fungi of this group produce vesicles)**, is a more subtle phenomenon than the ectotrophic mycorrhiza. The presence of a VAM fungus in a root is usually undetectable by the naked eye. There is no obvious morphological change, no mycelial mantle, no sudden flush of large fungal fruit bodies. Yet, as appropriate clearing and staining will show, roots are often extensively colonized (Fig. 17.1 A). The life cycle of a vesicular-arbuscular mycorrhizal fungus goes more or less as follows. Spores in the soil germinate, usually in conditions appropriate for plant seed

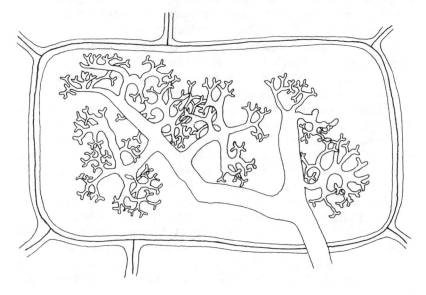

Fig. 17.3 Finely branched arbuscule of an endomycorrhizal fungus inside a root cell of the phytobiont.

germination and root growth. If the fungus encounters a receptive root or root hair, an appressorium is formed, and penetration occurs (often through 'short cells' of the exodermis, if these are present, because they are not yet suberized), in the elongation zone of the root. Symbiosis is initiated in juvenile tissues.

Hyphae grow in or between the cortical cells, but never enter meristematic cells or endodermal cells. Specialized hyphal branches enter individual cortical cells and form finely branched, tree-like structures called **arbuscules** (Fig. 17.1 A, 17.3), which are completely encapsulated by the host plasmalemma, and are the main sites of exchange between the fungus and the plant. The nucleus of the root cell is enlarged, and the volume of cytoplasm increases. We assume that phosphorus is being actively transferred to the plant throughout the life of each arbuscule. Polyphosphate granules, involved in P transport in the fungus, are present in hyphae, but not in the finest branches of the arbuscules, which contain acid and alkaline phosphatases. After 4-15 days, the arbuscule gradually breaks down, and the root cell returns to normal.

Many, though not all, vesicular-arbuscular mycorrhizal (VAM) fungi also form **vesicles** in the root. These are thin-walled, inflated structures without a basal septum, and are often full of lipids. I have seen up to 500 vesicles/cm in older leek roots, the root cortex looking like an almost solid mass of vesicles. Despite this, the root remains functional, since the stele is not colonized, and can still translocate substances to and from the active root tips. Vesicles are *not* formed by one actively endomycorrhizal genus, *Gigaspora.*

While the fungus is developing its **intramatrical** phase within the root, it is also developing an **extramatrical** hyphal network in the soil. Extramatrical hyphae extend at least 8 cm from the root. This means that a mycorrhizal plant can exploit several times the volume of soil available to a non-mycorrhizal plant. The extramatrical hyphae obtain phosphorus and translocate it to the plant, which reciprocates by supplying the fungus with photosynthates. These enable the latter to extend its hyphal network, and to produce its large, **asexual spores**. Spores may form in the soil singly, or in aggregations up to 2 cm in diameter called **sporocarps**. Individual spores are large: 50-600 µm in diameter. They may have walls up to 30 µm thick, are often darkly pigmented, and are filled with storage lipids, all features that emphasize their role in long-term survival when host plants are absent or dormant. Vesicles are sometimes regarded as 'intramatrical spores.' The spores will eventually germinate, producing hyphae which will once more grow through the soil and perhaps encounter another plant. The identity of the plant may not matter much, since VAM fungi can usually relate successfully to a very large number of host species (130 fungal taxa with 300,000 plant taxa).

Systematics of VAM Fungi and their Hosts

The taxonomy of the VAM fungi is in a state of ferment. Thirty taxa were recognized in 1974, about 120 by 1985, 130 by 1991. Only one of these obligately biotrophic fungi has ever been seen to undergo sexual reproduction, and they are different enough from all other known fungi to be something of a taxonomic enigma. For the present they are all placed in the family Glomaceae, order Glomales, Division Zygomycota of Kingdom Eumycota.

There are six unequivocally endomycorrhizal genera—*Acaulospora*, *Entrophospora*, *Gigaspora*, *Glomus*, *Sclerocystis* and *Scutellospora* (Fig. 17.4). Since these fungi are present in most soils around the world, I will provide a dichotomous key to these six genera.

Dichotomous Key to Genera of Arbuscular Mycorrhizal Fungi
(after Morton & Benny 1990)

---

1) Only arbuscules formed in mycorrhizal roots; "azygospores" produced at apex of a fertile hypha; auxiliary cells formed 2

1) Both arbuscules and vesicles formed in mycorrhizal roots; "chlamydospores" produced terminally or laterally on or in fertile hyphae; auxiliary cells not produced

                                    3

  2) Germ tubes produced directly through spore wall; inner flexible wall group absent; auxiliary cells ornamented (papillate or echinulate) . . . .*Gigaspora*

  2) Germ tubes arise from germination shield; inner flexible wall group always present; auxiliary cells knobby, papillate or smooth . . . .*Scutellospora*

3) Chlamydospores formed apically from fertile hyphae . .4

3) Chlamydospores formed from or within the neck of a sporiferous vesicle .5

  4) Spores always formed in a sporocarp; lateral walls of spores adhering to one another; connecting hyphae embedded in central plexus; chlamydospores in a single layer except at base; base of sterile hyphae . . . . . *Sclerocystis*

  4) Spores in a sporocarp not formed as in *Sclerocystis*; spores also formed singly or in aggregations in soil, less often in roots . . . . *Glomus*

5) Spores arise laterally from the neck of a sporiferous vesicle . . . .*Acaulospora*

5) Spores formed in the neck of the sporiferous vesicle . . .*Entrophospora*

Glomus (Fig. 17.4), the commonest genus, now has more than 50 species. These form globose, ellipsoid or irregular spores, 20-400 μm in diameter, with walls up to 30 μm thick. They are hyaline, yellow, red-brown, brown or black. They are attached to a single hypha, and are produced in the soil near plant roots, at the soil surface, or occasionally inside roots, and they may be solitary, in groups, or in large aggregates called **sporocarps**, 1-20 mm across. The sporocarps of a few species are formed at the surface of the soil, those of other species buried in the soil or in leaf litter. Sporocarps are commonest in undisturbed forest communities with perennial plants and a thick organic horizon.

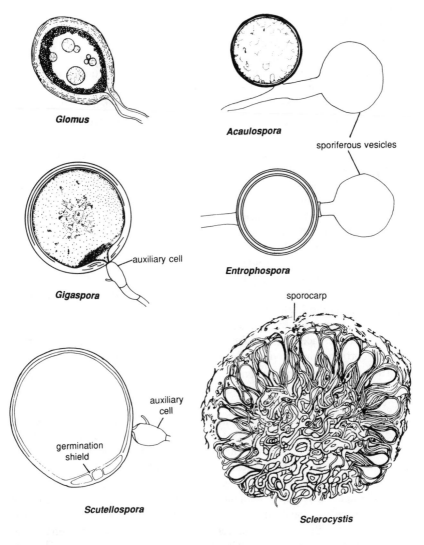

Fig. 17.4 Diagnostic spores and sporocarps of endomycorrhizal fungi (Glomales).

Sclerocystis (Fig. 17.4) produces spores up to 125 μm long, always in a sporocarp, radially arranged in a single layer around a central plexus of hyphae. Sporocarps may occur in masses up to several centimetres in diameter on the soil surface, or on leaves, twigs and mosses. No member of this genus has yet been persuaded to sporulate in pot culture.

The spores of *Acaulospora* species (Fig. 17.4) form on the side of thin-walled, terminal swellings that later collapse and vanish, or leave only an inconspicuous remnant. The spores are globose or ellipsoid, 100-400 μm in diameter, with walls up to 12 μm thick. Spores are hyaline to reddish-brown, and never occur in sporocarps.

Individual spores of *Gigaspora* species (Fig. 17.4) are 200-600 μm in diameter, with walls up to 20 μm thick, and develop singly at the end of a persistent, bulbous hypha, which may bear short lateral projections, the remains of collapsed hyphal branches. Spores range from hyaline to black, and may be ornamented. *Gigaspora* species also form unique 'ornamented vesicles,' 20-50 μm in diameter, borne singly or in clusters of 12 or more, typically on spiral hyphae.

Vesicular-arbuscular mycorrhizae have actually been seen in about 1,000 genera of plants from about 200 families. Although this is a small sample of the 350,000 extant species of higher plants, we believe that about 90% of vascular plants will normally have VAM fungi in their roots, especially if they are growing in poor soil. I can't mention all the families which we know or assume are endomycorrhizal. It is easier to list those few that are mostly non-endomycorrhizal. These are the Brassicaceae, Commelinaceae, Cyperaceae, Juncaceae, and Proteaceae, as well as some members of the Capparaceae, Polygonaceae, Resedaceae, Urticaceae, and herbaceous members of the Caryophyllales (Amaranthaceae, Caryophyllaceae, Chenopodiaceae, Portulacaceae); plus, of course, most of the 2,000 woody species that are ectomycorrhizal. Apart from this last group, most of the plants just mentioned are entirely non-mycorrhizal, and most are herbaceous (see Table 17.2 for a comparison between the hosts of endomycorrhizal and ectomycorrhizal fungi).

The only entirely non-mycorrhizal woody family is the Proteaceae, whose members have fine, brush-like roots and abundant root hairs. Many of the rest are weedy—vigorous pioneer herbaceous annuals with highly opportunistic lifestyles. They germinate quickly in poor soils, and some can flower and set seed in a few weeks. This means that they cannot wait for the local VAM fungi to find and colonize their roots. They have evolved finely branched roots with many root hairs: these enable them to dispense with mycobionts.

The endomycorrhizal relationship is extremely old, and it is hardly surprising that some plants may now be evolving different lifestyles. This is especially true of the herbaceous annuals, the newest group of plants. As well as being weedy, members of the Brassicaceae and related families have evolved chemical defences to repel herbivorous animals, and thus may have inadvertently discouraged their now inessential mycorrhizal fungi.

Since there are just under 400 families of higher plants, we estimate that all or most members of over 380 of these families associate with VAM fungi. Many of the 50 or so families of non-flowering vascular plants (Gymnosperms, Pteridophytes, etc.) are also endomycorrhizal. This means that about 300,000 plant species are receptive hosts for the incomparably smaller number of VAM fungi.

Sources of Vesicular-Arbuscular Mycorrhizal Inoculum

VAM fungi are obligately biotrophic, and can be maintained or multiplied only in **dual culture** with a host plant. All experimental work with these fungi involves the establishment of such cultures. The roots of experimental plants can be inoculated with infected soil, or infected roots, or spores, or a mixture of all three. Soil often contains more than one mycorrhizal fungus, and may even contain pathogens. Root inoculum can be used if it has been grown under more or less aseptic conditions, and if the original inoculum used to infect the roots was of a single, named species. The structures developing in roots, although diagnostic of VAM fungi as a group, are not usually identifiable to species. Most species can be identified only by their spores, which develop primarily on hyphae outside the roots. So spores may still be the best inoculum for laboratory experiments.

Since VAM fungi won't grow in axenic culture, the only source of spores is the soil near the roots of colonized plants. Agricultural soil contains up to 86 spores/gram, but if you need a lot of spores for experimental inoculum, those in naturally infected soil seem few and far between. Individual VAM fungi propagated in a dual culture, commonly called a **pot culture**, with no competition, can do much better, and there should be little contamination. Soil in which onions inoculated with *Scutellospora calospora* had been grown for 19 months contained over 300 spores/gram of dry soil. The only problem was how to get them out.

The first useful technique for extracting spores from soil was devized in 1955. Soil was shaken with water, and allowed to settle briefly. Then the liquid phase was sieved. Material that passed through a 1 mm mesh, but was retained by a 250 µm mesh, was washed and transferred to a petri dish, where the spores were picked out by hand under a dissecting microscope. This technique yielded as few as 100 spores per operator per day. Since 50-500 spores were needed to inoculate one pot, and an experiment often involved scores of pots, you can imagine what heroic efforts were required of researchers in those days.

A search for more efficient extractions began. Most methods still involve an initial wet sieving to concentrate the fine organic fraction, though dry separation is possible with a 'Dry particle analysis size elutriator,' in which particles are suspended in an airstream, the air velocity regulated to suspend particular size-classes of particles, and these collected on filter papers. Several ways of purifying spores have been devized.

(1) Centrifugation in a sucrose gradient (50% sucrose at the bottom, 25% sucrose above it, water at the top). Spores accumulate in the middle layer. This

method yielded 1500 spores per man-day, but the osmotic pressure exerted by the sugar solution sometimes damaged young spores.

(2) Differential sedimentation on gelatin columns—solidified 20% gelatin at the bottom, 15% above that, then 5%, and finally water. Upright columns are melted in a water bath at 32°C. Then the fine organic fraction is added to the water at the top. After 30 minutes the column is solidified at 4°C. Spores collect near the 5-15% interface. This segment is cut out, gently melted, and filtered to recover the spores. This method avoids osmotic stresses.

(3) The flotation-bubbling technique. The fine organic fraction is added to a column containing 50% aqueous glycerol, and compressed air injected at the bottom through a fritted disc. The small bubbles separate spores from soil and push them toward the surface. After settling, the supernatant is drawn off and sieved, giving 95% recovery of spores.

(4) Centrifugation in density gradients of radiopaque media (substances designed to be injected intravenously into humans for X-ray diagnostic procedures). These media have no deleterious effects, osmotic or otherwise, on the spores. Each gradient contains four dilutions of the medium—60%, 40%, 20%, and 10%. This is an effective way of cleaning up the spore concentrate derived from the flotation-bubbling process. But spores are not sterile when collected. They can be surface-sterilized in 0.05% aqueous Tween 20, followed by 2% Chloramine T; or in a filter-sterilized solution of 200 ppm Streptomycin and 100 ppm Gentamicin.

Soil-borne spores are no longer our only source of inoculum. Two other more easily handled inocula are now available. The first is the large sporocarps of *Glomus versiforme*, which are formed at the surface of the soil, and may contain up to 7 million spores each. Several sporocarps can be harvested every month from each pot without disturbing the culture, which can go on producing sporocarps for years.

Colonized roots also make good inoculum, and can easily be produced in large quantities. All that is necessary is to pull up the colonized plants, wash the entire root system, then use or store the infected roots. Regular staining and microscopic observation of root samples is needed to ensure that roots are not colonized by pathogens. Nevertheless, I think this kind of root inoculum may be commercially developed in the near future. Mycologists in England are already experimenting with tomato plants inoculated with VAM fungi, then grown with their roots in a thin film of recirculating nutrient solution. The colonized plants will give an improved yield of tomatoes, and later their chopped roots can be used to infect the next crop.

Storage of VAM inoculum is still problematic. Short-term storage in Ringer's solution at 4°C has been reasonably satisfactory. For extended storage, spores of some species survive lyophilization with or without prior freezing. Colonized roots survive only the two-stage procedure. Until we learn more about storing VAM inocula, they should be used as soon as possible after extraction.

Evaluation and Selection of VAM Fungi

As with ectomycorrhizal fungi, several factors must be considered when choosing endomycorrhizal partners: geographic distribution, frequency of occurrence in nature, host range, soil type, pH, fertility, moisture and organic matter, persistence of inoculum in the soil, speed of infection, and phosphorus efficiency. Inoculum production is also important—how easy it is to persuade the fungus to produce propagules on a large scale under controlled conditions, and to store, transport and deliver that inoculum without loss of viability.

We don't yet know the geographic range of most VAM fungi. Lacking such background information, we must take field samples to identify the local mycota, and perhaps to accumulate enough spores to establish pot cultures which will multiply the inoculum for future use. Despite the apparent lack of host specificity under the artificial conditions of pot culture, plants in the field select, or are selected by, certain indigenous VAM fungi in preference to others. Some VAM fungi have been linked to particular kinds of soil—*Glomus mosseae* with fine-textured, fertile, high pH soils; *Acaulospora laevis* with coarse-textured, acid soils; *Gigaspora* species with sand dune soil.

Before it is worthwhile to produce VAM inoculum on a large scale, it should be determined that the chosen species is a more efficient scavenger of phosphorus than other VAM fungi present in the local soil, or will boost the VAM fungal population to a level at which it can improve crop nutrition. Unfortunately, 'phosphorus efficiency' alone is no guarantee of success. In a non-sterilized field of birdsfoot trefoil (*Lotus corniculatus*), introduction of P-efficient VAM fungi improved yield, but only in the first year. In subsequent years the indigenous VAM fungi, presumably better adapted to local conditions, replaced the introduced strain, and yields returned to normal.

The response of VAM fungi to host plants can be measured in several ways. Spore production is one expression of the success of the symbiosis, but although some methods of recovery can give almost 100% retrieval, spore production is not usually used to quantify the success of a mycobiont. There are several reasons for this. (1) Spores may not be produced until the mycorrhizal relationship has been established for several months. (2) Spores may disappear or become inviable for a variety of reasons, e.g. they may be eaten by soil animals, or attacked by pathogenic fungi. (3) Spores vary greatly in size; some are too small to be easily separated from soil, others are concentrated in occasional sporocarps. (4) Some VAM fungi rarely or never produce spores.

If we want to follow the development of colonization during an experiment, or to assess the level of colonization in native plants collected in the field, we look at stained roots using the **gridline intersect** method. Roots are washed, cleared in KOH or hydrogen peroxide, and stained in acid fuchsin or trypan blue. Stained roots are spread out evenly over the bottom of a petri dish which is marked with a grid of lines delimiting 1/2 inch squares. The gridlines are scanned under a dissecting microscope, and presence or absence of colonization is recorded at each point at which a root intersects a line. If three sets of 100 intersects are recorded, and the mean value determined, the percentage of the root length colonized will be estimated fairly accurately. This technique also allows the total length of roots in the dish to be determined. If the distance between lines is 14/11 of the chosen measuring unit, the number of intersects equals the length of the roots, expressed in that unit. Conveniently, 14/11 cm = 1/2 in. So with a 1/2 inch grid, the number of grid intersects equals the total length of roots in cm.

VAM-induced improvements in yield are probably due to the increased volume of soil being exploited by the plant. So a measure of the amount and extent of the fine hyphae growing through the soil would be useful. Unfortunately, when we remove a root system from the soil, the delicate extramatrical mycelium is usually destroyed. A few estimates of these mycelia have been made, using such indicators as the degree to which hyphae bind together soil around roots. Fortunately, in several VAM fungi painstakingly examined, the amount of extramatrical mycelium was found to have a strong positive correlation with the much more easily observed level of root colonization.

Nevertheless, we have few comparative data on the respective abilities of various VAM fungi to absorb phosphorus from the soil, and to transport it to the host plant. Differentials may exist in both areas. The relationship between phosphorus efficiency and speed of colonization is also important, since the effectiveness of VAM fungi depends on both factors. Since plants normally need more phosphorus when young, the faster the root can be colonized, the better. So a phosphorus-efficient fungus may still be an unsuitable mycorrhizal partner because it colonizes the roots too slowly. It is obviously much easier and quicker to test fungi for rapid colonization than for their ability to increase phosphorus uptake.

The responses of host plants to VAM fungi can also be measured in several ways. An obvious parameter is dry weight production. Dry weight of the root and shoot systems should be recorded separately, since their responses may differ. Other, non-destructive measures are: differences in plant height, stem diameter, shoot volume, and leaf number and area—all of which can be measured repeatedly on the same plants at intervals. Crop yield, transplant survival and disease resistance are other valid criteria, and analyses of plant components and root exudates may reflect physiological changes resulting from VAM fungal colonization. Since the VAM fungus is often essentially parasitic on its host until it becomes established, the experimental growth period must be long enough for the positive effects of mycorrhization to show themselves.

Extramatrical hyphae have been shown to retrieve soluble and insoluble phosphorus 27 mm from a root—phosphorus that was completely unavailable to non-mycorrhizal roots at similar distances. The zone of depletion around mycorrhizal roots can be twice that around non-mycorrhizal roots. But even the most efficient VAM fungus will have little or no effect on a plant if available phosphorus is present at luxury levels. A relative mycorrhiza dependency factor can be calculated from the following formula:

$$100 \times \frac{\text{dry wt mycorrhizal plant} - \text{dry wt non–mycorrhizal plant}}{\text{dry wt of mycorrhizal plant}}$$

to be calculated for any given level of P availability. For example, at 100 µg/g available P, the relative mycorrhiza dependency of carrot is 99.2%, and that of wheat is 0%. This calculation also lets us compare the responses of any species of plant to different sources of P, and to different mycorrhizal fungi.

As yet we don't know much about the contributions to plant growth made by indigenous VAM fungi in field soils (although we extrapolate from the results of laboratory experiments). This is partly because any treatment that will kill all spores in the soil, and allow comparisons to be made, is sufficiently drastic that it will also change the chemical makeup of the soil, and probably alter its nutrient status.

Effects of Vesicular-Arbuscular Mycorrhizae on Plant Disease

The presence of VAM fungi in the roots of plants tends to reduce the incidence and severity of soil-borne diseases in those plants. I have found 56 reports of interactions between VAM fungi and 18 soil-borne plant pathogenic fungi, 8 plant parasitic nematodes, and 3 viruses, involving a total of 21 different crop plants. Most experiments showed that mycorrhizal plants had less disease, though virus symptoms were more severe. Various explanations have been put forward to explain the reductions in fungal disease. (1) The mycorrhizal plants were healthier and more able to resist the attacks of the pathogenic fungi. (2) The cells of mycorrhizal plants may partly digest the senescent arbuscules of the fungus. The same chitinolytic enzymes might be used on other invading fungi. (3) Possible infection sites on the surface of the plant roots may be preferentially occupied by the mycorrhizal fungus, to which the plant may well be more susceptible.

Field Application of VAM Inoculum

In setting up scientific experiments we must eliminate as many uncontrolled variables as possible, and the microbial population of natural soil injects too many variables. So most experiments establishing the benefits of VAM fungi have been done with pot cultures in controlled environment chambers or greenhouses, and the growth medium is usually fumigated or sterilized. This means that we can't tell how a VAM inoculum will survive, or what its effects will be, when it competes with an indigenous soil mycota. However, evolution appears to have equipped this ancient group of fungi with the ability to cope successfully with all natural hazards. It has recently been shown that even under field conditions, with an indigenous VAM spora present in phosphorus-poor soil, the growth of outplanted apple trees (Rosaceae) is significantly improved when they have been previously inoculated with an appropriate VAM symbiont.

What about field-sown crops, where we can't pre-inoculate the plants? Obviously, the way in which VAM inoculum is introduced to its host is crucial, since it will encounter competition from indigenous microorganisms. Several methods of applying inoculum have been tried. (1) Inoculum can be mixed into the soil. (2) Layers, pads, or pellets of inoculum can be placed beneath or alongside the seeds. (3) Seeds can be pelleted with inoculum, though this is obviously incompatible with the widespread practice of coating seeds with fungicide. Placing a layer of inoculum below citrus seed, or as a band alongside the seed, gives more infection than pelleting seed with inoculum. Crops that are transplanted, and therefore labour-intensive in any case, can be inoculated in the seed beds, where controlled conditions can ensure a high level of colonization. For field-sown crops our answers to the two major questions: how to mass-produce inoculum, and how to apply it effectively, are still tentative and incomplete.

Prospects

It has been said that: 'Most woody plants require mycorrhizae to survive, and most herbaceous plants need them to thrive,' so it seems only logical that both VAM and EM fungi must be of vital concern to *Homo sapiens*, a supposedly intelligent species that knows it is totally dependent on plants. Tragically, the endomycorrhizal rainforests are rapidly being destroyed by logging, agriculture, mining, road-building, urbanization and other human activities. Since these forests do not regenerate easily or quickly, they will often be replaced by plantations of fast-growing exotic ectomycorrhizal conifers. Conifers are also being established on many treeless areas. Existing forests need to be replanted after harvesting. It looks to me as though any research and biotechnological investments society makes in ectomycorrhizal fungi will be well repaid by the ease and speed with which the trees become established, and by the accelerated growth of the maturing forests. Tree nurseries and field crops are often heavily fertilized. This effectively discourages many mycorrhizal fungi, which are highly adapted to infertile soils. Commercial mycorrhizal inoculum may eventually wean forest nurserymen and farmers away from chemical fertilizers: increasing energy costs may provide the required impetus.

Further Reading

Harley, J.L. and S.E. Smith (1983) **Mycorrhizal Symbiosis**. Academic Press, London.

Kendrick, B. and S.M. Berch (1985) Mycorrhizae: Applications in Agriculture and Forestry. pp. 109-152 (in) **Comprehensive Biotechnology**. Vol. 3. (Ed.) C.W. Robinson. Pergamon, Oxford.

Molina, R. (Ed.) (1985) **Proceedings of the 6th North American Conference on Mycorrhizae**. Oregon State University, Corvallis.

Schenck, N.C. (Ed.) (1982) **Methods and Priniciples of Mycorrhizal Research**. American Phytopathological Society, St. Paul.

Fifth North American Conference on Mycorrhizae (1983) Keynote papers by various authors. Canadian Journal of Botany **61**: 907-1024.

Chapter 18

Fungi as Food: Mycophagy

Introduction

Throughout the English-speaking world, fungi are viewed with suspicion. Toadstools, perhaps because of their sudden appearance, strange shapes, bizarre colours, and reputedly poisonous nature, became associated in folklore with fairies, witches, or even the devil. These superstitions probably saved many lives over the centuries. People in forested areas of Central and Eastern Europe apparently directed their superstitious awe elsewhere (see Grimm's Fairy Tales...), and did not hesitate to eat mushrooms whenever they appeared. Information derived from these experiments gradually accumulated and was passed on, first in the oral tradition, later in books. A few agarics gained a reputation for killing those who ate them. These are dealt with in chapter 22. At the other end of the scale, a relatively small number of fungi eventually entered the culinary hall of fame: they are the chief subjects of this chapter.

'...Ravioli filled with fresh **black truffles** and celery in melted butter and parmesan cheese...sweetbreads with a soya sauce, **cloud ears** and julienne of many vegetables...lamb with kidney stuffing and potato crepe stuffed with spinach and **mushrooms**...warm sweetbread salad with girolles (**chanterelles**), oysters and leeks in **truffle** sauce...tiny veal kidneys with **chanterelle** mushrooms...cloud-like mousse of fattened livers of Bresse chickens with **truffles** raining over it.' These quotations are taken from a series of articles written by the restaurant critic of the Toronto 'Globe and Mail,' Joanne Kates, after a grand gourmet tour of France. The common denominator in this outpouring of haute cuisine: fungi as ingredients contributing flavour and texture.

Can we make any generalizations about the edibility of large fungi? Let's try a few. (1) Of about 10,000 species of fleshy fungi, only a handful are lethal: deadly poisonous. (2) Unfortunately, some of that handful are relatively common. (3) Representatives of only about 20 genera are regarded as prime edible fungi: check the list below. (4) **There are no simple ways of distinguishing between the edible and the poisonous**: all folkloric tests such as, 'If the cap peels, it's edible,' and 'If it doesn't blacken a silver spoon, it's OK,' are misleading and dangerous fictions. (5) **You should eat a mushroom only if you know its name with considerable precision (and by that, I mean its scientific name, its Latin binomial, a unique pair of epithets which specify its genus and species**). Don't assume that all is well if it looks like a picture in a book, or even if you can identify it to genus: genera which contain prized edible species may also have disagreeable or dangerous members—this is true of both *Amanita* and *Agaricus*. (6) In order to discover the proper name, you will probably have to refer to an expert: every handbook ever published is incomplete and fallible, and you will often need to examine microscopic features (such as basidiospores). (7) Do not accept the word of self-styled 'experts' without checking their credentials: after all, it's your life, not theirs. (8) The first few times you eat a mushroom that is new to you, don't eat much of it, because some people develop severe allergic reactions, even to species generally considered safe. (9) Sort your collections very carefully: don't mix species, and never eat old or shrivelled specimens. (10) If you are still determined to become a **mycophagist**, buy one or more of the well-illustrated manuals listed at the end of this chapter (the Lincoff, Phillips and Arora books are the most comprehensive), and join your local natural history or mushroom society. If you become fascinated by the strange and mysterious world of the fungi, then you will be ready to join NAMA—the North American Mycological Association—and perhaps subscribe to Mushroom Magazine. Good hunting.

Now for a quick tour of the better-known edible mushrooms. I will begin with those that have, tentatively or commercially, been brought into cultivation, then move on to those which are available only in nature. Mushroom cultivation may have an extremely bright future. Consider the following. If we use a hectare of land to produce beef, the yield of protein is about 80 kg/ha. If we use the same area for fish-farming, the yield may be as much as 660 kg/ha. But if we grow mushrooms, the protein yield is commonly 80,000 kg/ha; and fungi have the added advantage that they bioconvert cellulosic debris such as straw, sawdust and animal manure, which are produced in large quantities as essentially worthless by-products of other industries.

(1) *Agaricus brunnescens* or *A. bisporus* (depending on whether you follow Malloch or Singer) (Holobasidiomycetes, Agaricales, Agaricaceae). **The mushroom** of the western world: to many people, all other agarics are 'toadstools,' to be avoided. Sauteed in butter, the supermarket mushroom is an excellent accompaniment to steaks; dipped in batter and deep fried, it makes a truly greasy but tasty snack at many country pubs.

This is the one edible mushroom that every Westerner knows about. It was domesticated in the 17th century by the French, and has spawned a considerable industry in North America (sorry about that pun, it was quite unintentional). Annual world production of this species is estimated to be about 1,000,000 tonnes, and growing. As an interesting footnote to the end of the Cold War, the nuclear missile silos at Csasar in Hungary are now being used to grow mushrooms. The crop is exported to Germany, the very country at which the missiles were formerly aimed. Canadian consumption of *A. brunnescens* increased seven-fold between 1963 and 1983. Before I move on to the many other edible fungi, I must insert a warning. Mushrooms should **not** be eaten raw, because they contain significant amounts (0.6 ppm) of the carcinogenic 4-(hydroxymethyl)-benzenediazonium ion. Fortunately, this unstable ion is destroyed by cooking.

(2) *Pleurotus ostreatus* (Holobasidiomycetes, Agaricales, Tricholomataceae), the **oyster mushroom**, is another good find. It forms overlapping

clusters of large, non-stipitate basidiomata on dead or dying trees. In fact, no fewer than seven species of *Pleurotus* have been domesticated and marketed, notably *Pleurotus sajor-caju* with *P. ostreatus* a distant second, but some growers ran into an unexpected snag: the basidiospores are extremely allergenic, and cause severe reactions in many of the workers. World production is more than 20,000 tonnes/year.

(3) *Lentinus edodes* (Holobasidiomycetes, Agaricales, Tricholomataceae), the **shii-take** (shee-tah-kay) of Japan, the **xiang-gu** of China, is widely used in oriental cuisine. For 2,000 years the Japanese and Chinese have cultivated it by boring holes in specially stacked oak and chestnut logs and inoculating them with plugs of infected sawdust or wood. The fungus takes a year or more to fruit, though repeated crops (flushes) will arise from each log. A refined culture technique now grows the mycelium in a much cheaper hardwood sawdust medium supplemented with 8-25% of a starch-protein mixture and some calcium sulphate. This medium is autoclaved in a heat-resistant plastic bag, then inoculated. Twenty days in darkness are followed by 30-60 days in the light, all at 24-28°C, then 10 more days in darkness at 13-18°C. Finally, fruiting is induced by opening the bags, exposing them to light, and deliberately varying the temperature between 10° and 18°C. Fruiting may continue for 10 months. The effort is worthwhile, because dried shiitake retail for up to $40/kg in gourmet shops. In south-east Asia, it is estimated that 200,000 growers produce 150,000 tonnes of shiitake per year.

(4) *Volvariella volvacea* (Holobasidiomycetes, Agaricales, Pluteaceae), the **paddy straw mushroom**, is widely used in the Far East, as well as in Chinese cuisine in the west. It has been cultivated for centuries by preparing heaps of plant debris and watering them. It is now being grown on a more scientific basis, and pure mycelial inoculum (spawn) is available. When encountered in Chinese food, it can be easily recognized by the extremely well-developed volva or universal veil that virtually envelops the young basidioma. Although we usually see this fungus only in an immature condition, since it is harvested and canned before the cap expands, I was fortunate enough to visit a straw mushroom factory in Java in 1989. I took a few specimens back to my room and watched them first expand, then deposit a heavy pinkish spore-print. World production is more than 60,000 tonnes/year.

(5) *Flammulina velutipes* (Holobasidiomycetes, Agaricales, Tricholomataceae), the **winter** or **velvet stem mushroom**, long cultivated in Japan, where it is called **enokitake**, is now grown on a sawdust-bran mixture in North America. It is too early to say whether it will catch on here, but it suits our climate, since it will grow and fruit at low temperatures. The cultivated form has little resemblance to the natural fruit bodies, since it consists of long, narrow stipes with tiny caps at the top. World production is about 40,000 tonnes/year.

(6) *Pholiota nameko* (Holobasidiomycetes, Agaricales, Strophariaceae) is another lignicolous mushroom that has been domesticated in Japan, where it is called **nameko,** and about 15,000 tonnes a year are produced.

(7) *Auricularia polytricha* (Phragmobasidiomycetes, Auriculariales), the **tree ear** or **cloud ear** or **mu-er** of Chinese cuisine, is a jelly fungus that grows on dead trees (cf. Fig. 5.8 B). Its ear-like basidiomata are added to a variety of Chinese dishes; mostly, I suspect, for their slippery, crunchy texture. It has recently been suggested that something in these fungi reduces the clotting tendencies of human blood, and may help to explain the low rate of heart disease among the Chinese. About 8,000 tonnes a year are consumed.

(8) *Tuber melanosporum* (Ascomycetes, Pezizales, Tuberaceae), the **black, queen,** or **Perigord truffle** (Fig 4.10 G). This is what the French call the diamond of the kitchen. They also say: 'Ta femme, tes truffes et ton jardin, garde-les bien de ton voisin.' (Your wife, your truffles and your garden; guard them well from your neighbour). This old French saying will give you some idea of the high esteem in which truffles are held. Molière, who wrote much better stuff than that, was obviously fascinated by truffles, since he gave the old French name for a truffle, 'Tartuffe,' to the main character in his comedy of the same name, and named his estate 'Perigord,' after an area famous for its black truffles.

My introductory quotations from Joanne Kates' gastronomic tour show how heavily the best French cuisine leans on the subtle aroma emanating from truffles. Italian chefs place an equal premium on the extremely odoriferous **white** or **Piedmont truffle** (*Tuber magnatum*) that grows in northern Italy— Alba holds a great yearly truffle festival in its honour, which I hope some day to attend. In December of 1984 I visited the tiny mountain village of Scheggino in Umbria, another centre of truffle collecting, where both black and white truffles grow. As a guest of the Urbani family, who appear to have cornered much of the international trade in truffles, I overdosed on dishes laced with black and white truffles, and came to the conclusion that the smell of the white truffle was too overpowering for my taste (reminiscent of the overripe sock), but that the black truffle added real cachet to a meal. Needless to say, I did not mention these treasonable thoughts to my Italian hosts, voicing them to my companions only after we had crossed the border into France. At the truffle market in Carpentras, France, I watched as buyers and sellers haggled quietly and skilfully over baskets of the clay-daubed tubers (yes, you pay for the dirt, too), and acted as slightly bemused translator while one of my American companions paid $60 for a single fist-sized truffle. Such is the power of the legend.

Unfortunately for most of humanity, these culinary gems are native only to Europe (though more plebeian edible species like *Tuber gibbosum* are common in western North America). The truffles of haute cuisine are also hard to find: they fruit underground, and their subterranean ripeness must be sniffed out by female pigs or trained dogs such as Kiki, who stars in Fig. 18.1. The secrets of 'trufficulture' are gradually being unravelled by French scientists, who now inoculate the roots of oak and hazelnut seedlings (the mycorrhizal partners of Perigord truffles — see chapter 17) with a suspension of truffle ascospores, and obtain truffles as little as three years later. During my truffle tour, I visited two French truffle orchards, and in each case the trained dogs had little difficulty in sniffing out and unearthing a few of the black diamonds (Fig. 18.1). I also visited a new French company named 'Agritruffe,' which markets mycorrhizal seedlings. Almost all of my American fellow-travellers took home a batch of mycorrhizal seedlings, in the hope of establishing truffle orchards in Texas, Oregon, New York and places between. One of their incentives was the unpredictable and apparently diminishing French harvest (2,000 tonnes in 1889, 200 tonnes in 1976), which means that the North American price can be nearly a thousand dollars a kilogram. This isn't as absolutely prohibitive as it may seem,

Fig. 18.1 Kiki, the truffle dog, at work.

because unlike *Agaricus* and most other edible fungi, truffles are usually added to food only in small quantities, to enhance or embellish the flavours of the principal ingredients.

According to some people, truffles are also an aphrodisiac. Though this was long considered apocryphal, and perhaps just a story invented to jack up their

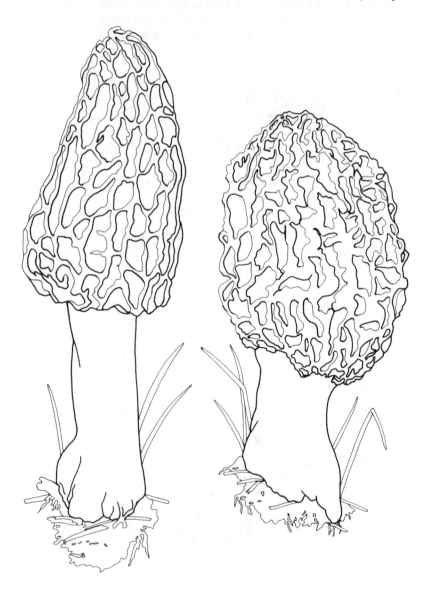

Fig. 18.2 Morels: ***Morchella esculenta***.

price even further, it has recently been discovered that one of the components of the odour of truffles is a steroid called alpha-androstenol (5-androst-16-en-3-ol). Alpha-androstenol is also found in the saliva, and hence on the breath, of rutting boars, where it serves as a pheromone, overcoming the sexual inhibitions of the young female pig. This explains the natural talent sows have for truffle-hunting. The same substance is found in the underarm perspiration of men, and in the urine of women. Although its sexual role in humans hasn't been clearly established, men rating photographs of normally dressed women for sexual attractiveness gave higher marks while sniffing alpha-androstenol. Women's reactions either haven't been tested, or we are being sheltered from the results: though if the advertising industry's usual dire warnings about underarm perspiration are to be believed, androstenol is unlikely to fulfill male fantasies. However, it is already being added to certain cosmetics...

(9) Species of *Morchella* (Ascomycetes, Pezizales, Morchellaceae), the spring-fruiting **morels**, with their distinctive ridged and pitted heads (Fig. 18.2), are to many people (including me), the supreme edible fungi. As an accompaniment to steak and a good bottle of red wine, they are unbeatable. Although morels occur over a wide geographical range, in most areas it is hard to find them in quantity (people are very secretive about their morel patches), and to make things worse, they fruit only in May. There is, however, at least one place where everyone can share the bounty: Michigan. In mid-May, half a million people head for the wooded hills to hunt, first for the black morel, *Morchella angusticeps*; then, a week or so later, for the white morel, *Morchella esculenta*. The rather similar *Verpa bohemica* (wrinkled thimble-cap) is also picked, though it doesn't taste as good as the true morels, and can make you disoriented if you eat too many caps.

Several morel festivals are held in Michigan, the most famous being that at Boyne City. This event celebrated its 25th year in 1984, when the winner of the National Mushroom Hunting Championship found over 500 morels in 90 minutes. But even that total pales into insignificance before the all-time record of over 900 morels collected by the champion in 1970. As part of the research involved in the preparation of this book, I attended the 1984, 1985 and 1991 festivals, and can personally vouch that even a newcomer to the area can find enough morels for a good feed if he or she is willing to tramp the woods for a few hours, and cultivate a morel-spotter's eye. In fact, in the 1985 championships, a visiting professional mycologist, Dr. Nancy Weber, outdid the local ladies by collecting 129 morels in the finals. It is worth noting that although morels are easy to recognize, several other fleshy ascomycetes, including the dangerous false morel, *Gyromitra esculenta*, fruit at the same time (see chapter 22). In 1991 a quart basket of black morels went for $5, but the same quantity of white morels would set you back $20. Although the white morel is thicker-fleshed and firmer than the black, I don't think the price differential reflects any real superiority: both species have a strong and unforgettable flavour.

Morel mycelium has been grown in pure culture on artificial media for many years, but only in 1982 was it finally persuaded to fruit. The dream of fresh morels available year-round may soon be realized. U.S. patent number 4,594,809 was granted in 1986 for the method by which it can be induced to fruit in culture. Morels are now being produced at a rate of about 250 kg per week on a regular basis, and all those who have ever eaten them hope that the process can be scaled up to a commercial level before long.

(10) *Dictyophora duplicata* (Holobasidiomycetes, Phallales), a large and beautiful stinkhorn, which has a white lace-like skirt below its receptacle, has long been avidly collected in its natural habitat under bamboos in Guangdong Province, China, where it is called **zhu-Sun** or 'bamboo sprouts.' It is now cultured on a small scale on a medium composed of sawdust, bagasse (sugarcane debris) and bamboo. The dried product, which is reported to have a 'pleasant sweetish smell,' sells for US$400-1,000/kg in Hong Kong. Because of its rarity it is served as a delicacy at state banquets, but it is widely sought because "according to Chinese medicals, it not only cures high blood pressure, but also reduces cholesterol content of the blood, and through long use, it effectively reduces the belly fat."

(11) *Tremella fuciformis* (Phragmobasidiomycetes, Tremellales), a jelly fungus, is widely cultured on wood blocks and in bags of sawdust in China, where it is called 'silver ear' or **yin-er** and is used in soups and as a tonic. I saw great mounds of the spherical, frilly colonies for sale in the fascinating market at Guang-zhou (Canton).

(12) *Ustilago esculenta* (Teliomycetes, Ustilaginales), a smut fungus, is inoculated into wild rice, *Zizania caduciflora*, in China. It causes the stem to become very thick and fleshy, and at maturity produces small pockets of teliospores scattered throughout this tissue. During my visit to China, I enjoyed the fungus-riddled, hypertrophied stem many times as a vegetable. For the Chinese it has the added advantage that it is supposed to have curative powers against fevers, conjunctivitis and kidney and bladder problems.

Although 'mushrooms' of 32 species in 16 genera are currently being cultivated commercially, only four or five are grown on a large scale. Many of them satisfy our demand for recycling and re-use, because they can be grown on various kinds of plant debris, a plentiful resource. *Agaricus* and *Volvariella* are grown on straw or similar substrates: by-products of agriculture. *Lentinus*, *Flammulina*, *Pholiota*, *Auricularia* and *Ganoderma* (this last is called **Reishi** in Japan, and **Ling Chi** in China, where it is used for medicinal purposes rather than being eaten) are grown on wood, sawdust or wood-chips: by-products of forestry. For those of you who would like to grow mushrooms in your basement or garden, there is now an excellent handbook called 'The Mushroom Cultivator.' This gives detailed instructions on all aspects of home mushroom culture, and deals with many species, including several which are hallucinogenic. Those specifically interested in cultivating *Lentinus edodes* should consult the 'Shiitake Growers Handbook.'

Now we move on to species that have never been commercially cultivated. These include some of the best of all edible fungi, so there is still room for research and lots of entrepreneurial spirit in bringing some of them to an eager public.

(13) *Boletus edulis* (Holobasidiomycetes, Agaricales, Boletaceae) is the celebrated **cep** of France, the **Steinpilz** of Germany, the **porcini** of Italy. Their large, plump basidiomata bear fleshy tubes rather than gills (Fig. 5.5 D). They are the basis for some European dried 'mushroom' soups, and are also imported in see-through plastic packages. The aroma emanating from an unopened packet, even after it has been sitting in a cupboard for months or even years, is unbelievably appetizing. Most members of the family Boletaceae are edible, though species with reddish or orange pore mouths, and those whose flesh turns blue when bruised, should be avoided. *Boletus edulis* is mycorrhizal with conifers in western North America, where it fruits from June to November. I collected it in June 1984 near the edges of melting snowbanks near Bend, Oregon, and in November 1990 along the southern coast of Oregon. I have also found it in the east, though it is less common there. About 25 varieties of this species have been described. The importance of the boletes to European mushroom hunters can be gauged by the fact that of about 850 tonnes of mushrooms a year offered in the Munich market at the turn of the century, over 500 tonnes were accounted for by *Boletus edulis* and another bolete, *Leccinum scabrum*. These mushrooms are the filling for Crêpes à la Bordelaise. The tubes are removed, the caps are cut into slices 1 cm thick, seasoned with salt and pepper, and browned in olive oil or butter for 5 minutes. Then they are cooked for 2 minutes in egg yolks beaten with sour cream, and finally rolled up inside thin pancakes and reheated in the oven. I also find *Boletus edulis* delightful on its own, simply sliced and fried in butter.

A former colleague of mine, Dr. Maria Pantidou, was the first to persuade boletes to fruit in pure culture. However, the fruit bodies were tiny, and despite further efforts at refining the medium, no one has yet managed to grow a commercially viable product.

(14) *Tricholoma matsutake* (Holobasidiomycetes, Agaricales, Tricholomataceae), the highly prized **matsutake** or pine mushroom of Japan, is thought by some to be the best of all edible mushrooms, and brings astronomical prices in Japan: up to $200/kg, fresh. It does not grow in North America, but the Japanese now import fresh *Tricholoma magnivelare* by air from western North America to supplement their own matsutake crop. Prices are volatile, depending on supply. Pickers in Oregon and Washington have been paid as much as $80/kg for grade 1 matsutake, as little as $1/kg for grade 7. The grading system works like this: Grade 1—tight buttons more than 6 cm long, no partial veil evident; grade 2—larger button with partial veil apparent but unbroken; grade 3—as grade 2, but with breaks in partial veil; grade 4—partial veil completely ruptured, gills fully visible, cap not expanded, still inrolled at margin; grade 5—cap expanded, but undamaged; grade 6—cap expanded, with breaks, holes or stains; grade 7—wormy but still firm.

In early December 1990, during a sabbatical visit to Oregon, I was fortunate enough to find a few good specimens of about Grade 3 on the mountains of the coast range. Their spicy aroma is unmistakeable, although it reminds different people of different things: some liken it to cinnamon; I thought it smelled like fresh watercress. These few large, solid agarics added a delicious new dimension to our diet for several days. I have since learned that, because of the high prices being paid, competition between mushroom hunters has reached the point at which guns are being pointed, and occasionally discharged, in disputes over collecting territory. The wild west has not totally vanished, it seems.

(15) *Cantharellus cibarius* (Holobasidiomycetes, Aphyllophorales, Cantharellaceae), the **chanterelle** or **girolle** of France, or **Pfifferlinge** of Germany, is widely collected, partly because its yellow, funnel-shaped basidiomata are easy to recognize (Fig. 5.4 D). It is eaten fresh, often sauteed in butter with a little parsley, chopped garlic, and freshly cracked pepper served on generously buttered hot toast. Since in many places it is found only during a short period of the year, it is commonly dried: many European kitchens I have visited boast a big jar of dried chanterelles, which add their delicate but distinctive flavour to stews and other dishes year round. Fresh chanterelles sold for $22/kg in Toronto in 1983. In Oregon, the white chanterelle, *Cantharellus subalbidus*, commonly accompanies *C. cibarius*, and is also considered desirable. A closely related species, *Craterellus cornucopioides*, the **horn of plenty**, though less common, and less substantial, is reputed to taste better than the chanterelle. As much as 2 million kg of chanterelles are picked in the North Western U.S. in a good year and shipped in barrels of brine to Germany.

(16) *Lactarius deliciosus* (Holobasidiomycetes, Agaricales, Russulaceae), the **saffron milk cap**, was mentioned by the Roman author, Pliny, and is represented in frescoes excavated at Pompeii, the Roman city buried in A.D. 79 by an eruption of the volcano, Vesuvius. *Lactarius*, which is mycorrhizal, fruits under conifers in Autumn. I must admit that as far as I am concerned, this species has two drawbacks: it is often already riddled with the borings of dipteran larvae by the time I encounter it; and I don't find the flavour particularly interesting. However, since I am not an early riser, and some of my acquaintances enjoy this species, I felt obliged to include it.

(17) *Clitocybe nuda* (Holobasidiomycetes, Agaricales, Tricholomataceae), the **blewit**, is a rare exception to the widespread British mycophobia, and is sold at markets in central and northern England. I find this strange, since this species is entirely lilac to blue or purple: distinctly poisonous-looking. But having been raised in Northern England, I can confirm that blewits make excellent eating. These species were formerly classified in *Tricholoma* or *Lepista*.

(18) *Marasmius oreades* (Holobasidiomycetes, Agaricales, Tricholomataceae), the **fairy ring mushroom**, is a small but numerous, summer-fruiting, pasture species that can be collected in fair quantity and is usually dried for use as a flavouring. Make sure the pasture in which you collect has not been treated with selective weedkillers.

(19) *Coprinus comatus* (Holobasidiomycetes, Agaricales, Coprinaceae), the **shaggy mane** or shaggy ink cap (Fig. 5.5 C, 8.5), is common on new lawns and disturbed ground in late autumn. Unfortunately, the ease with which we find it

is in inverse proportion to its flavour. I find shaggy manes, which must be eaten before the gills begin to darken and deliquesce, rather watery, although it can make a good contribution to a soup.

(20) *Calvatia gigantea* (Holobasidiomycetes, Lycoperdales), the **giant puffball** (Fig. 18.3), which can be eaten when the fruit body is young and its interior the colour and texture of marshmallow, is sold in Farmers' markets in Ontario. Thick slices brought $12/kg in 1989. It has an interesting texture, and can be a

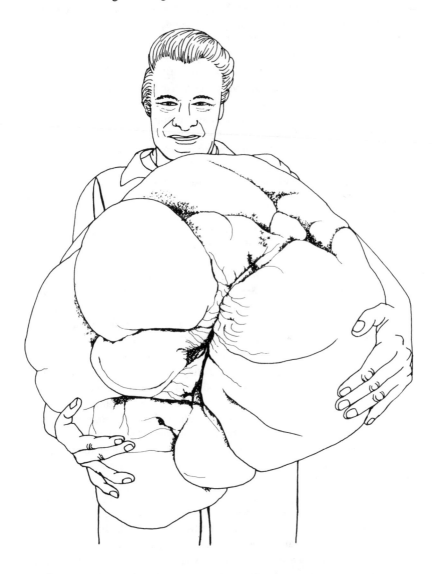

Fig. 18.3 Man holding the world's largest edible fungus, *Calvatia gigantea*.

vehicle for other flavours, but its own is too delicate to be of much interest. I suppose one of its attractions is that a single basidioma can feed a large number of people.

(21) *Armillaria mellea* (Holobasidiomycetes, Agaricales, Tricholo-mataceae), the **honey mushroom** (Fig. 14.3), actually comprises at least 11 genetically different strains in North America. It has been involved in a few poisonings, but this problem should not arise if only fresh young specimens are eaten, and if it is always well cooked. Many amateur mycologists swear by this species, which is very common in most woodlands, but it would seem prudent to eat only a few when trying them for the first time (as with any mushroom you have not eaten before). I have had some tasty dishes incorporating this fungus, but the common name refers to its colour, not its flavour.

(22) *Amanita caesarea* (Holobasidiomycetes, Agaricales, Amanitaceae), was the favourite mushroom of Roman emperors (who presumably had access to the best). *Amanita rubescens* (the blusher) is also reputed to be edible. Note that these species are congeneric with *Amanita phalloides* and *Amanita virosa*, perhaps the two deadliest mushrooms in the world. Although I have not eaten (nor even seen) *A. caesarea*, a close relative of that species, *Amanita umbonata*, grows in North America, and has been beautifully painted by the Canadian artist, H.A.C. Jackson (see 'Mr. Jackson's Mushrooms,' published by the National Museums of Canada).

Amanita caesarea starred in one of history's dramatic moments. Agrippina, wife of the Roman emperor, Claudius, coveted her husband's job for her son, Nero. She tried to kill Claudius with a dish of his favourite mushrooms, rendered lethal by judicious additions of *Amanita phalloides* juice. This plan went awry when Claudius threw up his dinner (Emperors often did this bulemic trick to make room for another meal). But the resourceful Agrippina had a back-up plan: the imperial physician was in her pay, and poison was resolutely, and as we know, successfully, administered to the doomed Claudius by enema.

(23) Various species of *Termitomyces* (Holobasidiomycetes, Agaricales, Amanitaceae), whose often very large basidiomata are found associated with termite mounds in Africa (Fig. 16.3), are collected and eaten. Perhaps the largest edible mushroom on record was a *Termitomyces* collected in Zambia which had a cap 66 cm across and weighed 2.5 kg. The size of these basidiomata is easier to understand when one knows that the mycelia from which these mushrooms arise are actually cultivated in special underground fungal gardens by the termites, which supply them with chewed-up wood, and rigorously exclude other fungi (see chapter 16 for the full story).

(24) Charles Darwin, circumnavigating South America in the "Beagle," noted that the golf-ball-like, compound ascomata of what was subsequently named *Cyttaria darwinii* (Ascomycetes, Cyttariales) parasitic on southern beech, *Nothofagus*, were an important part of the diet of the natives of Tierra del Fuego. The Araucans of Chile take advantage of the fact that *Cyttaria* contains up to 15% of fermentable sugars, and has on its surface the yeast, *Saccharomyces*, to prepare an alcoholic beverage from ripe ascomata.

Various amateur mycophagists of my acquaintance have told me that they really enjoy one or more of the following members of the Aphyllophorales (where I have tried them myself, I add my own evaluation): (25) 'hen-of-the-woods,' *Grifola frondosa* (Polyporaceae); (26) 'umbrella polypore,' *Polyporus umbellatus* (Polyporaceae); (27) 'chicken mushroom' or 'sulphur shelf,' *Laetiporus sulphureus* (Polyporaceae) [excellent, but only when young, and cooked thoroughly]; (28) 'sweet tooth,' *Dentinum repandum* and *D. umbilicatum* (Hydnaceae) [not exciting]; (29) 'clustered coral,' *Ramaria botrytis* (Clavariaceae); (30) 'cauliflower mushroom,' *Sparassis crispa* (Clavariaceae) [acceptable]; and (31) the 'beefsteak fungus,' *Fistulina hepatica* (Polyporaceae). Finally, (32) fried teliospore masses of corn smut, *Ustilago maydis* (Teliomycetes, Ustilaginales), are regarded as a treat by many Mexicans.

As a souvenir of my lecture tour of China in 1987, I have a beautifully illustrated book (all in Chinese except for Latin binomials) which a Chinese graduate student of mine assures me is titled 'Edible Mushrooms.' This book contains paintings of representatives of 70 genera of fungi, at least some of which I would be extremely reluctant to eat (e.g. *Paxillus involutus*, the 'poison pax'). I can only assume that the Chinese are more adventurous than us in these matters.

A Warning

In eastern Europe, other hazards accompany mycophagy. Since the Chernobyl disaster, wild mushrooms in Poland and Russia contain levels of radioactive Cesium many times higher than those found in other food sources, and radio stations frequently warn people not to eat too many. But it is only fair to point out that, wherever they grow, wild mushrooms tend to accumulate Cadmium and other toxic elements. By means of the Ames test for mutagenicity, it has also been established that some 'edible' mushrooms, including *Agaricus brunnescens*, shiitake (*Lentinus edodes*) and *Boletus edulis* contain base-pair substitution mutagens, and *B. edulis* also contains frameshift mutagens. While the mutagenic activity of *L. edodes* was not reduced by boiling for 20 minutes, that of *A. brunnescens* and *B. edulis* declined, but only by 50%. Since the mutagens have not yet been isolated and characterized, we don't know their implications for human health. They may or may not turn out to be significantly carcinogenic. So while eating mushrooms as an occasional treat may be fine, they should never be regarded as a dietary staple.

Other edible fungi

Many filamentous fungi do not produce large fruit bodies, but can grow on cheap substrates, and produce large amounts of mycelia high in protein. In Britain, a strain of *Fusarium graminearum*, the conidial anamorph of *Gibberella zeae* (Ascomycetes, Hypocreales), is being grown in submerged culture in 1300-litre fermentors on glucose syrup and ammonia. The dried mycelium has 45% protein of acceptable amino acid composition, 10-15% fat and 20-25% fibre. The nucleic acid content starts out at a gout-inducing 10%, but is reduced to an acceptable 1% by heating the mycelium to 64°C for 20 minutes. This inactivates proteolytic enzymes, but allows the organism's own ribonucleases to break down the nucleic acids to products that can be washed out of the cells. Successful feeding trials on animals and volunteer humans have led to conmercial production of this high-protein food, which is sold in various forms, under the name 'Quorn,' flavoured and textured to resemble traditional foods.

No discourse on fungi as food would be complete without some mention of yeasts. Species of *Saccharomyces* and *'Torula'* have been used as food supplements for many years, largely because they contain high levels of the B vitamins. But yeasts also commonly contain 40-50% dry weight of protein, can be grown on substrates such as the effluents from food-processing plants, and have a short generation time. They would seem to be obvious sources of SCP (single-cell protein), yet they have not yet been fully exploited. Why is this? First, the presence of high levels of nucleic acids has made yeast proteins unacceptable: if humans eat more than 2 grams of nucleic acid per day, hyperuricaemia (elevated levels of uric acid in the blood) will result, possibly leading to kidney stones and gout. Second, yeast proteins are nutritionally inferior because they are low in the amino acids, methionine and tryptophan. For yeast protein to be suitable as food, it must be separated from the indigestible chitinous wall material, must not be denatured, must have its nucleic acid level reduced, and should be supplemented with methionine. Apparently, if yeast cells are disrupted at pH 8.5 in the presence of succinic anhydride, 90% of the protein can be extracted without denaturation. If the pH is then lowered to 4.2-4.5, the protein is precipitated, leaving most of the nucleic acid (mainly RNA) in the supernatant fluid. The development of processes like this may bring acceptance of yeast SCP closer. Of course, no-one could be expected to eat yeast protein as it comes; it would presumably be used (as the still cheaper soy protein is used) to supplement the protein concentration of other, tastier foods. Yeastburgers, anyone?

Animal Mycophagy

I am sure none of you imagines that human beings are the only animals to appreciate the dietary value of fungi. One of the more dangerous myths used to establish edibility of mushrooms asserts that if they have been nibbled by larvae, slugs, snails or squirrels, they must be edible. In fact, many animals, both vertebrates and invertebrates, seem to be unaffected by the toxins found in agarics poisonous to us (this is especially true of some *Drosophila* species, as you will learn in chapter 22). *Elaphomyces*, the deer truffle or hart's truffle, is apparently eagerly sought and relished by the animals for which it is named. In the forests of California the red-backed vole, *Clethrionomys californicus*, lives almost exclusively on truffles (*Tuber* spp.) and false truffles (e.g. *Rhizopogon*); and many other small rodents feed on, and disperse, these hypogeous fungi. Wildlife biologists were surprised to find remains of flying squirrels, which live high in trees, in the faeces of bobcats and coyotes. Then mycologists spotted truffle ascospores and false truffle basidiospores in the guts of the flying squirrels: apparently the squirrels had been fatally lured onto the ground, away from the safety of the trees, by the odour of ripe truffles. Birds migrating across the deserts of Kuwait, including nine species of lark, find and eat desert truffles of the genus *Phaeangium*.

Flies of the genus *Helomyza* are also tuned in to truffles, since their larvae will eat nothing else. It is sometimes possible to find truffles by the swarms of egg-laden flies hovering over their hiding places. Many other insects are also extremely fond of mushrooms, as any collector of *Lactarius deliciosus* or boletes knows. Adult Mycetophilidae (fungus gnats) and members of many other groups (including some species of *Drosophila*) seek out fungal fructifications unerringly, so that their larval instars can fatten on the proper diet. Aphids, nematodes and amoebae have been found selectively feeding on the mycorrhizal fungi growing around conifer roots. Some Amphipods (freshwater crustaceans) graze preferentially on the conidiophores of amphibious hyphomycetes—fungi which colonize leaves that fall into streams (see chapter 11). Collembola (springtails) and oribatid mites (Acarina) have also been found to prefer a diet of fungal spores and mycelium.

Perhaps the most interesting examples of animal mycophagy are found among groups of insects that cannot themselves digest cellulose or lignin, but still manage to exploit these substrates through the mediation of specific fungi. The insects either carry the fungi around from tree to tree (Ambrosia beetles), or actually cultivate them in special subterranean gardens (the Attine ants of central and south America, and the mound-building termites of Africa and Asia). These special relationships are discussed in chapter 16.

Further Reading

Arora, D. (1986) **Mushrooms Demystified**. 2nd Edn. Ten Speed Press, Berkeley [one of the most comprehensive field guides yet published; everyone should have it, but it does focus on Western taxa].

Chang, S.T. and W.A. Hayes (1978) **The Biology and Cultivation of Edible Mushrooms**. Academic Press, New York.

Ingratta, F.J. and T.J. Blom (1980) **Commercial Mushroom Growing**. Ministry of Agriculture and Food, Ontario. Publ. 350.

Lincoff, G.H. (1981) **The Audubon Society Field Guide to North American Mushrooms**. Knopf, New York [relatively inexpensive; lots of good colour photographs; one of the more comprehensive guides for those in Eastern North America].

Malloch, D. (1976) *Agaricus brunnescens,* the cultivated mushroom. Mycologia **68**: 910-919.

Maser, Z., C. Maser and J.M. Trappe (1985) Food habits of the northern flying squirrel (*Glaucomys sabrinus*) in Oregon. Canadian Journal of Zoology **63**: 1084-1088.

McIlvainea: Journal of the North American Mycological Association.[this journal comes with your membership of NAMA: 336 Lenox Ave., Oakland, CA 94610].

McKenny, M., D.E. Stuntz and J.F. Ammirati (1987) **The New Savory Wild Mushroom**. University of Washington Press, Seattle [fine colour photographs; very suitable for beginners in the Pacific North-West].

Miller, O.K. (1979) **Mushrooms of North America**. Dutton, New York [the first of the modern guides, now superseded by more comprehensive books, including that of the same title by Roger Phillips].

Mushroom: the Journal of Wild Mushrooming. 861 Harold St., Moscow, ID 83843 [appears quarterly, and will keep you up-to-date on all things agaric].

Pacioni, G. (1981) **Simon & Schuster's Guide to Mushrooms** (U.S. Editor, G. Lincoff). Simon & Schuster, New York [cheap; lots of fine colour photographs].

Phillips, R. (1991) **Mushrooms of North America**. Phillips, Little, Brown & Co., Boston. [the newest and most comprehensive of North American guides: over 1000 colour photographs; best coverage of *Amanita, Cortinarius, Hygrophorus, Lactarius* and *Russula*].

Pomerleau, R. (1980) **Flore des Champignons au Québec**. Les Editions La Presse, Montreal [French text, excellent technical descriptions and line drawings, but poor colour photographs; suitable for anywhere in North-Eastern North America; an expanded English edition is in the works].

Przybylowicz, P. and J. Donoghue (1988) **Shiitake Growers Handbook**. Kendall/Hunt, Dubuque [if you really want to get serious].

Singer, R. (1984) *Agaricus brunnescens* Peck and *Agaricus bisporus* (Lange) Imbach. Mycotaxon 20: 479-482.

Smith-Weber, N. (1988) **A Morel Hunter's Companion**. TwoPeninsula Press, Lansing [simply the best book about morels and their relatives].

Stamets, P. and J.S. Chilton (1983) **The Mushroom Cultivator: a practical guide to growing mushrooms at home**. Agarikon Press, Olympia, Washington.

Toth, B. , K. Patil and H.-S. Jae (1981 Carcinogenesis of 4(hydroxymethyl)-benzenediasonium ion (tetrafluoroborate) of *Agaricus bisporus*. Cancer Research **41**: 2444-2449.

Ying, J.Z., J.D. Zhao, X.L. Mao, Q.M. Ma, L.W. Xu and Y.C. Zeng (1982) **Edible Mushrooms**. Academic Press, Beijing [beautiful, full-page paintings of many well-known, and some not-so-familiar, fungi].

Chapter 19

Fungi in Food Processing

'A loaf of bread, a jug of wine, and thou.' Omar Khayyam had it right. Even if the right 'thou' happens to be away, good bread and wine offer some consolation. Eating fungi in recognizable form can be fun (or occasionally fatal), as you may read in chapters 18 and 22, but even those who make a point of avoiding such gastronomic adventures eat fungi (or fungal byproducts) without even being aware of it. The reason for this is that a number of the basic items in our diet, as well as some of the most interesting tidbits, are 'processed' by fungi. No-one seems the slightest bit interested in the presence of the fungus itself, only in the changes it produces in the substrate. And what dramatic changes they are. Without fungi, French bread would be matzoh. Blue cheeses would be blah.

The wonderful texture of **bread** is created by the yeast, *Saccharomyces cerevisiae*, which ferments small amounts of sugars and liberates bubbles of carbon dioxide that become trapped in the dough and leaven it. Bread without yeast would be like a day without sunshine, or steak without wine, or watching a football match without beer. Whatever your tipple, its alcoholic component is ultimately derived from the activities of yeasts, again of the genus *Saccharomyces*, which ferment the sugar in grapes or malted barley, and liberate alcohol and carbon dioxide. The substrate and end products balance as follows:

$$C_6H_{12}O_6 \longrightarrow 2\ C_2H_5OH + 2\ CO_2$$

though the process is actually very complex, involving 22 enzymes, at least 6 coenzymes, and Mg and K ions. Bottled beer, crackling wines, and champagne all owe their fizz as well as their kick to yeast. So how come bread doesn't have any alcohol? Perhaps fortunately, it evaporates during the baking process, so we aren't all on the road to alcoholism with our first peanut butter sandwich (though we could be on our way to a different kind of intoxication, as you can read in chapter 21 on mycotoxins).

The manufacture of **beer** begins with the malting of barley, during which the barley's own amylase converts the starch in the grain to sugar, which is then fermented by the chosen yeast. Lager is produced by *Saccharomyces carlsbergensis*, ale by *Saccharomyces cerevisiae*. Although the making of beer appears to have been mechanized and standardized to a high degree, with tailor-made yeasts (see chapter 10) and precisely controlled conditions at every step, I have found many and different brews during sabbatical trips around the world, most of them pleasant enough. Although I was born in Britain, my preference is for German beer, so I was delighted to find a reasonable facsimile in Western Samoa — which used to be administered by the Germans. British beer ('best bitter'), drunk flat and almost warm, represents one end of the beer spectrum; some European beers, rather carbonated and cold, the other.

Wine has been aptly described as a chemical symphony, though the kind of organoleptic impression left on the consumer can vary enormously. For thousands of years people have made wine by crushing grapes to produce 'must,' and letting the wild yeasts always found on grape skins perform the alcoholic fermentation. Winemaking has been brought to a high art in parts of France (Bordeaux and Burgundy). Even some inexpensive French wines can be excellent, and the better ones are delectable. Having reverently assisted at the consumption of a bottle of Chateau Lafite-Rothschild, a 'Premier Grand Cru,' I can attest to the almost magical complexity and perfection of the best. Some French wines (e.g. Chateau Margaux '59) sold for over $500 a bottle in Ontario in 1985 (to whom, I do not know). The reasons for the continued supremacy of the best French wines are several.

First, the grape species used. Make no mistake, the best wine is made only from varieties of *Vitis vinifera*. For many years the winegrowers of New York and Ontario used a native North American grape, *Vitis labrusca*, with disastrous results. This species, used because it is hardier and more pest- and disease-resistant than the European grape, has now been largely replaced by *vinifera* hybrids, with considerable benefit to the resulting wines. The great wine-growing regions of France use different varieties. The great red burgundies are made from the Pinot noir grape, the red bordeaux from the Cabernet sauvignon. Excellent white wines are made from such varieties as Chardonnay, Sauvignon Blanc, and Chenin Blanc.

Second, the climate should provide a long growing season, to give a high sugar content, but should not be too hot, so that the sweetness of the grapes will be balanced by their acidity. These conditions are found in Bordeaux, the Rioja area of northern Spain, northern Italy, Yugoslavia, northern California. Less reliable summers in Germany, Austria, Switzerland, Oregon, Washington, New York, Ontario, and even Burgundy, mean that the grapes do not always become sweet enough, and the wine may be unbalanced. This explains the concept of 'vintage years.' Wine from warm summers may be much better than that from cooler, wetter years. Hot, sunny climates like those in southern California, southern Spain, Algeria, Cyprus, South Africa and Australia produce grapes with lots of sugar, but low acidity, that are often better as dessert wines than as table wines. No need for 'vintage' years in those areas.

Third, the soil. Some of the finest Burgundies are grown in some of the worst-looking soils I have ever seen: just a collection of small limestone rocks. Clearly, the soil must be limestone-based and extremely well-drained, to put it mildly.

Fourth, the yeast. If early winemakers were lucky, the yeast that got the lion's share of the action was *Saccharomyces cerevisiae* var. *ellipsoideus*. But other wild yeasts often dominated, with less than desirable results, and sometimes *Acetobacter* ruined things completely. It was that greatest of all Frenchmen, Louis Pasteur, who finally put the crucial fermentation stage of winemaking on a scientific footing in 1866 with his classic paper, 'Études sur le vin.' Most winemakers now suppress wild yeasts with sulphur dioxide, and add pure cultures of highly selected wine yeasts. Needless to say, there are yeasts for every kind of wine: riesling yeasts, chablis yeasts, etc. The actual fermentation is now kept relatively cool, to boost the production and retention of esters and other aromatic compounds which are largely responsible for the bouquet and aroma of the wine. The introduction of modern wine-making techniques to many parts of the world has given us a much wider selection of excellent wines than has ever been available before. Price is not the sole arbiter of quality. I have recently imbibed first class wines from Chile, Argentina, Australia and Spain, all costing much less than French wines of equivalent quality.

Fifth, the age and method of storage. Although Beaujolais (made with the Gamay grape) should be drunk young, some other red wines, particularly those made with the Cabernet sauvignon grape, contain an amazingly complex mixture of chemicals which sometimes needs years of aging to blend and smooth out into an ideal flavour. Such wines are often stored for a while in oak casks, which impart more tannin (firmness) to the wine. Then the wine spends several more years in bottle before arriving at its peak.

Wines are of two main kinds. Table wines usually have 10-14% alcohol. Aperitifs and dessert wines like port and sherry are fortified with brandy, which is itself distilled from wine, and have about 20% alcohol (40 proof). The brandy is sometimes added before the natural fermentation of the sugars is complete, leaving a sweet wine like port or muscatel.

There is another way of making a sweet wine that depends on a hyphomycete, *Botrytis cinerea*. This causes the 'noble rot'—'pourriture noble' in France, 'Edelfaul' in Germany, 'aszu' in Hungary. In good years, the grapes are left on the vines until they are overripe, and the *Botrytis* grows on them. The grapes crack open, the mould lives on the juice, and the sugar content increases. At just the right stage, they are ultimately individually picked, all mouldy and shrivelled, and made into wine. The very best Sauternes are made this way, as are the German 'Trockenbeerenauslesen,' and the Hungarian Tokay. I acquired some *Botrytis*-wine in South Africa, and found that its velvety texture, its concentration, and its great sweetness balanced by acidity, made a wonderful combination.

Ontario vintners recently began to make 'eiswein' (ice wine), long a European specialty. Like *Botrytis* wine, it is made from grapes that have been left on the vine until well past the normal harvest. In this case the grapes do not rot, but become frozen, in which state they are picked and pressed. As with the noble rot, a small amount of rich, sweet wine is produced. Ontario eiswein, made from the Vidal grape, is now regarded as the best in the world, and sells for $40 per half bottle.

Many fine books have been written about wine. If your interest in the subject has been whetted, I suggest you proceed to reading and tasting. Never forget that most wine is at its best as an accompaniment to food.

'Hard' drinks such as the whiskies also originate from a yeast fermentation. Bourbon is made from fermented corn, Scotch from fermented barley, Rye from fermented rye. The fermented grain broth is distilled to concentrate the alcohol, usually to 40% (80 proof), and aging in wood supplies further character.

The Araucans of Chile ferment the fleshy ascomata of *Cyttaria harioti* (Ascomycetes, Cyttariales) which contain as much as 15% of fermentable carbohydrates, and, like grapes, bear natural populations of *Saccharomyces*. The natives dry the fungus, grind it up, and mix it with warm water. Natural fermentation produces a refreshing, mildly alcoholic drink called 'chicha del llau-llau.'

Cheese has probably been with us since the domestication of animals, since it is an effective way of storing milk proteins for long periods. There are more than 500 different cheeses, many of them characteristic of a particular area. Only a small handful are processed by fungi, but they are among the most interesting we have in terms of texture and flavour. They are of two kinds: the soft-ripened Camembert-type, and the blue Roquefort-type.

Camembert, Brie, Thenay, Troyes and Vendome cheeses are all ripened by *Penicillium camembertii* or *Penicillium caseiolum* (Hyphomycetes). These moulds form a dense white mycelial mat on the outside of the cheese, and their extracellular proteases diffuse inward, digesting milk proteins and giving the cheese a wonderfully smooth, soft, almost buttery consistency. The interior of a really ripe Brie (my favourite) or Camembert will have a rather viscous, almost fluid texture, and may ooze gently when cut. The flavour of these cheeses is mild, and is probably generated largely by lactobacilli. It is unfortunate that these cheeses have a very high content of saturated fats.

The blue cheeses—Roquefort, Stilton, Gorgonzola, Danish Blue, and Wensleydale—are ripened by *Penicillium roquefortii*. When the curd is ready, breadcrumbs with *P. roquefortii* growing on them are added, then the cheese is incubated until ripe. *Penicillium roquefortii* can tolerate high carbon dioxide concentrations and low levels of oxygen, so it grows throughout the curd, assisted to some extent by holes punched in the substrate by the cheesemaker. The colour of the blue-green veins that develop is due to the presence of innumerable conidia. Not only the appearance, but also the taste of the cheese, is transformed by the mould. *P. roquefortii* oxidizes fatty acids to methyl ketones, particularly 2-heptanone, which are believed to give the cheese its penetrating smell and its unique, pungent flavour. Although under some conditions *P. roquefortii* produces a dangerous mycotoxin called PR toxin, happily this is not formed during the cheese-making process.

And with alcoholic beverages, bread and a few cheeses, we have exhausted the repertoire of fungus-processed foods manufactured in the Occident. But if we look to the Far East, we find a whole range of fungus-fermented foods, some of which are now gradually becoming more familiar to western palates.

Shoyu, better known to us as **soy sauce**, is such a standard part of the everyday Japanese diet that annual consumption in Japan is nearly 15 litres per person. Shoyu is made from a mixture of wheat and soybeans or soybean meal. One version of the process is as follows. The soybean is cooked and mixed with crushed, roasted wheat, then inoculated with *Aspergillus oryzae*, and incubated at 25°C for 18 days. It is then stirred and incubated at 30-35°C for 48 hours, then stirred again with brine and inoculated with a yeast and a *Lactobacillus*. Now it is incubated for up to 6 months, and finally matured for anything up to 2 years. I'll bet you had no idea soy sauce was so complicated to make.

Ket-jap is a simpler Indonesian variant on the soy sauce theme. It is made from black soybeans, which are boiled, then inoculated with *Aspergillus oryzae* or, as in the cottage ket-jap factory I visited in Java, with whatever mould spores fall into it from the air. It is incubated for 2-3 days, then kept in brine for 8 days. The result is filtered, cooked in several changes of water to extract all soluble components, then mixed with sugar (the Javanese have a sweet tooth) and other flavouring ingredients, and finally concentrated by slow boiling to a thick, syrupy consistency.

Miso is second in importance only to shoyu among fungus-fermented foods in Japan. It is a thick paste used as a spread, and can be made from soybeans and rice, soybeans and barley, or soybeans alone. Rice is steamed, then inoculated with *Aspergillus oryzae* and incubated for 2 days at 28°C to produce a starter called **Koji**. Meanwhile, soybeans are crushed, washed and soaked for a few hours, then steamed. After cooling, the soybean is inoculated with a yeast, *Saccharomyces rouxii*, and mixed with the koji and salt. The mixture ferments for a week at 28°C, then for two months at 35°C, and is finally ripened for two weeks at room temperature.

Hamanatto is another Japanese soybean product. Soybeans are soaked for 4 hours, steamed for 10 hours, cooled to 30°C then inoculated with *Aspergillus oryzae*. After incubation in trays for 20 hours, the beans become covered with *A. oryzae* (basically, green mouldy). They are then dried, put in baskets with ginger, soaked in brine, and aged for 6 months. A similar product is known as **tu-su** in China, and **tao-si** in the Philippines.

Tempeh, a kind of soybean cheese, is an important food in Indonesia. It is an attempt to make the notoriously indigestible soybean both edible and tasty by exploiting fungal enzymes. Soybeans are cooked, then inoculated with *Rhizopus oligosporus* (Zygomycetes: Mucorales). When I visited a cottage tempeh factory, I found that the fungal inoculum is now bought as a whitish powder in small plastic bags. The mycelium of this fast-growing fungus permeates the soybean, and its extracellular proteases break down some of the bean protein within a day. When fried, the result is not unpleasant to western taste buds. In Java, the basic tempeh is often made more tasty by adding sugar and sometimes hot peppers. **Sufu** is a Chinese version of soybean cheese, the fungus involved being *Actinomucor elegans* (Zygomycetes: Mucorales).

Ont-jom is another Indonesian food, this time made from press cake, which is the residue left after oil has been expressed from peanuts. The press cake is washed, steamed, put in small containers, and sprinkled with pink conidia of the *Chrysonilia* anamorph of *Neurospora sitophila* (Ascomycetes, Sordariales) from the previous batch of Ont-jom. The containers are incubated until the fast-growing fungus has thoroughly colonized the substrate, then the result is cut up and cooked.

Katsuobushi is made in Japan by fermenting cooked bonito fish with *Aspergillus glaucus* until it dries out. Shavings of the resulting hard, dark substance are used to flavour other foods.

It is obvious that we have no more than begun to explore the possible uses of fungi in predigesting and flavouring many basically nutritious but indigestible or tasteless food substrates. A world that welcomes the kind of gustatory trivia presented by most fast foods will surely embrace whatever comes after beer and wine, brie and roquefort.

Further Reading

Gray, W.D. (1959) **The Relation of Fungi to Human Affairs**. Holt, New York.

Gray, W.D. (1981) Food technology and industrial mycology. pp. 237-267 (in) **Biology of Conidial Fungi**. Vol. 2. (Eds.) G.T. Cole and B. Kendrick. Academic Press, New York.

Hesseltine, C.W. (1965) A millenium of fungi, food and fermentation. Mycologia **57**: 148-197.

Hesseltine, C.W. and H.L. Wang (1967) Traditional fermented foods. Biotechnology and Bioengineering **9**: 275-288.

Wood, B.J.B. and F.M. Yong (1975) Oriental food fermentations. pp. 265-280 (in) **The Filamentous Fungi**. Vol. 1. (Eds.) J.E. Smith and D.R. Berry. Arnold, London.

Chapter 20

Food Spoilage By Fungi, and Its Prevention

I have a great fondness for damson plum jam with all the tangy skin of the fruit in it. You just can't buy stuff like that at the supermarket. So when I found some damson plums at our local farmers' market, I carried them home in triumph, intending to make jam—very soon. A week later I remembered my plan, and retrieved the fruit, only to find that some of the plums had a mould sporulating on them. Can you suggest, from the nature of the substrate (a stone fruit), what that mould might have been? (Did you remember *Monilia*?) I quickly sorted out the mouldy fruit and put it aside for my undergraduate class. I then pitted the sound fruit and cooked it very briefly with what seemed like an enormous amount of sugar. I ladled the jam into sterilized jars, and covered it with a thin layer of melted paraffin wax before sealing the jars tightly. That story exemplifies the problem of food spoilage, and what we have to do to prevent it.

What is food spoilage? You may think the answer is obvious. But, as often happens when we sit down and try to define a phenomenon, it's not as clear-cut as it might seem. How about this definition: 'Changes in the appearance, texture, smell or taste of food, that cause it to be discarded.' One important flaw in this definition is that the criteria for acceptability are strongly affected by cultural or economic conditioning. So the quantification of the various criteria may have to be reformulated for different countries or ethnic groups.

Many kinds of food become visually unappealing only when fungi are seen to be fruiting on the surface. But you must be aware by now that the interior of the food will be riddled by assimilative hyphae, and permeated by fungal metabolites, long before visible sporulation occurs (especially if the surrounding air is dry). Those fungal metabolites may include **mycotoxins** (see chapter 21). Even the most fastidious consumer can't always tell when these are present. Many kinds of food are processed before they reach us, so the mouldiness that might be evident on raw peanuts will no longer be apparent after they have been turned into peanut butter.

Since ideas of what constitutes spoilage vary so much, no definition can be completely objective and scientific. But science has now added an important new criterion. Food must be regarded as spoiled, no matter how appealing it may look, smell or taste, if it contains potentially harmful levels of mycotoxins. (In bacterial terms, the same would obviously be true if it contained botulinus toxin). **Food is spoiled by fungi when they bring about unacceptable changes in its appearance, texture, smell, or taste, or contaminate it with potentially**

harmful levels of one or more mycotoxins. Toxigenic fungi are identified by an asterisk (*) in the text that follows.

Having defined the condition, our next problem is to establish how prevalent and important it is. Food may be living or dead, fresh or preserved, raw or processed. In the case of fruits and vegetables, spoilage can occur in the field before harvest. But since North Americans no longer shop every day, insist on eating many seasonal foods all year round, and demand many exotic foods, most spoilage problems occur during transportation or storage. Food that is wet or has a high moisture content, and an alkaline pH, tends to be spoiled by bacteria. Drier or more acid foods are usually spoiled by fungi.

It has been estimated that about a quarter of all produce harvested spoils before it can be eaten. Fungal spoilage falls into several categories, depending on the strategy of the fungus. (1) Some losses are caused by the ongoing activities of plant pathogenic fungi already established in the substrate. (2) Some fungi that cause storage problems, such as *Monilia fructigena* (soft rot of peaches and other stone fruits), are actually **necrotrophs**. Necrotrophs are fungi which, although they grow on living hosts, are not really biotrophic. They produce toxins that kill the plant cells before the fungal hyphae reach them, so the fungus is actually feeding saprobically. (3) Other storage fungi are strictly saprobic, but have one or more of the following unusual abilities: (a) coping with substrates of low moisture and/or high osmotic pressure (**xerotolerance**), (b) surviving high temperatures (**thermotolerance**), (c) growing at low temperatures (**psychrotolerance**), (d) growing in extremely acid media, (e) growing at low levels of oxygen and/or high levels of carbon dioxide.

The growth of any fungus presupposes: (1) the presence or introduction of fungal propagules or inocula of some kind; (2) an appropriate source of energy-rich carbon compounds and other basic nutrients; (3) an appropriate level of moisture in the substrate; (4) a tolerable pH; (5) adequate oxygen; (6) absence of inhibitory substances. I will examine each of these in turn (fungal physiology revisited), establish the limits of fungal tolerance, and thus show the kinds of criteria that our food processing and storage techniques must meet or exceed, if we are to be able to eat more of what we grow.

Since fungal spoilage of food can happen only if a fungus is present and active, there are two possible avenues of prevention. The first is to rigorously exclude fungi from the substrate; the second is to prevent them from growing even if they are present. Which do you think is the easier route? There isn't much doubt in my mind: the environment is teeming with fungal spores, and it is extremely difficult to exclude them completely. Only in laminar flow benches and 'clean' rooms are fungal spores virtually absent. In most places, the air contains from hundreds to thousands of spores per cubic metre. The surfaces of many substrates are colonized by fungi, and it is extremely difficult to remove them all. So we should accept fungal contamination as a fact of life. It is worth remembering, however, that the inner tissues of healthy plants and animals are usually uncontaminated by spoilage organisms (though symptomless fungal endophytes are common in many plants: see chapter 21), and that natural coverings such as the skin of fruits, the husks of grains, and the shells of nuts, often protect these tissues from spoilage for extended periods.

What practical ways are there of preventing fungi from exploiting our food? Fortunately we have devised several very effective techniques, which can be grouped into two categories: (1) those which kill the microorganisms; (2) those which inhibit their growth. I will list the methods in each category, then discuss them in turn. (1a) Heat sterilization, (1b) irradiation, (1c) filtration; (2a) drying, (2b) refrigeration, (2c) addition of chemical inhibitors, (2d) exclusion of oxygen.

(1a) **Heat sterilization** involves heating the food to a high enough temperature for long enough to kill all the fungal propagules present on or in it. This method often has to be teamed with other techniques for preventing subsequent re-contamination, or for inhibiting moulds that do find their way in. Food may, for example, be heat-processed and then vacuum-packed, canned, bottled or frozen. Some moulds are **thermotolerant**, and can grow at 55-60°C. These include species of *Aspergillus**, *Chrysosporium, Humicola, Malbranchea, Paecilomyces* and *Penicillium**, all hyphomycetes (dikaryomycotan anamorphs). Some species of *Talaromyces* and *Byssochlamys**, ascomycetous teleomorphs of *Penicillium* and *Paecilomyces*, have ascospores that can survive heating to 80°C. Certain foods have delicate textures or flavours that would be ruined by heating to 100°C, so other methods of preservation are often used. A final note of caution: heat sterilization is not a very effective way of getting rid of mycotoxins—some of them are very heat-stable.

(1b) **Irradiation** is one of the newest and most promising forms of sterilization. Food is sealed in airtight containers, to prevent later re-contamination, and treated with appropriate doses of gamma radiation. This kills all living things —bacteria, fungi, even insects—in the food, and endows it with a very long shelf-life. This method should be suitable for a wide range of foods, though it has not been very successful with fresh vegetables. Some misguided environmentalists have condemned this technique, ostensibly because it reduces vitamin levels, and produces free radicals (but more probably because it is associated with the hated nuclear industry). The free radicals, though in some cases potentially carcinogenic, are unstable and break down naturally after a while, and I am personally convinced that hungry people would rather eat food with reduced vitamin levels than lose it to bacteria, fungi or insects.

(1c) **Filtration** is obviously of very limited application; in fact it can probably be used only for clear fluids such as beer, wine, some fruit juices, and soft drinks. This is because the pores in the filter have to be small enough to filter out microbial propagules. If we include bacteria in this instance (which is logical because they tend to be the major spoilers of liquids), the pores must be less than 1 μm in diameter.

(2a) **Drying** is almost certainly the oldest method of preserving food. It works quite simply by denying the microorganisms the water they need to grow. Dryness is relative—by that I mean that we never need to remove **all** the water from food in order to extend its shelf-life. In fact we sometimes remove very little of the water, simply making it unavailable to fungi by manipulating the osmotic pressure of the system. This is commonly done by adding salt or sugar. These substances reduce the **water activity** of the food just as effectively as if we had physically removed the water.

Water activity (a_W) is an expression of the moistness of the food: to measure it, we keep a sample of the food in a small airtight enclosure until the water in the sample and in the air within the container have equilibrated. If the relative humidity of the air within the container is then 85%, the water activity of the food is said to be 0.85. Life can go on over a range of water activities from 1.0 down to about 0.6. Animals can function only when virtually saturated—at water activities from 0.99-1.0. Many plants wilt permanently at 0.98. Most microorganisms can grow only above 0.95. These figures make the drought tolerance of some fungi all the more remarkable. In fact, some conidial fungi and yeasts are the most xerotolerant organisms known. *Wallemia sebi*, which grows on salt fish, can tolerate a water activity of 0.75. *Chrysosporium fastidium* can grow at 0.69, and causes spoilage of dried prunes in Australia. But *Aspergillus echinulatus* is the champion, able to grow at water activities as low as **0.62**. Some osmotolerant yeasts do almost as well.

The xerotolerance of many moulds means simply that cheddar cheese at its normal moisture content will go mouldy if exposed to a little air, and the fact that many conidial fungi are also psychrotolerant means that this will happen even in the refrigerator. If we did dry the cheese to the point where fungi will not grow, it would not be cheddar cheese any more, but would take on the arid texture of the parmesan cheese we grate onto spaghetti. Some moulds are so xerotolerant that not even jams and jellies, with their high sugar content, are immune to spoilage, although the high osmotic pressure of jam slows the fungi down considerably. So when preparing home-made jam we have to sterilize the jamjars, put a layer of wax on top of the jam, and seal the jars tightly before storing them. Dried fruit, grains, and powdered milk have an a_W of less than 0.75, and are therefore susceptible to attack by only a few fungi (e.g. species of *Aspergillus*, *Wallemia* and *Chrysosporium*). Only by reducing the water activity of foods to 0.65 or less can we virtually eliminate fungal deterioration.

(2b) **Refrigeration** is commonly used to retard food spoilage, but everyone knows that if you leave food in the refrigerator long enough, it will spoil. Many moulds will grow, slowly but surely, at 4°C, and even at 0°C. Some psychrotolerant fungi will grow at temperatures several degrees below freezing. Several *Penicillium* spp.* grow at -2°C. *Cladosporium herbarum** grows down to -5°C, and *Fusarium poae** down to -7°C. So refrigerators are not insurance policies against spoilage: they merely extend the storage life of especially perishable foods like milk and meat. If we really want to use low temperature to prevent fungal spoilage of foods containing moderate amounts of moisture, we have to keep them at -18°C or below, the temperature range maintained by modern freezers.

(2c) **Addition of chemical inhibitors**. If you read the list of ingredients on the packaging of a loaf of bread, you will usually find **calcium propionate** among them. It slows down the germination and growth of moulds, and extends the shelf-life of bread by several days. Since it has little effect on yeasts, it can be added during the preparation of bread dough. Calcium propionate is also added to cheese spreads. **Sodium benzoate** is often added to jams, jellies, margarine, carbonated soft drinks, fruit salads, fruit juices, pickles, etc., to inhibit yeasts and moulds in acid conditions (pH 2.5-4.0) that some of them could normally tolerate. **Calcium, sodium** and **potassium sorbate** are used to inhibit moulds in the same range of foods, but at pH values above 4. **Sulphur dioxide** is used to disinfect wine-making equipment, and to preserve fruit juices and dried fruit. **Lactic acid** is developed during the natural fermentation of sauerkraut, dill pickles, green olives, many cheeses, and some sausages; and **propionic acid** forms naturally during the ripening of swiss cheese; but these acids are usually supplemented by other preservatives. In case you were wondering, the substances mentioned above are 'generally regarded as safe' (GRAS) food additives.

(2d) **Exclusion of oxygen**. Fungi are almost all aerobic (oxygen-requiring), so such strategies as canning, bottling, sealing under paraffin wax, or wrapping food in impermeable membranes, can effectively inhibit growth of most moulds. So can storage of food in inert atmospheres of carbon dioxide or nitrogen. A few species, such as *Penicillium roquefortii**, the mould that ripens blue cheeses, can grow at oxygen tensions only 10% of normal, but if most other cheeses are tightly sealed in aluminum foil or plastic wrap they will not become mouldy. Once the wrapping has been opened, conidia present on the cheese will soon germinate (even in the refrigerator, as we have seen), and visible mouldiness will not be far behind. Some common saprobic moulds such as *Gliocladium roseum** and *Trichoderma koningii** grow quite well in 1% oxygen, and the oxygen level has to be reduced to 0.2% before the growth of *Fusarium oxysporum** is much curtailed.

Keeping in mind the kind of techniques we have developed for preventing or retarding mould spoilage of foods, we can now make a quick survey of the main groups of foods, and the kinds of moulds that cause spoilage problems in each. Foods from plants fall into four broad categories: (1) cereals and nuts, (2) sugars, (3) vegetables, (4) fruits. Those of animal origin provide a further four categories: (5) meat and poultry, (6) eggs, (7) fish and other seafood, (8) milk and milk products. We will examine them in that order.

(1) **Cereals and nuts**. If promptly harvested and stored under dry conditions, most of these naturally dry foods are relatively immune to fungal spoilage. But if the growing season is wet, grain can become mouldy while still in the field. Some field moulds are notorious mycotoxin producers—*Fusarium* spp.* produce zearalenone, T-2 toxin and vomitoxin. Some storage moulds that attack grain and nuts are equally infamous—*Aspergillus flavus** and *A. parasiticus** produce aflatoxins. Rice, which is grown in warm, wet conditions, is often moulded by species of *Aspergillus* or *Penicillium*; and rice stained yellow by *P. citrinum**, *P. islandicum** and *P. citreoviride* often contains mycotoxins. Barley is often contaminated with ochratoxin produced by *P. verrucosum* var. *verrucosum**. Corn can be spoiled by *Fusarium graminearum** or *Aspergillus fla-*

vus*, which produce zearalenone and aflatoxins, respectively. Corn and winter wheat in the field are threatened by *Fusarium graminearum,** the source of vomitoxin, and wheat in storage is sometimes spoiled by members of the *Aspergillus glaucus* series, by *A. candidus*, *A. flavus**, *A. ochraceus**, and by some penicillia*.

If flour is stored at a moisture content of 13% or less, it won't mould, but the addition of water during baking makes the finished product available to fungi. The commonest moulds on bread are: the zygomycete, *Rhizopus stolonifer*, with its tall sporangiophores and black pinhead sporangia; the green-spored hyphomycetes, *Penicillium expansum** and *P. stoloniferum*, the black-spored *Aspergillus niger*, and the pinkish *Chrysonilia sitophila* anamorph of *Neurospora*. Species of the zygomycete genus *Mucor* and the filamentous yeast, *Geotrichum* may also be involved. Wheat bread is often moulded by *Penicillium brevicompactum**, *P. chrysogenum* and *P. verrucosum* var. *cyclopium**: rye bread by the last species and *P. roquefortii**, pastries by *Aspergillus repens* and *P. verrucosum* var. *cyclopium**.

(2) **Sugars**. Properly made jams and jellies have an a_w of 0.7 or lower, and are virtually inaccessible to fungi. But because manufacturers are now trying to cut down on calories or cost, many jams have a water activity nearer 0.8. This opens the door to such xerotolerant hyphomycetes as members of the *Aspergillus glaucus* series, *Penicillium corylophilum* and *Wallemia sebi*, and means that jam makers have had to resort to such supplementary measures as sterile filling of containers, refrigeration, and even chemical preservatives.

(3) **Vegetables**. Some vegetables, such as cabbages, potatoes and turnips, are relatively resistant to fungal spoilage. Others, such as lettuce and ripe tomatoes, have a much shorter shelf-life. The most serious fungal market diseases of vegetables are grey mould rot caused by *Botrytis* (Hyphomycetes), watery soft rot caused by the sclerotial anamorph of *Sclerotinia* (Ascomycetes, Leotiales), blue mould rot caused by *Penicillium,** *Fusarium** rot, *Alternaria** rot, *Cladosporium** rot, black mould rot caused by *Aspergillus niger* (the last five all hyphomycetes), and soft rot caused by *Rhizopus* (Zygomycetes).

(4) **Fruits**. The combination of senescent cells and high sugar and acid content makes many ripe fruits particularly susceptible to fungal spoilage by several hyphomycetes. *Botrytis cinerea* causes the extremely destructive grey mould of strawberries. *Penicillium expansum** and *Gloeosporium* spp. produce storage rots of apples. *Penicillium digitatum* and *P. italicum* destroy oranges and lemons. *Monilia* brown rot causes heavy losses of peaches, cherries, other stone fruits and pears. *Rhizopus stolonifer* (Zygomycetes) is also a common problem on ripe peaches. Tropical fruits are often attacked by species of *Colletotrichum** (Coelomycetes).

Fruits are often preserved by drying or canning (or by making into jam, as mentioned under heading 2), and fruit juices now support a whole industry. Apricots and peaches for drying are impregnated with sulphur dioxide to preserve their colour, and this also effectively prevents fungal spoilage. Unsulphured dried fruit can go mouldy. Prunes, especially, are sold in moist packs which have an a_w of 0.80-0.85. This makes them accessible to most xerotolerant moulds, which can be inhibited by sorbic or benzoic acid. Canned goods are usually heated to a high enough temperature to destroy fungal spores, but fruits with delicate textures are pasteurized at lower temperatures. Heating to 80°C will kill all zygomycete sporangiospores, and all hyphomycete conidia; but it won't kill ascospores of *Byssochlamys fulva** or *B. nivea*. These thermotolerant ascomycetes sometimes spoil canned strawberries, soft drinks and fruit juices (prune, grape, pineapple), and home-bottled fruit. If these fungi are cultured, their *Paecilomyces* anamorphs usually develop. Fruit juices are naturally contaminated with yeasts, and the normal course of events would involve an alcoholic fermentation which would ultimately, as in the case of wine, effectively preserve the substrate. But if the juice is refrigerated, moulds, rather than yeasts, will be favoured. Some fruit juices (blackcurrant, grape) are preserved with sulphur dioxide. In conclusion, it is worth pointing out that we can't blame all fruit losses on the fungi—bananas become brown and mushy through the action of their own enzymes.

Further Reading

Frazier, W.C. and D.C. Westhoff (1978) **Food Microbiology**. 3rd Edn. McGraw-Hill, New York.

Pitt, J.I. (1981) Food spoilage and biodeterioration (in) **Biology of Conidial Fungi**. Vol 2. (Eds.) G.T. Cole and B. Kendrick. Academic Press, New York.

Samson, R.A. and E.S. van Reenen-Hoekstra (1988) **Introduction to Food-borne Fungi**. 3rd Edn. Centraalbureau voor Schimmelcultures, Baarn (with contributions by 12 other authors).

Chapter 21

Mycotoxins in Food and Feed

Introduction

Foods are usually non-living but natural organic substances, which are excellent substrates for saprobic fungi, and accordingly tend to go mouldy if kept too long. The people of western countries, generally relatively wealthy and fastidious, will throw out most food that is obviously mouldy. But this is not necessarily true in the poorer nations, where food is often a precious commodity, not to be rejected because of a little surface discolouration. This attitude is reinforced in the Far East by the common use of moulds to prepare traditional fermented foods (see chapter 19). In some areas, indigenous peoples prefer the spicy flavour certain foods acquire when they go mouldy (cf. the blue cheese eaten by westerners). Animals will often accept mouldy feed. To compound the problem, the term mouldy refers only to food on which the contaminating fungi are already sporulating. But even food which looks perfectly edible may be riddled by the invisible assimilative hyphae of moulds, and contaminated by their metabolites. Do these things matter? Is mouldy food dangerous? This chapter will give you some answers.

Some fungi, including many common moulds (mostly hyphomycetes), produce **secondary metabolites**—usually steroids, carotenoids, alkaloids, cyclopeptides and coumarins. Many substances in the last three categories are toxic to animals and to other microorganisms at very low dosages, and are also persistent and often heat-stable. Such compounds are frequently produced in fungus-contaminated foodstuffs, remain there even after processing, sterilization or cooking, and are unsuspectingly eaten. They are called **mycotoxins**. Over 200 such substances, produced by about 150 different fungi, are now known, and more are being discovered every year.

Ergot Alkaloids and Saint Anthony's Fire

We have become aware of most mycotoxins and their insidious effects only since 1960, but the condition called **ergotism** has been known for thousands of years. This mysterious and dreadful disease struck the Spartans in 430 B.C. during their war with Athens. Epidemics during the Middle Ages have left bizarre accounts in which the screams of the dying, the stench of rotting flesh, and limbs actually dropping off, are recorded in grisly detail (sounds like a suitable plot for Stephen King's next movie). Supplications were naturally made to the Saints, and especially to one St. Anthony, the founder of monastic life, since sufferers who made pilgrimages to his shrine often gained relief. Grateful survivors founded a hospital brotherhood in his name, and to this day the condition is known as **St. Anthony's Fire**. What was really happening to the victims? How can we explain those 'miraculous' cures?

We now know that the victims had all eaten bread made from grain contaminated with sclerotia of the **ergot** fungus, *Claviceps purpurea* (Fig. 4.18 A-D). These sclerotia contain a complex cocktail of physiologically active substances: ten different groups with over 100 individual compounds. The disease-producing substances are alkaloids of two main kinds: (1) clavine alkaloids; (2) derivatives of lysergic acid—amides or peptides.

What was the disease like? Two main patterns were seen. (1) **Gangrenous ergotism**. This syndrome began with fatigue, and cold or prickling sensations in the limbs, then severe muscular pains. Limbs later became swollen and inflamed, and burning pains and sensations of heat alternated with those of icy coldness. Gradually the affected parts became numb. Feet and legs turned black and mummified. This dry gangrene spread upward, and the fingers and toes of victims, or even their hands and feet, literally sloughed off. (2) **Convulsive ergotism**. Here the central nervous system was most severely affected. Symptoms ranged from formication (check the spelling—it means feeling as if ants are crawling under your skin), to itching, numbness of hands and feet, twitching, and muscular cramps escalating into sustained convulsions. Fists became clenched, the hands in acute flexion; the body either rolled up in a ball, or bent rigidly backward as in tetanus. Convulsions alternated with periods of drowsiness. Between convulsions, patients often ate voraciously, and could not sleep. Some died within hours, others lingered for weeks. Severe non-fatal cases lasted up to two months, and brain damage was common. Mortality ranged from 11-60%.

At least 65 epidemics were documented between 1581 and 1889. A Frenchman named Dodart exposed the cause of the disease in 1673, but ignorance and stubbornness prevented much reduction in the death rate for another century. Finally, when a famine in 1770 precipitated many terrible epidemics, effective control measures were introduced. But *Claviceps* also attacks the ovaries of many wild grasses, and grazing livestock still sometimes suffer from ergotism.

The symptoms can be analyzed into two main components, caused by different groups of chemicals. (1) Effects on muscles: the alkaloids affect smooth muscle and cause vasoconstriction. This effect has been put to medical use in two areas. (A) **Ergotamine tartrate** is useful in the management of migraine. It reduces the diameter of the cranial arterioles, thus reducing pulsation pressure and the attendant headache. (B) **Ergometrine** has been widely used to induce labour (but not to procure abortions, since the uterine muscles become really sensitive to the compound only at full term), and to control bleeding after childbirth. (2) Effects on the central nervous system: **lysergic acid amides**, particularly lysergic acid diethylamide (**LSD**), are dramatically potent hallucinogens. Since this was discovered, more than 2,000 papers have appeared on the subject, and many more unofficial experiments have been conducted. Although the medical profession drily records the effects of LSD as 'hyperthermia, hyperglycemia, mydriasis, piloerection, tachypnoea and hyper-reflexia'

(I'll leave your own curiosity to drive you to look those words up: they aren't in the glossary), the really important immediate effects appear to be extremely subjective and less easily described. However, I'm sure you have all read, or heard at first hand, accounts of trips taken by devotees, with their dazzling visual hallucinations (**Lucy in the Sky with Diamonds**) and intense sexual experiences. Those who are tempted by such glowing accounts should be warned, not only of the temporary personality-dissolving effects, but also of the less well charted long-term sequelae. Perhaps the most promising use for this drug lies in the treatment of certain mental disorders—it is not recommended for most of us, who might describe ourselves as nearly normal neurotics.

So, on the one hand, ergot is now produced deliberately by the pharmaceutical industry, spores of the fungus being mechanically inoculated into the flowers of rye; on the other hand, ergot is now rigorously excluded from grain that will be ground for flour. No longer do we need to take pilgrimages to St. Anthony's shrine to give ourselves a break from an ergot-contaminated diet (Yes, that seems to have been the secret of those miraculous cures). Only animals and the occasional alkaloid-overdose patient now suffer from St. Anthony's Fire. A few years ago in England, ergotamine tartrate was prescribed for a woman suffering from migraine. Unhappily, the amount prescribed was a massive overdose, she developed gangrene in her feet, and her toes had to be amputated. In Canada a hog farmer lost most of his pigs to ergot poisoning. He was awarded $100,000 damages against the feed supplier, despite the fact that the grain had not exceeded the level of ergot contamination permitted by the Canadian Grain Commission. *Claviceps purpurea* has not lost its ancient powers, and its toxic effects can be avoided only by constant vigilance.

Aflatoxins—Toxins, Mutagens, Carcinogens

The modern awakening of scientists to an awareness of mycotoxins began in 1960, when tens of thousands of turkey poults in England began to die from a mysterious disease of unknown etiology—they sickened rapidly, they haemorrhaged subcutaneously, they died. Post-mortems showed that their livers had undergone extensive necrosis, and their bile ducts had hypertrophied. This condition was called 'Turkey X disease,' which is easy to remember, but not very informative. Elsewhere in Britain, large losses of partridges, pheasants and ducklings were reported, and later, calves and pigs were affected. Some slick detective work showed that the only factor common to all these different outbreaks was the incorporation of Brazilian peanut meal in the animals' feed. A high incidence of hepatoma in hatchery-raised trout was also linked to peanut meal. It wasn't long before the toxin was isolated, and found to originate with a fungus growing on the peanuts, rather than with the peanuts themselves. The fungus responsible was found to be a very common mould, *Aspergillus flavus* (Fig. 21.1 C), so the toxin was called **aflatoxin**. It soon transpired that there were four toxins, rather than one. When separated chromatographically and examined under U/V, two fluoresced blue, and two fluoresced green. The toxins were called aflatoxin B_1 and B_2, and aflatoxin G_1 and G_2. Under most conditions, aflatoxin B_1 is the major toxin produced. The chemical name for this group of compounds is bisfuranocoumarins.

The factor that made aflatoxins big news was not simply that they were toxic, but as was soon discovered, that they are extremely potent **carcinogens** in rats (and therefore, by implication, in humans). To make matters worse, the aflatoxins were discovered at a time when UNICEF, among others, was pushing peanut meal, with its high protein content, as a dietary supplement to prevent Kwashiorkor (gross protein deficiency) among children in many tropical countries. Did the discovery of aflatoxins mean that these people were at risk? Were they liable to sustain liver damage or even develop liver cancer? It became very important

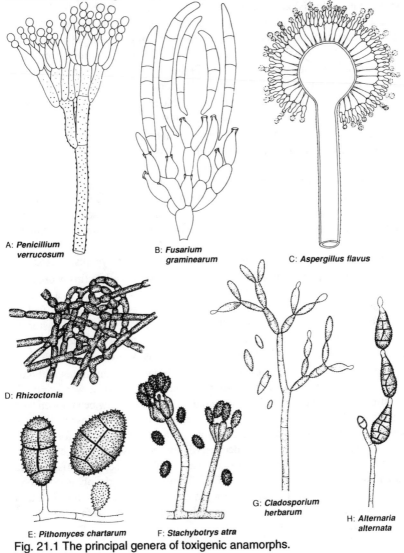

A: *Penicillium verrucosum*

B: *Fusarium graminearum*

C: *Aspergillus flavus*

D: *Rhizoctonia*

E: *Pithomyces chartarum*

F: *Stachybotrys atra*

G: *Cladosporium herbarum*

H: *Alternaria alternata*

Fig. 21.1 The principal genera of toxigenic anamorphs.

to know just what conditions led to the formation of aflatoxins, especially since *Aspergillus flavus* occurs on many grains in storage, and is even used in the Orient to prepare some kinds of vegetable cheese and soy sauce. Not only that—cows whose diet is contaminated with aflatoxin produce milk containing a derivative called aflatoxin M_1, and peanut butter is the staple diet of most North American children.

Although it was soon found that the range of conditions under which *Aspergillus flavus* could grow was much wider than that over which it formed aflatoxins, it was also discovered just how toxic aflatoxins are. Some typical LD_{50} figures (the dosage in mg/kg which will kill half of a population of experimental animals) are: ducklings—0.335, rabbits—0.3, cats—0.55, pigs—0.62, sheep—1.0. That's bad enough, but it was discovered that even if the diet didn't contain sufficient toxin to cause acute poisoning, prolonged exposure to much lower levels will often cause liver cancer. Many experiments have demonstrated this in rats. As little as 0.015 ppm in the diet over 70 weeks caused neoplasms in all rats tested. At 1 ppm this takes only 40 weeks. At 5 ppm it takes 9 weeks. Shasta trout are so sensitive that as little as 0.5 µg/kg (0.5 ppb) in their food over 20 months will produce similar results.

If we examine the incidence of liver cancer in human populations, we find it is exceptionally common in some developing countries, especially those of Subsaharan Africa and the Far East. The problem is well documented in Uganda, Swaziland, Kenya and Thailand. All have elevated levels of liver cancer, and the diet in each country is significantly contaminated with aflatoxins. Although we cannot of course prove experimentally that aflatoxins cause liver cancer in humans, the suspicion is strong enough to be almost a certainty (as with the connection between smoking and lung cancer). And we do know that in some other mammals, aflatoxins are the most potent carcinogens yet discovered.

What is being done to monitor and control the levels of aflatoxins in our diet? In Canada the allowable limit of contamination, originally 20 ppb in a finished product, has been reduced to 15 ppb. Germany allows only 10 ppb. I feel no detectable aflatoxin should be permitted. If proper attention was paid to storage and selection of peanuts for human consumption, and to appropriate dilution of mildly contaminated nuts, this standard could be easily attained.

Aspergillus flavus competes best in warm climates, on substrates that have low water contents (low 'water activities': see chapter 20). It was originally classfied as a storage mould, but some contamination has now been traced back to the field: the fungus can be an adventitious parasite, invading insect-damaged tissue. Serious aflatoxin contamination has been found in peanuts, brazil nuts, pistachio nuts, almonds, walnuts, pecans, filberts, cottonseed, copra, corn, grain sorghum, millet, palm, kernels, beans, wine, milk, cheese, dried fish, garlic, spaghetti, noodles, bread, flour, and figs. Aflatoxicosis is mainly encountered in warmer climates, and it is interesting to note peanuts now grown in Ontario seem to be free of aflatoxin—that's one advantage to living so far north.

Mycotoxins and Oesophageal Cancer

In at least two areas of the world, the incidence of oesophageal cancer is many times higher than might be expected. The reasons for this have only recently begun to be understood. In Lin Xian, China, not many years ago, oesophageal cancer killed 25% of the population, and the disease had tragically become an accepted part of existence. Folk wisdom held that if you had trouble in swallowing it was because you were unhappy. Scientists, however, suspected that nitrosamines were responsible.

The foods people ate did not contain elevated levels of nitrosamines, but it was established that these compounds could easily be produced in the stomach from nitrites and amines. Gradually, the pieces of the puzzle were fitted together. Although the local water was not initially very high in nitrite, people simmered their corn for hours, concentrating the nitrite, and then used the water to make soups. The soil was low in molybdenum, a deficiency which caused crop plants to accumulate nitrite in their leaves. So body levels of nitrite were found to be high, while vitamin C intake was low. Apparently, without adequate vitamin C, the body could not rid itself of the nitrites. The peasants made steamed bread from the corn. Nothing unusual in that, except that they made enough at one time to last for three weeks. Needless to say, the bread started to go mouldy after a few days. But this didn't bother the people of Lin Xian: they liked the spicy flavour of the mouldy bread (remember my comments on cultural determination of what constitutes food spoilage?) Scientists found that two of the fungi involved in the moulding caused levels of amines in the bread to increase seventeen-fold. Here was another piece of the puzzle. Rats fed nitrites and mouldy bread manufactured nitrosamines, and developed cancer. But it was also noted that some of the control rats, those fed only mouldy bread, also developed cancer. Some of the fungi must produce unknown carcinogens. Doctors also found that 90% of the cancers surgically removed from patients actually had these moulds growing inside them. This was another important observation, because many apparently healthy people already had pre-cancerous thickenings of their oesophagus, 72% of which harboured living moulds.

The etiology of the disease was now much clearer. Molybdenum-deficient soil led to nitrite accumulation in crops; vitamin C deficiencies permitted high body nitrite levels. Mouldy bread was high in amines and harboured fungi that produced carcinogens. Now it was time to institute preventive measures. Seeds are being treated with molybdenum. People are supplied with piped water free of nitrite. People are told to eat fresh vegetables, and to avoid mouldy food at all costs. Unfortunately, it takes years for a cancer to develop, and it will be ten years before the results of the cancer prevention campaign can be assessed. But this is certainly one disease where prevention, if possible, is a thousand times better than the attempt to cure, which involves drastic surgery and follow-up radiation treatments, and does not have a good prognosis.

A similarly high incidence of oesophageal cancer among the Xhosa people in some parts of the Transkei, South Africa, has also been connected with the consumption of mould metabolites in food (mainly corn) and in the native beer, which is made by preference from mouldy grain. This time the suspect fungus is *Fusarium moniliforme*, and the suspect metabolite is **fumonisin**, a secondary metabolite that has been characterized only recently, after 15 years of investigations. Again, preventive dietary changes would seem to be the answer. But as we all know, it is hard to get people to give up dangerous habits they enjoy, particularly those involving food, or 'legal' drugs such as alcohol and tobacco.

Each year in South Africa about 200 people suffer from an unnamed haemorrhagic disease with additional tremorgenic (neurotoxic) effects, plus associated liver and kidney symptoms. This complex syndrome is believed to result from drinking home-brewed native sorghum beer, often contaminated with at least two mycotoxins, tenuazonic acid produced by *Alternaria alternata* and *Phoma sorghina*, and cytochalasin produced by *Aspergillus clavatus*.

Trichothecenes and Haemorrhagic Syndrome

During World War II, and for some years after (especially 1942-1947), a serious and widespread haemorrhagic syndrome called **Alimentary Toxic Aleukia (ATA)** affected people in Siberia. Similar illnesses had been noted on earlier occasions, but had never before reached such epidemic proportions—in some areas 10% of the population developed the disease, and most cases were fatal. ATA was characterized by nausea, vomiting, haemorrhages in many organs, bleeding from nose and throat, bloody diarrhea, low leucocyte count, exhaustion of bone marrow, throat sepsis and necrosis. About a third of the deaths were due to strangulation resulting from internal swelling of the throat.

This disease occurred when much of the Russian population was starving and manpower shortages had prevented Fall harvesting of grain. When the grain was finally harvested in Spring, it proved to be extremely toxic. Not until years afterward was the epidemic linked to mycotoxins produced by moulds growing on the overwintered grain. Symptoms of ATA appeared after about 2 kg of contaminated grain had been eaten. Consumption of 6 kg was fatal. A similar haemorrhagic syndrome in animals is called **mouldy corn toxicosis**.

The two fungi found to be mainly responsible were *Fusarium poae* and *Fusarium sporotrichioides* (Hyphomycetes) (cf. Fig. 21.1 B), and the toxins they produced belonged to the group of tetracyclic sesquiterpenoids called **trichothecenes**, which are extremely poisonous, having an LD_{50} for many animals of less than 10 mg/kg. ATA is provoked by a trichothecene called **T-2 toxin**. The molecules of the more than 40 naturally occurring trichothecenes all contain a ring system called trichothecane, an olefinic bond at C-9,10, and an epoxy group at C-12,13 (Fig. 21.2). T-2 toxin has an LD_{50} for mice of 5.2 mg/kg.

Trichothecenes and Stachybotryotoxicosis in Horses

During the 1930's, horses in the Ukraine began to die in large numbers. They suffered mouth ulceration and swelling, fever, severe inflammation of the skin and respiratory tract, and depletion of leucocytes and blood platelets leading to complete failure of the blood-clotting mechanism. Death could occur in less than a day, or up to a month after the onset of symptoms. Scientists eventually connected the disease to fodder contaminated with macrocyclic trichothecenes produced by *Stachybotrys chartarum* (cf. Fig. 21.1 F), a common cellulose-decomposing hyphomycete growing on hay used as food and bedding. No fewer than five stable and persistent trichothecenes are produced by this fungus: **verrucarin J, roridin E**, and **satratoxins F, G** and **H**, though only satratoxins have been demonstrated in naturally contaminated straw associated with an outbreak among sheep in Hungary. Although typically reported in horses, this toxicosis can also affect cattle, pigs, poultry, sheep and even humans. Nikita Krushchev, who later became the Russian head of state, owed some of his early career success to his recognition that horses, so vital to the Russian economy and the Red Army transport system of the day, needed clean, dry fodder.

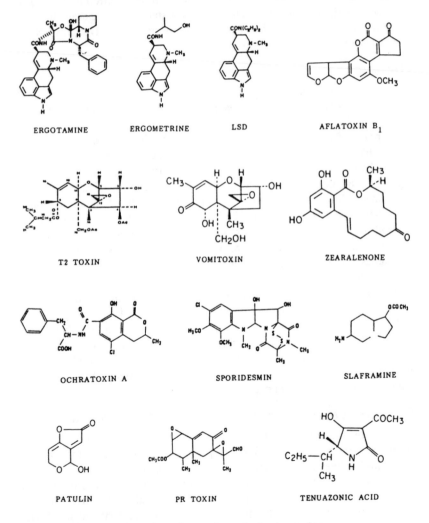

Fig. 21.2 Structural formulae of some important mycotoxins.

Equine Leucoencephalomalacia: 'Hole in the Head' Disease of Horses

In horses, donkeys and mules, the first signs of this condition are apathy, protruding tongue, unwillingness to move backward, and walking in circles. Eventually the animal becomes delirious and may run full tilt into fences. Finally it falls over, thrashes its legs in the air, and dies. Death may occur in seven hours or several days. A postmortem reveals areas of brain necrosis—large, irregular holes where the white matter has disintegrated. It was found that the disease condition could be reproduced by feeding the animals corn moulded by *Fusarium moniliforme* (the anamorph of *Gibberella fujikuroi*: Ascomycetes, Hypocreales). Field outbreaks of this mycotoxicosis have occurred in Argentina, Brazil, China, Egypt, South Africa and the U.S.A., but despite the dramatic signs and symptoms it produces, the nature of the mycotoxin involved has not yet been determined.

Trichothecenes and Yellow Rain

During the Vietnam war the U.S. government received many reports of chemical attacks launched by the invading Vietnamese in Laos and Kampuchea against troops and the civilian Hmong people. According to the reports, victims were sprayed with 'yellow rain,' an aerosol containing substances with toxic effects that did not match those of any known agents of chemical warfare. Eventually it was recognized that the symptoms—prolonged vomiting, diarrhea, headaches and dizziness, respiratory problems, blisters, internal haemorrhages, sometimes culminating in death—were like those produced by the trichothecenes. Samples of blood, urine and body tissues from victims, and leaves, water and soil from sprayed areas were found to contain several trichothecenes and zearalenone, typical *Fusarium* toxins. Control samples, including cereal grains, from areas adjacent to the places where attacks had taken place, contained no *Fusarium* toxins.

However, this issue was clouded by the remoteness of the location, and the unsatisfactory and inconclusive nature of the available evidence. Samples of the 'yellow rain' deposits were later shown to be largely made up of pollen, and it seems probable that these deposits were in fact nothing more than bee faeces, dropped during communal cleansing flights. The issue was carefully documented in an article titled 'Political Science' in The Atlantic Monthly, and I leave you to draw your own conclusions from that.

Trichothecenes: Vomitoxin, Refusal and Emesis in Pigs

Fusarium graminearum (Fig. 21.1 B), a common mould on damp corn, produces a **trichothecene** (3,7,15-trihydroxy-12,13-epoxytrichothec-9-en-8-one). This has been called **vomitoxin** because it was first discovered as a result of its powerful emetic effect on pigs, which will quickly learn to refuse food contaminated with it. Up to 40 ppm have been found in corn from Austria, Canada, France, Japan, South Africa and the U.S. It also contaminated barley and winter wheat. Since it affects pigs at concentrations as low as 0.7 ppm, many countries won't buy grain contaminated with it. Current vomitoxin limits for wheat used in pastry flour, and in bread or breakfast cereal, are 0.3 and 0.1 ppm, respectively. After one recent wet season, Ontario farmers growing winter wheat lost $17 million on a harvest of 670,000 tonnes, because of extensive vomitoxin contamination of the grain.

Zearalenone (F2 toxin) and Oestrogenic Syndrome in Pigs

Pig farmers sometimes find that their young female pigs ('gilts') develop swelling of the vulva, enlargement of mammary glands, enlargement of the uterus, and sometimes even rectal and vaginal prolapse—the vagina and associated structures swell and are often literally extruded. Internally, the ovaries atrophy. At the same time, the testes of young male pigs shrivel, and their mammary glands enlarge. Since all of these symptoms affect primary and secondary sexual characteristics, the involvement of some kind of sex hormone might be suspected. Once characterized, the syndrome was quickly linked with the presence of mouldy corn in the feed, and the fungus concerned was found to be the hyphomycete, *Fusarium graminearum* (Fig. 21.1 B). The toxin was named **zearalenone**. It obviously has many of the properties of oestrogen, one of the principal female sex hormones (it actually seems to be involved in regulating the development of sexual fructifications of the fungus). The toxin doesn't usually kill the animal, but complications following rectovaginal prolapse sometimes cause the whole herd to be destroyed. Lower levels of exposure are also serious in pigs, because they can cause infertility, small litters, and stillbirths.

Fusarium graminearum, the anamorph of *Gibberella zeae* (Ascomycetes, Hypocreales), develops as a pinkish mycelium on corn cobs stored wet over winter, and the toxin may reach levels of 50-100 ppm in the grain. Animals which aren't allowed to eat such mouldy feed will not develop oestrogenic syndrome. Zearalenone is not inevitably detrimental: when added to feed in very low doses, its hormonal properties produce accelerated growth in cattle and sheep, and it has been patented as a feed supplement (but not for pigs). It has also been used to treat post-menopausal syndrome in humans, and as an oral contraceptive.

Mouldy Sweet Potato Toxicosis

Cattle fed sweet potatoes affected by *Fusarium solani* storage rot develop acute symptoms of respiratory distress, and may die. The disease affects only the lungs, which become swollen and congested, with scattered haemorrhages. It has been found that four furanoterpenoid toxins are responsible for this condition: **4-ipomeanol**, **1-ipomeanol**, **ipomeanine**, and **1,4-ipomeadiol**. These compounds are not simply fungal metabolites, but are produced by a host-pathogen interaction. In response to stress, the sweet potato produces phytoalexins, such as 4-hydroxymyoporone, which are catabolised by *F. solani* to produce the toxic end-products. Humans in New Guinea for whom sweet potatoes are an important dietary item often suffer from a chronic respiratory syndrome that is sometimes fatal. The causation of this disease is still obscure, but the compounds discussed above must be strong suspects.

Ochratoxin, Mycotoxic Nephropathy in Pigs, and Balkan Nephropathy in Humans

In 1928 a new kidney disease of pigs was discovered in Denmark, but it was not until 1966 that the condition was proved to be a mycotoxicosis. It is caused by **ochratoxin-A**, a metabolite of *Aspergillus ochraceus* (and six other aspergilli: cf. Fig. 21.1 C), and *Penicillium viridicatum* (and five other penicilli: cf. Fig. 21.1 A). These fungi grow on damp feed grain, usually barley or oats. Epidemiological studies also link ochratoxin with Endemic Balkan Nephropathy, a fatal kidney condition reported among people living near the Danube River and its tributaries in Yugoslavia, Bulgaria and Roumania. The LD_{50} of ochratoxin-A for rats is 20 mg/kg. Ochratoxin-A is a dihydroisocoumarin moiety linked over its 7-carboxy group to L-β–phenylalanine. Its structure is shown in Fig. 21.2.

Sporidesmin and Facial Eczema of Sheep

For many years, New Zealand sheep (one of that country's principal industries) have been plagued by outbreaks of a condition known as facial eczema. They stop eating, develop diarrhea, then inflamed swellings on their lips, face, eyelids and vulva. They also become photophobic, trying to avoid bright light. Internally there is hypertrophy of the bile ducts and extensive liver necrosis. Affected animals sometimes die. The disease usually occurs in late summer, after warm rains.

Eventually, in 1963, the cause of the disease was found to be a toxin called **sporidesmin**, produced by a saprobic hyphomycete, *Pithomyces chartarum* (Fig. 21.1 E), growing on dead parts of forage grasses. The name of the disease is misleading, because the liver damage, rather than the skin problem, is life-threatening. The photosensitivity causing the 'facial eczema' is a secondary symptom caused by a porphyrin, **phylloerythrin**. This is a product of chlorophyll digestion that builds up in the peripheral circulation because the damaged liver cannot excrete it. Since it would be very expensive to spray large areas of grassland with fungicide, attempts are made to avoid the disease by forecasting weather conducive to sporulation of the fungus, and moving sheep to less susceptible grazing areas during such periods.

Lupinosis of Sheep

Sheep or other animals grazing on lupin stubble in Australia, New Zealand, South Africa, and Europe, especially a week or so after heavy rains, may become anorexic, feverish and listless, then jaundiced. Up to half of affected animals may die. The liver is clearly the main organ affected. It was first suggested as long ago as 1880 that the disease might be caused by toxins derived from fungi growing on the lupins, but final proof of this was not forthcoming until 1970.

Phomopsin A, the hepatotoxin responsible, is a cyclic hexapeptide produced by the coelomycete, *Phomopsis leptostromiformis* (the anamorph of *Diaporthe woodii*: Ascomycetes, Diaporthales). This fungus produces black pycnidial conidiomata on stems and pods of *Lupinus*, and the teleomorph has also been reported from this substrate. The fungus is a pathogen that continues growing saprobically after the death of the host, producing toxins in both phases. In Western Australia, where lupinosis is a serious problem, attempts are being made to breed lupins resistant to the *Phomopsis*.

Slaframine: Slobber Factor

In the U.S. Mid-West, cattle which are seen to slobber or drool, and then refuse to eat, may well have been feeding on red clover (*Trifolium*) attacked by a sterile basidiomycetous anamorph, *Rhizoctonia leguminicola* (Fig. 21.1 D), especially after cool, wet weather. The fungal metabolite that produces this reaction was named **slaframine**. It is an acetate ester of a bicyclic amine synthesized partly from lysine. This compound itself is physiologically inactive, but is transformed biologically to a quaternary amine similar in activity to acetylcholine: thus all cholinergic exocrine glands are stimulated. Although we know what causes the disease, it has proved impossible either to breed red clover resistant to the fungus, or to control the fungus with fungicides. Fortunately, there is a simple answer—farmers in the Midwestern United States have given up sowing red clover as a forage crop.

Apple Juice and Patulin

Patulin first attracted attention as a potential antibacterial antibiotic isolated in 1943 from *Penicillium patulum* and also from *Penicillium expansum* and *Penicillium claviforme*, as well as several other penicillia (Fig. 21.1 A) and aspergilli (Fig. 21.1 C). Interest in its antibacterial activity has now given way to concern about its toxic effects on plants and animals, and its possible role as a carcinogen. *Penicillium expansum* causes a very common storage rot in apples, so contamination of apple juice is likely, and should be monitored. The LD_{50} of patulin in mice is 8-10 mg/kg. Its structural formula is given in Fig. 21.2.

Tremorgens, the Shakes and Staggers

People in Western Nigeria are sometimes afflicted by a condition known as **Ijesha Shakes**. After eating, they become almost completely incapacitated by tremors of the legs. The condition may last for several days, but patients eventually recover completely. It is suspected that foods containing tremorgens—neurotoxins of fungal origin—are responsible. A disease of sheep and cattle, known as **Grass Staggers**, presents symptoms identical to those produced by the tremorgenic toxin **penitrem A** of *Penicillium cyclopium*. There is a strong possibility that the toxins responsible for this disease are produced by some symptomless endophytic fungi, including the *Acremonium* anamorph of *Epichloë typhina* (Ascomycetes, Clavicipitales) or other members of this order.

PR Toxin and Blue Cheese

You will have noted that many of the mycotoxins discussed in this chapter are produced by species of *Penicillium* or *Aspergillus* (Fig. 21.1 A,C). It so happens that various species of both genera have been used for many years in the preparation of traditional foods. Aspergilli are responsible for many oriental fungally fermented foods, while penicillia impart the unique and delicious flavours to some of our finest cheeses. The conjunction of these facts did not go unnoticed. Could both westerners and orientals be insidiously poisoning themselves with these delicacies? Scientists who set out to answer that question were rather dismayed to find that *Penicillium roquefortii*, the fungus responsible for all blue cheeses (Roquefort, Gorgonzola, Danish blue, Stilton), did in fact produce a toxin, which they called **PR toxin**. This substance was lethal to mice: when injected intraperitoneally it had an LD$_{50}$ of 6 mg/kg. Fortunately for those of us who are addicted to blue cheese, no trace of this toxin has been found in the cheese itself, and it appears that conditions prevailing during the cheese-making process prevent toxin formation. It has also been found that toxins are not normally produced during the preparation of **soy sauce** (shoyu), **ketjap**, **miso, hamanatto**, or **katsuobushi**, all of which involve species of *Aspergillus*. It seems that some kind of selection process has excluded toxigenic strains from most food processing applications, or the conditions involved have inhibited toxin production. However, some concerns remain. *Penicillium roquefortii* has also been found to produce two other toxins, **roquefortine** and **patulin**, and *Penicillium camembertii*, which ripens soft cheeses such as Brie and Camembert, produces **cyclopiazonic acid.** Whether these toxins are produced in dangerous quantities, or occur at all in cheeses, is not yet fully established.

Alternaria and Tenuazonic Acid

Alternaria (Fig. 21.1 H) is one of the commonest moulds on various crops, such as apples and tomatoes, and on deteriorating food, and it is now known to produce several mycotoxins, of which the most poisonous is **tenuazonic acid**. This has been detected in commercial tomato pastes at levels of 0.1-1 ppm, and warrants further attention. In South Africa it has been shown that the growth of native cattle is considerably retarded by the presence of tenuazonic acid in their diet.

Cladosporium and Epicladosporic Acid

Cladosporium (Fig. 21.1 G) is another extremely common mould of deteriorating plant materials, and again produces several mycotoxins. One of these, **epicladosporic acid**, may have been implicated in the outbreaks of alimentary toxic aleukia, since it was produced by one of the cladosporia isolated from samples of the grain consumed by ATA patients.

It must be obvious by now that mycotoxins are a growing cause for concern. Obviously, their presence in certain foods, such as peanut butter, must be continuously monitored. Can we detoxify contaminated food or, better still, prevent moulds from growing on it in the first place? If the substrate can be kept dry and cool, moulds cannot grow, and mycotoxins will not be produced. Mycotoxin-producing moulds are sometimes classified as either field moulds, which grow in substrates containing 22-25% moisture, or storage moulds, which need only 13-18% moisture. This is only a rough division, since some fungi can exploit both ranges, but it gives us some idea of the kind of conditions to aim for in food storage. Certain aspergilli are the world's most xerotolerant organisms, capable of growing at extremely low water activities (below 0.7), so it is not easy to eliminate them completely. Temperature is another important factor. The three most important toxigenic mould genera are *Penicillium*, *Fusarium* and *Aspergillus* (Fig. 21.1 A-C). The optimum temperatures for the members of these genera are rather different. Many *Fusarium* species grow best in the range 8-15°C; the optimum for *Penicillium* species is usually 25-30°C; and that for *Aspergillus* species is often 30-40°C. This information gives us some idea where to expect problems with each of these genera.

A recent compilation found that representatives of 46 genera of fungi are known to produce mycotoxins. When anamorph-teleomorph connections are taken into account, the number of holomorphic genera decreases to 35. Given that there are thousands of fungal genera, the number reported as toxigenic seems very low. But is that so surprising when we consider that we have detected most mycotoxins only after reacting to reports of toxicity, and we have not yet taken a pro-active attitude toward testing a wide range of fungi for toxin production? If and when such a survey is carried out, I predict a dramatic increase in the ranks of the toxigenic fungi.

Detection of Mycotoxins

The continuous monitoring of food for mycotoxin contamination requires regular sampling, efficient methods for extracting and purifying mycotoxins, and sensitive methods of detecting and quantifying them. Sampling can be a problem, because of the uneven distribution of mould growth (How many mouldy peanuts are there in a sack?) Mycotoxins are extracted with an organic solvent: chloroform, dichloromethane, acetonitrile, ethyl acetate, acetone or methanol. Repeated column chromatographic purification is often necessary, using such substances as silica gel, alumina, and Sephadex. Thin layer chromatography (TLC) or high performance liquid chromatography (HPLC) help in the final separation of the mycotoxins from other compounds extracted with them.

Aflatoxins can then be detected directly by their U/V fluorescence. Other toxins do not autofluoresce: sterigmatocystin fluoresces only after being sprayed with $AlCl_3$ in ethanol. The possibility that non-toxins will behave like toxins, and give false-positive results, can be reduced by running toxin standards in tandem with samples, but can be completely ruled out only by positive identification of the toxin. This is most reliably done by high resolution mass spectroscopy (MS), but in many cases, relatively simple chemical tests will suffice. For example, after 1-dimensional TLC, sterigmatocystin can be reacted with trifluoroacetic acid (TFA) to form a product with an R_F value lower than that of sterigmatocystin itself. This compound can then be detected by running the plate again in the second dimension, using the same solvent. Interfering substances that do not react with the TFA will finish up on the diagonal of the plate, since they will move the same distance each time. The sterigmatocystin-TFA derivative will move a smaller distance on the second run, and will thus stand out. It can also be checked against a similarly treated sterigmatocystin standard.

Detoxification

It seems that we will always have to deal with mycotoxin-contaminated food and feed. Are there ways of removing or destroying mycotoxins? Aflatoxin has been the subject of most detoxification research. Although this toxin is relatively heat-stable, heating a contaminated substrate to 100°C for 2 hours can degrade 80% of the aflatoxin present. Dry roasting nuts has a similar effect. But heat treatment won't eliminate aflatoxin. Chemical treatment can give more complete detoxification. Aflatoxins are degraded by aqueous solutions of strong acids and bases, so crude edible oils are now treated with NaOH solution to remove aflatoxin. Ammonia treatment will almost eliminate aflatoxin from peanut meal and grains, but may reduce their food value. Oxidizing agents will also destroy aflatoxins: NaOCl and hydrogen peroxide hold some promise. Bisulphite, already accepted as an antimicrobial additive in fruit juices and dried fruits, degrades aflatoxins, and may become widely used for this purpose if current research shows that it doesn't damage other food constituents.

Although more mycotoxins are being discovered and characterized each year, it seems unlikely that we will ever again have to resort to pilgrimages to give us a vital respite from a mycotoxin-contaminated diet. We should remember, however, that many people in the underdeveloped countries are still at risk, as are wild and domesticated animals. Mycotoxins may play no direct role in the metabolism of the fungi that produce them, but in an situation where a fungus and an animal are competing for a grain of corn, mycotoxins may have evolved as powerful weapons that help the fungi to deter or destroy the competition.

Further Reading

Christensen, C.M. (1975) **Molds, Mushrooms and Mycotoxins**. University of Minnesota Press, Minneapolis.

Egmond, H.P. van (1988) Mycotoxins, sampling and chemical detection. pp. 250-261 (in) **Introduction to Food-borne Fungi**. 3rd Edn. (Eds.) R.A. Samson & E.S. van Reenen-Hoekstra. Centraalbureau voor Schimmelcultures, Baarn.

Howell, M.V. (1982) The detection and determination of mycotoxins in food and feedingstuffs. Journal of the Science of Food and Agriculture **33**: 590-591.

Krogh, P. (Ed.) (1988) **Mycotoxins in Food**. Academic Press, New York.

Marasas, W.O. and P.E. Nelson (1987) **Mycotoxicology**. Pennsylvania State University Press, University Park.

Mirocha, C.J., R.A. Pawlosky, K. Chatterjee, S. Watson and W. Hayes (1983) Analysis for *Fusarium* toxins in various samples implicated in biological warfare in Southeast Asia. Journal of the Association of Official Analytical Chemists **66**: 1485-1499.

Pringle, P. (1985) Political science. The Atlantic Monthly. Vol. **256** (4): 67-81.

Purchase, I.F.H. (Ed.) (1974) **Mycotoxins**. Elsevier, Amsterdam.

Rodicks, J.V., C.W. Hesseltine and M.A. Mehlman (1977) **Mycotoxins in Human and Animal Health**. Pathotox Publishers, Park Forest South, Illinois.

Samson, R.A., E.S. vann Reenen-Hoekstra (and 12 others) (1988) **Introduction to Food-borne Fungi**. 3rd Edn. Centraalbureau voor Schimmelcultures, Baarn.

Scott, P.M., H.L. Trenholm and M.D. Sutton (Eds.) (1985) **Mycotoxins: a Canadian Perspective**. National Research Council of Canada, Ottawa.

Stoloff, L., S. Nesheim, L. Yin, J.V. Rodricks, M. Stack and A.D. Campbell (1971) A multi-mycotoxin detection method for aflatoxins, ochratoxins, zearalenone, sterigmatocystin and patulin. Journal of the Association of Official Analytical Chemists **54**: 91-97.

Wylie, T.D. and L.G. Morehouse (Eds.) (1977-78) **Mycotoxic Fungi, Mycotoxins, Mycotoxicoses**. Vols. 1-3. Marcel Dekker, New York.

Chapter 22

Poisonous and Hallucinogenic Mushrooms

Introduction

A man is brought to the Emergency Department of a hospital suffering from diarrhea, abdominal cramps, nausea and vomiting. His problem is diagnosed as gastro-enteritis. He is given atropine, donnatal, and intravenous fluids to combat dehydration, then sent home. The vomiting and diarrhea go on for another 24 hours. By now he is severely dehydrated, and has to be admitted to hospital. Over the next two days, his liver, kidney and heart begin to fail. Despite treatment of his symptoms with a battery of antibiotics, corticosteroids, vitamins, stimulants and intravenous fluid, he dies.

This is a true story. The only thing I didn't tell you was that the man had eaten a meal of wild mushrooms about 12 hours before the onset of his symptoms. By the time you have read this chapter, you should be able to diagnose his illness correctly, and suggest treatments that might have saved his life.

People can conveniently be divided into two groups: those who love to eat wild mushrooms, and those who would never dream of doing such a thing. There doesn't seem to be any middle ground on this issue: you are either a 'picker' or a 'kicker.' This characteristic seems to be culturally determined. Most people of Anglo-Saxon origin are kickers, while those from Central and Eastern Europe are pickers. Picking is a pastime that occasionally gets them into trouble. There are about 10,000 different species of fleshy fungi. The vast majority are perfectly innocuous. A relatively small number are hunted for their delicious flavour, and a cooperative few have been domesticated (see chapter 18). But another few are deadly poisonous, and many others can cause more or less serious discomfort if they are unwittingly eaten. During the course of human history I would suspect that all 10,000 species of agarics have been eaten. This chapter considers what we have learned from the trying, tragic or transcendental experiences of those who made random or unconventional choices of mushroom for their free meal.

The main problem is one of identification. There is no simple rule or test that will tell whether a mushroom is edible or deadly poisonous. Many people are blissfully unaware of this, and rely on tests which are irrelevant and fallacious. They are playing Russian roulette. You should eat wild mushrooms only if you know, or can determine, their scientific names. If you are sure, from observation (some of it through the microscope), or experience, that all of a particular collection of fungi belongs to, say, *Cantharellus cibarius* (the chanterelle: Fig. 5.4 D), or *Morchella esculenta* (the morel: Fig. 22.1 C), and that the fruit bodies are young and freshly picked, experience tells us that you can eat and enjoy them, as **mycophagists** have done for thousands of years (though some people are allergic to mushrooms). Every year, many people take unnecessary chances by eating unfamiliar mushrooms, or confuse poisonous species with edible ones, and every year some unfortunates are fatally poisoned.

Since most North Americans are kickers, they tend not to become mushroom poisoning statistics. Europeans, however, are pickers, and have suffered as many as 100 fatalities in two weeks. In 1975, a Swiss newspaper reported 54 local deaths during a short period in late summer. Which fungi killed these people? What are the toxins involved? We recognize eight different kinds of mushroom poisoning, which are listed in Table 22.1. A quick look at this table will show that fatalities are usually caused only by groups I, II and III. In fact, 50% of all serious mushroom poisonings, and 95% of all fatalities, are caused by members of a single genus, *Amanita*, which fruits in late summer and fall.

Table 22.1 Mushroom Toxins and their Occurrence

Toxins	Fungi
I. Amanitins (cyclopeptides)	*Amanita* bisporigera, A. ocreata, A. phalloides, A. verna, A. virosa, etc.
	Galerina autumnalis, G. marginata, etc.;
	Lepiota spp.
	Conocybe filaris.
II. Gyromitrin, monomethylhydrazine	*Gyromitra* brunnea, G. caroliniana, G. esculenta, G. fastigiata, G. infula
	(?) *Helvella* elastica, (?) H. lacunosa;
	(?) *Paxina* spp.
	Sarcosphaera crassa.
III. Orellanine	*Cortinarius* orellanus, C. orellanoides, C. rainierensis.
IV. Muscarine	*Clitocybe* cerussata, C. dealbata, C. rivulosa, C. sudorifica
	Inocybe geophylla, I. lilacina, I. pudica.
V. Ibotenic acid, muscimol	*Amanita* cokeri, A. cothurnata, A. gemmata, A. muscaria, A. pantherina
	(?) *Panaeolus* campanulatus.
VI. Coprine	*Coprinus* atramentarius, (?) Coprinus spp.;
	Clitocybe clavipes.
VII. Psilocybin, psilocin	*Conocybe* cyanopus;
	Gymnopilus spectabilis, (?) Gymnopilus spp.;
	Panaeolus foenisecii, P. subbalteatus;
	Psilocybe cubensis, P. cyanescens, P. semilanceata, P. silvatica.

VIII. Gastrointestinal
irritants

Agaricus hondensis, A. placomyces;

Amanita brunnescens;

Boletus luridus, other blueing *Boletus* spp.;

Chlorophyllum molybdites;

Entoloma grande, E. lividum, E. sinuatum, E. strictius;

Hebeloma crustuliniforme;

Lactarius piperatus, L. rufus, L. uvidus, L. vellereus;

Marasmius urens;

Naematoloma fasciculare;

Omphalotus olearius;

Pholiota squarrosa;

Russula emetica;

Scleroderma aurantium;

Tricholoma pardinum; etc.

Group I — Amanitin Poisoning

As a result of many inadvertent, and often fatal, experiments made by hapless or foolhardy volunteers, we can say that the basidiomata of several species of the agaric genera *Amanita* and *Galerina* (Fig. 22.1 B) contain toxins that are lethal to humans in extremely small doses. *Amanita virosa* (the 'destroying angel': Fig. 22.1 A), *Amanita phalloides* (the 'death cap'), and closely related species are notorious killers. They contain such high levels of toxin that a single bite can be fatal to a debilitated individual. The toxin molecules are made up of amino-acids in a double ring, and so are called **cyclic oligopeptides** or **cyclopeptides**. They come in two varieties, known as **amatoxins** (amanitins), which contain 8 amino-acid molecules, and **phallotoxins** (phalloidins), which contain 7 amino-acid molecules. When injected into mice, the phallotoxins are ten times more lethal than cyanide: their LD_{50} is 2 mg/kg. But when taken by mouth, they have no effect. They may be neutralized or broken down by digestive juices, or may not be absorbed by the gut. In contrast, the much more deadly amatoxins are actively toxic when eaten (**$LD_{50} = 0.1$ mg/kg**).

Amatoxins rapidly damage intestine, kidney and liver. Alpha-amanitin attacks the nucleus of cells, binding to RNA-polymerase II, the enzyme that transcribes DNA and produces messenger RNA. The synthesis of RNA ceases, and so, as a direct consequence, does the synthesis of protein. This ultimately brings the machinery of the cell to a standstill, and it dies. Cells of the intestinal lining, liver and kidney have a rapid turnover, so their loss and non-replacement will soon have serious effects on the organism. This is bad news, but there is worse to come. We still have no specific antidote to these toxins. And worst of all, the outward symptoms of amatoxin poisoning do not begin until after a great deal of the cell damage has been done. This makes it one of the most difficult forms of poisoning to treat.

One important step in understanding what may be going on in a poisoning case is to ascertain whether the mushrooms in the case contain amatoxins. The **Meixner test** provides a simple way of doing this. Liquid is expressed from a

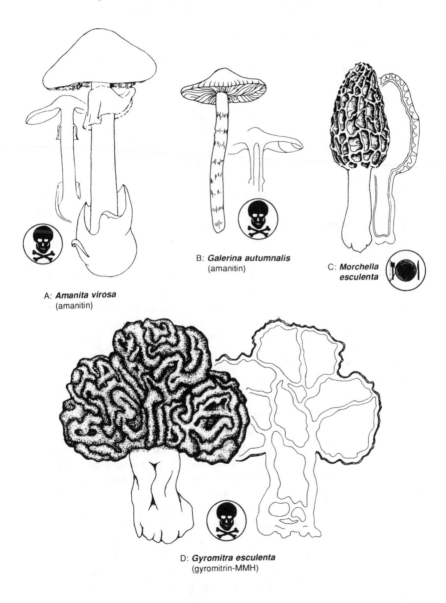

A: *Amanita virosa*
(amanitin)

B: *Galerina autumnalis*
(amanitin)

C: *Morchella esculenta*

D: *Gyromitra esculenta*
(gyromitrin-MMH)

Fig. 22.1 The deadly and the delicious.

piece of the fresh mushroom into a circle marked on a piece of newspaper, and allowed to dry (perhaps with a little help from a hair-dryer). A drop of concentrated hydrochloric acid is added to the dried spot. A blue colour, developing at any time over the next 20 minutes, indicates the presence of amatoxins. If the toxin is present in the agaric at high levels, the colour will probably develop in 1-2 minutes. Newsprint must be used, rather than high-quality paper, because the test is based on a reaction between amatoxin and lignin, which is catalyzed by the acid. A negative test does not prove that an agaric is edible.

The most poisonous mushroom in eastern North America is probably *Amanita virosa*. The large basidiomata of this innocent-looking species are pure white throughout, and have both ring and volva. In the West, the situation is complicated by the presence of *Amanita phalloides*, with a greenish cap, which is probably just as toxic as *A. virosa*. Those who have eaten these species report that they have a mild flavour. Subsequent events may be divided into four stages. (1) A latent period of 6-24 hours, most commonly about 12 hours. This asymptomatic interlude is long enough that the patient frequently does not even connect the subsequent illness with mushrooms. During this hiatus,the amanitin is attacking the cells of the liver, kidney and intestine. (2) Violent vomiting, diarrhea and abdominal pain, which last for a day or so. (3) A brief, misleading remission of symptoms. (4) Collapse of kidney and liver function, with secondary effects on the heart and brain, leading to coma and death.

What can be done for victims of amanitin poisoning? The biggest problem is the long delay in the appearance of overt symptoms. By the time the patient seeks medical aid, massive cell damage may already have been done. The first hurdle is to arrive at a correct diagnosis. *Amanita* poisoning is relatively rare in North America, and many doctors may not think of it unless the patient mentions mushrooms. Even then, most physicians (and this is no discredit to them) know virtually nothing about diagnosing mushrooms. No identifiable specimens may be available. With luck, the local mycologist will be called in, and will recognize the danger inherent in the delayed symptoms. Even if the problem is correctly diagnosed, there is currently no antidote for amanitin. Treatment consists of attempts to: (1) remove toxin from the system; (2) increase the rate at which the patient excretes it; (3) support the patient's various systems.

(1) **Removal of toxin**. If the condition is diagnosed within an hour or two, it is obviously appropriate to empty the stomach by emesis and gastric lavage (getting the patient to throw up, and then washing out the stomach). If the usual latent period has elapsed, this approach would be pointless. Three blood-cleansing techniques have been applied to late-diagnosed amanitin poisoning. (A) **Haemodialysis** (circulating the blood through a semipermeable membrane bathed in an isotonic medium) is used in long-term treatment of kidney failure, or until a transplant becomes available. Its use in *Amanita* poisoning is questionable, since it removes substances of molecular weight 300 or less. Amanitin itself has a molecular weight of 900, and it may often become complexed with much larger molecules, such as proteins. Nevertheless, in serious cases, where kidney failure threatens, haemodialysis may be useful under heading 3. (B)

Haemoperfusion (circulating the blood over activated charcoal) is used to support the detoxifying function of ailing livers. It has been used experimentally to treat *Amanita* poisoning in recent years, and has been shown to remove some toxin from amanitin-spiked blood.

Unfortunately, the amounts of amanitin detected in the blood of poisoning victims are usually very low, especially if more than 12 hours have elapsed since the mushrooms were eaten. Keeping in mind the possible unfavourable effect of haemoperfusion on a blood coagulatory pattern already unbalanced by the effects of the toxin, this technique should be applied with caution. It may, of course, be indicated if the effects of the toxin cause liver failure. (C) **Apheresis** (centrifuging the blood to segregate its major components—plasma, erythrocytes, leucocytes, platelets—then discarding and replacing the fraction containing the unwanted agent) is being increasingly used to treat many diseases of the immune system, and some kinds of poisoning. Again, the actual kinetics of amanitin in the body are not yet well-enough understood for us to be sure which blood fraction, if any, should be replaced. This technique may prove to be of value when the movements of amanitin in the body are better understood.

(2) **Increase excretion of toxin.** Although the body's natural excretion of amanitin is obviously not efficient enough to prevent cell damage, a new and sensitive radioimmunoassay for amanitin in body fluids has shown that the toxin is present in the urine of patients at far higher levels than can be found in their blood. This suggests that attempts to increase urine production by giving intravenous fluids, and an appropriate diuretic, might be helpful.

(3) **Supportive measures** involve careful monitoring of electrolyte and fluid balance, and blood sugar, with appropriate replacement therapy as required. Liver and kidney functions must be closely followed. If kidney and/or liver failure occurs, haemodialysis and/or haemoperfusion may be necessary. In addition, various researchers have suggested several other strategies to support the damaged liver or kidneys: intravenous infusion of B vitamins, vitamin K, Penicillin-G, corticosteroids, and thioctic acid (a coenzyme in the Krebs cycle). The therapeutic value of some of these agents has not been firmly established, but in a potentially fatal condition, the shotgun approach is worth trying.

The Bastien Treatment. A French physician, Dr. P. Bastien, has developed a new treatment for *Amanita* poisoning. It has three parts: (1) intravenous injections of 1 gram vitamin C twice a day; (2) two capsules of nifuroxazide three times a day; (3) two tablets of dihydrostreptomycin three times a day. The treatment is supplemented by measures to control fluid and electrolyte balance, and by penicillin. Bastien successfully treated 15 cases of *A. phalloides* poisoning between 1957 and 1969. In 1974 he ate 65 grams of *A. phalloides* and survived. In 1981 he ate 70 grams of *A. phalloides* and again successfully treated himself. It is reported that the Bastien treatment is now used throughout France, where it saves the lives of all those whose treatment has not been delayed until massive liver and kidney damage has occurred. This method should obviously be widely publicized and tested in North America.

As a fascinating biological footnote, I must mention that several myco-phagous species of *Drosophila* (the fruit fly genus) eat poisonous amanitas with impunity. It has been demonstrated that they can survive concentrations of amanitin hundreds of times greater than can their fruit-feeding relatives. They are, in fact, the most amanitin-tolerant species known. Although we do not know exactly how they deal with the toxin, we now know two things which may have driven the evolution of this tolerance. First, although the agarics in which mycophagous drosophilas breed are also sought out by crane flies and wood gnats, much larger insects, those competitors cannot survive in mushrooms that contain amanitin. Second, *Drosophila* larvae in amanitin-containing mush-rooms are never parasitized by the nematode, *Howardula*. This is an important selective advantage, because parasitized adults, which can represent up to 35% of the population, are often sterile or have reduced breeding success. There is an old saying: "It's an ill wind that blows nobody any good." It certainly seems that the presence of amanitin in some agarics is a real boon to *Drosophila*, if not to people.

Group II: Monomethylhydrazine Poisoning

The morel, *Morchella esculenta* (Fig. 22.1 C), is one of the finest edible fungi. A meal of morels, steak and good red wine is a truly memorable occasion. So the compound ascomata of this species are avidly hunted in spring. Fruiting at the same time, and looking similar to the untutored eye, is the false morel, *Gyromitra esculenta* (Fig. 22.1 D). This species is responsible for 2-4% of all fatal mushroom poisonings. Over a ten-year period in Poland, 100 people were hospitalized, and 6 died, as a result of eating *Gyromitra*. The toxin precursor in *G. esculenta* is called **gyromitrin**. When this is hydrolyzed, it becomes **monomethylhydrazine (MMH)**, which is used as a rocket fuel, and is, as researchers for the space program realized, extremely toxic. All species of *Gyromitra* are poisonous. Reports that those who ate the mushrooms were unaffected, while the cook became ill, were often discounted. But there is a rational explanation of these seemingly bizarre stories. The monomethylhy-drazine has a boiling point of 87.5°C, and its vapours are toxic. Certain cases in which some diners were unaffected, while others became very ill, were also difficult to explain until it was shown that there is a narrow margin between no effect and a lethal dose—an 'all-or-nothing' response. The same individual could eat *Gyromitra* several times without apparent effect, then on one occasion unwittingly exceed the limit and be poisoned. Symptoms of poisoning appear 2-12 hours (typically 6-8 hours) after the meal. An initial bloated feeling is followed by nausea, vomiting, diarrhea and abdominal cramps. Victims often experience faintness, loss of muscular control, and fever. In severe cases, jaundice and convulsions occur, and coma and death may ensue after 2-7 days.

The delay in the onset of symptoms gives a clue to the action of the toxin. As with the cyclopeptides, it is at the cellular level. It is haemolytic, toxic to the central nervous system, irritates the gastro-intestinal tract, and damages the liver. Methaemoglobin and free haemoglobin are present in the blood. Levels of bilirubin and liver enzymes rise, and blood sugar falls. Unless the toxic nature of the mushroom is diagnosed almost immediately after it has been eaten, there is little point in evacuating the gut. Pyridoxine hydrochloride should be administered as a specific physiological antagonist of MMH. The patient's blood sugar, liver and kidney function, and free haemoglobin level should be monitored. Intravenous glucose, forced diuresis if free haemoglobin rises, haemodialysis in severe cases, and other supportive measures, may be needed.

Group III: Orellanine Poisoning

In 1957 a report emerged from Poland of three outbreaks of mushroom poisoning caused by eating *Cortinarius orellanus*. Among 132 people poisoned, 19 died. Death was caused by kidney failure, and in most cases occurred two to three weeks after symptoms began (though some children died within a few days, and other deaths were delayed for months). The most unusual feature of this poisoning was the extremely delayed onset of symptoms. Even in severe and ultimately fatal cases, no symptoms were reported until 3-4 days after the mushrooms had been eaten. In milder cases, the latent period was longer, extending to 10-17 days.

Initial symptoms were an intense thirst, accompanied by burning and dryness of the mouth. Headache, chills, loin or abdominal pain, nausea and vomiting followed. Although urination was initially stimulated, it was soon reduced and in some cases ceased altogether. In serious cases, the BUN (blood urea nitrogen) rose, as might be expected following kidney damage.

Once this form of poisoning had been recognized and described, it was reported from France, Germany, Switzerland, and Czechoslovakia. No confirmed cases have been reported in North America. The nephrotoxin involved is called **orellanine**, and has been detected in another European species, *Cortinarius orellanoides*, as well as in the North American species, *Cortinarius rainierensis*. Orellanine has an oral LD_{50} (cat) of 4.9 mg/kg. It is estimated that 100-200 g of fresh *C. orellanus* contains enough orellanine to cause complete kidney failure. Although there do not appear to be any reports of kidney transplants in the literature, that procedure would now seem to be an appropriate response to total renal shutdown.

Group IV: Coprine (Antabuse-like) Poisoning

This kind of poisoning can occur at any time for up to 5 days after *Coprinus atramentarius* (Fig. 22.2 A) has been eaten. Strangely enough, the mushrooms by themselves are not toxic. Symptoms appear 30-60 minutes after the mushroom-eater has a drink containing **alcohol**: they include hot flushes of the face and neck, a metallic taste in the mouth, tingling sensations in the limbs, numbness in the hands, palpitations, a throbbing headache, nausea and vomiting. This is an unpleasant combination, but it isn't fatal. The only treatment necessary may be to control arrhythmia (irregular heartbeat). The syndrome will persist as long as there is any alcohol in the system—usually 2-4 hours—after which recovery is spontaneous, and the victim may well swear off booze.

The condition arises because *Coprinus atramentarius* contains **coprine**, a unique amino acid that blocks the metabolism of ethyl alcohol at the acetaldehyde stage. Coprine poisoning is really **acetaldehyde** poisoning. The rather excessive duration of this potential booby-trap for drinkers is due to the persistence of coprine in the body. **Antabuse** (disulfiram), which is prescribed to help alcoholics stay on the wagon, has an action almost identical to that of coprine, though the two substances are chemically different.

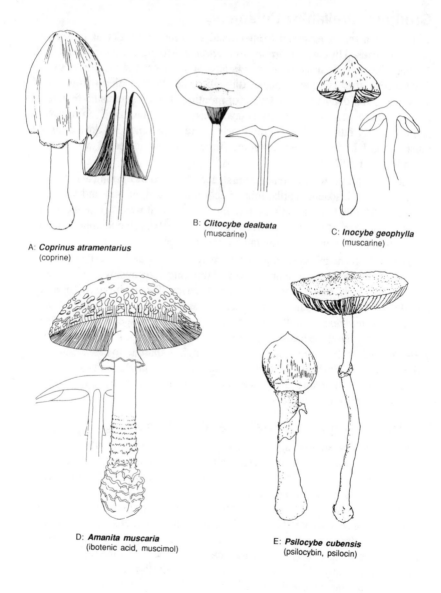

B: *Clitocybe dealbata*
(muscarine)

C: *Inocybe geophylla*
(muscarine)

A: *Coprinus atramentarius*
(coprine)

D: *Amanita muscaria*
(ibotenic acid, muscimol)

E: *Psilocybe cubensis*
(psilocybin, psilocin)

Fig. 22.2 Mushrooms that make you feel strange.

Group V: Muscarine Poisoning—PSL Syndrome

It is a good idea to avoid eating little white or brown mushrooms that grow in the grass, since some members of two common genera, *Clitocybe* (Fig. 22.2 B) and *Inocybe* (Fig. 22.2 C), contain significant amounts of **muscarine**. This is a toxin that, within 30 minutes to 2 hours of being consumed, stimulates the exocrine glands—the producers of sweat, saliva and tears—in what is called the 'PSL' syndrome (**perspiration, salivation, lachrymation**), and also causes constriction of the pupils, blurred vision, muscle spasms, diarrhea, slow heartbeat, and a drop in blood pressure. The only real danger here is that the heart may actually stop, if enough toxin has been absorbed. This has happened only rarely, and then in patients with existing cardiovascular disease. The appropriate treatment is carefully administered intravenous **atropine**.

Group VI: Ibotenic Acid-Muscimol Poisoning

Earlier in this chapter I described what happens when someone eats the deadly species of *Amanita*, those containing amatoxins. But other species of *Amanita* produce very different effects. *Amanita muscaria* (Fig. 22.2 D), the famous scarlet-capped, white-spotted mushroom so beloved of fairy-tale illustrators, is one of these. It induces muscle spasms, dizziness (and vomiting, if too many mushrooms have been eaten), then a deep sleep full of fantastic dreams, lasting about 2 hours. On waking, the subject usually experiences a 'good trip': a feeling of elation that persists for several hours. People often become hyperactive, making compulsive and uncoordinated movements, perhaps talking non-stop, and having altered perceptions of reality. Occasionally the experience is a 'downer.' Clearly, *Amanita muscaria* contains a substance that specifically affects the central nervous system. Needless to say, this was discovered long ago, and has been exploited by various peoples. The Soma hymns of the 3,000-year-old sacred Indian book, the Rig Veda, have been interpreted as a glorification of *A. muscaria* and its effects. Many tribes in Siberia used it for centuries as a religious or recreational intoxicant, and although it has now largely been replaced by vodka, some Siberians still prefer mushrooms.

Historical accounts suggest that the active principle is not destroyed in the body, but is excreted unaltered in the urine. Probably by watching their reindeer, which have a fondness for urine, the Siberians learned that the inebriant could be recycled. When mushrooms were in short supply, and only the richer tribesmen could afford them, the poor folk waited for the guests to relieve themselves, then drank the intoxicating liquid. Clearly, the motivation was very strong.

Although fresh mushrooms contain **ibotenic acid**, which has some effect on the nervous system, dried mushrooms have been found to be much more potent. This is because ibotenic acid degrades to **muscimol** on drying. Muscimol is 5-10 times more psychoactive than ibotenic acid. Dried mushrooms retain their potency for 5-10 years. Although very few deaths have been reported from this kind of poisoning, 10 or more mushrooms can constitute a fatal dose.

In most cases, the best treatment is no treatment. Recovery is spontaneous and complete within 24 hours. If many mushrooms have been eaten, severe convulsions may have to be controlled, and the stomach should be emptied. On no account should atropine be given: it will exacerbate the symptoms.

Group VII: Psilocybin-Psilocin 'Poisoning'

'Teonanacatl'—'the flesh of the Gods.' This is how the Aztecs of Mexico described the sacred mushrooms which have been used for thousands of years in Central America for religious rites of divining and curing. The practice was suppressed by the 'Christian' Spanish Conquistadors, and the secret of Teonana-catl was lost to the outside world until the twentieth century. The story of its rediscovery is a mycological classic. After penetrating the wall of silence with which the people of Oaxaca protected their shamanic ceremonies, two Americans were eventually allowed to participate, and to partake of the sacred mushrooms. After eating the mushrooms, they waited with their hosts, in the dark. The two visitors vomited. Again they waited. Nothing happened. Then one whispered to the other 'I'm seeing things.' 'That's all right,' said the other, 'so am I.' One of them later described the visions as being 'in colour...kaleido-scopic...they were angular and they would go fast or slow, responding to my wishes...I had delightful feelings...euphoria, peaceful feelings. The effects lasted about 4 1/2 hours. Then imperceptibly we all...fell asleep on the ground.'

After many similar experiences, the same author wrote: 'The sacred mush-rooms of Mexico seize hold of you with irresistible power. They lead to a temporary (state)...in which your body lies, heavy as lead, on the mat, and you take notes and compare experiences with your neighbour, while your soul flies off to the ends of the world and, indeed, to other planes of existence...some seem to experience only a divine euphoria, which may translate itself into uncontrollable laughter...I experienced hallucinations...visions of palaces, gardens, seascapes, and mountains.... With the speed of thought you are translated wherever you desire to be, and you are there, a disembodied eye, poised in space, seeing, not seen, invisible, incorporeal. I have placed stress on the visual hallucinations, but all the senses are equally affected, and the human organism as a whole is lifted to a plane of intense experience. (Everyday experiences are) transformed, leaving you breathless with wonder and delight. The emotions and intellect are similarly stepped up. Your whole being is aquiver with life.'

Experiences like these can be triggered by members of four agaric genera: *Psilocybe* (Fig. 22.2 E), *Panaeolus*, *Conocybe*, and *Gymnopilus*. The Mexican rites usually employ one of several *Psilocybe* species, particularly *P. caerules-cens*, *P. zapotecorum* and *P. mexicana*. In the United States, and in coastal areas of British Columbia, devotees of 'magic mushrooms' often collect hallucino-genic species of *Panaeolus* and *Conocybe*. *Psilocybe* species are often culti-vated, since spore prints of, for example, *Psilocybe cubensis* (Fig. 22.2 E) can be ordered by mail, and people in the Pacific Northwest avidly hunt for *Psilocybe semilanceata* and *P. pelliculosa*, the fabled 'liberty caps.' The psychoac-tive principles in these agarics are indole alkaloids called **psilocybin** and

psilocin, hydroxyltryptamine derivatives related to the neurotransmitter, serotonin. An average effective dose of psilocybin is 4-8 mg, the amount contained in about 2 g of dried mushrooms. If larger quantities of mushrooms are eaten, the hallucinogenic effects may be rather overwhelming, but serious poisoning is unlikely unless huge numbers of mushrooms are consumed. Adults on 'bad trips' may become extremely anxious or even paranoid, and may need considerable reassurance or, more rarely, tranquilizers. Children who eat hallucinogenic mushrooms may develop a high fever or convulsions. They should **not** be given aspirin. Tepid baths or wet sheets should be used. Hallucinations may be suppressed by chlorpromazine, and convulsions by diazepam.

Group VIII : Gastro-Intestinal Irritants

The seven kinds of poisoning already described are now fairly well understood. Most of the relatively few fungi involved are clearly identified as containing specific toxins which cause well-defined sets of symptoms. In contrast, the seventh kind of poisoning is caused by a grab-bag of fleshy fungi belonging to many different genera. They have only one thing in common: within 30-90 minutes of being eaten, all cause various degrees of digestive upset. The commonest symptoms are vomiting and diarrhea, with abdominal cramps. Fortunately, the similarity to amanitin poisoning ends there. Symptoms generally clear up spontaneously in 3-4 hours, and complete recovery takes only a day or so.

Little or nothing is known about the toxins involved, though the diversity of fungi causing these symptoms suggests that a number of different substances may eventually be implicated. Digestive disturbances can be caused by various members of the following genera: *Agaricus, Amanita, Boletus, Chlorophyllum, Entoloma, Hebeloma, Lactarius, Marasmius, Naematoloma, Omphalotus, Pholiota, Russula, Scleroderma, Tricholoma*, and possibly many others. Since we don't know what chemicals are causing the problem, treatment is restricted to emptying the stomach and, in elderly or debilitated patients, monitoring for dehydration, reduced blood pressure or impaired kidney function. Occasional fatalities have been caused by almost all of these fungi.

If we look back on the various kinds of poisoning examined in this chapter, and try to analyze the mechanisms involved, we can discern four basic patterns:

(1) Toxins that cause extensive cell destruction, but which produce overt symptoms only after a significant, and potentially fatal, delay (amanitin, orellanine, monomethylhydrazine).

(2) Toxins that act on the autonomic nervous system, causing symptoms either as soon as they have been absorbed, or whenever the appropriate substrate enters the system (muscarine, coprine).

(3) Toxins that act on the central nervous system, causing symptoms as soon as they have been absorbed (muscimol, psilocybin).

(4) Undetermined toxins that act on the alimentary canal, causing symptoms as soon as they have been absorbed.

Perhaps it is worthwhile, after that rather alarming litany of toxic effects, to suggest again that unless you are a mushroom expert, you should either refrain from eating wild mushrooms altogether, or stick to a few species whose characteristics you have learned in great detail. In addition to checking your fungi in the 'Audubon Society Field Guide to North American Mushrooms' by Lincoff 'Mushrooms Demystified' by Arora, or 'Mushrooms of North America' by Phillips, I recommend 'Funghi Velenosi' by Azzaretti et al., which has excellent colour pictures of most of the really dangerous species. In any case, if someone you know should be unfortunate enough to be poisoned by mushrooms, you will now be in a position to offer some practical advice, even to the medical profession.

Further Reading

Azzaretti, G., R. Galli, A. Bernini and F. Polani (1983) **Funghi Velenosi**. Edizioni La Tipotecnica, Milan.

Bastien, P. (1985) J'ai dû manger des Amanites mortelles. Flammarion, Paris.

Bauchet, J.M. (1983) Treatment of *Amanita phalloides* poisoning — the Bastien method. Bulletin of the British Mycological Society **17** (2): 110-111.

Faulstich, H., B. Kommerell and T. Wieland (1980) **Amanita Toxins and Poisoning**. Gerhard Witzstrock, Baden-Baden.

Jaenike, J. (1987) Of toxic mushrooms, flies, and worms. McIlvainea **8** (1): 32-34.

Lampe, K.F. (1991) Human poisoning by mushrooms of the genus *Cortinarius* pp. 497-521 (in) **Toxicology of Plant and Fungal Compounds**. (Eds.) R.S. Keeler & A.T. Tu. Marcel Dekker, New York.

Lincoff, G. and D.H. Mitchel (1977) **Toxic and Hallucinogenic Mushroom Poisoning**. Van Nostrand Reinhold, New York.

Litten, W. (1975) The most poisonous mushrooms. Scientific American **231**: 90-101.

Meixner, A. (1979) Amatoxin-Nachweis in Pilzen. Zeitschrift für Mykologie. **45**: 137-139.

Chapter 23

Medical Mycology

Introduction

Three rather different groups of fungi actually cause specific diseases. A few obligately parasitic fungi (dermatophytes) have evolved specifically to attack the outer surface of human beings. A few other fungi which cause disease in people are normally soil organisms, but have also adapted to life in the unusual and rather hostile environment of the human body, often responding to this environment by developing a different morphology (thermal dimorphic saprobes). A third group of opportunistic saprobes can attack us only when our defences are down—when our immune systems themselves are diseased or deficient, or when we artificially suppress them, as we must to prevent the rejection of transplanted organs.

We can divide fungal attacks on our persons into: (1) **cutaneous** infections, which involve the outer layers of the skin and cause an allergic or inflammatory response; (2) **subcutaneous** infections, usually involving fungi of low inherent virulence which have been introduced to the tissues through a wound of some kind, and which remain localized or spread only by direct mycelial growth; and (3) **systemic** infections, which are caused, either by true pathogenic fungi which can establish themselves in normal hosts, or by opportunistic saprobic fungi which could not infect a healthy host, but can attack individuals whose immune system is not working. Both kinds of fungi sometimes become widely disseminated through the body of the host.

Cutaneous Infections

Most cutaneous mycoses are caused by a specialized group of keratinolytic fungi called the **dermatophytes**, of which you have already learned something. There are about 40 species of dermatophytic hyphomycetes, placed in 3 genera. *Epidermophyton* has 2 species, *Microsporum* (Fig. 4.8 C) has 17, and *Trichophyton* has 24 species and varieties. Eight species of *Trichophyton* have teleomorphs in *Arthroderma*, and nine species of *Microsporum* have teleomorphs in *Nannizzia*. These teleomorphic genera are both members of the family Arthrodermataceae (Ascomycetes, Onygenales).

About half of the dermatophytes are found only on people, causing diseases commonly called **tinea** or, more colloquially, **ringworm**. These have no reservoir of infection in the soil or on animals: they can grow only on humans, although their arthric conidia can survive in carpets and upholstery for up to two years. Many of the rest are usually isolated from other mammals. *Microsporum canis* has its reservoir in the cat. It may move to dogs or humans, but will die out after one or two person to person transfers. If it is to survive, it must return to the cat for rejuvenation. About 5 species are recorded from both man and animals. The irritation caused by the presence of the fungus stimulates the epithelial cells of the host to divide more often than usual. This increases the amount of keratin available to the fungus, and also means that more flakes of skin containing infective mycelium will be shed. *Epidermophyton floccosum* causes transient infections, and relies on this exfoliated material for quick spread to other hosts. *Trichophyton rubrum* tends to cause chronic infections of the foot and toenails, so the host produces infective material over a period of years. Almost everyone is susceptible to short-term infection by *Epidermophyton floccosum*, but a chronic *Trichophyton rubrum* infection of one marriage partner may never be transmitted to the other. *Trichophyton concentricum* causes a chronic ringworm of the body in Polynesians, (tinea imbricata, tokelau) but is never transmitted to caucasians or blacks living in the same communities. *Trichophyton rubrum* can attack any part of the skin, but *Microsporum audouinii* and *Trichophyton tonsurans* are found mainly on the head (tinea capitis), and *Epidermophyton floccosum* usually infects the feet (tinea pedis, athlete's foot) or the groin (tinea cruris, jock itch). It must be emphasized that these fungi are not growing on living tissue. Their clinical effects are due to the various irritants they produce; enzymes such as proteases, peptidases and elastases, and other metabolites. The condition is really a form of toxic dermatitis.

The yeast, *Candida albicans* (Fig. 6.2 C), is a normal component of the gut microbiota, but excessive wetness, or very tight clothing, can trigger rapid overgrowth of skin by this fungus. It can cause diaper rash, infections around fingernails, in armpits and crotch, and under breasts. Mucous membranes are particularly susceptible to inflammation by the toxins of this fungus: oral candidiasis (thrush) is common in the newborn, arising when the normal flora of lactobacilli doesn't develop quickly enough. Pregnant women produce vaginal secretions with altered levels of glycogen. This encourages the growth of *Candida*, and vaginal candidiasis is common in pregnant women. Their husbands sometimes contract candida balanitis, a nasty infection of the penis, though this may also be a consequence of diabetes. If cutaneous candidiasis becomes chronic, it may be a sign of various abnormalities of the thymus, of the thyroid, of white blood cells (leucocytes), etc.

Subcutaneous Infections

This category includes such diseases as **chromoblastomycosis, entomophthoromycosis, mycetoma** and **sporotrichosis**. These are caused by fungi that are normally saprobic, but which, when introduced to wounds, can adapt to growth in man, often changing their morphology or physiology in the process. **Chromoblastomycosis** (verrucous dermatitis) is common throughout the tropics among people who go barefoot. The disease-causing agent is one of three soil hyphomycetes (*Phialophora verrucosa, Cladosporium carrioni*, or *Fonsecaea pedrosoi*) which is 'inoculated' by a thorn or a sliver. When the fungus starts to grow, the host cells respond by dividing rapidly, and produce unsightly, stalked, warty growths on the feet or legs. The fungus may spread through the lymphatic system.

Entomophthoromycosis is a clumsy word, but tells us that the disease is caused by a member of the order Entomophthorales (Zygomycota). *Basidiobolus ranarum* usually lives in rotting vegetation and in the guts of amphibia and reptiles. It may be introduced to the human body by insect bites, and causes the formation of a subcutaneous tumour that grows steadily and may involve a whole limb, or the chest or shoulder.

Mycotic mycetoma is another disease of barefoot tropical peoples. Again, the fungal agent enters the body through a wound. The fungus attacks various tissues and stimulates the formation of a tumour, within which are many compact fungal colonies called grains. If the surface of the skin eventually ruptures, some of these colonies may be extruded. They have been found to belong to fungi such as *Madurella mycetomatis* (Hyphomycetes), *Exophiala jeanselmei* (Hyphomycetes), *Pseudallescheria boydii* (Ascomycetes) and *Leptosphaeria senegalensis* (Ascomycetes).

Sporotrichosis is caused by *Sporothrix schenckii*, a cosmopolitan hyphomycete which may be an anamorph of *Ophiostoma*. The fungus enters the host through a wound made, for example, by a contaminated thorn. Once inside the host, the normally mycelial fungus becomes yeast-like (it is therefore dimorphic, but not related to the other dimorphic fungi discussed elsewhere in this chapter). The initial, localized infection may ulcerate, drain and heal. But all is not well. The infection spreads through the lymphatic system, and many secondary lesions may form. Eventually, the disease may become systemic, spreading first to the joints, then the bones, and finally the internal organs, through the bloodstream.

Systemic Mycoses

As I pointed out above, these diseases are of two very different types: those produced by specialized pathogens, and those caused by opportunistic saprobes. There are four true pathogens, all of which are **dimorphic**—this means they have one kind of morphology outside the host, another inside the host. Three of these diseases are extremely common in North America, and the fourth in South America. In the first three mentioned below, the causative fungi are readily isolated from soil. Although these and other mycoses occasionally have horrifying effects on the human body, I am not going to gross you out with pictures. If you really must know how bad things can get, there are many pathetic photographs in the main references listed at the end of this chapter.

Dimorphic Pathogens

(1) **Histoplasmosis**, commonly abbreviated to 'histo,' is caused by the *Histoplasma capsulatum* anamorph of *Ajellomyces capsulatus* (Ascomycetes). This anamorph grows well in high-nitrogen substrates like wild bird droppings, chicken manure and bat guano. Anyone who disturbs such deposits, or spends much time around them, is likely to become infected. Conidia of the fungus are

inhaled and cause primary infections in the lungs. About 95% of all cases produce no obvious clinical symptoms, and heal spontaneously, leaving the subject with only a small calcified lesion in the lung, and resistance to reinfection. In the other 5%, various clinical symptoms develop. The inhaled conidia assume a yeast-like form, and become parasitic within histiocytes (phagocytic host cells). At first 'flu-like, the disease may go on to produce a progressive lung disease that mimics tuberculosis. If untreated, it may even develop into a generalized, systemic infection which can attack all internal organs, ultimately with fatal results. Histoplasmosis is endemic in the Mississippi and Ohio Valleys of the U.S.A., where about 40 million people have had the disease (most of them without knowing it). It attacks males more commonly than females.

(2) **Coccidioidomycosis** is a nasty tongue-twister of a name, often contracted to 'coccy', for the disease caused by *Coccidioides immitis*. This fungus thrives in dry, saline soils, and is endemic in desert areas of the Southwestern U.S., where the disease is often called 'valley fever,' and Mexico (though it is strangely absent from the deserts of Africa and Asia). The process of infection, progress of the disease, and clinical symptoms, are very similar to those of histoplasmosis, though the fungus is not intracellular, and forms spherical structures containing spores. In culture, the same fungus produces chains of alternate thallic-arthric conidia, and has no known teleomorph. Millions of people in the U.S. Southwest have contracted the disease. Fortunately, as in histoplasmosis, most cases are benign, and healing is spontaneous. A few become systemic, and are usually fatal if untreated or misdiagnosed. The disseminated form of this disease is commoner among males than females, and among people with darkly pigmented skin.

(3) **Paracoccidioidomycosis** is a disease exclusive to Central and South America. It is caused by *Paracoccidioides brasiliensis*, which seems to occur mainly in tropical mountain forests. Inhalation of conidia causes a primary infection in the lungs. However, as with the other two diseases just discussed, though infection is common in endemic areas, serious disease is rare. When secondary infections do occur, they tend to provoke ulceration of the mucosa of mouth and nose, often causing loss of teeth. Less commonly, the pulmonary infection progresses, mimicking tuberculosis, and sometimes eventually involves other internal organs. In the host, the fungus occurs as large, multipolar budding yeast cells (cf. Fig. 6.1 A), while in culture it is a mycelial, *Chrysosporium*-like anamorph (cf. Fig. 4.20) . The teleomorph, if one exists, has not been discovered.

(4) **Blastomycosis** is caused by *Blastomyces dermatitidis*, a fungus rarely isolated in culture from soil or other natural substrates. However, the disease is endemic to several areas, including the Eastern U.S. and Canada. Infection often seems to be a result of disturbing plant debris. Again, the primary infection is in the lungs, forming large granulomas that contain many tiny abscesses. These lesions may heal, but the organism then crops up in another area, frequently the exposed parts of the face and neck. Warty, thickened patches develop, which spread widely and cause extensive scarring and destruction of tissue. Internally,

bones may become involved. Eventually other organs, especially the prostate and the brain, are attacked. *Blastomyces* is seen as a yeast cell in host tissue, but forms a *Chrysosporium*-like anamorph in culture, converting to a yeast-like form at 37°C. Mating of compatible strains produces the teleomorph, *Ajellomyces dermatitidis* (Ascomycetes).

Opportunistic Pathogens

Opportunistic infections are caused by diverse fungi—a few species of *Aspergillus*, *Candida*, *Cryptococcus*, and some members of the Mucorales. All grow well at body temperature, but do not otherwise seem particularly different from closely related non-pathogenic species. None of them can usually cause an infection in a normal, healthy individual. All rely on some breakdown in the mechanisms of resistance. This kind of systemic fungal infection is often a complication of diabetes, AIDS, advanced cancer, or is a sequel of steroid or antibiotic therapy.

Candidiasis (also called candidosis). The causal organism is *Candida albicans*. In children, oral candidiasis that becomes chronic, and spreads down the oesophagus, is probably a sign of genetic defects or multiple endocrine deficiencies. In adults, alimentary candidiasis may be associated with diabetes, AIDS, steroid or antibiotic therapy, cancer, blood disease, endocrine deficiencies, or other debilitating conditions. In leukemic patients, candidiasis may become truly systemic, or may produce a form of septicaemia. Either way, it can ultimately be fatal. This condition may also be produced by repeated entry of the fungus with injections self-administered by drug addicts, or as a sequel of long-term antibiotic or steroid therapy, or indwelling catheters. *Candida* septicaemia may also arise as a result of parenteral hyperalimentation (feeding by continuous direct injection of fluids, often undertaken during treatment of severe gastrointestinal disease). If patients remain on hyperalimentation for more than 20 days, more than half of them develop *Candida* septicaemia. Fortunately, in patients with intact immune responses, the infection often clears up if the needle is removed.

Zygomycosis is caused by several opportunistic members of the Mucorales (Zygomycota). *Rhizopus arrhizus* and *Rhizopus oryzae* are most commonly involved, but species of *Mucor*, *Rhizomucor* and *Absidia* have also been reported. Four kinds of systemic disease occur: rhinocerebral, thoracic, gastro-intestinal, and cutaneous. Rhinocerebral zygomycosis attacks acidotic diabetics (who have high blood sugar, high ketone levels, and usually some leucocyte dysfunction). The infection begins in the sinuses, then grows with dramatic rapidity outward to the eyes and inward to the brain. The eyes bulge and may become paralysed, the eyelids droop, and there is often some degree of facial paralysis. The disease usually progresses with devastating rapidity, and is often fatal within 7 days.

Thoracic zygomycosis strikes people with leukemia or lymphoma, and occasionally also diabetics, transplant patients undergoing steroid therapy, or patients on dialysis. The symptoms are those of bronchitis and pneumonia, with complications like thrombosis or infarction, caused by direct invasion of blood vessels by the fungus. This disease is also fatal if untreated.

Gastrointestinal zygomycosis almost always occurs in Third-World countries, attacking children who are already suffering from Kwashiorkor (chronic protein deficiency). The causal agent, *Absidia corymbifera* (Zygomycetes), invades the walls of the stomach and intestine, blocking the arteries. The resulting necrosis and perforations are fatal. Cutaneous zygomycosis occurs when zygomycetous fungi colonize burns. In a severely burned, and therefore extremely debilitated, patient, the infection may spread rapidly and be quickly fatal.

Cryptococcosis is caused by an encapsulated, budding basidiomycetous yeast, *Cryptococcus neoformans*, the anamorph of *Filobasidiella neoformans* (Aphyllophorales). The anamorph commonly grows on pigeon droppings, so everyone is exposed to the propagules of the fungus. Many people contract sub-clinical or asymptomatic cryptococcosis which resolves spontaneously. An unfortunate minority, often already suffering from leukemia or lymphoma, or on immunosuppressive therapy following organ transplants, develop lung disease which may then become systemic. This phase involves bones, or organs such as heart, testicle, prostate or eye, and is often fatal. A second form of the disease is cryptococcal meningitis. Patients complain of increasingly severe headaches, which eventually escalate into meningitis. Untreated cryptococcal meningitis is always fatal.

Aspergillosis. Although species of *Aspergillus* (Hyphomycetes) cause other health problems, such as acute and chronic aflatoxin poisoning, we are concerned here only with diseases caused by the growth of the fungus itself somewhere in the body. (1) Bronchopulmonary aspergillosis is usually caused by *Aspergillus fumigatus*, which colonizes mucus within the bronchi, evoking a severe allergic reaction. (2) In Aspergilloma, the fungus forms a mycelial ball in a lung cavity produced by an earlier attack of tuberculosis. The wall of the cavity may erode, causing the patient to spit blood, and necessitating surgical intervention. (3) Invasive aspergillosis is found only in patients who are severely debilitated, or are immunosuppressed, as in AIDS. The fungus grows outward from the lung, invading blood vessels and spreading to other organs through the bloodstream. This insidious disease is usually fatal, and is often diagnosed only when an autopsy is performed.

Since the rise in the number of immunocompromised patients, those suffering from cancer and AIDS, as well as those with transplanted organs, new groups of opportunistic fungi have been observed. **Phaeohyphomycosis** is the general term for such diseases produced by about 40 darkly pigmented conidial fungi. **Hyalohyphomycosis** is a general term for opportunistic infections caused by about a dozen non-pigmented conidial fungi. *Fusarium* is one of the commonest among these.

AIDS and Mycoses

Since the searing advent of AIDS—Acquired Immune Deficiency Syndrome —to our societal consciousness, medical mycologists have become aware that many AIDS patients suffer from a variety of mycoses. Patients who developed certain opportunistic mycoses in the absence of any obvious predisposing factors were automatically investigated to see whether they also had AIDS. The "diagnostic" mycoses included Aspergillosis, Candidiasis, Cryptococcosis, and Zygomycosis. Oesophageal candidiasis and cryptococcosis of the central nervous system were regarded as being particularly strong indicators of AIDS. Candidiasis of mucous membranes is seen in two-thirds of AIDS patients. Cryptococcosis is found in 6-10% of AIDS patients in North America, but in one-third of patients in Zaire. The dermatophytes, *Trichophyton rubrum* and *T. interdigitale*, also cause more protracted and more severe infections in AIDS patients.

Treatment of Mycoses

Although **potassium iodide** (KI) has been used successfully in the treatment of sporotrichosis since 1903, there were no really effective drugs to combat most other fungal diseases. Until fairly recently, several of these diseases, such as blastomycosis, mucormycosis, and disseminated forms of histoplasmosis, coccidioidomycosis, cryptococcosis, candidiasis, and aspergillosis, were almost always fatal. Antibacterial antibiotics usually had little or no effect on fungi, and might actually make things worse by knocking out the competition. Fortunately, a number of effective antifungal antibiotics are now available (though they are not without side effects). Most important until very recently were two **polyene antibiotics** produced by *Streptomyces* spp. The first, **Nystatin**, introduced in 1950, is an effective treatment for superficial and oesophageal candidiasis. Drs. Brown and Hazen, the two women scientists who discovered this antibiotic, philanthropically gave their profits to establish a foundation that finances research in medical mycology.

The second polyene antibiotic, **Amphotericin B** (Fungizone), which became available in 1957, represented a major breakthrough. It is effective against most of the potentially fatal deep-seated mycoses when administered intravenously. But it is a very toxic substance with many side-effects: patients often need secondary treatment to cope with the attendant nausea, phlebitis (inflammation of major blood vessels), headaches and impairment of kidney function. This drug should be given only to patients whose condition is potentially fatal. Although Amphotericin B usually works, some resistant strains of fungi, especially *Aspergillus flavus*, have been encountered, and one of my colleagues has had the truly terrible experience of watching a 14-year-old die slowly as his brain was slowly destroyed by this fungus. **Miconazole** (Monistat) is also used intravenously to treat several of the major systemic fungal infections, but it, too, has unpleasant side-effects, especially nausea and phlebitis. Cryptococcosis is now treated with a combination of **5-fluorocytosine** and Amphotericin B. Another antibiotic, **Griseofulvin**, derived from *Penicillium griseofulvum* (Hyphomycetes), is useful in oral doses of up to 1 g per day for treating dermatophyte infections. Newer, topical treatments for athlete's foot and ringworm are **Tolnaftate** (Tinactin), **Canesten** (Clotrimazole), haloprogin, miconazole nitrate, iodochlorhydroxyquin, thiabendazole, or glutaraldehyde. Topical and systemic treatments are often used in parallel for stubborn cases. In 1981, a new antifungal antibiotic, **Ketoconazole** (Nizoral), became available. But although it can cure severe cases of some systemic mycoses, it should be used only in extreme cases, because it has severe side-effects: adrenal suppression in both sexes, and aspermia and impotence in males.

Perhaps I should conclude this chapter by telling you not to worry too much after reading it. Although coccy, histo and blastomycosis are endemic in many areas of North America, most people will never contract a serious mycosis. You are far more likely to come to grief crossing the road, riding your bicycle, or cooking dinner. But you will most probably be infected several times during your life by dermatophytes.

Further Reading

Ainsworth, G.C. and P.K.C. Austwick (1973) **Fungal Diseases of Animals**. 2nd Edn. Commonwealth Agricultural Bureaux, Slough.

Campbell, C.K. and G.C. White (1989) Fungal infection in AIDS patients. The Mycologist 3(1): 7-9.

Delacretaz, J., D. Grigoriu and G. Ducel (1976) **Color Atlas of Medical Mycology**. Hans Huber, Bern.

Emmons, C.W., C.H. Binford, J.P. Utz and K.J. Kwon-Chung (1977) **Medical Mycology**. Lea and Febiger, Philadelphia.

Rippon, J.W. (1988) **Medical Mycology**. 3rd Edn. Saunders, Philadelphia.

Speller, D.C.E. (1980) **Antifungal Chemotherapy**. Wiley, New York.

Vanden Bossche, H., D.W.R. Mackenzie and G. Cauwenbergh (1987) *Aspergillus* **and Aspergillosis**. Plenum, New York.

Sources of Illustrations

Frontispiece: after C. & D. Hughes, National Geographic, January 1983/ Fig. 1.1 after Margulis & Guerrero 1991/ Fig. 2.1 after Koevenig in Alexopoulos 1962/ Fig. 2.2 after Golder in Margulis & Schwartz 1988/ Fig. 2.3 after Golder in Margulis & Schwartz 1988/ Fig. 2.4 after Meszoly in Margulis & Schwartz 1988/ Fig. 2.5 A after Cooney, Barr & Barstow 1985; B-E after Barr 1991/ Fig. 2.6A: after Barr pers. comm.; B: after Webster 1980; C: after Karling 1977; D: after Sparrow 1960 and Whisler 1978/ Fig. 2.7 after Webster 1980 and Fuller 1978/ Fig. 2.8A,B: after Webster 1980; C: after Mueller & Loeffler 1976; D: after Hughes 1971 and Webster 1980/ Fig. 2.9B: after Smith 1938/ Fig. 2.10 after Alexopoulos 1962/ Fig. 2.11 after Alexopoulos 1962/ Fig. 2.12 after Alexopoulos 1962/ Fig. 3.1: after Ingold 1973/ Fig. 3.2: after Hawksworth, Sutton & Ainsworth 1983/ Fig. 3.3A-D: after O'Donnell 1978/ Fig. 3.4B: after Webster 1980/ Fig. 3.5A: after Webster 1980; B: after O'Donnell 1979; C: after Benjamin 1958; D: after Benjamin 1959/ Fig. 3.6A: after Jensen 1969; B,C: after Buller 1934; D,F: after Webster 1970; E: after Rees 1932/ Fig. 4.2: after Corner 1929/ Fig. 4.5A-D: after Cole & Samson 1979/ Fig. 4.7A-C: after Cole & Samson 1979/ Fig. 4.8A-C: after Cole & Samson 1979, Carmichael 1971 and Matsushima 1971/ Fig. 4.9A: after Smith 1938; B: after Webster 1979/ Fig. 4.12: after Mueller & Loeffler 1976/ Fig. 4.13A: after Scagel, Bandoni et al. 1969; B: after Ames 1961; D: after Berlese 1905/ Fig. 4.14A-E: after Webster 1980/ Fig. 4.15 from Samuels & Rossman 1979/ Fig. 4.16: after Pirozynski/ Fig. 4.17J-O: after DiCosmo, Nag Raj & Kendrick 1984/ Fig. 4.18B,C: after Smith 1938; D,F after Tulasne & Tulasne 1865/ Fig. 4.19B: after Tulasne 1865; E: after Royle 1978/ Fig. 4.20: from Currah 1984/ Fig. 4.22: after Thaxter 1896/ Fig. 4.23: after Pirozynski 1967 & Mueller & von Arx 1962/ Fig. 5.1C: after Bracker & Butler 1963; D: after Butler & Bracker 1970/ Fig. 5.2: after Gaeumann & Dodge 1928/ Fig. 5.3B: after Oberwinkler 1982/ Fig. 5.4A: after Eriksson 1973; C,D,: after Pomerleau 1980; G: after Scagel, Bandoni et al. 1969/ Fig. 5.5B,C: after Pomerleau 1980; E-G: after Moore-Landecker 1972/ Fig. 5.6A-E: after Oberwinkler 1977/ Fig. 5.7A: after Brodie 1951; D-F: after Dring 1973/ Fig. 5.8: after Smith 1938/ Fig. 5.9A: after Couch 1931; B-E: after Oberwinkler 1982/ Fig. 5.10: after Scagel, Bandoni et al. 1969/ Fig. 6.1: after von Arx 1980/ Fig. 6.2A,D-F: after von Arx 1979; B: after von Arx 1970; C: after Cole & Nozawa 1981/ Fig. 7.1B-D: after Brodo 1981/ Fig. 8.1A: after Bourke 1969; B: after Bourke 1964/ Fig. 8.2A,C,D: after Cole & Samson 1979; B: after Benjamin 1959/ Fig. 8.3: after Webster 1980/ Fig. 8.4: after Blumer 1933/ Fig. 8.5: after Buller 1924/ Figs. 10.3, 10.4: after Berka & Barnett 1989/ Fig. 11.1: after Buller/ Figs. 11.4, 11.5: after Michaelides & Kendrick 1982/ Fig. 11.6: after Deacon 1984/ Fig. 12.1: after Cruickshank, Stewart & Wastie 1982/ Fig. 12.2A: after Plant Protection Division ICI; B: after Coffey 1975/ Fig. 12.3A: after James 1971; B: after Large & Doling 1963/ Fig. 15.1: after Barron 1980/ Fig. 15.2: after Barron 1977/ Fig. 15.3: after Barron 1987/ Fig. 15.4: after Barron 1977/ Fig. 15.5: after Barron 1977/ Fig. 15.6: after Barron 1981/ Fig. 15.7A,C: after Barron 1977; B: after Barron 1981/ Fig. 16.1: after Batra & Batra

1967/ Fig. 16.2: after Batra & Batra 1967/ Fig. 16.3: after Dixon 1983/ Fig. 17.4: after Trappe & Schenck 1982/ Fig. 21.1A: after Samson, Hoekstra & van Oorschot 1981; B: after Booth 1971; C: after Raper & Fennell 1965; D: after Barnett 1960; E: after Ellis 1971; H: after Ellis 1971/ Fig. 22.1: after Pomerleau 1980/ Fig. 22.2B-D: after Pomerleau 1980; E: after Lincoff & Mitchel 1977.

Glossary

ABSCISSION: separation, as of conidia from a conidiophore.

ABSORB: to obtain food by taking up water and dissolved substances across a membrane; this is how fungi operate (cf. INGEST).

ACERVULAR CONIDIOMA (ACERVULUS): a flat, covered sporoma produced by Coelomycetes; often subcuticular or subepidermal (in host tissue).

ACROPETAL: describes chains of conidia in which the youngest conidium is at the tip of the chain; a pattern of apical growth.

ACTIVE TRANSPORT: the pumping of a substance across a cellular membrane from a point of lower concentration to one of higher concentration; requires energy.

ADAPTIVE ENZYME: see ENZYME.

AECIA (sing. = AECIUM): pustules of rust fungus containing aeciospores.

AECIOSPORES: the dikaryotic 'transfer' spores of Uredinales, which are formed on the alternate host in macrocyclic rusts, but can infect only the primary host.

AERO-AQUATIC FUNGI: pond-inhabiting fungi producing elaborate floating propagules which are on hand to colonize autumn-shed leaves as they fall into the water, then 'condition' them in near-anaerobic conditions at the bottom of the pond (cf. AMPHIBIOUS fungi).

AEROBIC: requiring free oxygen for respiration.

AEROBIOLOGY: the study of fungal (and other) propagules in the atmosphere.

AFLATOXIN: virulent toxin produced by the Hyphomycetes, *Aspergillus flavus* and *A. parasiticus*, growing on foodstuffs, esp. nuts: highly carcinogenic.

AGAR: phycocolloid produced by the red alga, *Gelidium*; used to solidify culture media used in mycology and bacteriology.

AGARIC: a gill- or tube-bearing mushroom of the order Agaricales (Holobasidiomycetes).

AIDS: Acquired Immune Deficiency Syndrome, an ultimately fatal condition produced when a virus destroys the T cells of the body's immune system; AIDS patients are attacked and sometimes killed by opportunistic fungi.

ALGAE (sing. = ALGA): unicellular or simple multicellular organisms with chlorophyll, lacking the multicellular sex organs typical of plants. Comprise several protoctistan Divisions (some, like the kelps, large and plant-like), plus the prokaryotic 'blue-green algae' (Cyanobacteria).

ALIMENTARY TOXIC ALEUKIA (ATA): a mycotoxicosis caused by T-2 toxin (q.v.) which killed many people in Russia during and after World War II.

ALKALOIDS: nitrogen-containing organic compounds produced by plants; physiologically active in vertebrates; many have a bitter taste and some are poisonous.

ALLANTOID: sausage-shaped.

ALLELE: one of the two or more alternative states of a gene that occupy the same position (locus) on homologous chromosomes; alleles are separated from each other at meiosis.

ALLERGY: hypersensitivity, often to external agents, in which mast cells of the immune system initiate inflammation.

ALTERNATE HOST: the second host of heteroecious rusts: that which does not bear the sexual state (the teliospores); see PRIMARY HOST.

ALTERNATION OF GENERATIONS: succession of haploid and diploid thalli in the life cycle.

AMANITINS: see AMATOXINS; the cause of most fatal mushroom poisonings (see BASTIEN TREATMENT).

AMATOXINS: cyclic octopeptides (including: and alpha-amanitin) found in some spp. of *Amanita*, *Galerina*; extremely toxic to humans.

AMBIMOBILE: describes systemic fungicides which can move upward in the xylem or downward in the phloem.

AMBROSIA FUNGI: symbiotic wood-inhabiting fungi associated with wood-wasps and wood-inhabiting beetles; the fungi feed the larvae, and are dispersed by the adults.

AMEROSPORES: non-septate spores.

AMOEBOID: without a cell wall or a definite shape, moving and feeding by means of pseudopodia (temporary cytoplasmic protrusions).

AMORPHOUS: shapeless, formless.

AMPHIBIOUS FUNGI: specialized stream-inhabiting, leaf-colonizing fungi which have aquatic anamorphs often producing tetraradiate conidia (q.v.), and emergent or terrestrial teleomorphs.

AMPHOTERICIN-B (Fungizone): an antifungal polyene antibiotic derived from actinomycetes (*Streptomyces* spp.); used to treat systemic mycoses.

AMYLASE: an enzyme which hydroyzes starch.

AMYLOID: turning blue in iodine (Melzer's reagent (q.v.)), reacting like starch, as do many ascus tips, basidiospore walls or ornamentations; I^+.

ANAEROBIC: describing cells which can live without oxygen and utilize another substrate, e.g., sulphur, as an electron acceptor.

ANALOGOUS: of similar form and/or function, but of different evolutionary origin; see HOMO-LOGOUS.

ANAMORPH: the asexual reproductive manifestation of a fungus: usually produces conidia, but may also be sclerotial.

ANASTOMOSIS: fusion of somatic hyphae; characteristic of Dikaryomycota.

ANDROSTENOL: mammalian pheromone produced by truffles.

ANEUPLOID: having a chromosome number which is not a multiple of the haploid set.

ANION: a negatively charged ion.

ANISOGAMY: fusion of gametes of different size, as in *Allomyces* (Blastocladiales: Chytridiomycota).

ANNELLIDIC: describes blastic conidia produced in sequence by short percurrent extensions of a conidiogenous cell, which leave annular scars (annellations) on the cell.

ANNULUS: a ring around the stem of mushrooms, the remains of the partial veil.

ANTABUSE (Disulfiram): substance which, for several days after it has been ingested, will interrupt the catabolism of alcohol at the acetaldehyde stage, causing headache, numbness of extremities, metallic taste, palpitation, nausea, vomiting, blurring of vision; used to treat chronic alcoholism; see COPRINE.

ANTHERIDIUM (pl. = ANTHERIDIA): male gametangium.

ANTIBIOTIC: a diffusible substance produced by one microorganism that is damaging to others, thereby conferring a competitive advantage on the producer.

ANTICHOLINERGIC: interfering with the transmission of nerve impulses.

APHERESIS: fractionation of blood by centrifugation, so that specific components can be replaced.

APICAL APPARATUS or APICAL RING: a specialized structure found in the tips of many unitunicate-inoperculate asci, acting as a valve or sphincter that controls the forcible expulsion of ascospores.

APICULATE: having an apiculus, a small pointed projection at the tip.

APOPLASTIC: describing the movement of substances via the cell walls: not entering the living cells (cf. SYMPLASTIC).

APOTHECIAL ASCOMA (APOTHECIUM): the usually cup- or saucer-like ascoma of the 'discomycetes'; the hymenium is exposed at maturity, as in cup fungi and morels.

APPLE SCAB: disfiguring disease of apple leaves and fruit caused by the *Spilocaea pomi* anamorph of *Venturia inaequalis* (Dothideales: Ascomycetes).

APPRESSORIUM: a swelling on a germ-tube or hypha, which adheres to the surface of a host, and facilitates subsequent penetration.

ARBUSCULAR MYCORRHIZA: see ENDOMYCORRHIZA.

ARBUSCULE: a finely branched organ produced by endomycorrhizal fungi inside host root cells; the interface at which fungus and plant exchange phosphorus and photosynthates.

ARCHAEASCEOUS: (of asci) essentially bitunicate, splitting at the tip; part of the inner wall may protrude; common in lichens.

ARCHAEOBACTERIA: an ancient line of bacteria, including the methanogenic, halophilic and thermoacidophilic groups found in hot springs and sea-floor vents; their ribosomes are distinctive, and they also differ from eubacteria (q.v.) in their ribosomal RNA, wall chemistry, and lipids.

ARTHRIC: describes thallic conidia which form by the breaking up of fertile hyphae at the septa.

ASCOGENOUS HYPHAE: the restricted dikaryophase of Ascomycetes; the dikaryotic hyphae which grow out from the fertilized ascogonium and eventually give rise to asci.

ASCOGONIUM (pl. = ASCOGONIA): in many ascomycetes, the female gametangium that receives nuclei from the antheridium.

ASCOMA (pl. = ASCOMATA): any multihyphal structure producing asci; formed by the Ascomycetes; see APOTHECIAL, CLEISTOTHECIAL, PERITHECIAL, PSEUDOTHECIAL ASCOMATA.

ASCOMYCOTINA: Subdivision of Dikaryomycota; form endogenous meiospores in asci and have a restricted dikaryon; generally called Ascomycetes.

ASCOSPORE: meiospore produced in an ascus; usually 8 per ascus.

ASCUS (pl. = ASCI): the meiosporangium of the Ascomycetes: originally as a spore-gun.

ASEPTIC: free or freed from contaminating organism(s); (of microbiological technique) pertains to working under sterile conditions and using sterile techniques, e.g., working in a laminar flow bench, using flame sterilized inoculating loops and instruments.

ASEXUAL REPRODUCTION: a form of reproduction neither preceded nor followed by meiosis; in fungi, commonly involves mitospores, such as, sporangiospores or conidia.

ASPERGILLOMA: a 'fungus ball' composed principally of hyphae of *Aspergillus*, found in a pre-existing cavity (esp. in an upper lobe of the lung) or a bronchus; usually relatively benign or asymptomatic (cf. ASPERGILLOSIS).

ASPERGILLOSIS: any disease in man or animals caused by *Aspergillus* (esp. *A. fumigatus*).

ASYMPTOMATIC: not showing any clinical manifestations.

ATHLETE'S FOOT: infection of the skin between the toes caused by dermatophytes (conidial anamorphs of the Arthrodermataceae, Onygenales: Ascomycetes).

ATP (ADENOSINE TRIPHOSPHATE): the major source of usable chemical energy in metabolism; on hydrolysis, ATP loses one phosphate to become adenosine diphosphate (ADP), releasing usable energy.

ATTENUATED: (1) tapered, narrowed; (2) (of a pathogen) having reduced pathogenicity or virulence.

AUTOCLAVING: sterilization by steam under pressure (15 lb./in^2) for prescribed time periods; better than dry heat, as sterilization is achieved at lower temperatures (121°C).

AUTOECIOUS: describes rust fungi which complete their life cycle on a single host (cf. HETEROECIOUS).

AUTOIMMUNE DISEASES: diseases caused by the body's immune system attacking its own tissues or organs, e.g. rheumatoid arthritis, juvenile diabetes.

AUTOLYSIS: self-digestion resulting in cell breakdown and often liquefaction.

AUTOTROPHIC: capable of synthesizing energy-rich carbon compounds.

AUXILIARY CELL: cell from which the extramatrical spores of *Gigaspora* and *Scutellospora* (Glomales: VAM fungi) arise.

AUXINS: plant growth hormones; some are produced by ectomycorrhizal fungi.

AUXOTROPH: a biochemical mutant deficient for one or more substances; it will grow on minimal medium only if it has been supplemented with these substances.

AXENIC: describes a condition in which an organism grows alone, with no other organisms (host, symbionts or parasites) present, as in 'axenic culture'.

AZYGOSPORES: extramatrical spores of some VAM fungi that resemble zygosporangia, but are not the result of any sexual process.

BALLISTOSPORE: a forcibly discharged spore.

BASAUXIC: growing from the base, rather than at the apex.

BASIDIOMA (pl. = BASIDIOMATA): any multihyphal structure producing basidia; formed by most basidiomycetes, e.g., mushroom, puffball.

BASIDIOMYCOTINA: Subdivision of Dikaryomycota (q.v.) forming exogenous meiospores on basidia, and have an extended dikaryon; generally called Basidiomycetes.

BASIDIOSPORES: exogenous meiospores produced on a basidium; usually 4 per basidium.

BASIDIUM: the meiosporangium of the subdivision Basidiomycotina; produces exogenous meiospores (usually 4) on special projections called sterigmata.

BASIPETAL: describes a chain of conidia to which new units are added at the base (cf. ACROPETAL).

BASTIEN TREATMENT: an apparently successful treatment for amanitin poisoning, involving: (1) twice-daily injection of 1 g vitamin C, (2) 2 capsules of nifuroxazide, three times a day, (3) two tablets of dihydrostreptomycin, three times a day, (4) penicillin therapy, (5) maintenance of fluid and electrolyte balance.

BATCH CULTURE: the growth of microorganisms in a fixed volume of medium.

BENOMYL (Benlate): the first successful systemic fungicide: one of the Benzimidazoles, has very low toxicity to plants and animals, and controls ascomycetous fungal pathogens by interfering with spindle formation during nuclear division.

BENZIMIDAZOLES: systemic fungicides, including Benomyl (q.v.).

BIFLAGELLATE: having two flagella, as in zoospores of the Oomycota.

BINDING HYPHAE: thick-walled, narrow, highly branched, non-septate hyphae found only in trimitic basidiomata (cf. SKELETAL, GENERATIVE hyphae).

BINOMIAL: the unique double name given to each known species: composed of generic epithet and a species, or 'trivial', epithet.

BIOCIDE: a substance which kills living organisms.

BIOCONTROL: the control of undesirable organisms by other organisms.

BIOCONVERSION: the enzyme-mediated conversion of organic substrates, such as cellulose, to other more valuable substances, such as protein, by other organisms.

BIODEGRADABLE: capable of being broken down by microorganisms (bacteria and/or fungi).

BIOLOGICAL ACCUMULATION: the acccumulation of toxic substances, e.g., DDT, in higher levels of the food web by consumption of organisms of the same or lower levels which have acquired the substance but which have not been affected by it.

BIOLOGICAL CONTROL: see BIOCONTROL.

BIOMASS: the total mass (amount) of living organism(s) in a particular area or volume.

BIOTECHNOLOGY: the large-scale exploitation of microorganisms, including fungi, to produce pharmaceuticals, feedstuffs, or other valuable metabolites.

BIOTROPHIC: growing on another living organism, in intimate asssociation with its cytoplasm.

BIPOLAR: (1) describes a system of heterothallism in which sexual compatibility is controlled by many different alleles which occur at a single locus (cf. TETRAPOLAR); (2) describes yeasts in which budding occurs at opposite ends of the long axis of the cell, by percurrent proliferation: they are blastic-annellidic.

BIRD'S NEST FUNGI: members of the order Nidulariales (Gasteromycetes): the basidiospores are in peridioles ('eggs') and the 'nest' is a splash-cup dispersal mechanism.

BITUNICATE: describes a type of ascus with two distinct, persistent wall layers: the 'jack-in-a-box' ascus that is diagnostic of the Bitunicatae and is found in pseudothecial ascomata (cf. UNITUNICATE).

BLASTIC: one of two basic modes of conidium development: there is marked enlargement of a recognizable conidium initial before the initial is delimited by a septum; derived from budding (cf. THALLIC).

BLASTOMYCOSIS: a disease in man caused by *Blastomyces dermatitidis* (teleomorph *Ajellomyces dermatitidis*).

BLIGHT: a general name for many diseases of plants esp. when leaf damage is sudden and serious, e.g., potato blight, late blight (*Phytophora infestans*); early blight (*Alternaria solani*).

BLISTER RUST: a disease of 5-needled pines, caused by *Cronartium ribicola* (Uredinales: Teliomycetes).

BLUE CHEESES: cheeses ripened and flavoured by *Penicillium roquefortii* (Hyphomycetes), e.g., Roquefort, Stilton, Gorgonzola, Danish Blue.

BLUE MOULD: a downy mildew of tobacco, caused by *Peronospora tabacina* (Peronosporales: Oomycota).

BLUE STAIN: a blue-grey colouration of worked wood paradoxically caused by the growth of brown fungal hyphae in the surface layers of wood cells.

BLUEING REACTION: a colouration of bruised or broken tissues in some agarics (esp. Boletaceae), caused by an oxidative reaction.

BOLETE: a fleshy agaric with tubes instead of gills.

BORDEAUX MIXTURE: the first practical fungicide used by Millardet in 1883-1885 against downy mildew of grape vine (*Plasmopara viticola*), and still in general use for controlling many plant diseases; it contains 4 parts copper sulphate, 4 parts quicklime, 500 parts water.

BRACKET FUNGI: corky or woody, often perennial, basidiomata of the polypores (Aphyllophorales: Basidiomycetes).

BROAD SPECTRUM: (of fungicides) active against a wide range of organisms.

BROMATIA: enlarged hyphal tips induced by Attine (leaf-cutting) ants in their domesticated fungus, and eaten by them.

BROWN ROT: wood rot produced by a basidiomycete that can degrade cellulose but not lignin.

BUDDING: a process of growth or multiplication by development of a new cell from a small outgrowth of the parent cell (cf. BLASTIC).

BULBIL: a small sclerotium-like structure of relatively few cells.

BULLER DROP: the tiny droplet of liquid which appears at the base of a basidiospore just before it is discharged.

CANDIDIASIS: a disease of man and animals caused by species of *Candida*, esp. *C. albicans*; also called moniliasis and candidosis.

CANKER: plant disease producing sharply delimited necrosis of cortical tissue.

CAP: the spreading, often umbrella-like, gill- or tube-bearing part of an agaric, more technically known as the pileus.

CAPILLITIUM: sterile filamentous elements among the spores in some gasteromycetes and Myxostelida.

CARBOHYDRATE: organic compound consisting of a chain of carbon atoms to which hydrogen and oxygen are attached in a 2:1 ratio, e.g., sugars, starch, glycogen, cellulose.

CARBOXAMIDES (Carboxin, Vitavax): systemic fungicides used as seed dressing to control smut on barley and wheat.

CARCINOGENS: substances which induce cancer.

CARDINAL TEMPERATURES: the minimum, maximum and optimum temperatures of growth of an organism.

CAROTENOIDS: fat-soluble pigments including carotenes (yellow and orange) and xanthophylls (yellow).

CATABOLIC: describes metabolic chemical reactions resulting in the breakdown of complex materials and the release of energy in the metabolic process (cf. ANABOLIC).

CATION: a positively charged ion.

CELL: a unit of protoplasm containing a functional genome and often enclosed by a wall.

CELLULASE: an enzyme that can degrade cellulose; a cellulolytic enzyme.

CELLULOSE: principal polysaccharide of plant cell walls; a polymer of glucose; walls of Oomycetes are partly composed of a similar substance called 'fungal cellulose'.

CENTRIOLE: cytoplasmic organelle identical to a kinetosome; found in flagellated cells of protoctistan fungi; the centriole divides and organizes spindle fibres during mitosis and meiosis.

CENTROMERE: that part of the chromosome to which the spindle fibres are attached.

CENTRUM: the structures inside an ascoma, which are concerned with development of the asci.

CEPHALODIA: a delimited part of a lichen thallus containing a blue-green alga, while the main thallus contains a green alga.

CHANTERELLE: the edible *Cantharellus cibarius* (Aphyllophorales: Basidiomycetes).

CHEMOTAXIS: movement of a motile organism up a chemical concentration gradient (cf. CHEMOTROPISM).

CHEMOTROPISM: growth of an organism up a chemical concentration gradient.

CHESTNUT BLIGHT: a devastating disease caused by *Endothia parasitica* (Diaporthales: Ascomycetes) which has wiped out the edible chestnut (*Castanea dentata*) in North America.

CHITIN: the principal polysaccharide in cell walls of most fungi (but not Oomycetes); a polymer of N-acetylglucosamine.

CHLAMYDOSPORE: an often thick-walled, resistant mitospore, formed by many fungi.

CHLOROPLAST: a chlorophyll-containing plastid; the site of photosynthesis.

CHOKE: a disease of grasses caused by *Epichloë*; the stroma of the teleomorph encircles the main axis of the grass and prevents it from flowering.

CHOLINERGIC: stimulating or augmenting the transmission of nerve impulses (acetylcholine is an important agent of neurotransmission across synapses).

CHROMATID: one of the two daughter strands of a duplicated chromosome which are joined by a single centromere.

CHROMATOGRAPHY: a separation technique which uses the differential rates of diffusion of different sizes of molecules in gas (GC), liquid (HPLC), on paper, and in thin layers of silicate on glass, aluminum or plastic plates (TLC). Now much used in lichenology.

CHROMOBLASTOMYCOSIS: fungal skin disease of humans caused by species of *Phialophora* (Hyphomycetes).

CHROMOSOMES: in eukaryotes, usually elongated structures in the nucleus along which the genes are located; actually long DNA molecules with associated protein; seen as several to many threads or rods which appear in contracted form during mitosis and meiosis. In prokaryotes there is only one, circular chromosome.

CHYTRIDIOMYCOTA: Division of protoctistan fungi with posteriorly uniflagellate zoospores; hence, chytrid.

CIRCADIAN RHYTHMS: regular rhythms of growth and activity, which occur in an approximately 24-hour cycle.

CLAMP CONNECTIONS: short, backwardly directed branches on many dikaryotic basidiomycetous hyphae, providing a bypass for one of the nuclei produced during synchronous division of the dikaryon, insuring their equal distribution between the new cells; croziers are possible homologues.

CLASS: taxonomic rank above order, but below Division (or Phylum); suffix is **-mycetes**.

CLASSIFICATION: the systematic arrangement of organisms, based on everything we know about them.

CLEISTOTHECIAL ASCOMA (CLEISTOTHECIUM): an ascoma, which is closed at maturity; the unitunicate but frequently evanescent asci are often spherical and are not arranged in an hymenium; characteristic of Eurotiales.

CLONING: producing organisms all of which contain copies of the same gene: the desired gene is removed from the donor, inserted into a vector (usually a plasmid), the vector is used to transform a host culture, then those hosts which have taken up the vector are selectively cultured.

CLUB FUNGI: members of family Clavariaceae (Aphyllophorales: Basidiomycetes).

COCCIDIOIDOMYCOSIS: deep-seated mycosis caused by *Coccidioides immitis* (Hyphomycetes); common in dry S.W. of U.S.A.

CODON: sequence of three adjacent nucleotides (in DNA or RNA) that form the code for a single amino acid; a sequence of codons specifies the amino acids that constitute a protein.

COELOMYCETES: anamorphic fungi in which the conidia are produced within a protective structure, an acervular or pycnidial conidioma.

COENOCYTIC: describes multinucleate hyphae lacking cross-walls, as in protoctistan fungi and many zygomycetes.

COENZYME: an organic molecule, which plays an accessory role in enzyme-catalyzed processes, often by acting as a donor or acceptor of a substance involved in the reaction; ATP and NAD are common coenzymes.

COFACTOR: non-protein component(s) needed by an enzyme to be functional; some cofactors are metal ions, others are coenzymes (q.v.).

COLLARETTE: the often flaring wall of a phialide distal to the conidiogenous locus.

COLONY: a discrete mycelium of a fungus, often derived from a single spore.

COLUMELLA: a continuation of the stalk into the head of a spore-producing structure; found in sporangia of Mucoraceae (Zygomycetes).

COMPATIBLE: able to undergo sexual fusion: of opposite mating types.

COMPLETE MEDIUM: see MEDIUM.

COMPOUND ASCOMA: a teleomorphic fructification incorporating several to many distinct ascomata on or in a single structure, as in the Clavicipitales.

CONDITIONING: the process by which fungi must enzymically soften up substrates like dead leaves before the detritivorous animals can eat them.

CONIDIA: see CONIDIUM.

CONIDIATION: the process of producing conidia.

CONIDIOGENESIS: the process by which individual conidia develop; see also: ACROPETAL, ANNELLIDIC, ARTHRIC, BASIPETAL, BLASTIC, PHIALIDIC, RETROGRESSIVE, SYMPODIAL, SYNCHRONOUS, THALLIC.

CONIDIOGENOUS: giving rise to conidia.

CONIDIOMA (pl. = CONIDIOMATA): any multihyphal structure producing conidia, .e.g, synnematal, sporodochial, acervular, or pycnidial conidiomata.

CONIDIOPHORE: a specialized hypha, simple or branched, on which conidia are formed.

CONIDIUM (pl. = CONIDIA): a non-motile fungal mitospore not formed inside a sporangium; typical of dikaryomycotan anamorphs.

CONJUGATION: the kind of sexual fusion of somatic cells seen in Zygomycetes; an adaptation to the absence of motile gametes.

CONSTITUTIVE ENZYME: see ENZYME (cf. ADAPTIVE ENZYME).

COPRINE: a rare amino acid found in the agaric, *Coprinus atramentarius*; its effects mimic those of antabuse (q.v.)

COPROPHILOUS FUNGI: fungi living on dung; include many zygomycetes, ascomycetes and basidiomycetes.

CORAL FUNGI: Hymenomycetes with highly branched, upright basidiomata, usually arising from the ground; some members of the family Clavariaceae (Aphyllophorales, Holobasidiomycetes).

CORTINA: (of agarics) a filamentous or web-like partial veil covering the mature gills; typical of the rusty-brown-spored mycorrhizal genus *Cortinarius*.

CROSS-WALLS: SEPTA (q.v.)

CROSSING-OVER (CROSSOVER): exchange of genetic material between two homologous chromosomes by the breakage and joining of sister chromatids; occurs during meiosis.

CROZIER: in ascogenous hyphae, a terminal hook in which conjugate nuclear division takes place just prior to nuclear fusion, meiosis, and ascus formation.

CRUCIATELY-SEPTATE: describes the basidia of order Tremellales (Phragmobasidiomycetes) which are divided into four more or less equal parts by vertical cross-walls.

CRUSTOSE: describes a lichen thallus that adheres closely to the substrate (often rock) (cf. FOLIOSE, FRUTICOSE, SQUAMULOSE).

CRYPTIC: inconspicuous or hidden.

CRYPTOCOCCOSIS: a systemic mycosis caused by a basidiomycetous yeast, *Cryptococcus neoformans* (teleomorph: *Filobasidiella neoformans*).

CRYPTOGAM: a plant, fungus, or protoctistan that propagates by spores rather than by seeds (fungi, algae, bryophytes, ferns).

CUP FUNGUS: a 'discomycete': any ascomycete with an open, shallow, cupulate apothecial ascoma; a hetergeneous grouping because the asci may be unitunicate operculate, unitunicate inoperculate, or in many lichens, bitunicate.

CUTICLE: waxy or fatty layer on outer wall of epidermal cells.

CYANOBACTERIA: prokaryotic chlorophyllous organisms often capable of fixing nitrogen; blue-green algae.

CYCLOHEXIMIDE (ACTIDIONE): an antibacterial and antifungal antibiotic derived from *Streptomyces*, which is used in isolating fungi pathogenic to humans.

CYCLOPEPTIDES (CYCLIC OLIGOPEPTIDES): substances formed of amino acids joined in a ring (cf. AMATOXINS, CYCLOSPORINE).

CYCLOSPORINE: a cyclic polypeptide, produced by the Hyphomycete, *Tolypocladium inflatum*; used as an effective immunosuppressant after organ transplantation.

CYSTIDIA (sing. = CYSTIDIUM): sterile cells, frequently of distinctive shape, occurring at any surface of a basidioma, particularly the hymenium, from which they frequently project.

CYTOPLASM: all the living contents of the cell, except the nucleus.

CYTOPLASMIC INHERITANCE: see EXTRACELLULAR INHERITANCE.

DAMPING-OFF: a rotting of seedlings at soil level; commonly caused by species of *Pythium*, *Phytophthora*, *Fusarium*, and *Rhizoctonia*.

DECIDUOUS: falling off, as leaves that are shed in the autumn; used to describe the sporangia of downy mildew fungi (Peronosporales: Oomycota).

DEER TRUFFLE: *Elaphomyces* (Elaphomycetales, Ascomycetes).

DEFINED MEDIUM: see MEDIUM.

DEHISCENCE: the opening of a structure to permit the escape of spores; the separation of spores from the structure that produced them.

DELIQUESCE: to liquefy; to autolyse, as in the gills of the agaric, *Coprinus*, or 'Prototunicate' asci.

DERMATITIS: non-contagious but often chronic skin inflammation; sometimes caused by fungal infections.

DERMATOPHYTES: anamorphs of some Onygenales (Ascomycetes), which live on keratin and can cause skin disease in humans (see MYCOSES, RINGWORM, TINEA).

DESTROYING ANGEL: the pure white agaric, *Amanita virosa*: ingestion of 1 mL of this fungus can prove fatal; its toxins are cyclic polypeptides, esp. amanitins.

DETRITIVORE: animal which eats organic 'garbage,' dead remains of other life forms.

DEXTRINOID: staining yellowish brown or reddish brown in Melzer's reagent (q.v.).

DIAGEOTROPISM: the tendency to grow in a direction horizontal to the surface of the earth.

DICHOTOMOUS: describes branching in which the two arms are equal (as in a capital Y).

DICTYOSEPTATE: having cross-walls running horizontally and vertically, like the layers of cement between bricks (also described as muriformly septate).

DICTYOSOME: see GOLGI BODY.

DICTYOSPORES: spores which are dictyoseptate (q.v.).

DIDYMOSPORES: one-septate spores (i.e., with two cells or compartments).

DIKARYOMYCOTA: Division of eumycotan fungi comprising the Subdivisions Ascomycotina and Basidiomycotina and their anamorphs; characterized by hyphae with chitinous walls and perforate septa, and (usually) the occurrence of a dikaryotic phase.

DIKARYON: a nuclear phenomenon unique to Division Dikaryomycota, in which compatible nuclei pair off and cohabit without copulating; restricted to ascogenous hyphae in ascomycetes; the dominant phase in basidiomycetes; the paired nuclei always divide synchronously.

DIKARYOTIC: having two separate but compatible nuclei in each cell or compartment; a nuclear condition unique to the fungi.

DIMITIC: describes basidiomata constructed from two different kinds of hyphae: generative and skeletal.

DIMORPHIC: having two distinct forms, as in some fungal pathogens of humans, which are yeast-like in the host, but mycelial in culture; also sometimes used to describe sexual dimorphism; having an anamorph and teleomorph.

DIPLOID: having two complements of haploid chromosomes in a single nucleus (a condition often labelled '2n') (cf. DIKARYOTIC).

DISCOLICHENS: lichens in which the mycobiont forms apothecial ascomata.

DISCOMYCETES: cup fungi; an informal grouping of ascomycetes which mostly form unituni-cate asci in apothecial ascomata, though many lichenized taxa have bitunicate or archaeasceous asci.

DITHIOCARBAMATES: organic fungicides; **dimethyl-** (DMDC): thiram, ferbam, ziram; **ethyl-ene-bis-** (EBDC): nabam, maneb, mancozeb, zineb.

DIVISION: a major taxon of fungi or plants above Class but below Kingdom. There are five Divisions of fungi: Dikaryomycota and Zygomycota (Eumycotan), Oomycota, Chytridiomycota and Hyphochytriomycota (Protoctistan). Divisions represent evolutionary pathways that diverged hundreds of millions of years ago (cf. PHYLUM).

DNA (DEOXYRIBOSE NUCLEIC ACID): carrier of genetic information in living organisms; composed of chains of phosphate, sugar molecules (deoxyribose), purines (guanine and adenine) and pyrimidines (cytosine and thymine); capable of self-replication as well as of determining RNA synthesis.

DNA LIGASE: an enzyme which repairs breaks in the phosphate backbone of DNA.

DOLIPORE: the complex barrel-shaped septal pore apparatus found in basidiomycetes other than Uredinales and Ustilaginales.

DOMINANT: (of an allele) exerting its full phenotypic effect despite the presence of another allele of the same gene, whose phenotypic expression it blocks.

DORMANT SPRAYS: sprays used when plants are dormant, to control overwintering pathogens.

DOWNY MILDEWS: serious plant diseases caused by obligately parasitic fungi, such as *Perono-spora* and *Plasmopara* (Peronosporales: Oomycota).

DRY ROT: wood-rot caused by certain basidiomycetes, e.g., *Serpula lacrymans* (Meruliaceae: Aphyllophorales).

DUAL CULTURE (POT CULTURE): fungus plus host plant or phytobiont; the only way yet known of growing certain obligately biotrophic fungi (e.g. VAM fungi) in reasonably controlled conditions.

DUAL ORGANISMS: organisms which invariably consist of two interdependent symbionts, e.g. lichens. In fact, most plants are also dual or multiple organisms because of their intimate association with endo- or ecto-mycorrhizal fungi. The eukaryotic cell is widely believed to have arisen as a multiple symbiosis.

DUTCH ELM DISEASE: a usually fatal disease of the American elm tree, *Ulmus americana*, caused by *Ophiostoma ulmi* (Ophiostomatales: Ascomycetes); the fungus is spread by a bark-bee-tle vector.

EAR FUNGI: the gelatinous, edible basidiomata of the Auriculariales.

EARTH-BALLS: the non-ostiolate basidiomata of the Sclerodermatales.

EARTH STARS: specialized soil-inhabiting puffballs (Lycoperdales: Gasteromycetes) in which the outer peridium splits and curls back in segments, raising the basidiospore mass (gleba) above the dead leaves, etc.

ECTOMYCORRHIZA or **ECTOTROPHIC MYCORRHIZA**: mycorrhiza in which a dikaryo-mycotan mycelium ramifies through the soil, forms a mantle around individual rootlets, and grows between cells of the root cortex, forming a Hartig net (the interface between the symbionts). The fungus exchanges phosphorus for photosynthates from the root. Many forest trees, esp. Pinaceae, Fagaceae, have ectomycorrhizal associations with agarics or boletes (cf. ENDOMYCORRHIZA); see MYCORRHIZA.

ELECTROPHORESIS: a technique which uses the differential mobility of differently charged molecules in an electric field to separate them within a stationary gel.

EMESIS: vomiting (sometimes caused by EMETICS).

ENDEMIC: natural to (always present in) one geographical region.

ENDOCRINE GLANDS: ductless glands which secrete hormones; include the pituitary, adrenal, thyroid.

ENDODERMIS: the differentiated, innermost layer of the cortex of roots, rhizomes and certain non-seedbearing vascular plant stems; surrounds the stele.

ENDOGENOUS : formed within another structure, as are the meiospores of Ascomycetes (cf. EXOGENOUS).

ENDOMYCORRHIZA or **ENDOTROPHIC MYCORRHIZA**: an ancient symbiosis of fungi with green plants; hyphae gathering nutrients from the soil, esp. phosphorus, are continuous with others that grow between and within root cells and produce arbuscules (q.v.); found in 90% of angiosperms and conifers, except Pinaceae; also called vesicular-arbuscular mycorrhizae (cf. ECTOMYCORRHIZA); see MYCORRHIZA.

ENDOPHYTIC FUNGI: fungi (such as some anamorphs of Clavicipitales) which grow systemically within plants without causing symptoms; now known to produce neurotoxins that discourage herbivores, and therefore to be participating in a mutualistic symbiosis.

ENDOPLASMIC RETICULUM (er): extensive system of membranes in eukaryotic cells.

ENDOSYMBIONT: an organism which lives in a mutualistic symbiosis within the cells of another organism.

ENTOMOGENOUS: living in or on insects, esp. as pathogens.

ENTOMOPATHOGENIC: causing disease in insects.

ENZYME: a protein that, even in low concentration, speeds up (catalyzes) specific chemical reactions; usually becomes inactivated or unstable at high temperatures; name usually derived from substrate or function, with suffix -ase; see AMYLASE, CELLULASE, DNA LIGASE, PROTEASE, RESTRICTION ENDONUCLEASE. CONSTITUTIVE enzymes are produced even in the absence of the substrate; ADAPTIVE enzymes are not produced until the presence of the substrate has been recognized.

EPIDEMIC: (of disease) prevalent and spreading rapidly among many individuals in an population at the same time.

EPIDERMIS: the surface tissue of plant organs, composed of living parenchyma cells.

EPIGEOUS: fruiting above the surface of the ground (cf. HYPOGEOUS).

EPIPHYTOTIC: an unnecessary coining meaning an EPIDEMIC among plants.

EPITHET: one of the words which makes up the binomial of an organism.

EPIZOOTIC: an unnecessary coining meaning an EPIDEMIC among animals.

ERADICANT: a fungicide which can kill a pathogen both outside and inside the host, because it is systemic (cf. PROTECTANT).

ERGOMETRINE (D-lysergic acid propanolamide): an alkaloid of *Claviceps purpurea* sclerotia; used to induce labour.

ERGOT: (1) a disease of cereals and grasses, caused by species of *Claviceps*, esp. ergot of rye (*C. purpurea*); (2) the sclerotium of the ergot fungus, which contains many toxic and psychogenic alkaloids.

ERGOTAMINE: a 3-amino acid cyclopeptide derivative of lysergic acid from *Claviceps purpurea* sclerotia; ergotamine tartrate is used to manage migraine by causing vasoconstriction of cranial arterioles, thereby reducing the pulsation pressure and attendant headache.

ERGOTISM: ergot poisoning, of two main types in man: the gangrenous and the convulsive; historically known as 'St. Antony's Fire'.

ERYTHROCYTES: red blood cells.

ETIOLATED: (of plants) excessively tall and lacking chlorophyll.

ETIOLOGY: the cause or origin of a disease.

EUBACTERIA: all bacteria which are not archaeobacteria; include all gram-positive bacteria with peptidoglycan walls, all gram-negative bacteria, all photosynthetic bacteria, all bacteria without a rigid cell wall.

EUCARPIC: with thallus divided into vegetative and reproductive structures (cf. HOLOCARPIC).

EUKARYOTIC: having nuclei which are delimited by nuclear membrane, contain 2 or more discrete chromosomes, and divide mitotically: the cytoplasm also contains organelles, such as mitochondria (cf. PROKARYOTIC).

EUMYCOTA: the Kingdom to which the Divisions Zygomycota and Dikaryomycota belong.

EVANESCENT: short-lived, soon disappearing.

EXOCRINE GLANDS: those which release their secretions through ducts, e.g. salivary glands, sweat glands, lachrymal (tear) glands.

EXODERMIS: in plant roots, the layer of cells immediately inside the epidermis; cells may be dimorphic, and variably suberized, influencing entry of VAM fungi and pathogens.

EXOGENOUS: formed externally to the parent cell, as are the meiospores of basidiomycetes.

EXTRAMATRICAL: VAM structures (mycelium, spores) developing outside the roots of the phytobiont.

EXTRANUCLEAR INHERITANCE: transmission of genetic information in the cytoplasm by DNA present in organelles, such as mitochondria.

FACULTATIVE: (of a parasite) able to live as a saprobe (cf. OBLIGATE, OPPORTUNISTIC).

FAIRY RING: rings of mushrooms arising at the periphery of a radially spreading underground mycelium; common in grasslands, and around conifers.

FALSE MOREL: *Gyromitra esculenta* (Ascomycetes), which is poisonous; see GYROMITRIN.

FALSE TRUFFLE: a hypogeous, ectomycorrhizal gasteromycete, e.g., *Rhizopogon*.

FAMILY: taxonomic group above genus, but below order; suffix is **-aceae**.

FERMENTATION: chemical changes in organic substrates caused by enzymes of living micro-organisms.

FERTILIZATION: the fusion of two gametes to form a diploid zygote.

FLAGELLUM (pl. = FLAGELLA): a long whip-like locomotory organelle projecting from a cell; found in zoospores of the protoctistan fungi: Oomycota, Chytridiomycota and Hyphochytriomycota; has similar ultrastructure in all three Divisions.

FOLIAR: relating to leaves.

FOLIOSE: describes a lichen thallus which has broad lobes attached to, but easily removed from the substrate (cf. CRUSTOSE, FRUTICOSE, SQUAMULOSE).

FRUTICOSE: describes a lichen thallus which is shrub-like, erect or hanging, and branched (cf. CRUSTOSE, FOLIOSE, SQUAMULOSE).

FUNGI (sing. = FUNGUS): non-photosynthesizing (i.e., heterotrophic) eukaryotes that produce exoenzymes and absorb their food: usually producing, and living inside, a network of apically extending, branched tubes called hyphae; may belong to Kingdom Protoctista or Kingdom Eumycota.

FUNGICIDE: an agent designed to kill fungi; may be chemical or biological.

'FUNGI IMPERFECTI': an unfortunate and obsolete name for anamorphic fungi which are, or are suspected to be, the anamorphs of ascomycetes or basidiomycetes; better called 'conidial fungi.' They are no less perfect than the teleomorphs some of them possess.

GAMETANGIUM (pl. = GAMETANGIA): a single-celled structure producing gametes or gametic nuclei.

GAMETE: cell, motile or non-motile, which can fuse with another compatible gamete to form a zygote.

GASTEROMYCETES: Holobasidiomycetes with basidioma closed at basidiospore maturity, hymenium present or absent, spore-shooting mechanism lost: basidiospores passively dispersed by a variety of interesting methods; a heterogeneous group.

GENE: a unit of heredity in the chromosome; a sequence of nucleotides in a DNA molecule that codes for a polypeptide.

GENERATIVE HYPHAE: thin-walled, branched hyphae which are the only kind found in monomitic basidiomata (cf. SKELETAL, BINDING hyphae).

GENETIC RECOMBINATION: the reassortment of genes, which can be brought about by several different processes, but in sexually reproducing organisms mainly by crossing-over during meiosis.

GENOME: the total genetic material of an organism (chromosomes plus cytoplasmic genes).

GENOTYPE: the sum of the genetic potential of an organism: in many fungi only part of this is expressed at any given time (see HOLOMORPH, ANAMORPH, TELEOMORPH).

GENUS (pl.= GENERA): taxonomic rank below Family, but above Species.

GEOTROPIC: growing directionally downward under the influence of gravity.

GERM PORE: a differentiated, thin area, or hollow, in a spore wall through which a germ tube may emerge.

GERM SLIT: a thin area of a spore wall running the length of the spore.

GERM TUBE: the hypha that emerges from germinating spores of true fungi.

GERMINATION BY REPETITION: the production and forcible release of a secondary ballistospore by a recently released basidiospore; characteristic of the Phragmobasidiomycetes.

GILLS: flat, vertically oriented plates of tissue that bear the hymenium in most agarics; also called lamellae.

GLEBA: basidiospore mass of a gasteromycete.

GLUCOSE: a six-carbon sugar ($C_6H_{12}O_6$); the commonest monosaccharide in most organisms.

GLYCOGEN: an insoluble carbohydrate, similar to starch; a reserve food found in fungi, bacteria and animals.

GLYCOLYSIS: a process in which sugar is changed anaerobically to pyruvic acid, with the liberation of a small amount of usable energy.

GOLGI BODY/APPARATUS: an intracellular organelle that consists of flat, disc-shaped vesicles often forming tubules at the edges; sites of accumulation and synthesis of cell products, e.g., wall material; in plants, sometimes called DICTYOSOMES.

GRANULOMA: a nodule of firm tissue formed as a reaction to chronic irritation.

GRISEOFULVIN: a chlorine-containing antifungal antibiotic from *Penicillium griseofulvum*, and *P. nigricans*; has been used as a systemic fungicide against plant pathogens and orally against dermtophyte infections in animals and humans.

GYROMITRIN: a heat-labile, carcinogenic, cellular toxin produced by *Gyromitra esculenta* (the False Morel); breaks down to monomethylhydrazine (MMH), which is also extremely toxic.

HALLUCINOGEN: a psychoactive substance which causes disturbances of perception, e.g. psilocybin.

HAMANATTO: an Oriental food obtained by fermenting whole soybeans with *Aspergillus oryzae*; tao-cho (Malaysia); tao-si (Philippines); tu su (China).

HAPLOID: having a single set of chromosomes (often denoted by 'n').

HARTIG NET: the intercellular hyphal network formed by an ectomycorrhizal fungus in the surface layers of a root; the effective interface between the symboints.

HAUSTORIUM (pl. = HAUSTORIA): in parasitic fungi, a specialized absorptive structure that penetrates and draws food from the host cell.

HEART ROT: decay of the inner wood of trees, caused by basidiomycetes.

HELICOSPORE: a spore which curves through more than 180°, and often through several complete gyres, coiling in two or three dimensions.

HEPATIC: concerning the liver, as in HEPATOMA (liver cancer).

HERBICIDE: a substance which kills plants.

HETEROECIOUS: describes fungi which need two hosts to complete their life-cycle, e.g. many rust fungi (Uredinales), Coelomomyces (Chytridiomycota) (cf. AUTOECIOUS).

HETEROKARYOTIC: containing genetically dissimilar nuclei.

HETEROTHALLIC: describes fungi in which two genetically distinct but compatible mycelia must meet before sexual reproduction can take place (cf. HOMOTHALLIC).

HETEROTROPHIC: unable to derive energy from photosynthesis or from inorganic chemical reactions, cf. AUTOTROPHIC.

HETEROZYGOUS: having two different alleles at the same locus on homologous chromosomes.

HISTOPLASMOSIS: deep-seated mycosis of humans caused by *Histoplasma capsulatum* (Hyphomycetes); common in the Mississippi Valley.

HOLOBASIDIOMYCETES: Basidiomycetes in which the basidia are not subdivided by septa (cf. PHRAGMOBASIDIOMYCETES).

HOLOBASIDIUM (pl. = HOLOBASIDIA): a meiosporangium not divided by septa which usually gives rise to 4 exogenous basidiospores (cf. PHRAGMOBASIDIUM).

HOLOCARPIC: with thallus becoming entirely converted into reproductive structures (cf. EUCARPIC).

HOLOMORPH: all manifestations of a genotype: in a fungus this frequently means one or more anamorphs plus teleomorph.

HOMOLOGOUS: (1) with the same evolutionary origin though now often different in form and/or function; (2) (of chromosomes) bearing genes for the same characters.

HOMOTHALLIC: describes fungi in which a single strain can undertake sexual reproduction; self-compatible (cf. HETEROTHALLIC).

HOMOZYGOUS: having identical alleles at the same locus on homologous chromosomes.

HONEY FUNGUS: the agaric, *Armillaria mellea*, which is parasitic on trees and causes serious root rots.

HORMONES: usually peptides or steroids, which are produced in one part of an organism and trigger specific rections in cells elsewhere.

HOST: an organism on or in which a parasitic, necrotrophic or symbiotic fungus lives.

HYDROLYSIS: splitting of a molecule into two parts by adding hydrogen and hydroxyl ions derived from water.

HYMENIUM (pl. = HYMENIA): fertile layer in fungi; bears asci in ascomata, basidia in basidiomata, conidia in pycnidia or acervuli.

HYMENOMYCETES: Holobasidiomycetes with hymenium exposed at maturity, basidiospores shot off (cf. GASTEROMYCETES).

HYPERPARASITE: an organism that parasitizes either another parasite, or an organism closely related to itself.

HYPERSENSITIVITY: the condition in which the host tissue dies at the point of attack by a pathogen, so that the infection does not spread.

HYPERTROPHY: excessive or abnormal growth.

HYPHA (pl. = HYPHAE): the tubular architectural module of almost all fungi, its wall chitinous in eumycotan fungi, cellulosic in oomycetes.

HYPHOCHYTRIOMYCOTA: Division of protoctistan fungi with anteriorly uniflagellate zoospores; hence, hyphochytrid.

HYPHOMYCETES: conidial anamorphs (mostly ascomycetous, some basidiomycetous) producing exposed conidiophores, not enclosed in any protective structure (cf. COELOMYCETES).

HYPOGEOUS: describes fungi which fruit underground.

IBOTENIC ACID: a metabolite of *Amanita muscaria*; changes to muscimol, a hallucinogen, when the basidiomata are dried.

IMMUNOSUPPRESSANT: a substance, such as the fungal metabolite, cyclosporine, (produced by the hyphomycete, *Tolypocladium inflatum*) which partially or completely suppresses the immune system; used to prevent rejection of transplanted organs.

INGEST: to obtain food by engulfing it (see PHAGOTROPHIC) (cf. absorb, which is what fungi do).

INOCULATE: to put a microorganism into an organism or a substratum.

INOCULUM: a small amount of a fungus used to inoculate fresh culture medium or to infect a host organism.

INOPERCULATE: describes sporangia, esp. some unitunicate asci, which have no specialized operculum or cap that opens to permit spore discharge (cf. OPERCULATE).

INTERCALARY: among or between cells; refers to such things as non-apical chlamydospores in many fungi.

INTRAMATRICAL SPORES: another name for the vesicles produced in host roots by most endomycorrhizal fungi.

ION: a charged atom or group of atoms.

IRRADIATION: exposure to some form of radiant energy.

ISIDIA: simple or branched protuberances of the cortex in lichens, which may break off and act as a form of vegetative propagule.

ISOGAMY: fusion of morphologically identical gametes.

JACK-IN-A-BOX ASCI : see BITUNICATE.

JELLY FUNGI: wood-inhabiting basidiomycetes with gelatinous basidiomata; Orders: Tremellales, Auriculariales (Phragmobasidiomycetes); Dacrymycetales (Holobasidiomycetes).

KARYOGAMY: the fusion of sexually compatible haploid nuclei.

KARYOLOGY: the study of the behaviour of nuclei in eukaryotes.

KATSUOBUSHI: a Japanese fermented food; cooked bonito fish is fermented by *Aspergillus glaucus* until dry; the product is shaved into ribbons and used for flavouring other foods.

kb: kilobases, an abbreviation for 1000 base pairs of DNA.

KERATIN: the protein that is the main component of skin, hair, nails, feathers and horns.

KERATINOPHYLIC: capable of decomposing keratin, as are many of the fungi that cause superficial mycoses in man; see DERMATOPHYTES, RINGWORM, TINEA.

KETJAP: an Oriental fermented food; Indonesian soy sauce; black soybeans are fermented for 2-3 days by *Aspergillus oryzae; the root of Ketchup and Catsup.*.

KETOCONAZOLE (Nizoral): an antifungal antibiotic.

KINETOSOME: basal body; self-replicating organelle at the base of flagellum, similar to a centriole.

KINGDOM: the highest taxonomic category, of which 5 are currently recognized (Monera, Protoctista, Eumycota, Plantae, Animalia); fungi constitute the Eumycota, and have 3 Divisions in Kingdom Protoctista.

KOJI: a 'starter' consisting of *Aspergillus oryzae* cultured on roasted wheat or barley (for hamanatto) or *A. orzyae* or *A. soyae* cultured on rice (for miso), which is then inoculated on the appropriate substrate.

KREBS CYCLE: the series of reactions that results in the oxidation of pyruvic acid to hydrogen atoms, electrons, and carbon dioxide; the electrons, passed along electron-carrier molecules, then go through the phosphorylation and terminal oxidation processes; also called the tricarboxylic acid cycle or TCA.

LAMELLAE (sing. = LAMELLA): see GILLS.

LD$_{50}$: LD = lethal dose; LD$_{50}$ = that dose which kills 50% of the spores, cells or individuals of the test organism.

LESION: a wound, injury, or area of diseased tissue.

LEUCOCYTES: white (non-haemoglobin-containing) blood cells of many types, including phagocytic MACROPHAGES and antibody-producing LYMPHOCYTES.

LICHEN: a dual organism in which a fungus (usually an Ascomycete) maintains a green alga or a cyanobacterium captive within its thallus in a symbiosis that approaches balanced parasitism.

LIGNIN: a polymer of phenylpropanoid units that is an important constituent of wood: very resistant to biodegradation, but degraded by many basidiomycetes.

LIPIDS: molecues containing a fatty acid with a long hydrocarbon chain, e.g., triglycerides (ester of a fatty acid plus glycerol), phospholipids (triglyceride containing 2 fatty acid chains and phosphate as a polar group).

LIRELLATE: long and thin.

LOCULE: a spore-containing cavity, esp. one secondarily developed within a pseudothecial ascoma, or in the basidiomata of Lycoperdales and Sclerodermatales.

LOCUS (pl. = LOCI): (1) a specific location; (2) the position on a chromosome occupied by a particular gene, hence often used synonymously with gene.

LSD: LYSERGIC ACID DIETHYLAMIDE, a powerful hallucinogen derived from *Claviceps* sclerotia.

LYOPHILIZATION: freeze-drying, a technique used to preserve fungal cultures in a state of suspended animation.

MACROCYCLIC: describes rust fungi which produce all 5 developmental stages—basidiospores, spermatia, aeciospores, urediniospores, and teliospores (cf. MICROCYCLIC).

MACRONUTRIENTS: chemical elements required in large amounts for plant or fungal growth, e.g., nitrogen, carbon, potassium, calcium, phosphorus, magnesium, and sulphur.

MACROSCOPIC: big enough to be seen by the naked eye.

MAGIC MUSHROOMS: typically, hallucinogen-containing species of *Psilocybe*, but also spp. of *Gymnopilus*, *Panaeolus*, *Conocybe*, and *Amanita muscaria*.

MANNITOL: a polyhydric alcohol, often found as a storage compound in ectotrophic mycorrhizal mantles.

MANTLE: a compact layer of hyphae enclosing short feeder roots of ectomycorrhizal plants; connected to the Hartig net on the inside, and to the extramatrical hyphae on the outside; acts as a sink for nutrients.

MASTIGONEMES: hair-like processes on the surface of tinsel flagella.

MATSU-TAKE: *Tricholoma matsutake*; an important edible fungus in Japan; grows in association with pine.

MEDIUM, culture: a substance or solution for the culture of microorganisms. DEFINED MEDIUM—of a prescribed composition, used for determining the biochemical capabilities of the organism, e.g., auxotrophs; COMPLETE MEDIUM—containing all nutrients required for growth; MINIMAL MEDIUM—the simplest chemically defined medium on which the wild type (prototroph) of a species will grow and which must be supplemented by one or more specific substances for the growth of auxotrophic mutants derived from the wild type; SELECTIVE MEDIUM: medium containing certain chemical components which restrict the growth of some microorganisms but encourages the growth of others.

MEIOSIS: reduction division: a diploid nucleus produced (usually) 4 haploid nuclei by 2 successive nuclear divisions in which the chromosome number is halved from diploid (2n) to haploid (n), and genetic segregation and recombination occur.

MEIOSPORANGIUM (pl. = MEIOSPORANGIA): a sporangium within which meiosis occurs before spore formation (e.g., basidium, ascus); produces meiospores. (cf. MITOSPORANGIUM).

MEIXNER TEST: for amatoxins: (1) express fluid from agaric onto newsprint, (2) dry, (3) add a drop of concentrated hydrochloric acid, (4) blue colour developing in 1-20 mins. indicates presence of amatoxin, higher levels produce colour sooner.

MELZER'S REAGENT: used to elicit amyloid or dextrinoid reactions in spores, asci, hymenial tissues, etc.; chloral hydrate: 100 g, potassium iodide: 5g, iodine -1.5 g, distilled water: 100 mL.

MEROSPORANGIUM (pl. = MEROSPORANGIA): (of Zygomycetes) a cylindrical outgrowth from the swollen end of a sporangiophore in which a chain-like series of sporangiospores is generally produced.

MESOPHILIC: describes organisms which grow at temperatures between 10-40°C (opt. 20-35°C) (cf. PSYCHROPHILIC, THERMOPHILIC).

MESOZOIC: the geological era comprising the Triassic, Jurassic and Cretaceous period (225-65 million years before present).

METABOLISM: the sum of all chemical processes occurring within a living cell or organism; PRIMARY METABOLISM — metabolism associated with the normal maintenance and growth of the organism; SECONDARY METABOLISM — processes which use primary metabolites available after growth has ceased, producing substances with no known role in primary metabolism.

METAMORPHOSIS: a dramatic reorganization leading to a change in appearance, as in the developmental change from caterpillar larva to butterfly.

METULAE: special cells at the apex of a conidiophore which support phialides, as in many species of *Penicillium*, *Leptographium*.

mg: see MILLIGRAM.

MICROBODY: cellular organelle bounded by a single membrane, and containing enzymes; derived from endoplasmic reticulum.

MICROCYCLIC: describes rust fungi in which some stages of the life cycle are bypassed (cf. MACROCYCLIC).

MICROGRAM: one-millionth of a gram: written as 'μg'.

MICROMETRE: one-thousandth of a millimetre or one millionth of a metre: written as μm (see also MICRON).

MICRON: see MICROMETRE.

MICROPORES: extremely narrow connectives penetrating the septa of some mycelial yeasts, e.g. *Geotrichum*.

MICROTUBULE: narrow (about 25 nanometres in diam.), elongate, non-membranous tubule of indefinite length occurring in the cytoplasm of many eukaryotic cells; the major component of the mitotic spindle and flagella; made of a protein called tubulin.

MIDDLE LAMELLA: pectin-rich layer between the walls of adjacent plant cells; this layer is attacked and dissolved by damping-off fungi.

MILLIGRAM: one-thousandth of a gram: written as 'mg'.

MINIMAL MEDIUM: see MEDIUM.

MISO: an Oriental food product, used for soups and as flavouring agent, composed of rice and cereals + soybeans fermented by *Aspergillus oryzae* and *Saccharomyces rouxii*.

MITOCHONDRIA: intracellular organelles concerned with the Krebs cycle and electron transport: the chief source of ATP in non-photosynthesizing cells.

MITOSIS: nuclear division involving chromosomes that are replicated and distributed equally between the daughter nuclei.

MITOSPORANGIUM (pl. = MITOSPORANGIA): a sporangium producing mitospores (q.v.) (cf. MEIOSPORANGIUM).

MITOSPORE: a spore receiving a nucleus or nuclei resulting from mitotic division; characteristic of asexual reproduction; see CONIDIUM, ZOOSPORES.

MONERA: the Kingdom for prokaryotic organisms (bacteria and blue-green algae).

MONILIOID: describes closely-septate hyphae with swollen cells, constricted at the septa.

MONOCULTURE: condition in which one species is grown in an extensive pure stand; describes most agricultural situations.

MONOKARYON: in ascomycetes and basidiomycetes, the haploid phase in which the hyphae contain only one kind of nuclei (cf. DIKARYON).

MONOMER: a simple molecule that can form polymers by combining with identical or similar molecules.

MONOMETHYL HYDRAZINE (MMH): see GYROMITRIN.

MONOMITIC: describes basidiomata constructed of only one kind of hypha, the generative type (cf. DIMITIC, TRIMITIC).

MOREL: a large, edible ascoma of the genus *Morchella* (Pezizales, Ascomycetes); fruits in Spring.

MOULDS: fungi, usually either zygomycetes or hyphomycetes, associated with deterioration of food or manufactured goods of organic origin.

MUCILAGINOUS: composed of mucilage.

MUCORMYCOSIS: a disease of man or animals caused by one of the Mucorales, e.g., *Absidia corymbifera*, but sometimes also applied to infections caused by members of the Entomophthorales.

MULTILOCULAR: with several to many internal spore-producing cavities or chambers.

MULTIPOLAR: describes yeasts in which each successive blastic conidium arises from a different point on the mother cell.

MUSCARDINE DISEASES: diseases of certain insects, esp. silkworms, caused by hyphomycetes; GREEN MUSCARDINE — *Metarhizium anisopliae*; WHITE MUSCARDINE — *Beauveria bassiana*; YELLOW MUSCARDINE — *Paecilomyces farinosus*.

MUSCARINE: toxic quaternary ammonium compound found in species of *Clitocybe* and *Inocybe*; causes perspiration-salivation-lacrymation syndrome.

MUSCIMOL: a hallucinogenic derivative of ibotenic acid; formed in *Amanita muscaria* when basidiomata are dried.

MUSHROOM: a fleshy basidioma, usually stalked and with a cap (pileus) beneath which gills or fleshy tubes are covered with or lined with the hymenium; edible or poisonous; see AGARIC, BOLETE.

MUTAGEN: an agent that increases the mutation rate.

MUTATION: a permanent change in a gene.

MUTANT: a mutated gene, or an organism carrying a gene that has undergone a mutation; may be biochemical, fermentation, resistance, suppressor, physiological, in nature.

MUTUALISM: a kind of symbiosis in which both or all partners gain from the association, e.g. mycorrhizae.

MYCANGIA: special organs of some wood-inhabiting beetles and wood-wasps in which they carry their symbiotic ambrosia fungus.

MYCELIUM (pl. = MYCELIA): collective term for hyphae; the vegetative thallus of a fungus excluding organs of sporulation or sclerotia.

MYCETOMES: pouches at the beginning of the midgut in anobiid beetles in which their endosymbiotic yeasts are stored.

MYCOBIONT: the fungal partner in a symbiotic relationship (mycorrhiza or lichen).

MYCOHERBICIDE: a prepartion of phytopathogenic fungi used to kill weeds.

MYCOINSECTICIDE: a preparation of entomopathogenic fungi used to kill insects.

MYCOLOGY: the study of fungi.

MYCOPARASITE: a fungus which attacks other fungi (sometimes called HYPERPARASITE).

MYCOPHAGOUS: eating fungi.

MYCORRHIZA: symbiotic relationship between a filamentous fungus and the roots of a hight plant; see ECTOMYCORRHIZA, ENDOMYCORRHIZA.

MYCOSES (sing. = MYCOSIS): diseases of humans or animals caused by fungi (e.g., ringworm, histoplasmosis, coccidioidomycosis, athlete's foot).

MYCOTOXIN: a fungal secondary metabolite which is poisonous to man or animals.

MYXAMOEBA: amoeboid stage of Myxostelida, feeds phagotrophically and later becomes a plasmodium.

NANOMETRE: one-billionth of a metre: written as 'nm'.

NECROSIS: death of cells or tissues.

NECROTROPH: an organism that kills tissues of living hosts by releasing toxins, then lives saprobically on the dead tissues.

NEMATODES: threadworms or roundworms; members of Phylum Nematoda, pseudocoelomate metazoa, 10,000 spp.; common in soil, decaying organic matter and as parasites of plants and animals.

NEPHROPATHY: kidney damage, sometimes caused by mycotoxins.

NEUROTOXIN: a toxin which affects the nervous system.

nm: see NANOMETRE.

NOBLE ROT: a condition in which the mould *Botrytis* grows on overripe grapes. A rich, sweet, expensive wine is made in small quantities from such grapes (Sauternes, Trockenbeerenauslese, Botrytis-wine).

NOMENCLATURE: the naming of Fungi is governed by the International Code of Botanical Nomenclature as adopted by each International Botanical Congress; any proposals to change the Code are published, debated, and voted on at such Congresses. This is why major evolutionary lines of fungi are called Divisions, not Phyla. If more than one name has been applied to a fungus, the rules help decide which is the proper one. The rules also allow separate binomials for anamorph and holomorph.

NON-TARGET ORGANISMS: organisms found with or near those being treated with a chemical or biological control agent; it is important that these agents have as little effect as possible on non-target organisms.

NUCLEAR CAP: a mass of RNA and ribosomes near the nucleus in some zoospores.

NUCLEOLUS: organelle found in the nucleus of eukaryotic cells; composed mainly of ribosomal RNA in the process of being transcribed from multiple copies of rRNA genes.

NUCLEOTIDE: a single unit of nucleic acid, composed of a phosphate, a five-carbon sugar (either ribose or deoxyribose), and a purine or a pyrimidine.

NUCLEUS: a specialized body within the eukaryotic cell bounded by a double membrane and containing the chromosomes.

NYSTATIN: an antifungal antibiotic derived from *Streptomyces noursei*, used to treat candidiasis.

OBLIGATE: invariably found in a particular situation; usually used in reference to organisms that must live in intimate association with a living host (cf. FACULTATIVE, OPPORTUNISTIC).

OCHRATOXINS: toxins of *Aspergillus ochraceus, Penicillium viridicatum*, etc.; cause kidney damage in sheep, cattle and pigs.

OESTROGENIC SYNDROME: a condition in which the mycotoxin, zearalenone, a steroid, causes severe sexual dysfunction in pigs (vaginal prolapse, shrivelled testes).

OLFACTORY: having to do with the sense of smell.

ONTJOM: an Indonesian fermented food, prepared from peanut press cake, which has been surface inoculated with the *Monilia* anamorph of *Neurospora sitophila* (Sordariales: Ascomycetes).

OOGAMY: sexual reproduction in which the larger female gamete (egg) is non-motile, while the smaller male gamete may be motile or non-motile: typical of all Oomycota and order Monoblepharidales of Division Chytridiomycota.

OOGONIUM (pl. = OOGONIA): single-celled female gametangium giving rise to one or more 'eggs'.

OOMYCOTA: Division of protoctistan fungi with biflagellate zoospores; oogamous, with non-motile gametes; have cellulose walls, and diploid vegetative thalli; hence, Oomycetes.

OOSPHERE: unfertilized female gamete in oogamous fungi, esp. Oomycota.

OOSPORE: thick-walled resting spore developing from a fertilized egg of the Oomycetes.

OPERCULATE: describes sporangia (esp. some unitunicate asci), having a special lid or cap (operculum) that opens to permit spore discharge (cf. INOPERCULATE).

OPPORTUNISTIC: (relating to pathogens) fungi which are normally saprobic, but occasionally act as pathogens when conditions unusually favourable for infection arise (cf. FACULTATIVE, OBLIGATE).

ORDER: taxonomic rank above Family, but below Class; suffix is **-ales**.

ORDERED TETRAD: the linear arrangement in the ascus of spores resulting from meiosis.

ORGANELLES: specialized sub-cellular structures which perform specific functions in eukaryotic cells, e.g., mitochondria, nucleoli, ribosomes: these are now believed to have been prokaryotic organisms which entered a symbiotic union with the ancestral eukaryotic cells.

ORGANOLEPTIC QUALITIES: attributes affecting the senses (taste, smell).

ORGANOMERCURIAL (RHgX): organic fungicides incorporating mercury.

ORGANO-TIN (RSnX): organic fungicides incorporating tin.

OSMOTIC PRESSURE: the potential pressure developed by a solution separated from pure water by a selectively permeable membrane that permits the passage of water, but not the dissolved substance.

OSMOTOLERANT: capable of growing under conditions of high osmotic pressure, as some yeasts and moulds on concentrated sugar solutions.

OSTIOLE: the opening at the top of many fungal fruit bodies (perithecia, pycnidia, puffball basidiomata) through which spores escape or are expelled.

OXIDATIVE PHOSPHORYLATION: the formation of ATP from ADP and inorganic phosphate that takes place in the electron transport chain of the mitochondrion.

PAINT FUNGI: wood-inhabiting basidiomycetes with thin, spread out, indefinite basidiomata; many Corticiaceae and Thelephoraceae: Aphyllophorales.

PALAEOZOIC: the geological era covering the period from 600-225 million years before present (m.y.b.p.); includes the Cambrian, Ordovician, Silurian, Devonian, Carboniferous and Permian periods.

PAPILLA: a nipple-like extension, as on the auxiliary cells of some VAM fungi.

PARAPHYSIS (pl. = PARAPHYSES): sterile hyphae growing up between the asci in the hymenium of many ascomycetes.

PARASEXUALITY: genetic recombination during the mitotic cycle, best known in conidial fungi (ascomycetous anamorphs, such as *Aspergillus*).

PARASITIC: deriving nourishment from another living organism (the host) (cf. NECROTROPHIC, SAPROBIC).

PARENCHYMATOUS: describes tissues or thalli made up of thin-walled, apparently randomly arranged cells, packed tightly together and thus usually polygonal.

PARENTHESOME: a perforated dome of membrane that covers each end of a dolipore.

PARTIAL VEIL: membrane enclosing gill cavity during development in some agarics; after rupture, it remains as a ring or annulus on the stipe (cf. UNIVERSAL VEIL).

PATHOGEN: an organism that causes disease.

PATULIN: a mycotoxin from *Aspergillus clavatus, Penicillium patulum, P. expansum*; antibacterial and antifungal; toxic to plants and animals (carcinogenic to mice) and the cause of neurotoxicosis in cattle.

PEACH LEAF CURL: a leaf hypertrophy caused by *Taphrina deformans* (Taphrinales: Ascomycetes).

PENICILLIN: an antibacterial antibiotic produced by *Penicillium* spp. (Hyphomycetes).

PENITREM A: a mycotoxin produced by various *Penicillium* spp., incl. *P. cyclopium*, which affects the nervous system, causing tremors; see NEUROTOXIN, TREMORGEN.

PERCURRENT: growing on through the scar left by release of a previous terminal spore; see ANNELLIDIC.

PERIDIOLES: the 'eggs' in bird's-nest fungi; disc-shaped bodies within which the basidiospores are borne, and which are splashed out of the cup-shaped basidioma by raindrops.

PERIDIUM (pl. = PERIDIA): outer covering of various sporangia in the Zygomycetes, and of the gleba in many Gasteromycetes.

PERITHECIAL ASCOMA: walled ascoma usually having an ostiole through which spores can be expelled at maturity; the asci are arranged in an hymenium; characteristic of many ascomycetes with unitunicate-inoperculate asci.

PERMEASE: transport protein or carrier molecule that assists in the movement of substances across cellular membranes; not permanently altered in the process.

pH (potential Hydrogen): a symbol for hydrogen ion concentration in a solution; pH values run from 0 to 14 on a logarithmic scale, the lower the value, the greater the concentration of hydrogen ions, and the more acidic a solution is; pH 7 is 'neutral', pH less than 7 is acidic, pH greater than 7 is alkaline or basic.

PHAGOTROPHIC: feeding by ingestion; engulfing food (no fungus does this).

PHENOTYPE: the physical expression of the genotype.

PHEROMONE: an intraspecific chemical signal, such as a sexual attractant liberated in minute quantities, yet capable of inducing chemotaxis of the 'target' at a considerable distance.

PHIALIDE: a conidiogenous cell which produces a basipetal succession of blastic conidia from an open end without any change in the length of the cell.

PHIALIDIC: describes conidia produced by a phialide.

PHLOEM: food-conducting tissue in vascular plants; basically composed of sieve elements, various kinds of parenchyma cells, fibres and sclereids.

PHOSPHOLIPIDS: see LIPIDS.

PHOSPHORYLATION: a reaction in which phosphate is added to a compound, e.g., the formation of ATP from ADP and inorganic phosphate.

PHOTOSYNTHETIC: having the ability to convert light energy to chemical energy; able to produce carbohydrates from carbon dioxide in the presence of chlorophyll.

PHOTOTROPISM: growth toward a light source, as in many dung-inhabiting fungi, e.g., *Pilobolus* (Zygomycetes), *Sordaria, Ascobolus* (Ascomycetes).

PHRAGMOBASIDIOMYCETES: Basidiomycetes in which the basidia are subdivided by primary septa (Orders: Tremellales, Auriculariales) (cf. HOLOBASIDIOMYCETES, TELIOMYCETES).

PHRAGMOBASIDIUM (pl. = PHRAGMOBASIDIA): a basidium with three transverse septa, characteristic of the Phragmobasidiomycetes (q.v.) and also the Teliomycetes.

PHRAGMOSPORE: a spore which has two or more transverse septa; septa appearing like the rungs of a ladder.

PHTHALIMIDES: the protectant fungicides: Captan, Captafol/Difolatan, Folpet/Phaltan.

PHYCOBIONT: the algal partner in a symbiotic relationship, as in a lichen.

PHYLOGENETIC: classification of organisms according to their evolutionary sequence, reflecting genetic relationships.

PHYLOGENY: evolutionary relationships among organisms; developmental history of a group of organisms.

PHYLUM (pl. = PHYLA): a taxon above Class, but below Kingdom, among the Animals and most Protoctista; the fungal and plant equivalent is DIVISION.

PHYSIOLOGY: the study of the activities and processes of living organisms.

PHYTOALEXIN: a metabolite, produced by a plant in response to infection by a pathogen (or by an abiotic factor), which inhibits the pathogen.

PHYTOBIONT: the plant partner in a mutualistic symbiosis, e.g. a mycorrhiza.

PILEIPELLIS: the superficial layer of cells covering the upper side of the cap of an agaric.

PILEUS: the spore-bearing cap or head of a mushroom or other large fungal fructification.

PLANKTON: free-floating aquatic organisms; usually microscopic.

PLASMALEMMA: or plasma membrane; outer boundary of the protoplast, next to the cell wall; consists of a single membrane; also called cell membrane and ectoplast.

PLASMID: a relatively small, circular fragment of DNA which can exist free in the cytoplasm and can be used as a vector in gene cloning.

PLASMODIUM: a naked, multinucleate, phagotrophic, amoeboid thallus, as in Myxostelida.

PLASMOGAMY: fusion or mixing of the cytoplasm of two cells; follows anastomosis and often precedes karyogamy.

PLASTIDS: organelles in the cells of certain groups of eukaryotes which manufacture and store food; plastids are bounded by a double membrane, e.g., chloroplasts.

PODETIA: upright, cylindrical structures in lichens (esp. *Cladonia*) which often bear apothecial ascomata at their apex.

POLYMER: a compound made by linking many identical smaller molecules (monomers).

POLYPEPTIDES: organic compounds made up of amino-acids linked by peptide bonds.

POLYPHYLETIC: genetically heterogeneous, because of having arisen from different ancestral groups.

POLYPORES: the shelf- or bracket-fungi; hymenomycetes living on dead (or sometimes living) trees and often producing perennial basidiomata in which the hymenium lines annual layers of corky, vertically oriented tubes.

POLYSACCHARIDE: a polymer made up of many linked monosaccharides, e.g., cellulose, a polymer of glucose.

POWDERY MILDEWS: plant diseases caused by obligately parasitic fungi (Erysiphales: Ascomycetes).

ppb: parts per billion; a measure of concentration.

ppm: parts per million; a measure of concentration.

PRECAMBIAN: geological era from the earliest days of the earth until 600 million years ago, at the end of which the earth's atmosphere is believed to have attained a level of oxygen capable of supporting multicellular, eukaryotic organisms.

PRECURSOR: a substance that precedes and is the source of another substance.

PREDACEOUS: preying upon other organisms, as in the nematode-exploiting fungi.

PREDACEOUS FUNGI: specialized fungi of several Divisions which trap or infect nematodes, rotifers, collembola, amoebae, tardigrades, etc., exploiting them either as principal diet or as a nitrogen supplement.

PRIMARY HOST: the principal host of heteroecious rust fungi, which bears the sexual phase (the teliospores); see ALTERNATE HOST.

PRIMARY METABOLISM: see METABOLISM.

PRIMARY PRODUCTION: elaboration of complex, energy-rich organic compounds by photosynthetic organisms. Fungi and animals are ultimately totally dependent on this process.

PRIMORDIUM: the first stage of development of an organ or sporoma.

PROKARYOTIC: lacking a membrane-bound nucleus and paired chromosomes; also lacking cytoplasmic organelles such as ribosomes, mitochondria and golgi apparatus: describes the bacteria and the cyanobacteria (cf. EUKARYOTIC).

PROLAPSE: a condition in which an organ becomes displaced (see oestrogenic syndrome in pigs).

PROMOTER: a nucleotide sequence in a gene to which RNA polymerase attaches in order to begin transcription of mRNA.

PROTEASE: an enzyme that digests protein.

PROTECTANT: a fungicide that can give protection from a pathogen by killing its spores or germ tubes while they are still outside the host, but cannot cure an existing infection (cf. ERADICANT).

PROTEIN: a long chain of amino acids (usually more than 100) joined by peptide bonds.

PROTOCTISTA: eukaryotic Kingdom of unicellular organisms and their multicellular descendants (e.g. macroscopic red, green and brown algae); contains over 35 Phyla, and three of them fungal.

PROTOCTISTAN FUNGI: the Divisions Chytridiomycota, Hyphochytriomycota and Oomycota; all produce some flagellate cells.

PROTOPLASM: fluid living content of a cell, the cytoplasm and nucleoplasm.

PROTOPLAST: the membrane-bounded living contents of a cell from which the wall has been removed enzymically to facilitate transformation.

PROTOTROPH: the wild type, as found in nature, which can synthesize a substance which a corresponding auxotroph (q.v.) mutant cannot.

PROTOTUNICATE: describes a kind of ascus that is basically unitunicate, but whose wall lyses at or before maturity; such asci may develop in a hymenium or may be distributed randomly in the interior of the ascoma.

PR TOXIN: a toxin produced by *Penicillium roquefortii*, fortunately not during the ripening of blue cheeses.

PSEUDOPARAPHYSES: specialized hyphae found in some bitunicate ascomycetes; they grow down from the roof of the pseudothecial ascoma and dissolve a space for the developing asci.

PSEUDOPARENCHYMATOUS: describes 'tissue' made up of very densely packed fungal hyphae which in mass have come to resemble a perithecial ascoma.

PSEUDOTHECIAL ASCOMA: ascoma containing bitunicate asci; often resembling a perithecial ascoma, though developing differently.

PSILOCIN and PSILOCYBIN: hallucinogenic indoles found in many species of *Psilocybe*, and some species of *Panaeolus, Gymnopilus* and *Conocybe*.

PSYCHEDELIC: mind-altering, hallucinogenic, psychoactive.

PSYCHROTOLERANT: growing at temperatures below 10°C (opt. below 20°C).

PUFFBALL: a gasteromycete basidioma in which the basidiospore mass (gleba) is enclosed by a papery peridium at maturity; an ostiole allows compression or wind suction to disperse basidiospores in the Lycoperdales and Tulostomatales; the basidiomata of the Sclerodermales have no ostiole.

PUFFING: a phenomenon in which thousands of asci in an apothecial ascoma discharge their ascospores simultaneously, producing a visible cloud of spores.

PULLEYWHEEL OCCLUSION: the structure blocking the septal pore in hyphae of the rust fungi (Uredinales).

PYCNIDIAL CONIDIOMA: a flask-shaped sporoma produced by Coelomycetous anamorphs.

PYRENOLICHENS: lichens in which the mycobiont produces perithecial or pseudothecial ascomata.

RADIOIMMUNOASSAY: an immunoassay in which radioactive tracers are introduced into the substance to be analyzed.

RECEPTACLE: the head of the stinkhorns, bearing the slimy gleba.

RECEPTIVE HYPHAE: special hyphae arising from spermagonia of rust fungi; the spermatia from other spermagonia fuse with them and initiate the dikaryon.

RECESSIVE: describes a gene whose phenotypic expression is masked by a dominant allele.

RECOMBINANT DNA: DNA of two different species spliced together in the laboratory (see CLONING).

REDUCTION DIVISION: see MEIOSIS.

REINDEER 'MOSS': the lichen, *Cladonia rangiferina*, and similar species.

RELATIVE HUMIDITY (RH): an index of water content, expressed as a percentage of the saturated value.

RESTRICTION ENDONUCLEASE: an enzyme used to cleave DNA at specific base pairs.

RESUPINATE: describes basidiomata that lie flat or spread out in a thin layer on the substrate, with a superficial hymenium: 'paint fungi' of families Thelephoraceae, Corticiaceae (Aphyllophorales: Basidiomycetes).

RETINA: a light-sensitive area, as in the subsporangial vesicle of *Pilobolus*.

RETROGRESSIVE: a mode of blastic conidiogenesis in which the short cylindrical segments of the conidiogenous cell differentiate into conidia; the conidiogenous cells becomes shorter during conidiation.

RHEXOLYTIC: secession of conidia involving the circumscissile rupture or breakdown of the longitudinal wall of the cell below the conidium (cf. SCHIZOLYTIC).

RHIZOIDS: very narrow, branched, usually enucleate, assimilative filaments found in the microscopic thalli of Chytridiomycota, etc.

RHIZOMORPH: a root-like, macroscopic aggregation of hyphae with a cortex of dark cells and a central core of long, unpigmented cells; functions in translocation of food; characteristic of *Armillaria mellea*.

RHIZOMYCELIUM: extensive nucleate rhizoidal system found in some Chytrids; possibly the precursor of true hyphae.

RIBONUCLEIC ACID (RNA): type of nucleic acid formed on chromosomal DNA and involved in protein synthesis; composed of chains of phosphate, sugar molecules (ribose), and purines (adenine, guanine) and pyrimidines (cytosine, uracil).

RIBOSOMES: organelles which are the site of protein synthesis.

RING: see PARTIAL VEIL.

RINGWORM: superficial mycoses caused by keratinophilic Hyphomycetes; see DERMATO-PHYTES, TINEA.

RNA: see RIBONUCLEIC ACID; tRNA = transfer RNA; mRNA = messenger RNA; rRNA = ribosomal RNA.

ROCK TRIPE: rock-inhabiting lichens of the genus *Umbilicaria*.

ROOTLET: part of the cytoskeleton supporting the base of a flagellum.

RUMPOSOME: honeycomb-like organelle of unknown function in Chytridiomycete zoospores.

RUSTS: plant diseases caused by obligately parasitic fungi (Uredinales: Teliomycetes).

SAPROBE: a heterotrophic organism that derives food from dead organisms, or from organic substances liberated by living ones (cf. PARASITE, NECROTROPH, SYMBIONT).

SCHIZOLYTIC: secession of conidia involving a splitting of the delimiting septum so that one half of the crosswall becomes the base of the seceding conidium and the other half covers the apex of the conidiogenous cells (cf. RHEXOLYTIC).

SCLEROTIUM (pl. = SCLEROTIA): a firm, frequently rounded, mass of hyphae with or without the addition of host tissue or soil, normally having no spores in or on it (cf. BULBIL, STROMA); a sclerotium may give rise to a fruit body, or mycelium.

SCOLECOSPORES: spores which are very long and thin (length/width ratio more than 15:1).

SECONDARY METABOLISM: see METABOLISM.

SELECTIVE MEDIUM: see MEDIUM.

SEPTA (sing. = SEPTUM): bulkheads occurring at regular intervals in most eumycotan fungi; they strengthen hypha and define the compartments, but are perforate and in many cases allow passage of cytoplasm and nuclei.

SEQUESTRATE: describes fungal fruit bodies which have evolved from exposed hymenia and forcibly discharged spores to a closed or even hypogeous habit in which the spores are retained in the fruit body until it decays or is eaten by an animal vector. Many sequestrate taxa can be clearly recognized a s being derived from specific spore-shooting ancestors, e.g. *Rhizopogon* from *Suillus* (Boletaceae).

SESSILE: not stalked; sitting directly on substrate.

SEXUAL REPRODUCTION: the fusion of gametes followed by meiosis and recombination at some point in the life cycle.

SHII-TAKE: *Lentinus edodes*; a domesticated edible agaric used in Japanese and Chinese cuisine; the fungus is grown on logs of Fagaceae (oak, beech).

SHORT CELLS: cells of a dimorphic plant root exodermis which remain unsuberized long enough to permit ingress by VAM fungi.

SHOYU (SOY SAUCE): an Oriental sauce of soybeans and wheat fermented by *Aspergillus*, yeasts, and bacteria.

SIRENIN: a hormone secreted by female gamete of *Allomyces* which attracts male gametes.

SKELETAL HYPHAE: thick-walled, little branched, non-septate hyphae found in dimitic and trimitic basidiomata (cf. BINDING, GENERATIVE hyphae).

SLAFRAMINE: a mycotoxin produced by *Rhizoctonia leguminicola*; causing excessive salivation or slobbering in ruminants feeding on certain fungus infected legume forage crops.

SMUTS: plant diseases, often specific to higher plant sex organs, caused by the Ustilaginales (Teliomycetes).

SOMATIC: pertaining to the vegetative or assimilative body of an organism.

SOREDIA (sing. = SOREDIUM): lichen propagules — small aggregations of fungal hyphae around algal cells; formed by the break up of a thallus.

SORUS: a simple fruiting structure produced by rust and smut fungi; an aggregation of spore-bearing cells bursting through the host epidermis.

sp.- abbreviation for one species.

spp.: abbreviation for more than one species.

SPECIES: the lowest-ranking taxon normally used (though subspecies, variety and race are subspecific taxa); comprises individuals very similar in all major respects; often used for organisms that are normally capable of interbreeding; among anamorphic fungi has a mainly morphological/developmental connotation.

SPERMAGONIUM: flask-shaped sporoma producing spermatia; found in rust fungi.

SPERMATIUM (pl. = SPERMATIA): non-motile male gamete, as in the rust fungi.

SPHAEROCYSTS: large, turgid, thin-walled cells, found clustered in the tissues of *Russula* and *Lactarius* (Agaricales), and accounting for the peculiar brittle texture of their flesh.

SPINDLE FIBRES: a group of microtubules that extend from the centromere of chromosomes to the poles of the spindle or from pole to pole in a dividing cell.

SPORANGIOLE: a reduced sporangium containing only one or a few spores; characteristic of some zygomycetous anamorphs.

SPORANGIOPHORE: specialized hyphal branch bearing one or more sporangia in Oomycetes, Zygomycetes, etc.

SPORANGIUM: a specialized cell within which a spore or spores are developed. See MITOSPO-RANGIUM, MEIOSPORANGIUM, SPORANGIOLE, ZOOSPORANGIUM.

SPORE: specialized microscopic propagule, usually an agent of dispersal, in fungi, cryptogamic plants, many protoctista, and bacteria: capable of developing into an adult without fusion with another cell.

SPORE PRINT: a visible deposit of basidiospores obtained by allowing an agaric to drop spores onto white paper overnight; the colour of this deposit is an important aid to identification.

SPORIDESMIN: hepatotoxic mycotoxin formed by *Pithomyces*, causes facial eczema in sheep.

SPORIFEROUS VESICLE: a thin-walled accessory cell distal to, or behind and to one side of, the chlamydospore of some VAM fungi.

SPOROCARPS: discrete aggregation of spores of some arbuscular-mycorrhizal fungi formed in or on the soil.

SPORODOCHIAL CONIDIOMA (SPORODOCHIUM): a cushion-like sporoma produced by some hyphomycetous anamorphs.

SPOROMA (pl. = SPOROMATA): any multicellular structure specially developed to produce spores.

SPOROTRICHOSIS: a lymphatic mycosis caused by *Sporothrix schenckii* (Hyphomycetes).

SQUAMULOSE: describes lichen thalli which consist of small scales.

STACHYBOTRYOTOXIN: a mycotoxin produced by the hyphomycete, *Stachybotrys*, growing on hay; implicated in serious poisoning of horses.

STALING: accumulation of metabolites which slow or stop growth of the organism which produces them.

STAUROSPORES: spores with three to many radiating extensions.

STELE: the central cylinder of conductive tissue in roots.

STERIGMA (pl. = STERIGMATA): a short apical outgrowth of a basidium, with a minute, pointed extremity on which a basidiospore is produced and from which it is forcibly discharged. (N.B.: sometimes incorrectly applied to small phialides and other peg-like structures on which spores are borne).

STERILIZATION: the process whereby all microorganisms and their propagules are killed by exposure to heat (see AUTOCLAVING), radiation, or chemicals, or removed by filtration.

STEROL-INHIBITORS: systemic but non-selective fungicides, e.g., bitertanol (Bayor); triadime-fon (Bayleton); fenarimol (Rubigan, Bloc); triforine (Funginox, Saprol); etaconazole (Vangard); triarimol (Trimidal); prochloraz (Sportak); fenapanil which inhibit sterol formation, and thus membrane formation.

STINKHORN: basidioma of some members of the order Phallales (Gasteromycetes).

STIPE: a stalk which lacks true vascular tissue, as in mushrooms.

STIPITATE: stalked.

STOMATE: a minute, intercellular fissure in the epidermis, surrounded by guard cells.

STRIATED DISC: flattened, fan-shaped assemblage of microtubules and fibrils extending from the side of the kinetosome in zoospores of the Monoblepharidales.

STROMA (pl. = STROMATA): mass of fungal tissue within which or from which perithecial or other fructifications are formed (cf. SCLEROTIUM, BULBIL).

SUBDIVISION: taxon above Class but below Division; suffix is -**mycotina**, e.g. Ascomycotina, Basidiomycotina.

SUBERIN: fatty material found in plants in the cell walls of cork tissue, of the endodermis (the Casparian band), and of the exodermis; its presence can prevent fungal penetration.

SUBICULUM: a wool- or crust-like growth of mycelium under fruit bodies.

SUBSTRATE: (1) the food of a fungus; (2) substance acted on by an enzyme.

SUCROSE: a disaccharide, $C_{12}H_{22}O_{11}$, consisting of glucose and fructose monomers.

SUMMER SPORES: (of rust fungi) see UREDINIOSPORES.

SURFACTANT: an agent which reduces the surface tension of a liquid, e.g., detergents.

SUSPENSORS: the empty walls of the two gametangia which remain attached to maturing zygosporangia.

SWARMER: see ZOOSPORE.

SYMBIOSIS: a state of intimate association or living together; the relationship benefits both partners in MUTUALISTIC symbioses, or one partner at the expense of the other in PARASITISM, or may be neutral, as in COMMENSALISM.

SYMPLASTIC: entering living cells (cf. APOPLASTIC).

SYMPODIAL: describes blastic conidia formed on a conidiogenous cells by the growth of a succession of apices, each originating below and to one side of the last.

SYNANAMORPH: one of two or more different anamorphs which develop simultaneously, or are otherwise known to be associated with a single teleomorph.

SYNCHRONOUS: describes blastic conidia initiated simultaneously in a cluster or on a specialized cell.

SYNERGISM: a condition in which two substances, e.g. fungicides, when used together, have a greater effect than either could produce alone.

SYNNEMATAL CONIDIOMA (SYNNEMA): the sporoma of some hyphomycetes, in which many conidiophores are aggregated into a column.

SYSTEMIC: describes a fungicide or pathogen which enters and becomes widely distributed within the body of a plant or animal.

TAKE-ALL: a cereal disease caused by *Gaeumannomyces graminis* (Diaporthales: Ascomycetes).

TARGET ORGANISM: the organism against which a treatment is directed (cf. NON-TARGET ORGANISM).

TAXA (sing. = TAXON): groupings of organisms made for systematic purposes: range in rank from species to Kingdom.

TAXONOMY: the classification of organisms on the basis of their evolutionary relationship; see CLASSIFICATION.

TELEOMORPH: the sexual manifestation of a fungus; unknown in many taxa (cf. ANAMORPH, HOLOMORPH).

TELIOMYCETES: Class of basidiomycetes including the orders Uredinales and Ustilaginales. Their teleomorphs consist of teliospores from which basidia develop.

TELIOSPORES: thick-walled resting spores that essentially constitute the teleomorph of the Uredinales and Ustilaginales; karyogamy takes place in them, and they germinate to produce a basidium.

TEMPEH: an Oriental food made by fermenting soybeans with *Rhizopus oligosporus*.

TEONANACATL: 'the Flesh of the Gods,' magic mushrooms used in Central American curing and divining ceremonies.

TERATOGENIC: causing abnormalities of growth of a fetus.

TERTIARY: the geological era covering the period from 65-1 million years ago: include the Palaeocene, Eocene, Oligocene, Miocene, and Pliocene periods; if the last million years, the Pleistocene, is included, this 65 million year span is often called the Cenozoic era.

TETRAPOLAR: describes a system of heterothallism in which sexual compatibility is controlled by many alleles, all occurring at 2 loci (cf. BIPOLAR).

TETRARADIATE: describes the staurospores of some stream-inhabiting fungi; the four (sometimes more) arms ensure a stable three-point landing on the substrate.

THALLIC: one of two basic modes of conidium development; if there is any enlargement of the conidium initial, it occurs only after the initial has been cut off by a septum; derived from conversion of pre-existing hyphal elements (cf. BLASTIC).

THALLUS (pl. = THALLI): the usually ill-defined 'body' of a fungus.

THERMOTOLERANT: capable of growing at high temperatures (up to 60°C, opt. 40-50°C) (cf. PSYCHROTOLERANT).

THRUSH: a yeast infection of the mouth and throat, esp. in children, caused by *Candida albicans*.

TINEA: a superficial infection caused by dermatophytes (q.v.).

TINSEL FLAGELLUM: a flagellum with lateral flimmers or mastigonemes (cf. WHIPLASH flagellum).

TISSUE: a group of similar cells organized into a structural and functional unit.

TOADSTOOL: see MUSHROOM, AGARIC; toadstool is a confused term—it is assumed to refer to poisonous agarics, but many so-called toadstools are harmless; use 'agaric' instead, and join the cognoscenti.

TOOTH FUNGI: members of the family Hydnaceae (Aphyllophorales: Basidiomycetes) in which the hymenium covers downwardly directed teeth.

TOXIGENIC: producing toxins.

TRACE ELEMENTS: elements essential for growth, but required only in minute amounts.

TRAMA: the sterile tissue of a basidioma, esp. that in the centre of the gills.

TRANSCRIPTION: the enzyme-catalyzed assembly of an RNA molecule along a strand of DNA.

TRANSFER SPORES: (of rust fungi) see AECIOSPORES.

TRANSFORMATION: a genetic change produced by the introduction of foreign DNA.

TRANSLATION: the assembly of a protein on a ribosome, amino-acids being brought to the site by tRNA (transfer RNA) and their order of assembly being specified by mRNA (messenger RNA).

TRANSLOCATION: movement of nutrients or other substances within an organism.

TREHALOSE: a crystalline sugar, $C_{12}H_{22}O_{11}$, characteristically found in fungi.

TREMORGEN: a mycotoxin inducing a neurotoxicosis (tremor) in man and other mammals; a NEUROTOXIN.

TRICARBOXYLIC ACID CYCLE (TCA CYCLE): see KREBS CYCLE.

TRICHOGYNE: an extension of the ascogonium (in some Ascomycetes) which facilitates fertilization.

TRICHOMYCETES: an inconspicuous Class of Zygomycota, found attached to the gut walls of insects.

TRICHOTHECENES: mycotoxins (scirpenes) of *Fusarium tricinctum, F. sporotrichioides, F. poae,* and *Trichothecium* (Hyphomycetes).

TRIMITIC: describes basidiomata constructed of three different types of hyphae, generative, skeletal and binding.

TRUFFLE: an edible hypogeous ascoma of the genus *Tuber* (Pezizales: Ascomycetes).

TUNING-FORK BASIDIA: the typical basidia of the order Dacrymycetales (Holobasidiomycetes), which have only two spore-bearing extensions.

T-2 TOXIN: a mycotoxin of the trichothecene group, produced by several *Fusarium* spp.; the cause of alimentary toxic aleukia.

UNITUNICATE: describes a type of ascus with only one distinct, functional wall layer (cf. BITUNICATE).

UNIVERSAL VEIL: membrane totally enclosing some young agaric basidiomata (as in *Amanita*); after rupture it remains as the volva around base of the stipe, and often also as scales on the cap (cf. PARTIAL VEIL).

UREDINIOSPORES: the dikaryotic 'summer spores' of Uredinales, which spread the fungus from plant to plant of the primary host during the growing season.

VAM: vesicular arbuscular mycorrhizal (endomycorrhizal).

VASOCONSTRICTION: constriction of blood vessels.

VECTOR: an organism which consciously or unconsciously aids in the dispersal of another, e.g., dipteran flies are vectors for stinkhorns.

VEGETABLE CATEPILLAR: a mummified lepidopteran larva from which arises the stromatic teleomorph of a species of *Cordyceps* (Clavicipitales: Ascomycetes).

VEIL: see ANNULUS (partial veil), VOLVA (universal veil).

VESICLE: (1) small, intracellular, membrane-bounded sac in which substances are transported or stored; (2) swollen, lipid-filled cells produced inside plant roots by most endomycorrhizal fungi (sometimes called intramatrical spores); (3) swelling at apex of sporophore in fungi like *Apergillus*.

VESICULAR-ARBUSCULAR MYCORRHIZAE: endomycorrhizae; plant roots colonized by mutualistic fungi of the Glomales (some of which do **not** produce vesicles).

VIRULENCE: the degree or measure of pathogenicity.

VOLVA: a sheath around the base of the stipe in some agarics, esp. the poisonous *Amanita*; remains of the universal veil.

VOMITOXIN: 4-Deoxynivalenol, a trichothecene; a mycotoxin produced by *Fusarium graminearum* (Hyphomycetes); esp. in barley and winter wheat; has an emetic effect on livestock.

WATER ACTIVITY (a_w): expresses the available water in a substrate as a decimal fraction of the amount present when the substrate is in equilibrium with a saturated atmosphere (an equilibrium relative humidity of 70% around the substrate means that the substrate has a water activity of 0.70).

WATER MOULDS: members of the Order Saprolegniales (Oomycetes).

WHIPLASH FLAGELLUM: a flagellum with a smooth shaft (cf. TINSEL flagellum)

WHITE ROT: a wood rot produced by basidiomycetes that can degrade both cellulose and lignin.

WHITE RUST: disease of crucifers caused by Albuginaceae (Peronosporales: Oomycota).

WILT: a plant disease, caused by species of *Verticillium* and *Fusarium* (Hyphomycetes), characterized by loss of turgidity and collapse of leaves.

WINTER SPORES: (of rust fungi) see TELIOSPORES.

WITCHES' BROOMES: massed outgrowths (proliferations) of the branches of woody plants caused by mites, viruses, etc., and fungi, esp. rust fungi.

WORONIN BODIES: two small spherical objects that sit, one on each side, near the pore of the ascomycete septum.

XEROTOLERANT: able to grow under dry conditions.

XYLEM: lignified water-conducting tissue in vascular plants.

XYLOSE: a pentose sugar, $C_5H_{10}O_5$, found in the cell walls of basidiomycetes.

YEASTS: fungi which in many cases are unicellular, though some produce hyphae; most yeasts are anamorphs; their cells are conidia, and they multiply by various kinds of conidiogenesis. Some can produce asci, some can form basidia, and some appear to be anamorphic holomorphs—entirely asexual.

ZEARALENONE: a mycotoxin produced by *Fusarium graminearum* (teleomorph, *Gibberella zeae*); the cause of oestrogenic syndrome (vulvovaginitis and infertility) in pigs.

ZOOSPORANGIA (sing. = ZOOSPORANGIUM): sporangia within which zoospores (flagellate spores) develop.

ZOOSPORES: flagellate, motile, asexual spores released by protoctistan fungi.

ZYGOMYCOTA: Division of true fungi; fast-growing, terrestrial, largely saprobic fungi with no motile cells; produce zygosporangia by fusion of usually similar gametangia; also asexual sporangia containing 1 to many non-motile spores, and borne on simple to complex sporangiophores; generally called zygomycetes.

ZYGOSPORANGIUM: the teleomorph of the zygomycetes; a usually thick-walled, often ornamented, multinucleate resting sporangium formed following anastomosis of gametangia arising from compatible mycelia (in heterothallic species) or from the same mycelium (in homothallic species).

ZYGOTE: a diploid cell or protoplast formed as a result of fusion of two haploid nuclei during sexual reproduction; zygotes often become resting spores, but ultimately germinate to produce either a diploid generation (very few fungi, many algae, all higher plants) or undergo meiosis and, following this genetic recombination, re-establish the haploid phase.